WESTERN WOODS
USE BOOK

STRUCTURAL DATA AND DESIGN TABLES

Western
Wood Products
Association

Published by
WESTERN WOOD PRODUCTS ASSOCIATION
1500 Yeon Building, Portland, Oregon 97204

PRICE $10.00 PER COPY

WESTERN WOODS USE BOOK

COPYRIGHT 1973 BY

WESTERN WOOD PRODUCTS ASSOCIATION

Library of Congress # 73-77089

**Printed in U.S.A. by Metropolitan Printing Company
Composition by Times-Litho-Print**

First Edition
First Printing-April 1973 — 5M
Second Printing August 1973 — 5M
Third Printing January 1974 — 5M

Preface:

The Western Woods Use Book had its beginnings in the Structural Timber Handbook on Pacific Coast Woods published in 1916. In 1930 the first Douglas Fir Use Book was published and the 1961 Edition was the latest revision. To engineers, architects and others engaged in the construction industry, who require accurate and reliable information concerning the qualities and uses of the Western species, the Western Wood Products Association offers this first edition of the Western Woods Use Book.

In changing from a book relating only to Douglas Fir to one covering the Western species, major revisions were necessary. All design tables relating to varying species properties have been revised and the book format and organization of material have been changed to reflect a more logical process of design. All chapters have been brought up to date to reflect information contained in the latest standards. A new chapter on Sound Control has been added and the section on Lateral Forces — Design has been revised to include plywood.

The cooperation and assistance of the National Forest Products Association, American Plywood Association, American Institute of Timber Construction, Southern Forest Products Association and the American Wood Preservers Institute are hereby acknowledged and greatly appreciated.

The Western Woods Use Book is intended for the use of architects, engineers, and students preparing for these professions. Data and formulas given are technical and should be used with knowledge of engineering principles and assumptions, as many factors other than simple fundamental formulas enter into structural analysis. It is recommended, therefore, that structural problems be referred to a qualified engineer or architect.

Additional technical information on the use of lumber and wood products is available from the Western Wood Products Association and the following organizations:

American Institute of Timber Construction
333 West Hampden Avenue
Englewood, Colorado 80110

American Plywood Association
1119 A Street
Tacoma, Washington 98401

American Wood Preservers Institute
1651 Old Meadow Road
McLean, Virginia 22101

National Forest Products Association
1619 Massachusetts Avenue, N. W.
Washington, D. C. 20036

Southern Forest Products Association
P. O. Box 52468
New Orleans, Louisiana 70150

WESTERN WOODS USE BOOK

TABLE OF CONTENTS

TABLE OF CONTENTS

TABLE OF CONTENTS

CHAPTER I

The Western Woods

THE WESTERN WOODS

The major softwood supply of the United States is contained in the growing region of the seventeen species of Western Woods. Covering the twelve western states, the area extends east and west from the Black Hills of South Dakota to the Pacific Ocean and from the Mexican border on the south to the Canadian border on the north.

The hills and mountains of this region have produced many billions of feet of lumber in the diverse range of soil and climatic conditions. In addition to the stands of mature trees ready for harvesting, there are millions of acres of new forests developing into a mature crop. Protection from fire and disease and scientific forest management practices assure a permanent supply of forest products manufactured from the Western Woods.

These timber stands also provide a prime recreational area of millions of acres because the timber-producing practices of the region are geared to the compatible use of the land for many purposes, including wildlife habitat, water production and grazing. The forest roads built and maintained for timber management also provide access to millions of people for camping, fishing, hunting, skiing and many other ways of enjoying this important national resource.

The hundreds of sawmills in this region, in addition to providing employment and stability in their communities, produce the wood products necessary to build and furnish millions of homes and apartments needed for adequate housing for the nation. In addition, Western Woods are used in churches, schools, farm buildings, warehouses, bridges and various other types of engineered timber structures. Modern prefabricated construction utilizes increasing amounts of lumber due to its ease of fabrication and high strength to weight ratio.

Species and Marketing Combinations

The seventeen species of Western Woods are combined into eleven principal marketing groups since a number of the species are grown, harvested, manufactured and marketed together and have similar performance properties which make them interchangeable in use. For identification and standardization of recommended design values and because some species cannot be visually separated in lumber form, some species are given a common designation and assigned common design values. The principal species and species combinations manufactured by mills of the Western Woods region for which design values are assigned are shown below.

Table 1.1

Commercial Species	Botanical Species Included
Douglas Fir— Larch	Douglas Fir — Pseudotsuga menziesii Western Larch — Larix occidentalis
Douglas Fir— South	Douglas Fir — Pseudotsuga menziesii[1]
Western Hemlock	Western Hemlock— Tsuga heterophylla

Table 1.1 Continued

Commercial Species	Botanical Species Included

Hem-Fir	Western Hemlock —Tsuga heterophylla
	True Firs
	  Pacific Silver Fir-- Abies amabilis
	  White Fir — Abies concolor
	  Grand Fir — Abies grandis
	  California Red Fir — Abies magnifica
	  Noble Fir — Abies procera

Mountain Hemlock	Mountain Hemlock — Tsuga mertensiana
Subalpine Fir	Subalpine Fir — Abies lasiocarpa
Engelmann Spruce	Engelmann Spruce — Picea engelmannii
Lodgepole Pine	Lodgepole Pine — Pinus contorta
Ponderosa Pine — Sugar Pine	Ponderosa Pine — Pinus ponderosa Sugar Pine — Pinus lambertiana
Idaho White Pine	Idaho White Pine — Pinus monticola
Western Cedars	Incense Cedar — Libocedrus decurrens Western Red Cedar — Thuja plicata

[1]**Grown in Arizona, Colorado, Nevada, New Mexico and Utah.**

Because of timber stand composition and mill manufacturing and marketing practices, some other species combinations are shipped and design values for the lowest valued species in the combination are applicable.

PHYSICAL PROPERTIES

Wood is an aggregate of cells, essentially cellulose in composition, which are cemented with lignin. Although cells of the western softwoods vary in shape and size according to their function, the greater portion are elongated and are positioned vertically in the standing tree. Known as tracheids, they vary from ⅛ to ⅓ of an inch in length and 1/100 of these dimensions in width.

Annual Growth Rings

New wood cells are formed in the cambium, a microscopic layer between the bark and the wood. Through the winter months, the trees are dormant. In the spring, the cambium begins to form new thin-walled springwood cells with large cavities. Through the summer, cell walls increase in thickness and, in the fall, newly formed summerwood cell cavities gradually decrease in size until growth virtually ceases. Differences in cell-wall thicknesses between those last formed in the fall and the thin-walled cells formed in the spring result in rings of annual growth which are visible on the ends of lumber. This change in growth characteristics occurs annually and, thus, the age of the tree may be determined by counting the growth rings.

Heartwood and Sapwood

The end of a log shows three distinct zones: the bark, a light-colored zone just beneath it called the sapwood, and an inner zone, often darker in color, called heartwood. At the structural center of the heartwood is the pith or "heart center."

The young tree is composed primarily of sapwood which functions in sap conduction and food storage. As the tree increases in diameter, inner

THE WESTERN WOODS

sapwood cells cease their conductive function and form the inactive heartwood. Deposits in these inactive cells give the heartwood of many species a darker color than the sapwood.

As all heartwood was once sapwood, there is no consistent difference between heartwood and sapwood in dry weight or in strength. For normal uses, no distinction need be made between heartwood and sapwood. Toxic extractives in the cells generally make heartwood more durable when in contact with soil and under other conditions conducive to decay. Where wood is to be treated with preservative, deeper and more effective penetration can be attained in sapwood than in heartwood.

Weight of Western Woods

Solid wood substance is heavier than water, its specific gravity being about 1.5 regardless of the species. Despite this fact, dry wood of most species floats in water because a portion of its volume is occupied by air-filled cavities. Variation among species in the size of cells and in the thickness of cell walls affects the amount of solid wood substance present and, hence, the specific gravity. Thus, specific gravity of wood is a measure of its solid wood substance and an index of its strength properties.

The relationship of strength to specific gravity has been used extensively in determining the range of strength and stiffness properties which exist throughout the growth range of a species. The specific gravity of over 30,000 trees of the western softwoods has recently been determined by the U.S. Forest Service. These data are incorporated in the current strength, stiffness and weight assignments herein.

Table 1.2

Species	Specific Gravity	Weight Lbs. Per Cu. Ft.	Weight* Factor
Douglas Fir — Larch	.48	36.3	.252
Douglas Fir South	.43	32.5	.226
Hem-Fir	.42	31.8	.221
Mountain Hemlock — Hem-Fir	.42	31.8	.221
Subalpine Fir	.31	23.5	.163
Engelmann Spruce	.32	24.6	.171
Lodgepole Pine	.39	29.5	.205
Ponderosa Pine — Sugar Pine	.39	29.5	.205
Idaho White Pine	.37	27.9	.194
Western Cedars	.35	26.5	.184
Western Hemlock	.42	31.8	.221

*To calculate the weight per lineal foot for a particular size and species, multiply the cross sectional area of the member in square inches by the species weight factor shown.

To determine the weight per cubic foot or per linear foot at higher moisture contents, multiply the above weights by the following factors.

Moisture Content	Adjustment Factor
30%	1.073
40%	1.156
50%	1.238
60%	1.321
70%	1.403

The specific gravity as determined on the basis of green volume, oven-dry weight is shown in the preceding table. Also shown is the average weight per cubic foot of wood and factors to determine the weight of lumber when used at a maximum moisture content of 19 per cent such as in most covered structures. Adjustment factors for other moisture content conditions, such as exposed use, are also provided. Weights for species combinations are based on the heaviest species in the combination, thus providing conservative estimates of building weights for design purposes.

Moisture in Wood

The moisture content of wood is the weight of the water in wood expressed as a percentage of the weight of the wood from which all water has been removed (oven dry). Moisture is removed from lumber either by air drying or by use of special drying kilns. Wood may contain moisture in two forms, either as "free water" in the cell cavities or as "absorbed water" in the cell walls.

When green wood begins to lose moisture, the cell walls remain saturated until the free water has been evaporated. The point at which evaporation of free water is complete and cell walls begin to lose their moisture is called the "fiber saturation point." This point occurs between 25 and 30 percent moisture content for the western softwoods.

Moisture content is determined by weighing a representative sample, drying it at $200°$-$212°$ F until no further loss in weight takes place, weighing after drying and then dividing the difference between the original and final weights by the final oven-dry weight.

Electric moisture meters are also available for determining the moisture content of wood. Since their operation depends only upon inserting small needles into the surface of lumber, individual pieces may be non-destructively tested for moisture content. The resistance type of portable meter measures the relation between the electrical resistance of wood and its moisture content. Most resistance-type meters are designed to measure moisture content between 6 and 70 percent. The dependable accuracy range is between 6 and 30 percent. While not as accurate, the higher range is useful in indicating an approximate moisture content for comparative purposes.

Capacitance-type portable meters are also available and utilize the relationship between the dielectric constant of wood and its moisture content. This type of moisture meter generates a radio frequency current through electrodes which only require surface contact. The power loss in the circuit is indicated, and, since the specific gravity of the wood also influences the current through the circuit, conversion tables based on the average specific gravity of each species are necessary. Variation in specific gravity within a species also affects the accuracy of moisture content determinations made with this type of meter. The range of capacitance-type meters lies between zero and 25 percent moisture content.

THE WESTERN WOODS

Dimensional Stability and Strength

Moisture content variations above the fiber saturation point have no effect upon the volume or strength of wood. As wood dries below the fiber saturation point and begins to lose moisture from the cell walls, shrinkage begins and strength and stiffness properties increase. With slight seasonal variations, wood in use over a period of time attains an equilibrium moisture content (emc) corresponding to the humidity and temperature of the surrounding air. For example, at 70° F., the (emc) of wood varies from 20.6 percent at 90 percent relative humidity to 6 percent at 29 percent relative humidity.

Wood in service usually is exposed to both long-term (seasonal) and short-term (daily) changes in the relative humidity and temperature of the surrounding air. The changes in moisture content of the wood caused by these conditions are usually gradual and short-term fluctuations tend to influence only the wood surfaces.

Moisture content standards of the grading rules generally provide for maximum 12 percent for dry finish-type lumber and maximum 19 percent for dry framing-type lumber. Lumber may be ordered unseasoned, and the size standards provide for larger sizes to account for shrinkage as the lumber reaches equilibrium moisture content. The average shrinkage of softwood lumber, which is compensated for by unseasoned size differentials, is 2.35 percent in thickness and 2.80 percent in width.

Increase in strength begins when the cell walls begin to lose moisture, as the wood is dried below the fiber saturation point. Design values for Western Woods reflect these increases which are different for various strength and stiffness properties. Where lumber is to be used under moisture conditions exceeding 19 percent, design values should be reduced. Reduction factors are shown in the design value section. See page 20.

Effect of Moisture on Decay

Wood maintained either constantly dry or continuously submerged in water does not decay. Decay is caused by certain fungi which are microscopic plants that require warmth, oxygen, food and moisture for survival. Moisture in particular is the key to understanding the activity of such a fungus. The moisture in wood below the fiber saturation point of 25 to 30 percent is held semi-chemically by the cell walls and is not available to the fungus. As discussed previously, the equilibrium moisture content of wood in normal use is usually below 19 percent. Therefore, except in such special uses as tanning factories, where steam or water spray may be present, the moisture content of the wood is too low to support the decay causing fungi.

It is thus obvious that the term "dry rot" is misleading and unfortunate. It perpetuates the incorrect assumption that wood is subject to decay under all conditions, wet or dry. The term "dry rot" is descriptive only of the condition of a piece of wood which has repeatedly been wet enough for decay to occur and later is observed in a dry and decayed condition.

Where conditions are present which are conducive to decay, preservative treatment or durable species are usually required by building codes. For foundation plates and sills, FOUNDATION LUMBER of Western Red Cedar or Incense Cedar is frequently specified due to the effective durability of the heartwood of these species.

Thermal Conductivity

The western softwoods have relatively low thermal conductivity and thus provide significant insulation value. The term commonly used to rate thermal conductivity of various materials is "k", the amount of heat (Btu's) transferred in one hour through one square foot of material one inch thick with a difference in temperature of 1° F. The thermal conductivity of wood increases with increased moisture content and with increased density. The "k" values for the Western Woods are shown in the table below.

Table 1.3

Species	"k" Value*
Douglas Fir — Larch	1.05
Douglas Fir South	.96
Hem-Fir	.94
Mountain Hemlock	.94
Subalpine Fir	.74
Engelmann Spruce	.75
Lodgepole Pine	.88
Ponderosa Pine — Sugar Pine	.88
Idaho White Pine	.85
Western Cedars	.81
Western Hemlock	.94

*"k" values shown are for wood at 12 percent moisture content. For other moisture contents, there is a change in "k" of approximately 0.01 for each 1 percent moisture content difference — an increase in "k" for an increase in moisture content and a decrease in "k" for a decrease in moisture content.

Thermal Expansion

In most structural design, the coefficient of thermal expansion (increase in dimension per unit of length, thickness or width for a temperature rise of 1° F) of wood can be neglected since it is very small.

Longitudinally, the coefficient of thermal expansion is independent of specific gravity and varies from 0.0000017 to 0.0000025 for different species. Across the grain, the values vary directly with the specific gravity from 0.000014 to 0.000022 for the Western Woods.

The coefficient of thermal expansion varies slightly with temperature, but for all ordinary uses may be considered constant. In the longitudinal direction, thermal expansion of wood is from 1/10 to 1/3 as great as the expansion of metals, concrete and glass.

Electrical Properties

Dry wood is an excellent insulator against transmission of direct electrical current and low frequency alternating current. Electrical resistance of wood, however, varies appreciably with wood

THE WESTERN WOODS

moisture content. Variations in the distribution of a fixed amount of moisture in the area of measurement also have a considerable effect upon electrical resistance. Variations in species, specific gravity and amount of inorganic ash content have a much smaller effect upon electrical resistance.

Below fiber saturation point (25 to 30% moisture content) electrical resistance of wood increases very rapidly with decrease in moisture content, whereas above fiber saturation point electrical resistance changes much more slowly. Resistance is also affected by temperature, approximately doubling with each drop of 10° C.

Electrical resistivity (specific resistance) of a material is the electrical resistance in ohms between opposing faces of a cubic centimeter unit. Electrical resistivity of wood varies from about 10^{16} to 10^{18} ohm-centimeters for oven dry wood to 10^5 to 10^6 ohm-centimeters for wood at fiber saturation.

Dielectric Constant
The ratio of the capacitance of a condenser having a wood dielectric to the capacitance of the same condenser with a vacuum dielectric is termed the dielectric constant for the wood used. Dielectric constant values differ along the grain from across the grain, being as much as 30 per cent greater in the parallel-to-grain direction.

Increases in wood density and in moisture content both result in appreciable increase in dielectric constant values. The capacitance type of moisture meter is based upon the variation of the dielectric value of wood with corresponding moisture content changes. Over the range of frequencies from middle audio to high radio frequency, the dielectric constant ranges from less than 10 for dry wood to about 50 for wet wood.

Resistivity of Wood at Radio Frequencies
Low frequency parallel resistivity of wood is much greater than corresponding resistivity at high (radio) frequencies. The resistivity (r) of wood is approximately inversely proportional to the frequency (f) as evident in the following equation where the power factor (cos Ø) and the dielectric constant (ε) vary only slightly with frequency:

$$r = \frac{1.8 \times 10^{12}}{\varepsilon \, f \cos Ø}$$

This reduction in resistivity with increase in current frequency is the principle upon which the curing of glue lines in wood by radio frequency heating is based.

Where wood is employed as a dielectric (as in high-frequency gluing) the power (P) dissipated in the wood as heat is proportional to the capacitance of the condenser (C), the power factor of the wood (cos Ø), the voltage (E) and the frequency (f). This is indicated in the equation:

$$P = 2 \pi f E^2 C \cos Ø$$

As high voltage (E) in the foregoing equation is difficult to generate, presents insulating problems and tends to produce arcing, the power (P) necessary to produce heat is best increased by increasing the current frequency (f). The heat thus generated affords a rapid means of polymerizing synthetic resin wood glues.

Chemical Resistance
The Western Woods are highly resistant to a number of chemicals and are thus used for various types of tanks, containers and equipment in which chemicals are used and for structures near such equipment.

Wood owes its extensive use in chemical equipment largely to its superiority over cast iron and steel in resistance to mild acids and solutions of acidic salts. Iron is superior to wood in resistance to alkalies.

The spread between strength properties of the species after exposure to chemicals is not great. The table below shows the percentage of original (wet-breaking strength) in tests after exposure to different solutions for the duration of exposure indicated. In designing for chemical resistance, the wet-use design values are applicable when there is exposure to aqueous solutions.

Table 1.4 **Percentage of Original Wet Breaking Strength Remaining After Exposure for the Duration Indicated***

J.D. Ross, Forest Products Journal, January, 1956.

	Acids				Bases		Salts				
	*1	2	3	4	5	6	7	8	9	10	11
Douglas Fir	91	67	65	99	51	105	111	106	107	32	56
Hem-Fir and Western Hemlock	92	68	67	100	59	92	107	108	103	12	56
Western Red Cedar	82	71	59	94	40	90	84	120	121	25	43
Incense Cedar	90	52	60	85	39	110	84	93	102	48	55
Ponderosa Pine	90	64	65	98	43	87	92	93	98	4	52
Sugar Pine	86	65	62	87	33	85	103	98	113	18	45
Idaho White Pine	86	68	67	95	54	87	100	100	104	17	63
Western Larch	85	66	58	102	40	89	86	125	93	20	51

* 1 — 5% Sulfuric acid, room temperature, 105 days.
  2 — 5% Hydrochloric acid, room temperature, 71 days.
  3 — 5% Nitric acid, room temperature, 72 days.
  4 — 5% Acetic acid, room temperature, 176 days.
  5 — 1% Sodium Hydroxide, room temperature, 87 days.
  6 —   Calcium Hydroxide, saturated, room temperature, 151 days.

7 — 20% Sodium carbonate, room temperature, 93 days.
8 — 20% Calcium chloride, room temperature, 105 days.
9 — 20% Sodium chloride, room temperature, 161 days.
10 — 5¼% Sodium hypochlorite, room temperature, 21 days.
11 — 5% Sodium carbonate, boiling, 36 days.

THE WESTERN WOODS

Friction Properties

The coefficient of friction depends on the moisture content of the wood and surface roughness, and varies little with species. Coefficients of static friction on unpolished steel of 0.65 for dry wood and 0.40 for green wood have been established. Coefficients of static friction for smooth wood on smooth wood are 0.60 for dry wood and 0.83 for green wood.

Coefficients of sliding friction differ from those for static friction, and depend on the rate of relative movement between the rubbing parts. Coefficients for wood on steel of 0.70 for dry wood and 0.15 for green wood have been established at a relative movement of 4 meters per second.

CHAPTER II

Lumber Standards

LUMBER STANDARDS

Several significant developments have been made in standards affecting the use of Western Woods in recent years. Chronologically, the major developments have been:

1. Completion of the *Western Wood Density Survey, Report No. 1, U.S.D.A. Forest Service Research Paper FPL-27* .... July, 1965.

2. The inauguration of the American Society for Testing and Materials (ASTM) in establishing and publishing clear wood strength values: *ASTM D 2555, Standard Methods for Establishing Clear Wood Strength Values*, original adoption................... 1966

3. A major revision of *ASTM D 245, Standard Methods for Establishing Structural Grades and Related Allowable Properties for Visually Graded Lumber.* This was the first major revision of this Standard since 1949 and incorporated new research and technical information concerning lumber performance 1968

4. A resampling of the strength of Engelmann Spruce throughout the entire growth range and publication of *Mechanical Properties and Specific Gravity of A Randomly Selected Sample of Engelmann Spruce. U.S.D.A. Forest Service Research Paper FPL 128* .... January, 1970

5. The culmination of several years work by the lumber industry on lumber standards to supersede Simplified Practice Recommendation 16-53 with the publication of *Product Standard 20-70, American Softwood Lumber Standard,* by the U. S. Department of Commerce................. September, 1970

6. Publication of new grade rules, based on the new Standards, by all of the softwood lumber rules writing agencies.............. 1970

Western Wood Density Survey

This Survey conducted by the U. S. Forest Service and Forest Products Laboratory was planned to obtain, by systematic sampling, adequate data on the average specific gravity and related quality characteristics, the magnitude of differences between species and the range of variation within the species for the commercial softwood timber stands of the West. Non-destructive calibrated increment borer techniques were used in the sampling of 30,326 trees on 4,225 plots systematically located on commercial forestlands extending throughout the Western Woods growing area. An increment borer is a hollow drill which extracts a core from living trees suitable for analysis of wood density, age, sapwood width, rate of growth and other quality factors. Since density is related to mechanical properties with known correlation, the average and variability of mechanical properties were determined for the species surveyed. The Western Woods included in Report No. 1 were Douglas Fir, five True Firs, Western Hemlock and Western Larch. These data were incorporated into *ASTM Standard D 2555* and were used for determination of design values for Western Woods shown herein.

ASTM D 2555

Commonly called the Clear Wood Standard, the *Standard Methods for Establishing Clear Wood Strength Values, ASTM D 2555,* is the first formal standard ever published dealing with the basic clear wood mechanical properties of U. S. and Canadian woods. The data obtained in the *Western Wood Density Survey* were incorporated for the species surveyed.

The development of safe and efficient design values for lumber has, as a starting point, the need for an authoritative compilation of clear wood strength values for the commercially important species. A primary feature of this Standard are tables presenting the most reliable basic information developed on the strength of clear wood and its variability.

The Standard also provides procedures for establishing, from these data, values applicable to groups of similar species where necessitated by efficient marketing. The Standard establishes limits that determine when a species may be included in a combination without reducing the average properties for the combination. If a species is to be included and the limits are exceeded, the assigned property value for the combination must be reduced to a value such that the limits are not exceeded.

ASTM D 245

Titled, Standard Methods for Establishing Structural Grades and Related Allowable Properties for Visually Graded Lumber, this Standard covers the basic principles for visually grading structural lumber and for establishing related recommended design values.

The Standard includes necessary procedures for the formulation of structural grades of any desired strength ratio. The term strength ratio represents the anticipated proportionate remaining strength after making allowance for the effect of maximum permitted knots, cross grain and other strength-reducing characteristics in a given grade as compared to clear, straight-grained lumber.

In addition to providing for the effects of strength-reducing characteristics, the Standard provides other modifications for design use. Methods are provided for determining allowable stresses at the 5 percent exclusion limit (the allowable stress which is less than the stress permissible for 95 percent of the pieces in a species and grade). The 5 percent exclusion limit is further modified to account for the effect of size, moisture content, duration of load, multiple-member systems and a factor of safety. Details of the methods and calculations for the Western Woods are shown in Determination of Recommended Design Values for Western Softwood Lumber, *1970 Standard Grading Rules,* published separately by the Western Wood Products Association.

Some of the major changes in this Standard over past practices are related to Modulus of Elasticity (E values), tension parallel to grain (Ft values), repetitive member values and the effect of moisture content.

Formerly, all grades of a lumber species were assigned a single modulus of elasticity value. However, in recent years research has shown that the modulus of elasticity varies with grade quality and ASTM D 245 now requires the reduction of 10 percent or 20 percent in E values for grades lower in quality than Select Structural, No. 1 or Appearance.

Since tension parallel to grain values are significantly higher than extreme fiber in bending values in small clear specimens, tension values were formerly assigned the same values developed for bending. With the recent development of equipment capable of testing full-size structural lumber in tension, it was learned that in these sizes, grade characteristics have a more severe effect on tension stresses than for bending. The tension values assigned herein reflect this new information with tension values based on 55 percent of the strength ratio in bending.

Tests have demonstrated that the interaction of assemblies of three or more closely spaced load-carrying members, such as joists, rafters, studs or decking, yield a greater capacity than can be predicted for the sum of the individual members. Therefore, the current design values for such members which are contiguous or are spaced not more than 24 inches and are joined by transverse floor, roof or other load-distributing element reflect an increase in bending values of 15 percent over values for single members.

Modifications in strength and stiffness assignments due to the effect of moisture content are now related to the net dimensions of lumber, and different increases for strength and stiffness due to drying are now specified than formerly when both dry and unseasoned lumber were manufactured to the same size.

American Softwood Lumber Standard
The current softwood lumber standard is *Product Standard PS 20-70,* a voluntary standard developed by the National Bureau of Standards in cooperation with producers, distributors and users. PS 20-70, in common with product standards for other materials, establishes dimensional requirements for standard sizes, technical requirements for the product and methods of grading and marking these products. In addition, however, this Standard provides for a standing American Lumber Standards Committee and an independent Board of Review to determine the competency of inspection agencies engaged in the grading of lumber, to inspect and police the grading of lumber and to require continuing conformance of grading rules to American Lumber Standards.

PS 20-70 has several improvements over the previous lumber standard including (1) sizes related to moisture content resulting in the same end-use sizes for both green and dry lumber, (2) requirements for the establishment of design values including ASTM D 2555 and ASTM D 245 and (3) establishment of the National Grading Rule for dimension lumber.

Under the Standard, uniform grade descriptions and names are established for all softwood species for lumber 2" to 4" in thickness. Grading rules of an agency shall not be certified as conforming to American Lumber Standards if the dimension lumber rules fail to conform to the National Grading Rule. The National Grading Rule for Dimension Lumber classifies dimension into two width categories and five use categories. Dimension up to 4" wide is classified as "Structural Light Framing," "Light Framing" and "Studs." Dimension 6" and wider is classified as "Structural Joists and Planks." In addition, a single "Appearance Framing" grade of 2" and wider dimension is designed for those special uses where a high bending strength ratio coupled with high appearance is needed. The grades established under these classifications are shown in the WWPA Grade Chart on page 14.

The standard provides for the grading of lumber by mechanical means. Denoted Machine Stress Rated Lumber by the Western Wood Products Association, it is lumber that has been evaluated by mechanical stress rating equipment. Machine Stress-Rated Lumber is distinguished from visually stress graded lumber in that each piece is nondestructively tested and marked to indicate: Machine Rated, the extreme fiber stress in bending rating and the modulus of elasticity rating. Equipment and methods of certification are subject to approval of the Board of Review of the American Lumber Standards Committee. Machine Stress-Rated Lumber is also required to meet certain visual grading requirements.

The inspection provisions of the Standard provide that, subject to freedom of agreement between buyer and seller as to the settlement of complaints, the purchase, sale or shipment of American Standard grades of lumber involves agreement to submit to reinspection by the certified inspection agency under whose published rules the lumber was graded, any complaint involving grades, sizes, moisture content or tally. Grading agencies may not inspect lumber which has been used, such as lumber in place in structures, as the Standard provides that material be held intact and properly protected.

When American Standard Lumber is grade marked, the grade marking must be under regular mill supervision by an agency certified by the Board of Review of the American Lumber Standards Committee as competent and having adequate facilities for such supervision. Facsimiles of the grade marks of the certified grading and inspection agencies, such as the Western Wood Products Association, are available from the American Lumber Standards Committee. An explanation of the meaning of the symbols of the WWPA grade marking appears in the Grading Rule Section.

CHAPTER III

WWPA Grading Rules

WWPA GRADING RULES

Every piece of lumber, due to the individuality of the tree from which it is produced, has individual characteristics; consequently an infinite number of lumber grades could be developed. For economy and convenience in distribution and merchandising, it is necessary to limit the number of grades.

Each lumber grade is a grouping of pieces, all slightly different but all suitable for the use for which the grade is intended. The purpose of a grading rule is to describe as accurately as possible the pieces which may be accepted in each grade. For those use and size classifications for which design values are provided, the grading rules limit the strength reducing characteristics and provide an important part of the basis of the development of design values described in the Lumber Standard Chapter. Though grade descriptions list the maximum characteristics which may be accepted, the majority of pieces that fall within a grade will contain less than the maximum characteristics permitted.

The first grading rules used in the West in the 1880's were modifications of those used in the Great Lakes region. By 1906, predecessors of the Western Wood Products Association had established the first set of rules written especially for grading the principal western species.

Since 1924, manufacturers, distributors and users of western lumber have used grading rules developed within the framework of the voluntary product standards. The current WWPA grading rules comply with all the provisions of PS 20-70, the American Softwood Lumber Standard adopted in 1970.

Grade Classifications
The grade and size classifications of the WWPA Grading Rules for Western Lumber are shown in the charts on pages 14 and 15. All grades are shown except Shop and Factory Lumber. Descriptive titles show the use and range of sizes in each classification of grades. The numbers preceding each grade refer to the section numbers of the grading rules.

New Grading Provisions
Significant differences in current WWPA grading rules from previous grading provisions are:

1. All dimension and timber grades are now graded uniformly for the full length. Pieces may be cross cut and the same stress assignment is retained in the shorter pieces. Lumber may be used as supporting members over single or multiple spans without stress reduction for the multiple spans.

2. Standard sizes are now related to moisture content at the time of surfacing with green lumber sizes larger than dry sizes. A complete size table is shown on page 16. The result of the size relationships in dimension lumber is to permit designing universally to dry sizes, regardless of whether green or dry lumber is used in construction. This is possible because the green sizes will shrink to essentially the same size as dry lumber when they both reach the same equilibrium moisture content in the structure. Design values for dry lumber also apply to lumber manufactured green.

3. The grade stamp indicates the condition of seasoning at time of manufacture. When unseasoned lumber is grade stamped, it is stamped "S-GRN" (Surfaced Green) to indicate it was over 19% when surfaced. When lumber is manufactured at a maximum moisture content of 19% and is grade stamped, it is stamped "S-DRY" (Surfaced Dry). Dimension or boards seasoned to 15% or less in moisture content, and Selects, Finish, Shop and Moulding Stock may be stamped "MC-15".

4. Grade designations apply to dimension and timbers of all western species. The dimension grade descriptions and grade names of Light Framing, Studs, Structural Light Framing, Appearance Framing and Structural Joists and Planks are the same for all U.S. softwood species.

The Grade Stamp
A WWPA grade stamp on a piece of lumber indicates its assigned grade, species or species combination, moisture condition at time of surfacing, the mill of origin and may also give other useful information. At buyers' request, mills authorized to use WWPA grade stamps will grademark the lumber they ship.

This is the official Association certification mark. It denotes that the product was graded under WWPA supervision. The symbol is registered with the U. S. Patent Office and may be used only when authorized by the Western Wood Products Association.

12 Each mill is assigned a permanent number. Some mills are identified by mill name or abbreviation instead of by mill number.

2 COM This is an example of an official grade name abbreviation, in this case 2 Common Boards as described in the WWPA Grading Rules. Its appearance in a grade mark identifies the grade of a piece of lumber.

This is a species mark identifying the tree species from which the lumber is sawn, in this case Douglas Fir.

S-DRY
MC 15
S-GRN These marks denote the moisture content of the lumber when manufactured. "S-DRY" indicates a moisture content not exceeding 19 percent. "MC 15" indicates a moisture content not exceeding 15 percent. "S-GRN" indicates that the moisture content exceeded 19 percent.

12 When an Inspection Certificate issued by the Western Wood Products

Association is required on a shipment of lumber and specific grade marks are not used, the stock is identified by an imprint of the Association mark and the number of the shipping mill or inspector.

All of the above components may appear in various combinations in the official grade stamps as shown in the following example:

When the fiber stress in bending value appears on the grade stamp, it will be the single member design value. Single member design values are discussed on page 20.

Machine Stress-Rated Lumber

Machine stress-rated lumber is lumber that has been evaluated by mechanical stress rating equipment. MSR lumber is distinguished from visually stress graded lumber in that each piece is nondestructively tested and marked to indicate the modulus of elasticity. MSR lumber is also required to meet certain visual requirements as set forth in the Grading Rules.

To meet structural needs for a broad range of engineered construction, 14 "f-E" classifications are available. "E" designates the modulus of elasticity in one million pounds per square inch and "f" indicates a correlated fiber stress in bending for edge loading in pounds per square inch.

The "f-E" classifications and other recommended design values are shown in the design value tables on page 27.

Grade Marking Requirements

A grade stamp on machine stress-rated lumber indicates the stress rating system used meets requirements of the grading agency's certification

WWPA GRADING RULES

and quality control procedures. The grade stamp will show the agency trademark, the mill name or number, will include the phrase "Machine Rated," the species identification and conditions of moisture content.

Grade Stamp Example

Lumber Graded Under Other Rules

Listed below are certain products manufactured by some WWPA mills under West Coast Lumber Inspection Bureau (WCLIB) rules:

Barge Framing, Planking and Decking
Industrial Clears
Ladder and Pole Stock
Ladder Rails
Margin Plank
Pipe Stave Stock
Railroad Ties
Railway and Car Material
Ship Decking
Ship Plank
Tank Stock
Transmission Crossarms, Planks and Timbers

Special Products Rules

Some special grades and product specifications are not included in the WWPA grading rules and are available in supplementary WWPA publications. These include:

Laminated Decking
Laminated 2 x 4's
Sheet Board
Sheet Deck
Structural-Glued Vertically-Laminated
  Idaho White Pine Beams
Laminating Stock

WWPA GRADING RULES

WWPA GRADE CHART

Grade Classifications
of the National Grading
Rules for Dimension
Lumber Are Underlined.
"Economy" grade
listed therein is
not a National Grading
Rule grade

PANELING

10.00 SELECTS AND FINISH
   10.10 Selects
   (4/4 & Thicker, 2" & Wider)
     10.11 B & Btr 1 & 2 clear (IWP-Supreme)
     10.12 C Select (IWP-Choice)
     10.13 D Select (IWP-Quality)
     10.17 Australian Clears
     10.18 Pitch Selects
     10.19 Stained Selects

14.00 CLEAR PANELING
   10.10 Selects
   (4/4 & Thicker, 2" & Wider)
     10.11 B & Btr 1 & 2 clear (IWP-Supreme)
     10.12 C Select (IWP-Choice)
     10.13 D Select (IWP-Quality)

     10.19 Stained Selects

10.50 FINISH
   (3/8" to 4" Thick, 2" to 16" Wide)
     10.51 Superior
     10.52 Prime
     10.53 E

10.50 FINISH
   (3/8" & Thicker, 2" & Wider)
     10.51 Superior
     10.52 Prime
     10.53 E

30.10 BOARDS (COMMONS)
   (3/4" & Thicker, 2" & Wider)
     30.11 1 Common (IWP-Colonial)
     30.12 2 Common (IWP-Sterling)
     30.13 3 Common (IWP-Standard)
     30.14 4 Common (IWP-Utility)
     30.15 5 Common (IWP-Industrial)

30.20 KNOTTY PANELING
   30.10 Boards (Commons)
   (3/4" to 16/4", 2" & Wider)
     30.22 Selected No. 2 Common
     30.23 Selected No. 3 Common

20.10 FINISH, PANELING AND CEILING
   (2" & Thinner, 2" & Wider)
     20.11 Clear Heart
     20.12 A
     20.13 B

17.00 LATH
   (3/8" Thick, 1½" Wide,
   32" or 48" Long)
     17.11 No. 1 Lath
     17.12 No. 2 Lath

109 V.G. STEPPING K.D.
   (1¼" x 12")
     109c "C & Btr" V.G. Stepping
     109d "D" V.G. Stepping

30.50 118 ALTERNATE BOARDS
   (3/4", 1", 1¼", & 1½" Thick, 2" & Wider)
     118 a "Select Merchantable"
     118 b "Construction"
     118 c "Standard"
     118 d "Utility"
     118 e "Economy"

40.00 LIGHT FRAMING
   (2" to 4" Thick, 2" to 4" Wide)
     40.11 Construction
     40.12 Standard
     40.13 Utility
     40.14 Economy

41.00 STUDS
   (2" to 4" Thick, 2' to 4" Wide, 10' & Shorter)
     41.13 Stud
     41.14 Economy Stud

51.00 APPEARANCE FRAMING
   (2" to 4" Thick, 2" & Wider)
     51.10 Appearance

52.00 MACHINE STRESS-RATED LUMBER
   (2" & Less in Thickness, 2" & Wider)
   Fourteen "f-E" Classifications
   are available

62.00 STRUCTURAL JOISTS AND PLANKS ⑥
   (2" to 4" Thick, 6" & Wider)
     62.10 Select Structural
     62.11 No. 1
     62.12 No. 2
     62.13 No. 3
     62.14 Economy

70.00 BEAMS AND STRINGERS ⑥
     70.10 Select Structural
     70.11 No. 1
     70.12 No. 2 (No. 1 Mining)
     70.13 No. 3 (No. 2 Mining)

80.00 POSTS AND TIMBERS ⑥
     80.10 Select Structural
     80.11 No. 1
     80.12 No. 2 (No. 1 Mining)
     80.13 No. 3 (No. 2 Mining)

Chart hierarchy (left to right):

Lumber

- **Boards**
  - **Appearance Grades**
    - Selects and Finish
    - Boards (Commons)
    - Bevel or Bungalow
    - Special Western Red Cedar Rules
    - Specialties
  - **Boards, Sheathing, and Form Lumber**
- **Dimension** ⑦
  - **Framing**
  - **Special Dimension**
  - **Joists and Planks**
- **Timbers** ⑧
  - **Beams and Stringers**
    (5" & Thicker, Width More Than 2" Greater Than Thickness)
  - **Posts and Timbers**
    (5" & Thicker, Width Not More Than 2" Greater Than Thickness)

CEILING AND SIDING

12.00 CEILING, DROP SIDING AND RUSTIC
(1" & Thinner, 4" & Wider)
10.10 Selects
10.11 B & Btr 1 & 2 clear (IWP-Supreme)
10.12 C Select (IWP-Choice)
10.13 D Select (IWP-Quality)

10.19 Stained Selects

10.50 FINISH

10.51 Superior
10.52 Prime
10.53 E

30.10 BOARDS (COMMONS)

30.11 No. 1 Common (IWP-Colonial)
30.12 No. 2 Common (IWP-Sterling)
30.13 No. 3 Common (IWP-Standard)

16.00 BEVEL OR BUNGALOW SIDING ①
(1/2" & 3/4" Thick, 4" to 12" Wide)
16.11 Superior
16.12 Prime

21.00 BEVEL SIDING ④
(1/2", 5/8", & 3/4" Thick,
4" to 12" Wide)
21.11 Clear V.G. Heart
21.12 A
21.13 B
21.14 C

113 BATTENS
(1/4" x 3",
1" Thick, 2", 2½", & 3" Wide)
113a "Battens"

CASING AND BASE

11.00 CASING AND BASE
(1" & Thinner, 3" to 6" Wide)
10.10 Selects
10.11 B & Btr 1 & 2 clear (IWP-Supreme)
10.12 C Select (IWP-Choice)
10.13 D Select (IWP-Quality)

10.50 FINISH
10.51 Superior
10.52 Prime
10.53 E
92.10 MOULDINGS

112 GUTTER
(Run to Pattern)
112a "Clear Gutter"

30.60 STRESS-RATED BOARDS
(1", 1¼" & 1½" Thick
2" to 16" Wide)

FLOORING

13.00 FLOORING
(2" & Thinner, 3", 4", & 6" Wide)
10.10 Selects
10.11 B & Btr 1 & 2 clear (IWP-Supreme)
10.12 C Select (IWP-Choice)
10.13 D Select (IWP-Quality)

10.50 FINISH
10.51 Superior
10.52 Prime
10.53 E

115 PICKETS
(1¼" & 1½" sq.
& 1" x 3" flat)
115a "Pickets"

42.00 STRUCTURAL LIGHT FRAMING ⑥
(2" to 4" Thick, 2" to 4" Wide)
42.10 Select Structural
42.11 No. 1
42.12 No. 2
42.13 No. 3
42.14 Economy

54.00 FOUNDATION LUMBER ⑤
(2" & Thicker, 4" & Wider)
54.00 Foundation

55.00 DECKING
(2" to 4" Thick,
4" & Wider)
55.11 Selected Decking
55.12 Commercial Decking

58.00 SCAFFOLD PLANK ②
(1¼" & Thicker,
8" & Wider)
58.11 Scaffold No. 1
58.12 Scaffold No. 2

① ALL SPECIES EXCEPT WESTERN RED CEDAR

② DOUGLAS FIR ONLY

③ STRESS-RATED BOARDS ARE GRADED UNDER THE PROVISIONS OF LIGHT FRAMING, STRUCTURAL LIGHT FRAMING AND STRUCTURAL JOISTS AND PLANKS AND DESIGN VALUES ARE ASSIGNED.

④ WESTERN RED CEDAR ONLY

⑤ WESTERN CEDARS ONLY

⑥ DOUGLAS FIR AND LARCH MAY BE SPECIALLY SELECTED FOR "DENSE" MATERIAL PER PARAGRAPH 53.00

⑦ DESIGN VALUES ARE ASSIGNED TO ALL DIMENSION GRADES EXCEPT ECONOMY AND FOUNDATION.

⑧ DESIGN VALUES ARE ASSIGNED TO ALL TIMBER GRADES EXCEPT NO. 2 AND NO. 3

WWPA GRADING RULES

Table 3.1 Standard Lumber Sizes/Nominal, Dressed, Based On WWPA 1970 Rules

Product	Description	Nominal Size: Thickness In.	Nominal Size: Width In.	Dressed Dimensions: Thicknesses and Widths In. Surfaced Dry	Dressed Dimensions: Thicknesses and Widths In. Surfaced Unseasoned	Lengths Ft.
DIMENSION	S4S	2	2	1-1/2	1-9/16	6 ft. and longer in multiples of 1′
		3	3	2-1/2	2-9/16	
		4	4	3-1/2	3-9/16	
			6	5-1/2	5-5/8	
			8	7-1/4	7-1/2	
			10	9-1/4	9-1/2	
			12	11-1/4	11-1/2	
			Over 12	Off 3/4	Off 1/2	
SCAFFOLD PLANK	Rough Full Sawn or S4S	1 1/4 & Thicker	8 and Wider	Same	Same	Same
				Thickness In.	Width In.	
TIMBERS	Rough or S4S	5 and Larger		1/2 Off Nominal		Same

Product	Description	Nominal Size: Thickness In.	Nominal Size: Width In.	Dressed Dimensions: Thickness In.	Dressed Dimensions: Width In.	Lengths Ft.
DECKING	2″ Single T&G	2	6	1 1/2	5	6 ft. and longer in multiples of 1′
Decking is usually surfaced to single T&G in 2″ thickness and double T&G in 3″ and 4″ thicknesses			8		6 3/4	
			10		8 3/4	
			12		10 3/4	
	3″ and 4″ Double T&G	3	6	2 1/2	5 1/4	
		4		3 1/2		
FLOORING	(D & M), (S2S & CM)	3/8	2	5/16	1 1/8	4 ft. and longer in multiples of 1′
		1/2	3	7/16	2 1/8	
		5/8	4	9/16	3 1/8	
		1	5	3/4	4 1/8	
		1 1/4	6	1	5 1/8	
		1 1/2		1 1/4		
CEILING AND PARTITION	(S2S & CM)	3/8	3	5/16	2 1/8	4 ft. and longer in multiples of 1′
		1/2	4	7/16	3 1/8	
		5/8	5	9/16	4 1/8	
		3/4	6	11/16	5 1/8	
FACTORY AND SHOP LUMBER	S2S	1 (4/4)	5 and wider (4″ and wider in 4/4 No. 1 Shop and 4/4 No. 2 Shop)	25/32 (4/4)	Usually sold random width	4 ft. and longer in multiples of 1′
		1 1/4 (5/4)		1 5/32 (5/4)		
		1 1/2 (6/4)		1 13/32 (6/4)		
		1 3/4 (7/4)		1 19/32 (7/4)		
		2 (8/4)		1 13/16 (8/4)		
		2 1/2 (10/4)		2 3/8 (10/4)		
		3 (12/4)		2 3/4 (12/4)		
		4 (16/4)		3 3/4 (16/4)		

ABBREVIATIONS

Abbreviated descriptions appearing in the size table are explained below.

S1S — Surfaced one side.
S2S — Surfaced two sides.
S4S — Surfaced four sides.
S1S1E — Surfaced one side, one edge.
S1S2E — Surfaced one side, two edges.
CM — Center matched.
D & M — Dressed and matched.
T & G — Tongue and grooved.
EV1S — Edge vee on one side.
S1E — Surfaced one edge.

WWPA GRADING RULES

Table 3.1 Standard Lumber Sizes/Nominal, Dressed, Based On WWPA 1970 Rules

Product	Description	Nominal Size		Dressed Dimensions		
		Thickness In.	Width In.	Thickness In.	Width In.	Lengths Ft.
SELECTS AND COMMONS S-DRY	S1S, S2S, S4S, S1S1E, S1S2E....	4/4 5/4 6/4 7/4 8/4 9/4 10/4 11/4 12/4 16/4	2 3 4 5 6 7 8 and wider	3/4 1 5/32 1 13/32 1 19/32 1 13/16 2 3/32 2 3/8 2 9/16 2 3/4 3 3/4	1 1/2 2 1/2 3 1/2 4 1/2 5 1/2 6 1/2 3/4 Off nominal	6 ft. and longer in multiples of 1'
FINISH AND BOARDS S-DRY	S1S, S2S, S4S, S1S1E, S1S2E ...	3/8'' 1/2'' 5/8'' 3/4'' 1'' 1 1/4'' 1 1/2'' 1 3/4'' 2'' 2 1/2'' 3'' 3 1/2'' 4''	2 3 4 5 6 7 8 and wider	5/16'' 7/16'' 9/16'' 5/8'' 3/4'' 1'' 1 1/4'' 1 3/8'' 1 1/2'' 2'' 2 1/2'' 3'' 3 1/2''	1 1/2 2 1/2 3 1/2 4 1/2 5 1/2 6 1/2 3/4 off nominal	3' and longer. In Superior grade, 3% of 3' and 4' and 7% of 5' and 6' are permitted. In Prime grade, 20% of 3' to 6' is permitted.
RUSTIC AND DROP SIDING	(D & M) .... If 3/8'' or 1/2'' T & G specified, same over-all widths apply. (Shiplapped, 3/8-in. or 1/2-in. lap) ..	1	6 8 10 12	23/32	5 3/8 7 1/8 9 1/8 11 1/8	4 ft. and longer in multiples of 1'
PANELING AND SIDING	T&G or Shiplap.................	1	6 8 10 12	23/32	5 7/16 7 1/8 9 1/8 11 1/8	4 ft. and longer in multiples of 1'
CEILING AND PARTITION	T&G	5/8 1	4 6	9/16 23/32	3 3/8 5 3/8	4 ft. and longer in multiples of 1'
BEVEL SIDING	Bevel or Bungalow Siding........ Western Red Cedar Bevel Siding available in 1/2'', 5/8'', 3/4'' nominal thickness. Corresponding thick edge is 15/32'', 9/16'' and 3/4''. Widths for 8'' and wider, 1/2'' off nominal.	1/2 3/4	4 5 6 8 10 12	15/32 butt, 3/16 tip 3/4 butt, 3/16 tip	3 1/2 4 1/2 5 1/2 7 1/4 9 1/4 11 1/4	3 ft. and longer in multiples of 1'

Product	Description	Nominal Size		Dressed Dimensions			
		Thickness In.	Width In.	Surfaced Dry	Surfaced Unseasoned	Surfaced Dry	Surfaced Unseasoned
STRESS RATED BOARDS	S1S, S2S, S4S, S1S1E, S1S2E....	1 1 1/4 1 1/2	2 3 4 5 6 7 8 and Wider	3/4 1 1 1/4	25/32 1 1/32 1 9/32	1 1/2 2 1/2 3 1/2 4 1/2 5 1/2 6 1/2 Off 3/4	1 9/16 2 9/16 3 9/16 4 5/8 5 5/8 6 5/8 Off 1/2

(Lengths for Stress Rated Boards: 6 ft. and longer in multiples of 1')

MINIMUM ROUGH SIZES   Thicknesses and Widths Dry or Unseasoned All Lumber (S1E, S2E, S1S, S2S)

80% of the pieces in a shipment shall be at least 1/8'' thicker than the standard surfaced size, the remaining 20% at least 3/32'' thicker than the surfaced size. Widths shall be at least 1/8'' wider than standard surfaced widths.

When specified to be full sawn, lumber may not be manufactured to a size less than the size specified.

CHAPTER IV

Lumber Design Values

LUMBER DESIGN VALUES

The recommended design values listed in the tables on the following pages are for lumber of species manufactured and shipped by mills in the 12 western states. The values for visually graded lumber are for normal loading conditions and computed in accordance with the requirements of "Methods for Establishing Clear Wood Strength Values" ASTM D-2555 and "Methods for Establishing Structural Grades for Visually Graded Lumber" ASTM D-245 published by the American Society for Testing and Materials.

The recommended design values for Machine Stress-Rated (MSR) Lumber are established to provide an extensive range of values for many use categories. Each piece is nondestructively tested and grade-marked to indicate the "f-E" classification. "E" designates the modulus of elasticity in units of one million pounds per square inch and "f" indicates the fiber stress in bending for edge loading in pounds per square inch. MSR lumber is also required to meet certain visual requirements as set forth in the Grading Rules. Rigid quality control standards and procedures are maintained including laboratory strength tests, certification of machines, plant testing on every production shift and continual quality inspections.

Design values are assigned to six basic properties of wood. These are extreme fiber stress in bending (Fb), tension parallel to grain (Ft), horizontal shear (Fv), compression parallel to grain (Fc), compression perpendicular to grain (Fc⊥) and modulus of elasticity (E). In the interest of safety, design values are calculated by assuming that any piece of a particular grade can have the maximum strength reducing characteristics described in the rules and will be loaded to the full maximum design load for a period of ten years. Details of the development of design values are described on page 8.

Fiber stress in bending values for all size catagories apply to pieces loaded on the narrow face as beams, joists and rafters, and to pieces loaded on the wide face as planks or decking, with the following exceptions:

1. Bending stresses for Beams and Stringers apply only to pieces loaded on the narrow face.

2. Bending stresses for Decking and Scaffold Plank apply only to pieces loaded on the wide face.

DESIGN CONSIDERATIONS

Single Member Design Values
Single member fiber stress in bending "Fb" design values are recommended for use where the strength of an individual piece, such as a beam, girder or post is or may be responsible for carrying a specific design load.

Repetitive Member Design Values
In structures where 2" to 4" thick lumber is used repetitively such as joists, studs, rafters and decking, the pieces side by side share the load and the strength of the entire assembly is enhanced. Therefore, where 3 or more members are adjacent or are not more than 24" apart and are joined by floor, roof or other load distributing elements, the repetitive member design values for fiber stress in bending "Fb" shown in the design value tables are recommended.

Effect of Moisture Content on Design Values
The recommended design values shown in the design value tables are applicable to lumber that will be used under dry conditions such as in most covered structures. The section properties of lumber for use in design should be based on the surfaced sizes shown herein. For 2" to 4" thick lumber the DRY or MC15 surfaced size should be used. In calculating design values, the natural gain in strength and stiffness that occurs as lumber dries has been taken into consideration as well as the reduction in size that occurs when unseasoned lumber shrinks. The gain in load carrying capacity due to increased strength and stiffness resulting from drying more than offsets the design effect of size reductions due to shrinkage. For 5" and thicker lumber, the surfaced sizes also may be used because design values have been adjusted to compensate for any loss in size by shrinkage which may occur.

Design values for Machine Stress-Rated Lumber are based on DRY surfaced sizes and a condition of use where moisture content will not exceed 19%. Design values for Scaffold Plank are based on exposed conditions of use.

Because of the built-in adjustments explained above, surfaced sizes should be used for design purposes in all instances. There are three situations where the tabulated design values should be adjusted.

Adjustment Factors for MC15 Lumber
(Use only when moisture content will not exceed 15% in use)

When 2" to 4" thick lumber is manufactured at a maximum moisture content of 15% and used in a condition where the moisture content does not exceed 15%, the design values may be multiplied by the following adjustment factors:

Extreme Fiber in Bending "Fb"	Tension Parallel to Grain "Ft"	Horizontal Shear "Fv"	Compression Perpendicular to Grain "Fc⊥"	Compression Parallel to Grain "Fc"	Modulus of Elasticity "E"
1.08	1.08	1.05	1.00	1.17	1.05

When 2" to 4" thick lumber is designed for exposed uses where the moisture content will exceed 15% for an extended period of time, the MC 15 design values should be multiplied by the following adjustment factors:

Extreme Fiber in Bending "Fb"	Tension Parallel to Grain "Ft"	Horizontal Shear "Fv"	Compression Perpendicular to Grain "Fc⊥"	Compression Parallel to Grain "Fc"	Modulus of Elasticity "E"
0.79	0.80	0.95	0.67	0.61	0.92

Adjustment Factors for Nominal 2" to 4" Thick Lumber
(Use only when moisture content will exceed 19% in use.)

When 2" to 4" thick lumber is designed for

exposed uses where the moisture content will exceed 19% for an extended period of time, the design values shown in the tables should be multiplied by the following adjustment factors: (Note that these factors apply to the DRY Decking values.)

Extreme Fiber in Bending "Fb"	Tension Parallel to Grain "Ft"	Horizontal Shear "Fv"	Compression Perpendicular to Grain "Fc⊥"	Compression Parallel to Grain "Fc"	Modulus of Elasticity "E"
0.86	0.84	0.97	0.67	0.70	0.97

Adjustment Factors for 5″ and Thicker Lumber
(Use only when moisture content will exceed 19% in use)

When lumber 5″ and thicker is designed for exposed uses where the moisture content will exceed 19% for an extended period of time, the design values should be multiplied by the following adjustment factors:

Extreme Fiber in Bending "Fb"	Tension Parallel to Grain "Ft"	Horizontal Shear "Fv"	Compression Perpendicular to Grain "Fc⊥"	Compression Parallel to Grain "Fc"	Modulus of Elasticity "E"
1.00	1.00	1.00	0.67	0.91	1.00

Notes on Horizontal Shear (Fv)
All horizontal shear values are established as if a piece were split full length and as such the values are reduced from those permitted to be assigned in accordance with ASTM standards. This reduction is made to compensate for any degree of shake, check or split that might develop in a piece.

2″ Thick Lumber
The horizontal shear values for 2″ Dimension shown herein are based on dry lumber manufactured at a maximum of 19% moisture content. When such lumber is manufactured unseasoned, the tabulated values should be multiplied by a factor of 0.92.

For convenience, the tables below may be used to determine horizontal shear values for any grade of 2″ thick lumber in any species when the length of split or check is known:

When length of split is:	Multiply Tabulated Fv value by:
No split	2.00
½ x wide face	1.66
1 x wide face	1.34
1½ x wide face or more	1.00

3″ and Thicker Lumber
Horizontal shear values for 3″ and thicker lumber also are established as if a piece were split full length. When specific lengths of splits are known and any increase in them is not anticipated, the following adjustments may be applied:

When length of split on wide face is:	Multiply Tabulated Fv value by:
No split	2:00
½ x narrow face	1.68
1 x narrow face	1.36
1½ x narrow face	1.04
2 x narrow face or more	1.00

LUMBER DESIGN VALUES

The horizontal shear values for 3″ and 4″ thick Dimension shown herein are based on dry lumber manufactured at a maximum of 19% moisture content. When such lumber is manufactured unseasoned, the tabulated values should be multiplied by a factor of 0.92.

Effect of Depth on Design Values
ASTM standards now provide means to adjust fiber stress in bending values depending on width, thickness and how a piece of lumber is used (on edge or flatwise). For stress rated boards and dimension 2″ to 4″ in thickness when used flatwise, the recommended design values for fiber stress in bending shown in the design value tables may be multiplied by the factors shown in the following table.

Adjustment Factors for Depth Effect
(Apply to Design Values for Extreme Fiber in Bending (Fb))

Lumber Width	When used as a plank Nominal Thickness			
	1″	2″	3″	4″
2″ to 4″	1.19	1.10	1.04	1.00
6″ and wider	1.32	1.22	1.16	1.11

For all widths of Decking and Scaffold Plank, use factors listed above for 2″ to 4″ widths.

Duration of Loading
The values shown in the design value tables are for normal loading conditions and are applicable in all conditions other than those for which specific exceptions are made. Normal load duration contemplates stressing a member to the allowable stress by the application of the full maximum design load for a duration of approximately 10 years either continuously or cumulatively, without encroaching on the factor of safety.

When the duration of the full maximum load does not exceed the period indicated, increase the design values shown in the tables as follows:

> 15 percent for 2 months' duration, as for snow.
> 25 percent for 7 days' duration.
> 33⅓ percent for wind or earthquake.
> 100 percent for impact.

Design values given in the tables herein for normal loading conditions, may be used without regard to impact if the stress induced by impact does not exceed the allowable unit stress for normal loading. The above increases are not cumulative. The resulting structural members shall not be smaller than required for a longer duration of loading. These provisions do not apply to modulus of elasticity.

Where a member is fully stressed to the maximum allowable stress for more than 10 years, either continuously or cumulatively under the condition of maximum design load, use working stresses 90 percent of those in the tables. These provisions do not apply to modulus of elasticity; however, they do apply to mechanical fastenings, except as otherwise noted.

LUMBER DESIGN VALUES

Table 4.1 LIGHT FRAMING and STUDS—2″ to 4″ Thick, 2″ to 4″ Wide
Recommended Design Values in Pounds Per Square Inch

Grades Described In
Sections 40.00 and 41.00
WWPA Grading Rules

Species or Group	Grade	Extreme Fiber Stress in Bending "Fb"		Tension Parallel to Grain "Ft"	Horizontal Shear "Fv"	Compression		Modulus of Elasticity "E"
		Single	Repetitive			Perpendicular "Fc ⊥"	Parallel to Grain "Fc"	
DOUGLAS FIR-LARCH	Construction¹	1050	1200	625	95	385	1150	1,500,000
	Standard¹	600	675	350	95	385	925	1,500,000
	Utility¹	275	325	175	95	385	600	1,500,000
	Studs	800	925	475	95	385	600	1,500,000
DOUGLAS FIR SOUTH	Construction¹	1000	1150	600	90	335	1000	1,100,000
	Standard¹	550	650	325	90	335	850	1,100,000
	Utility¹	275	300	150	90	335	550	1,100,000
	Studs	775	875	450	90	335	550	1,100,000
HEM-FIR	Construction¹	825	975	475	75	245	925	1,200,000
	Standard¹	450	525	275	75	245	750	1,200,000
	Utility¹	225	250	125	75	245	500	1,200,000
	Studs	625	725	375	75	245	500	1,200,000
MOUNTAIN HEMLOCK	Construction¹	875	1000	525	95	370	900	1,000,000
	Standard¹	500	575	275	95	370	725	1,000,000
	Utility¹	225	275	125	95	370	475	1,000,000
	Studs	675	775	400	95	370	475	1,000,000
MOUNTAIN HEMLOCK—HEM-FIR	Construction¹	825	975	475	75	245	900	1,000,000
	Standard¹	450	525	275	75	245	725	1,000,000
	Utility¹	225	250	125	75	245	475	1,000,000
	Studs	625	725	375	75	245	475	1,000,000
SUBALPINE FIR (White Woods) (Western Woods)	Construction¹	625	725	375	60	195	650	800,000
	Standard¹	350	400	200	60	195	525	800,000
	Utility¹	175	200	100	60	195	350	800,000
	Studs	475	550	275	60	195	350	800,000
ENGELMANN SPRUCE (Engelmann Spruce-Lodgepole Pine)	Construction¹	675	775	400	70	195	650	1,000,000
	Standard¹	375	425	225	70	195	525	1,000,000
	Utility¹	175	200	100	70	195	350	1,000,000
	Studs	525	600	300	70	195	350	1,000,000
LODGEPOLE PINE	Construction¹	775	875	450	70	250	800	1,000,000
	Standard¹	425	500	250	70	250	675	1,000,000
	Utility¹	200	225	125	70	250	425	1,000,000
	Studs	600	675	350	70	250	425	1,000,000
PONDEROSA PINE-SUGAR PINE (Ponderosa Pine-Lodgepole Pine)	Construction¹	725	825	425	70	250	775	1,000,000
	Standard¹	400	450	225	70	250	625	1,000,000
	Utility¹	200	225	100	70	250	400	1,000,000
	Studs	550	625	325	70	250	400	1,000,000
IDAHO WHITE PINE	Construction¹	725	850	425	65	240	825	1,100,000
	Standard¹	400	475	250	65	240	675	1,100,000
	Utility¹	200	225	125	65	240	450	1,100,000
	Studs	550	650	325	65	240	450	1,100,000
WESTERN CEDARS	Construction¹	750	850	425	75	295	875	900,000
	Standard¹	425	475	250	75	295	725	900,000
	Utility¹	200	225	125	75	295	475	900,000
	Studs	575	650	325	75	295	475	900,000
WESTERN HEMLOCK	Construction¹	925	1050	550	90	280	1050	1,300,000
	Standard¹	525	600	300	90	280	850	1,300,000
	Utility¹	250	275	150	90	280	550	1,300,000
	Studs	700	800	425	90	280	550	1,300,000

¹Fb, Ft and Fc recommended design values apply only to the 4″ widths of these grades. See table 4.6 for 2″ width and Table 4.7 for 3″ width.

Table 4.2 STRUCTURAL LIGHT FRAMING and APPEARANCE—2″ to 4″ Thick, 2″ to 4″ Wide
Recommended Design Values in Pounds Per Square Inch

Grades Described in
Sections 42.00 and 50.00
WWPA Grading Rules

Species or Group	Grade	Extreme Fiber Stress in Bending "Fb"		Tension Parallel to Grain "Ft"	Horizontal Shear "Fv"	Compression		Modulus of Elasticity "E"
		Single	Repetitive			Perpendicular "Fc ⊥"	Parallel to Grain "Fc"	
DOUGLAS FIR-LARCH	Select Structural*	2100	2400	1200	95	385	1600	1,800,000
	No. 1*/Appearance	1750	2050	1050	95	385	1250/1500	1,800,000
	No. 2*	1450	1650	850	95	385	1000	1,700,000
	No. 3	800	925	475	95	385	600	1,500,000
DOUGLAS FIR SOUTH	Select Structural	2000	2300	1150	90	335	1400	1,400,000
	No. 1/Appearance	1700	1950	975	90	335	1150/1350	1,400,000
	No. 2	1400	1600	825	90	335	900	1,300,000
	No. 3	775	875	450	90	335	550	1,300,000
HEM-FIR	Select Structural	1650	1900	975	75	245	1300	1,500,000
	No. 1/Appearance	1400	1600	825	75	245	1000/1200	1,500,000
	No. 2	1150	1300	675	75	245	800	1,400,000
	No. 3	625	725	375	75	245	500	1,200,000
MOUNTAIN HEMLOCK	Select Structural	1750	2000	1000	95	370	1250	1,300,000
	No. 1/Appearance	1450	1700	850	95	370	1000/1200	1,300,000
	No. 2	1200	1400	700	95	370	775	1,100,000
	No. 3	675	775	400	95	370	475	1,000,000
MOUNTAIN HEMLOCK-HEM-FIR	Select Structural	1650	1900	975	75	245	1250	1,300,000
	No. 1/Appearance	1400	1600	825	75	245	1000/1200	1,300,000
	No. 2	1150	1300	675	75	245	775	1,100,000
	No. 3	625	725	375	75	245	475	1,000,000
SUBALPINE FIR (White Woods) (Western Woods)	Select Structural	1250	1400	725	60	195	900	900,000
	No. 1/Appearance	1050	1200	600	60	195	700/850	900,000
	No. 2	850	1000	500	60	195	550	900,000
	No. 3	475	550	275	60	195	350	800,000
ENGELMANN SPRUCE (Engelmann Spruce-Lodgepole Pine)	Select Structural	1350	1550	775	70	195	900	1,200,000
	No. 1/Appearance	1150	1300	675	70	195	725/875	1,200,000
	No. 2	950	1100	550	70	195	575	1,100,000
	No. 3	525	600	300	70	195	350	1,000,000

(Table Continued Page 23)

LUMBER DESIGN VALUES

(Continued From Page 22)

Table 4.2 STRUCTURAL LIGHT FRAMING and APPEARANCE—2″ to 4″ Thick, 2″ to 4″ Wide
Recommended Design Values in Pounds Per Square Inch

Grades Described in
Sections 42.00 and 50.00
WWPA Grading Rules

Species or Group	Grade	Extreme Fiber Stress in Bending "Fb"		Tension Parallel to Grain "Ft"	Horizontal Shear "Fv"	Compression		Modulus of Elasticity "E"
		Single	Repetitive			Perpendicular "Fc⊥"	Parallel to Grain "Fc"	
LODGEPOLE PINE	Select Structural	1500	1750	875	70	250	1150	1,300,000
	No. 1/Appearance	1300	1500	750	70	250	900/1050	1,300,000
	No. 2	1050	1200	625	70	250	700	1,200,000
	No. 3	600	675	350	70	250	425	1,000,000
PONDEROSA PINE-SUGAR PINE (Ponderosa Pine-Lodgepole Pine)	Select Structural	1400	1650	825	70	250	1050	1,200,000
	No. 1/Appearance	1200	1400	700	70	250	850/1000	1,200,000
	No. 2	1000	1150	575	70	250	675	1,100,000
	No. 3	550	625	325	70	250	400	1,000,000
IDAHO WHITE PINE	Select Structural	1450	1650	850	65	240	1150	1,400,000
	No. 1/Appearance	1250	1400	725	65	240	925/1100	1,400,000
	No. 2	1000	1150	600	65	240	725	1,300,000
	No. 3	550	650	325	65	240	450	1,100,000
WESTERN CEDARS	Select Structural	1450	1700	850	75	295	1250	1,100,000
	No. 1/Appearance	1250	1450	725	75	295	975/1150	1,100,000
	No. 2	1000	1200	600	75	295	775	1,000,000
	No. 3	575	650	325	75	295	475	900,000
WESTERN HEMLOCK	Select Structural	1800	2100	1050	90	280	1450	1,600,000
	No. 1/Appearance	1550	1800	900	90	280	1150/1350	1,600,000
	No. 2	1300	1450	750	90	280	900	1,400,000
	No. 3	700	800	425	90	280	550	1,300,000

*For dense values, see Table 4.8

Table 4.3 STRUCTURAL JOISTS and PLANKS and APPEARANCE—2″ to 4″ Thick, 6″ and Wider
Recommended Design Values in Pounds Per Square Inch

Grades Described in
Sections 62.00 and 50.00
WWPA Grading Rules

Species or Group	Grade	Extreme Fiber Stress in Bending "Fb"		Tension Parallel to Grain "Ft"	Horizontal Shear "Fv"	Compression		Modulus of Elasticity "E"
		Single	Repetitive			Perpendicular "Fc⊥"	Parallel to Grain "Fc"	
DOUGLAS FIR-LARCH	Select Structural*	1800	2050	1200	95	385	1400	1,800,000
	No. 1*/Appearance	1500	1750	1000	95	385	1250/1500	1,800,000
	No. 2*	1250	1450	825	95	385	1050	1,700,000
	No. 3*	725	850	475	95	385	675	1,500,000
DOUGLAS FIR SOUTH	Select Structural	1700	1950	1150	90	335	1250	1,400,000
	No. 1/Appearance	1450	1650	975	90	335	1150/1350	1,400,000
	No. 2	1200	1350	775	90	335	950	1,300,000
	No. 3	700	800	450	90	335	600	1,100,000
HEM-FIR	Select Structural	1400	1650	950	75	245	1150	1,500,000
	No. 1/Appearance	1200	1400	800	75	245	1000/1200	1,500,000
	No. 2	1000	1150	650	75	245	850	1,400,000
	No. 3	575	675	375	75	245	550	1,200,000
MOUNTAIN HEMLOCK	Select Structural	1500	1700	1000	95	370	1100	1,300,000
	No. 1/Appearance	1250	1450	850	95	370	1000/1200	1,300,000
	No. 2	1050	1200	675	95	370	825	1,100,000
	No. 3	625	700	400	95	370	525	1,000,000
MOUNTAIN HEMLOCK-HEM-FIR	Select Structural	1400	1650	950	75	245	1100	1,300,000
	No. 1/Appearance	1200	1400	800	75	245	1000/1200	1,300,000
	No. 2	1000	1150	650	75	245	825	1,100,000
	No. 3	575	675	375	75	245	525	1,000,000
SUBALPINE FIR (White Woods) (Western Woods)	Select Structural	1050	1200	700	60	195	800	900,000
	No. 1/Appearance	900	1050	600	60	195	700/850	900,000
	No. 2	750	850	475	60	195	600	900,000
	No. 3	425	500	275	60	195	375	800,000
ENGELMANN SPRUCE (Engelmann Spruce-Lodgepole Pine)	Select Structural	1150	1350	775	70	195	800	1,200,000
	No. 1/Appearance	975	1150	650	70	195	725/875	1,200,000
	No. 2	800	925	525	70	195	600	1,100,000
	No. 3	475	550	300	70	195	375	1,000,000
LODGEPOLE PINE	Select Structural	1300	1500	875	70	250	1000	1,300,000
	No. 1/Appearance	1100	1300	750	70	250	900/1050	1,300,000
	No. 2	925	1050	600	70	250	750	1,200,000
	No. 3	525	625	350	70	250	475	1,000,000
PONDEROSA PINE-SUGAR PINE (Ponderosa Pine-Lodgepole Pine)	Select Structural	1200	1400	825	70	250	950	1,200,000
	No. 1/Appearance	1050	1200	700	70	250	850/1000	1,200,000
	No. 2	850	975	550	70	250	700	1,100,000
	No. 3	500	575	325	70	250	450	1,000,000
IDAHO WHITE PINE	Select Structural	1250	1450	825	65	240	1000	1,400,000
	No. 1/Appearance	1050	1200	700	65	240	925/1100	1,400,000
	No. 2	875	1000	575	65	240	775	1,300,000
	No. 3	500	575	325	65	240	475	1,100,000
WESTERN CEDARS	Select Structural	1250	1450	850	75	295	1100	1,100,000
	No. 1/Appearance	1050	1250	725	75	295	975/1150	1,100,000
	No. 2	875	1000	575	75	295	825	1,000,000
	No. 3	525	600	325	75	295	525	900,000
WESTERN HEMLOCK	Select Structural	1550	1800	1050	90	280	1300	1,600,000
	No. 1/Appearance	1350	1550	900	90	280	1150/1350	1,600,000
	No. 2	1100	1250	725	90	280	975	1,400,000
	No. 3	650	750	425	90	280	625	1,300,000

*For dense values, see Table 4.8

LUMBER DESIGN VALUES

Table 4.4 BEAMS and STRINGERS—5″ and Thicker
Width More Than 2″ Greater Than Thickness
Recommended Design Values in Pounds Per Square Inch

Grades Described
in Section 70.00
WWPA Grading Rules

Species or Group	Grade	Extreme Fiber Stress in Bending "Fb" Single Members	Tension Parallel to Grain "Ft"	Horizontal Shear "Fv"	Compression Perpendicular "Fc⊥"	Parallel to Grain "Fc"	Modulus of Elasticity "E"
DOUGLAS FIR-LARCH	Select Structural*	1600	1050	85	385	1100	1,600,000
	No. 1*	1350	900	85	385	925	1,600,000
DOUGLAS FIR SOUTH	Select Structural	1550	1050	85	335	1000	1,200,000
	No. 1	1300	850	85	335	850	1,200,000
HEM-FIR	Select Structural	1250	850	70	245	900	1,300,000
	No. 1	1050	700	70	245	775	1,300,000
MOUNTAIN HEMLOCK	Select Structural	1350	900	90	370	875	1,100,000
	No. 1	1100	750	90	370	750	1,100,000
MOUNTAIN HEMLOCK—HEM-FIR	Select Structural	1250	850	70	245	875	1,100,000
	No. 1	1050	700	70	245	750	1,100,000
SUBALPINE FIR (White Woods) (Western Woods)	Select Structural	950	625	60	195	625	900,000
	No. 1	800	525	60	195	525	900,000
ENGELMANN SPRUCE (Engelmann Spruce-Lodgepole Pine)	Select Structural	1050	700	65	195	650	1,100,000
	No. 1	875	575	65	195	550	1,100,000
LODGEPOLE PINE	Select Structural	1150	775	65	250	800	1,100,000
	No. 1	975	650	65	250	675	1,100,000
PONDEROSA PINE-SUGAR PINE (Ponderosa Pine-Lodgepole Pine)	Select Structural	1100	725	65	250	750	1,100,000
	No. 1	925	625	65	250	625	1,100,000
IDAHO WHITE PINE	Select Structural	1100	750	60	240	800	1,200,000
	No. 1	925	625	60	240	675	1,200,000
WESTERN CEDARS	Select Structural	1100	750	70	295	875	1,000,000
	No. 1	950	625	70	295	725	1,000,000
WESTERN HEMLOCK	Select Structural	1400	950	85	280	1000	1,400,000
	No. 1	1150	775	85	280	850	1,400,000

*For dense values, see Table 4.8

Table 4.5 POSTS and TIMBERS—5″ x 5″ and Larger
Width Not More than 2″ Greater Than Thickness
Recommended Design Values in Pounds Per Square Inch

Grades Described
in Section 80.00
WWPA Grading Rules

Species or Group	Grade	Extreme Fiber Stress in Bending "Fb" Single Members	Tension Parallel to Grain "Ft"	Horizontal Shear "Fv"	Compression Perpendicular "Fc⊥"	Parallel to Grain "Fc"	Modulus of Elasticity "E"
DOUGLAS FIR-LARCH	Select Structural*	1500	1000	85	385	1150	1,600,000
	No. 1*	1200	825	85	385	1000	1,600,000
DOUGLAS FIR SOUTH	Select Structural	1400	950	85	335	1050	1,200,000
	No. 1	1150	775	85	335	925	1,200,000
HEM-FIR	Select Structural	1200	800	70	245	950	1,300,000
	No. 1	975	650	70	245	850	1,300,000
MOUNTAIN HEMLOCK	Select Structural	1250	825	90	370	925	1,100,000
	No. 1	1000	675	90	370	800	1,100,000
MOUNTAIN HEMLOCK—HEM-FIR	Select Structural	1200	800	70	245	925	1,100,000
	No. 1	975	650	70	245	800	1,100,000
SUBALPINE FIR (White Woods) (Western Woods)	Select Structural	875	600	60	195	675	900,000
	No. 1	725	475	60	195	575	900,000
ENGELMANN SPRUCE (Engelmann Spruce-Lodgepole Pine)	Select Structural	950	650	65	195	675	1,100,000
	No. 1	775	525	65	195	600	1,100,000
LODGEPOLE PINE	Select Structural	1100	725	65	250	850	1,100,000
	No. 1	875	600	65	250	725	1,100,000
PONDEROSA PINE—SUGAR PINE (Ponderosa Pine-Lodgepole Pine)	Select Structural	1000	675	65	250	800	1,100,000
	No. 1	825	550	65	250	700	1,100,000
IDAHO WHITE PINE	Select Structural	1050	700	60	240	850	1,200,000
	No. 1	850	575	60	240	750	1,200,000
WESTERN CEDARS	Select Structural	1050	700	70	295	900	1,000,000
	No. 1	850	575	70	295	800	1,000,000
WESTERN HEMLOCK	Select Structural	1300	875	85	280	1100	1,400,000
	No. 1	1050	700	85	280	950	1,400,000

*For dense values, see Table 4.8

LUMBER DESIGN VALUES

Table 4.6   LIGHT FRAMING—2″ and Less in Thickness[1], 2″ Wide
Recommended Design Values in Pounds Per Square Inch
Horizontal Shear "Fv", Compression Perpendicular "Fc ⊥"
and Modulus of Elasticity "E" values are shown in Table 4.1, Light Framing.

Grades Described
in Section 40.00
WWPA Grading Rules

Species or Group	Grade	Extreme Fiber Stress in Bending "Fb"		Tension Parallel to Grain "Ft"	Compression Parallel to Grain "Fc"
		Single	Repetitive		
DOUGLAS FIR-LARCH	Construction Standard Utility	950 450 125	1100 500 150	500 225 75	1150 925 375
DOUGLAS FIR SOUTH	Construction Standard Utility	900 425 125	1050 475 150	475 225 75	1000 850 350
HEM-FIR	Construction Standard Utility	750 350 100	875 400 125	400 175 50	925 750 300
MOUNTAIN HEMLOCK	Construction Standard Utility	800 375 125	925 425 125	425 200 50	900 725 300
MOUNTAIN HEMLOCK-HEM-FIR	Construction Standard Utility	750 350 100	875 400 125	400 175 50	900 725 300
SUBALPINE FIR (White Woods) (Western Woods)	Construction Standard Utility	575 250 75	650 300 100	300 150 50	650 525 225
ENGELMANN SPRUCE (Engelmann Spruce-Lodgepole Pine)	Construction Standard Utility	625 275 100	700 325 100	325 150 50	650 525 225
LODGEPOLE PINE	Construction Standard Utility	700 325 100	800 375 125	375 175 50	800 675 275
PONDEROSA PINE-SUGAR PINE (Ponderosa Pine Lodgepole Pine)	Construction Standard Utility	650 300 100	750 350 100	350 150 50	775 625 250
IDAHO WHITE PINE	Construction Standard Utility	650 300 100	750 350 100	350 175 50	825 675 275
WESTERN CEDARS	Construction Standard Utility	675 300 100	775 350 100	350 175 50	875 725 300
WESTERN HEMLOCK	Construction Standard Utility	825 375 125	950 450 125	450 200 75	1050 850 350

[1]On 1″, 1¼″ and 1½″ nominal thickness, "SRB" designating "Stress Rated Boards" will be shown on grade stamps.

Table 4.7   LIGHT FRAMING—3″ and Less in Thickness[1], 3″ Wide
Recommended Design Values in Pounds Per Square Inch
Horizontal Shear "Fv", Compression Perpendicular "Fc ⊥"
and Modulus of Elasticity "E" values are shown in Table 4.1, Light Framing.

Grades Described
in Section 40.00
WWPA Grading Rules

Species or Group	Grade	Extreme Fiber Stress in Bending "Fb"		Tension Parallel to Grain "Ft"	Compression Parallel to Grain "Fc"
		Single	Repetitive		
DOUGLAS FIR-LARCH	Construction Standard Utility	875 550 150	1000 625 175	500 300 100	1150 925 450
DOUGLAS FIR SOUTH	Construction Standard Utility	825 525 150	950 600 175	475 300 75	1000 850 400
HEM-FIR	Construction Standard Utility	675 425 125	800 500 125	375 225 50	925 750 350
MOUNTAIN HEMLOCK	Construction Standard Utility	725 450 125	825 525 150	400 250 75	900 725 350
MOUNTAIN HEMLOCK-HEM-FIR	Construction Standard Utility	675 425 125	800 500 125	375 225 50	900 725 350

(Table 4.7 Continued Page 26)

LUMBER DESIGN VALUES   Table 4.7 (continued from page 25)

Species or Group	Grade	Extreme Fiber Stress in Bending "Fb"		Tension Parallel to Grain "Ft"	Compression Parallel to Grain "Fc"
		Single	Repetitive		
SUBALPINE FIR (White Woods) (Western Woods)	Construction Standard Utility	525 325 100	600 375 100	300 175 50	650 525 250
ENGELMANN SPRUCE (Engelmann Spruce-Lodgepole Pine)	Construction Standard Utility	550 350 100	650 400 125	325 200 50	650 525 250
LODGEPOLE PINE	Construction Standard Utility	625 400 125	725 450 125	350 225 75	800 675 325
PONDEROSA PINE-SUGAR PINE (Ponderosa-Pine-Lodgepole Pine)	Construction Standard Utility	600 375 100	675 425 125	325 200 50	775 625 300
IDAHO WHITE PINE	Construction Standard Utility	600 375 100	700 425 125	350 225 75	825 675 325
WESTERN CEDARS	Construction Standard Utility	600 375 125	700 450 125	350 225 75	875 725 350
WESTERN HEMLOCK	Construction Standard Utility	750 475 150	875 550 175	425 275 75	1050 850 400

¹On 1", 1¼" and 1½" nominal thickness, "SRB" designating "Stress Rated Boards" will be shown on grade stamps.

Table 4.8   DENSE DOUGLAS FIR—LARCH
Recommended Design Values in Pounds Per Square Inch

Grades Described in Section 53.00 WWPA Grading Rules

Species or Group	Grade	Extreme Fiber Stress in Bending "Fb"		Tension Parallel to Grain "Ft"	Hori-zontal Shear "Fv"	Compression		Modulus of Elasticity "E"
						Perpen-dicular "Fc ⊥"	Parallel to Grain "Fc"	
		Single	Repetitive					
STRUCTURAL LIGHT FRAMING	Dense Sel. Struc. Dense No. 1 Dense No. 2	2450 2050 1700	2800 2400 1950	1400 1200 1000	95 95 95	455 455 455	1850 1450 1150	1,900,000 1,900,000 1,700,000
STRUCTURAL JOISTS AND PLANKS	Dense Sel. Struc. Dense No. 1 Dense No. 2	2100 1800 1450	2400 2050 1700	1400 1200 950	95 95 95	455 455 455	1650 1450 1250	1,900,000 1,900,000 1,700,000
BEAMS AND STRINGERS	Dense Sel. Struc. Dense No. 1	1900 1550		1250 1050	85 85	455 455	1300 1100	1,700,000 1,700,000
POSTS AND TIMBERS	Dense Sel. Struc. Dense No. 1	1750 1400		1150 950	85 85	455 455	1350 1200	1,700,000 1,700,000

Table 4.9   DECKING—2" to 4" Thick. 4" to 12" Wide Design Values in Pounds Per Square Inch For Flatwise Use Only. ²

Grades Described in Section 55.00 WWPA Grading Rules

Species	Grade	DRY¹		MC 15¹	
		Extreme Fiber Stress in Bending "Fb" Repetitive	Modulus of Elasticity "E"	Extreme Fiber Stress in Bending "Fb" Repetitive	Modulus of Elasticity "E"
DOUGLAS FIR—LARCH	Selected Decking Commercial Decking	2000 1650	1,800,000 1,700,000	2150 1800	1,900,000 1,700,000
DOUGLAS FIR SOUTH	Selected Decking Commercial Decking	1900 1600	1,400,000 1,300,000	2050 1750	1,500,000 1,300,000
HEM-FIR	Selected Decking Commercial Decking	1600 1300	1,500,000 1,400,000	1700 1450	1,600,000 1,500,000
MOUNTAIN HEMLOCK	Selected Decking Commercial Decking	1650 1400	1,300,000 1,100,000	1800 1500	1,300,000 1,200,000
MOUNTAIN HEMLOCK—HEM-FIR	Selected Decking Commercial Decking	1600 1300	1,300,000 1,100,000	1750 1450	1,300,000 1,200,000
SUBALPINE FIR (White Woods) (Western Woods)	Selected Decking Commercial Decking	1200 1000	900,000 900,000	1300 1050	1,000,000 900,000
ENGELMANN SPRUCE (Engelmann Spruce—Lodgepole Pine)	Selected Decking Commercial Decking	1300 1100	1,200,000 1,100,000	1400 1150	1,300,000 1,200,000
LODGEPOLE PINE	Selected Decking Commercial Decking	1450 1200	1,300,000 1,200,000	1550 1300	1,400,000 1,200,000
PONDEROSA PINE—SUGAR PINE (Ponderosa Pine—Lodgepole Pine)	Selected Decking Commercial Decking	1350 1150	1,200,000 1,100,000	1450 1250	1,300,000 1,100,000
IDAHO WHITE PINE	Selected Decking Commercial Decking	1400 1150	1,400,000 1,300,000	1500 1250	1,500,000 1,300,000
WESTERN CEDARS	Selected Decking Commercial Decking	1400 1200	1,100,000 1,000,000	1500 1250	1,100,000 1,000,000
WESTERN HEMLOCK	Selected Decking Commercial Decking	1750 1450	1,600,000 1,400,000	1900 1600	1,700,000 1,500,000

¹Dry and MC 15 design values apply to lumber manufactured at a maximum moisture content of 19% and 15% respectively.

²For decking 4" and less in thickness, see page 21 for adjustment factors for depth effect.

LUMBER DESIGN VALUES

Table 4.10 ALLOWABLE STRESSES MACHINE STRESS-RATED LUMBER — 2" thick or less, 2" and wider
Recommended Design Values In Pounds Per Square Inch

Grades Described In Section 52.00 WWPA Grading Rules

"f—E" Classification	Extreme Fiber Stress in Bending "Fb" (1) Single	Repetitive	Modulus of Elasticity "E"	Tension Parallel to Grain "Ft"	Compression Parallel to Grain "Fc"
1200f — 1.2 E	1200	1400	1,200,000	600	950
1500f — 1.4 E	1500	1750	1,400,000	900	1200
1650f — 1.5 E	1650	1900	1,500,000	1020	1320
1800f — 1.6 E	1800	2050	1,600,000	1175	1450
2100f — 1.8 E	2100	2400	1,800,000	1575	1700
2400f — 2.0 E	2400	2750	2,000,000	1925	1925
2700f — 2.2 E	2700	3100	2,200,000	2150	2150
3000f — 2.4 E	3000	3450	2,400,000	2400	2400
3300f — 2.6 E	3300	3800	2,600,000	2650	2650

The above listed f-E classifications are those that have customarily been used for trussed rafters and other engineered 2x4 construction. The classifications listed below are designed to provide MOE levels with corresponding lower Fb requirements, especially for joist use. Although the tables are separated primarily on the basis of rafter and joist use, any f-E classification may be ordered which meets the requirement of design.

900f — 1.0 E	900	1050	1,000,000	350	725
900f — 1.2 E	900	1050	1,200,000	350	725
1200f — 1.5 E	1200	1400	1,500,000	600	950
1350f — 1.8 E	1350	1550	1,800,000	750	1075
1800f — 2.1 E	1800	2050	2,100,000	1175	1450

Douglas Fir & Larch	Hem-Fir	Pine (2)	Engelmann Spruce	Cedar(3)
Compression Perpendicular to Grain "Fc ⊥"				
385	245	240	195	295
Horizontal Shear "Fv"				
95	75	65	70	75

(1) The tabulated Extreme Fiber in Bending values "Fb" are applicable to lumber loaded on edge. When loaded flatwise, these values may be increased by multiplying by the following factors:

Nominal Width (In.)	3"	4"	6"	8"	10"	12"	14"
Factor	1.06	1.10	1.15	1.19	1.22	1.25	1.28

(2) Idaho White, Lodgepole, Ponderosa or Sugar Pine.

(3) Incense or Western Red Cedar.

Table 4.11 SCAFFOLD PLANK—Douglas Fir and Larch 1¼" and Thicker, 8" and Wider [1]

Recommended Design Values in Pounds Per Square Inch — Exposed Uses For Flatwise Use Only

Grades Described In Section 58.00 WWPA Grading Rules

Grade	Extreme Fiber Stress in Bending (Fb)	Modulus of Elasticity (E)
No. 1	2200	1,600,000
No. 2	2000	1,600,000

[1] For Scaffold plank 4" and less in thickness, see page 21 for adjustment factors for depth effect.

CHAPTER V

Section Properties
and
Design Loads

SECTION PROPERTIES AND DESIGN LOADS
TABLE 5.1 PROPERTIES OF SECTIONS — SAWN LUMBER

JOISTS AND BEAMS:

Nominal Size in Inches b ▽ h ▽	Surfaced Size For Design in Inches b ▽ h ▽	Area (A) A = bh (In²)	Section Modulus (S) $S = \frac{bh^2}{6}$ (In³)	Moment of Inertia (I) $I = \frac{bh^3}{12}$ (In⁴)	Board Feet Per Lineal Foot of Piece
2 x 2	1.5 x 1.5	2.25	0.562	0.422	0.33
2 x 3	1.5 x 2.5	3.75	1.56	1.95	0.50
2 x 4	1.5 x 3.5	5.25	3.06	5.36	0.67
2 x 6	1.5 x 5.5	8.25	7.56	20.80	1.00
2 x 8	1.5 x 7.25	10.88	13.14	47.63	1.33
2 x 10	1.5 x 9.25	13.88	21.39	98.93	1.67
2 x 12	1.5 x 11.25	16.88	31.64	177.98	2.00
2 x 14	1.5 x 13.25	19.88	43.89	290.78	2.33
3 x 3	2.5 x 2.5	6.25	2.60	3.26	0.75
3 x 4	2.5 x 3.5	8.75	5.10	8.93	1.00
3 x 6	2.5 x 5.5	13.75	12.60	34.66	1.50
3 x 8	2.5 x 7.25	18.12	21.90	79.39	2.00
3 x 10	2.5 x 9.25	23.12	35.65	164.89	2.50
3 x 12	2.5 x 11.25	28.12	52.73	296.63	3.00
3 x 14	2.5 x 13.25	33.12	73.15	484.63	3.50
3 x 16	2.5 x 15.25	38.12	96.90	738.87	4.00
4 x 4	3.5 x 3.5	12.25	7.15	12.51	1.33
4 x 6	3.5 x 5.5	19.25	17.65	48.53	2.00
4 x 8	3.5 x 7.25	25.38	30.66	111.15	2.67
4 x 10	3.5 x 9.25	32.38	49.91	230.84	3.33
4 x 12	3.5 x 11.25	39.38	73.83	415.28	4.00
4 x 14	3.5 x 13.25	46.38	102.41	678.48	4.67
4 x 16	3.5 x 15.25	53.38	135.66	1034.42	5.33
6 x 6	5.5 x 5.5	30.25	27.73	76.26	3.00
6 x 8	5.5 x 7.5	41.25	51.56	193.36	4.00
6 x 10	5.5 x 9.5	52.25	82.73	392.96	5.00
6 x 12	5.5 x 11.5	63.25	121.23	697.07	6.00
6 x 14	5.5 x 13.5	74.25	167.06	1127.67	7.00
6 x 16	5.5 x 15.5	85.25	220.23	1706.78	8.00
6 x 18	5.5 x 17.5	96.25	280.73	2456.38	9.00
6 x 20	5.5 x 19.5	107.25	348.56	3398.48	10.00
8 x 8	7.5 x 7.5	56.25	70.31	263.67	5.33
8 x 10	7.5 x 9.5	71.25	112.81	535.86	6.67
8 x 12	7.5 x 11.5	86.25	165.31	950.55	8.00
8 x 14	7.5 x 13.5	101.25	227.81	1537.73	9.33
8 x 16	7.5 x 15.5	116.25	300.31	2327.42	10.67
8 x 18	7.5 x 17.5	131.25	382.81	3349.61	12.00
8 x 20	7.5 x 19.5	146.25	475.31	4634.30	13.33
8 x 22	7.5 x 21.5	161.25	577.81	6211.48	14.67
8 x 24	7.5 x 23.5	176.25	690.31	8111.17	16.00
10 x 10	9.5 x 9.5	90.25	142.90	678.76	8.33
10 x 12	9.5 x 11.5	109.25	209.40	1204.03	10.00
10 x 14	9.5 x 13.5	128.25	288.56	1947.80	11.67
10 x 16	9.5 x 15.5	147.25	380.40	2948.07	13.33
10 x 18	9.5 x 17.5	166.25	484.90	4242.84	15.00
10 x 20	9.5 x 19.5	185.25	602.06	5870.11	16.67
10 x 22	9.5 x 21.5	204.25	731.90	7867.88	18.33
12 x 12	11.5 x 11.5	132.25	253.48	1457.51	12.00
12 x 14	11.5 x 13.5	155.25	349.31	2357.86	14.00
12 x 16	11.5 x 15.5	178.25	460.48	3568.71	16.00
12 x 18	11.5 x 17.5	201.25	586.98	5136.07	18.00
12 x 20	11.5 x 19.5	224.25	728.81	7105.92	20.00
12 x 22	11.5 x 21.5	247.25	885.98	9524.28	22.00
12 x 24	11.5 x 23.5	270.25	1058.48	12437.13	24.00

SECTION PROPERTIES AND DESIGN LOADS

TABLE 5.1 PROPERTIES OF SECTIONS — Continued

PLANKS:

Nominal Size in Inches b　h	Surfaced Size For Design in Inches b　h	Area (A) $A = bh$ (In²)	Section Modulus (S) $S = \dfrac{bh^2}{6}$ (In³)	Moment of Inertia (I) $I = \dfrac{bh^3}{12}$ (In⁴)	Board Feet Per Lineal Foot of Piece
3 x 2	2.5 x 1.5	3.75	0.938	0.703	0.50
4 x 2	3.5 x 1.5	5.25	1.312	0.984	0.67
6 x 2	5.5 x 1.5	8.25	2.062	1.547	1.00
8 x 2	7.25 x 1.5	10.88	2.719	2.039	1.33
10 x 2	9.25 x 1.5	13.88	3.469	2.602	1.67
12 x 2	11.25 x 1.5	16.88	4.219	3.164	2.00
4 x 3	3.5 x 2.5	8.75	3.646	4.557	1.00
6 x 3	5.5 x 2.5	13.75	5.729	7.161	1.50
8 x 3	7.25 x 2.5	18.12	7.552	9.440	2.00
10 x 3	9.25 x 2.5	23.12	9.635	12.044	2.50
12 x 3	11.25 x 2.5	28.12	11.719	14.648	3.00
14 x 3	13.25 x 2.5	33.12	13.802	17.253	3.50
16 x 3	15.25 x 2.5	38.12	15.885	19.857	4.00
6 x 4	5.5 x 3.5	19.25	11.229	19.651	2.00
8 x 4	7.25 x 3.5	25.38	14.802	25.904	2.67
10 x 4	9.25 x 3.5	32.38	18.885	33.049	3.33
12 x 4	11.25 x 3.5	39.38	22.969	40.195	4.00
14 x 4	13.25 x 3.5	46.38	27.052	47.341	4.67
16 x 4	15.25 x 3.5	53.38	31.135	54.487	5.33

DECKING:

Nominal	Surfaced	Area (A)	Section Modulus (S)	Moment of Inertia (I)	Board Feet
2	12 x 1.5	18.00	4.50	3.375	2.00
3	2.5	30.00	12.00	15.625	3.00
4	3.5	42.00	24.50	42.875	4.00

Table 5.2 Weights of Studs, Joists and Rafters — Douglas Fir and Larch

Nominal Size	Spacing					
	12" c.c.		16" c.c.		24" c.c.	
	Weight* lbs. per sq. ft.	Board Feet per sq. ft.	Weight* lbs. per sq. ft.	Board Feet per sq. ft.	Weight* lbs. per sq. ft.	Board Feet per sq. ft.
2 x 3	0.9	0.50	0.7	0.38	0.5	0.25
2 x 4	1.3	0.67	1.0	0.50	0.7	0.34
2 x 6	2.1	1.00	1.6	0.75	1.0	0.5
2 x 8	2.7	1.33	2.1	1.00	1.4	0.67
2 x 10	3.5	1.67	2.6	1.25	1.7	0.84
2 x 12	4.3	2.00	3.2	1.50	2.1	1.00
3 x 6	3.5	1.50	2.6	1.13	1.7	0.75
3 x 8	4.6	2.00	3.4	1.50	2.3	1.00
3 x 10	5.8	2.50	4.4	1.88	2.9	1.25
3 x 12	7.1	3.00	5.3	2.25	3.5	1.50
3 x 14	8.3	3.50	6.3	2.63	4.2	1.75
4 x 8	6.4	2.67	4.8	2.00	3.2	1.34
4 x 10	8.2	3.33	6.1	2.50	4.1	1.67
4 x 12	9.9	4.00	7.4	3.00	5.0	2.00
4 x 14	11.7	4.67	8.8	3.50	5.8	2.34
4 x 16	13.5	5.33	10.1	4.00	6.7	2.67

* Based on surfaced (S4S) size and used at an equilibrium moisture content of 15%, the maximum found in most covered structures.

SECTION PROPERTIES AND DESIGN LOADS
TABLE 5.3 STRUCTURAL GLUED LAMINATED TIMBER SECTION PROPERTIES

3⅛" WIDTH

No. of 1½" Lams	d	C_F	A	S	I
2	3.00	1.00	9.4	4.7	7.0
3	4.50	1.00	14.1	10.5	23.7
4	6.00	1.00	18.8	18.8	56.3
5	7.50	1.00	23.4	29.3	109.9
6	9.00	1.00	28.1	42.2	189.8
7	10.50	1.00	32.8	57.4	301.5
8	12.00	1.00	37.5	75.0	450.0
9	13.50	0.99	42.2	94.9	640.7
10	15.00	0.98	46.9	117.2	878.9
11	16.50	0.97	51.6	141.8	1,169.8
12	18.00	0.96	56.3	168.8	1,518.8
13	19.50	0.95	60.9	198.0	1,931.0
14	21.00	0.94	65.6	229.7	2,411.7
15	22.50	0.93	70.3	263.7	2,966.3
16	24.00	0.93	75.0	300.0	3,600.0

5⅛" WIDTH

No. of 1½" Lams	d	C_F	A	S	I
3	4.50	1.00	23.1	17.3	38.9
4	6.00	1.00	30.8	30.8	92.3
5	7.50	1.00	38.4	48.0	180.2
6	9.00	1.00	46.1	69.2	311.3
7	10.50	1.00	53.8	94.2	494.4
8	12.00	1.00	61.5	123.0	738.0
9	13.50	0.99	69.2	155.7	1,050.8
10	15.00	0.98	76.9	192.2	1,441.4
11	16.50	0.97	84.6	232.5	1,918.5
12	18.00	0.96	92.3	276.8	2,490.8
13	19.50	0.95	99.9	324.8	3,166.8
14	21.00	0.94	107.6	376.7	3,955.2
15	22.50	0.93	115.3	432.4	4,864.7
16	24.00	0.93	123.0	492.0	5,904.0
17	25.50	0.92	130.7	555.4	7,081.6
18	27.00	0.91	138.4	622.7	8,406.3
19	28.50	0.91	146.1	693.8	9,886.6
20	30.00	0.90	153.8	768.8	11,531.3
21	31.50	0.90	161.4	847.5	13,348.9
22	33.00	0.89	169.1	930.2	15,348.1
23	34.50	0.89	176.8	1,016.7	17,537.6
24	36.00	0.88	184.5	1,107.0	19,926.0

6¾" WIDTH

No. of 1½" Lams	d	C_F	A	S	I
4	6.00	1.00	40.5	40.5	121.5
5	7.50	1.00	50.6	63.3	237.3
6	9.00	1.00	60.8	91.1	410.1
7	10.50	1.00	70.9	124.0	651.2
8	12.00	1.00	81.0	162.0	972.0
9	13.50	0.99	91.1	205.0	1,384.0
10	15.00	0.98	101.3	253.1	1,898.4
11	16.50	0.97	111.4	306.3	2,526.8
12	18.00	0.96	121.5	364.5	3,280.5
13	19.50	0.95	131.6	427.8	4,170.9
14	21.00	0.94	141.8	496.1	5,209.3
15	22.50	0.93	151.9	569.5	6,407.2
16	24.00	0.93	162.0	648.0	7,776.0
17	25.50	0.92	172.1	731.5	9,327.0
18	27.00	0.91	182.3	820.1	11,071.7
19	28.50	0.91	192.4	913.8	13,021.4
20	30.00	0.90	202.5	1,012.5	15,187.5
21	31.50	0.90	212.6	1,116.3	17,581.4
22	33.00	0.89	222.8	1,225.1	20,214.6
23	34.50	0.89	232.9	1,339.0	23,098.3
24	36.00	0.88	243.0	1,458.0	26,244.0
25	37.50	0.88	253.1	1,582.0	29,663.1
26	39.00	0.88	263.3	1,711.1	33,366.9
27	40.50	0.87	273.4	1,845.3	37,367.0
28	42.00	0.87	283.5	1,984.5	41,674.5
29	43.50	0.87	293.6	2,128.8	46,301.0
30	45.00	0.86	303.8	2,278.1	51,257.8
31	46.50	0.86	313.9	2,432.5	56,556.4
32	48.00	0.86	324.0	2,592.0	62,208.0

8¾" WIDTH

No. of 1½" Lams	d	C_F	A	S	I
6	9.00	1.00	78.8	118.1	531.6
7	10.50	1.00	91.9	160.8	844.1
8	12.00	1.00	105.0	210.0	1,260.0
9	13.50	0.99	118.1	265.8	1,794.0

(continued — 3⅛"/5⅛" group, middle column top)

No. of 1½" Lams	d	C_F	A	S	I
10	15.00	0.98	131.3	328.1	2,460.9
11	16.50	0.97	144.4	397.0	3,275.5
12	18.00	0.96	157.5	472.5	4,252.5
13	19.50	0.95	170.6	554.5	5,406.7
14	21.00	0.94	183.8	643.1	6,752.8
15	22.50	0.93	196.9	738.3	8,305.7
16	24.00	0.93	210.0	840.0	10,080.0
17	25.50	0.92	223.1	948.3	12,090.6
18	27.00	0.91	236.3	1,063.1	14,352.2
19	28.50	0.91	249.4	1,184.5	16,879.6
20	30.00	0.90	262.5	1,312.5	19,687.5
21	31.50	0.90	275.6	1,447.0	22,790.7
22	33.00	0.89	288.8	1,588.1	26,204.1
23	34.50	0.89	301.9	1,735.8	29,942.2
24	36.00	0.88	315.0	1,890.0	34,020.0
25	37.50	0.88	328.1	2,050.8	38,452.2
26	39.00	0.88	341.3	2,218.1	43,253.4
27	40.50	0.87	354.4	2,392.0	48,438.6
28	42.00	0.87	367.5	2,572.5	54,022.5
29	43.50	0.87	380.6	2,759.5	60,019.8
30	45.00	0.86	393.8	2,953.1	66,445.3
31	46.50	0.86	406.9	3,153.3	73,313.8
32	48.00	0.86	420.0	3,360.0	80,640.0
33	49.50	0.85	433.1	3,573.3	88,438.7
34	51.00	0.85	446.3	3,793.1	96,724.7
35	52.50	0.85	459.4	4,019.5	105,512.7
36	54.00	0.85	472.5	4,252.5	114,817.5
37	55.50	0.84	485.6	4,492.0	124,653.9
38	57.00	0.84	498.8	4,738.1	135,036.6
39	58.50	0.84	511.9	4,990.8	145,980.4
40	60.00	0.84	525.0	5,250.0	157,500.0
41	61.50	0.83	538.1	5,515.8	169,610.3
42	63.00	0.83	551.3	5,788.1	182,326.0

10¾" WIDTH

No. of 1½" Lams	d	C_F	A	S	I
7	10.50	1.00	112.9	197.5	1,037.0
8	12.00	1.00	129.0	258.0	1,548.0
9	13.50	0.99	145.1	326.5	2,204.1
10	15.00	0.98	161.3	403.1	3,023.4
11	16.50	0.97	177.4	487.8	4,024.2
12	18.00	0.96	193.5	580.5	5,224.5
13	19.50	0.95	209.6	681.3	6,642.3
14	21.00	0.94	225.8	790.1	8,296.3
15	22.50	0.93	241.9	907.0	10,204.1
16	24.00	0.93	258.0	1,032.0	12,384.0
17	25.50	0.92	274.1	1,165.0	14,854.1
18	27.00	0.91	290.3	1,306.1	17,632.7
19	28.50	0.91	306.4	1,455.3	20,737.8
20	30.00	0.90	322.5	1,612.5	24,187.5
21	31.50	0.90	338.6	1,777.8	28,000.1
22	33.00	0.89	354.8	1,951.1	32,193.6
23	34.50	0.89	370.9	2,132.5	36,786.2
24	36.00	0.88	387.0	2,322.0	41,796.0
25	37.50	0.88	403.1	2,519.5	47,241.2
26	39.00	0.88	419.3	2,725.1	53,139.9
27	40.50	0.87	435.4	2,938.8	59,510.3
28	42.00	0.87	451.5	3,160.5	66,370.5
29	43.50	0.87	467.6	3,390.3	73,738.6
30	45.00	0.86	483.8	3,628.1	81,632.8
31	46.50	0.86	499.9	3,874.0	90,071.2
32	48.00	0.86	516.0	4,128.0	99,072.0
33	49.50	0.85	532.1	4,390.0	108,653.3
34	51.00	0.85	548.3	4,660.1	118,833.2
35	52.50	0.85	564.4	4,938.3	129,629.9
36	54.00	0.85	580.5	5,224.5	141,061.5
37	55.50	0.84	596.6	5,518.8	153,146.2
38	57.00	0.84	612.8	5,821.1	165,902.1
39	58.50	0.84	628.9	6,131.5	179,347.3
40	60.00	0.84	645.0	6,450.0	193,500.0
41	61.50	0.83	661.1	6,776.5	208,378.4
42	63.00	0.83	677.3	7,111.1	224,000.5
43	64.50	0.83	693.4	7,453.8	240,384.5
44	66.00	0.83	709.5	7,804.5	257,548.5
45	67.50	0.83	725.6	8,163.3	275,510.8
46	69.00	0.82	741.8	8,530.1	294,289.3
47	70.50	0.82	757.9	8,905.0	313,902.4
48	72.00	0.82	774.0	9,288.0	334,368.0
49	73.50	0.82	790.1	9,679.0	355,704.5

12¼" WIDTH

No. of 1½" Lams	d	C_F	A	S	I
8	12.00	1.00	147.0	294.0	1,764.0
9	13.50	0.99	165.4	372.1	2,511.6
10	15.00	0.98	183.8	459.4	3,445.3
11	16.50	0.97	202.1	555.8	4,585.7
12	18.00	0.96	220.5	661.5	5,953.5
13	19.50	0.95	238.9	776.3	7,569.4
14	21.00	0.94	257.2	900.4	9,453.9
15	22.50	0.93	275.6	1,033.6	11,627.9
16	24.00	0.93	294.0	1,176.0	14,112.0
17	25.50	0.92	312.4	1,327.6	16,926.8
18	27.00	0.91	330.8	1,488.4	20,093.1
19	28.50	0.91	349.1	1,658.3	23,631.4
20	30.00	0.90	367.5	1,837.5	27,562.5
21	31.50	0.90	385.9	2,025.8	31,907.0
22	33.00	0.89	404.2	2,223.4	36,685.7
23	34.50	0.89	422.6	2,430.1	41,919.1
24	36.00	0.88	441.0	2,646.0	47,628.0
25	37.50	0.88	459.4	2,871.1	53,833.0
26	39.00	0.88	477.8	3,105.4	60,554.8
27	40.50	0.87	496.1	3,348.8	67,814.1
28	42.00	0.87	514.5	3,601.5	75,631.5
29	43.50	0.87	532.9	3,863.3	84,027.7
30	45.00	0.86	551.2	4,134.4	93,023.4
31	46.50	0.86	569.6	4,414.6	102,639.3
32	48.00	0.86	588.0	4,704.0	112,896.0
33	49.50	0.85	606.4	5,002.6	123,814.2
34	51.00	0.85	624.8	5,310.4	135,414.6
35	52.50	0.85	643.1	5,627.3	147,717.8
36	54.00	0.85	661.5	5,953.5	160,744.5
37	55.50	0.84	679.9	6,288.8	174,515.4
38	57.00	0.84	698.2	6,633.4	189,051.2
39	58.50	0.84	716.6	6,987.1	204,372.5
40	60.00	0.84	735.0	7,350.0	220,500.0
41	61.50	0.83	753.4	7,722.1	237,454.4
42	63.00	0.83	771.8	8,103.4	255,256.3
43	64.50	0.83	790.1	8,493.8	273,926.5
44	66.00	0.83	808.5	8,893.5	293,485.5
45	67.50	0.83	826.9	9,302.3	313,954.1
46	69.00	0.82	845.2	9,720.4	335,352.9
47	70.50	0.82	863.6	10,147.6	357,702.7
48	72.00	0.82	882.0	10,584.0	381,024.0
49	73.50	0.82	900.4	11,029.6	405,337.6
50	75.00	0.82	918.8	11,484.4	430,664.1
51	76.50	0.81	937.1	11,948.3	457,024.1
52	78.00	0.81	955.5	12,421.5	484,438.5
53	79.50	0.81	973.9	12,903.8	512,927.8
54	81.00	0.81	992.2	13,395.4	542,512.7
55	82.50	0.81	1,010.6	13,896.1	573,213.9
56	84.00	0.81	1,029.0	14,406.0	605,052.0

KEY TO CHART
COLUMN HEADS

Number of Laminations
d —Depth (inches)
C_F—Size Factor
A —Area (inches^2)
S —Section Modules (inches^3)
I —Moment of Inertia (inches^4)

SECTION PROPERTIES AND DESIGN LOADS

The forces exerted on structures by their own weight, the dead loads, or by imposition, the live loads, are usually vertical or horizontal. Those that act at an angle may, for convenience, be resolved into vertical and horizontal components. There are several kinds of loadings in the live load category, but only those most often encountered will be covered in this chapter, some by reference only.

Dead Loads
A dead load is the weight permanently supported by a structure. It may include such items as roofing, sheathing, flooring, ceiling, the weight of supporting members and other objects permanently affixed and is usually expressed in pounds per square foot (psf). Tables 5.6 and 5.7 give weights of materials commonly encountered.

Live Loads
A live load is any load that a structure is required to support in addition to the dead load. Live loads are usually expressed in pounds per square foot (psf). Most live loads fluctuate, but some are as permanent as the structure itself. There are numerous kinds of live loadings but only the more commonly encountered, fluctuating live loads and their application to timber structures will be covered. These are:

> Floor Live Loads
> Moving Loads
> Roof Live Loads
> Snow Loads
> Wind Loads
> Earthquake Loads

Floor Live Loads
Buildings and structures are usually built for a specific occupancy or use. Long experience with the actual use of various buildings and structures has guided the establishment of practical live load requirements. A compilation of occupancy loadings, as recommended by the American National Standards Institute (ANSI) is given in Table 5.4.

Occupancy live loads vary in magnitude because the number of people, quantities of merchandise, volume of commodities, etc., are constantly changing and infrequently reach the maximum design load. It is loading such as this that is contemplated as normal loading on the lumber members of structures. The conditions of "normal loading" are described in detail on Page 21.

In addition to the dead load, floors should be designed to safely support the uniformly distributed live loads shown in Table 5.4 or a concentrated load as shown in Table 5.5, whichever produces the greater stress. Unless otherwise specified, the tabulated concentrated loads are assumed to occupy an area 2½ feet square and are so located as to produce a maximum stress condition in structural members.

Since uniformly distributed loading is not truly representative of real service conditions for floors, most authorities permit floor live loads of 100 psf or less on any member supporting more than 150

square feet of surface area, to be reduced at the rate of 0.08% per square foot of area supported by the member, except that no reduction should be made for areas to be occupied as places of public assembly, for garages or for roofs. The reduction should exceed neither N (in percent) as determined by the following formula, nor 60%:

$$N = 23.1 \left(1 + \frac{DL}{LL}\right)$$

Where N = reduction in percent
DL = dead load per square foot of area supported by the member.
LL = design floor live load per square foot of area supported by the member.

For floor live loads exceeding 100 psf, no reduction should be made, except that the design floor live loads on columns may be reduced 20%.

Table 5.4
MINIMUM UNIFORMLY
DISTRIBUTED LIVE LOADS[a]

Occupancy or Use	Live Load, (psf)
Apartments (see Residential)	
Armories and drill rooms	150
Assembly halls and other places of assembly:	
Fixed seats	60
Movable seats	100
Platforms (assembly)	100
Balcony (exterior)	100
On one and two family residences only and not exceeding 100 sq ft	60
Bowling alleys, poolrooms, and similar recreational areas	75
Corridors:	
First floor	100
Other floors, same as occupancy served except as indicated	
Dance halls and ballrooms	100
Dining rooms and restaurants	100
Dwellings (see Residential)	
Fire escapes	100
On multi- or single-family residential buildings only	40
Garages (passenger cars only)	50
For trucks and buses use AASHO* lane loads (see Table 5.5 for concentrated load requirements)	
Grandstands (see Reviewing stands)	
Gymnasiums, main floors and balconies	100
Hospitals:	
Operating rooms, laboratories	60
Private rooms	40
Wards	40
Corridors, above first floor	80
Hotels (see Residential)	
Libraries:	
Reading rooms	60
Stack rooms (books & shelving at 65 pcf) but not less than	150
Corridors, above first floor	80

SECTION PROPERTIES AND DESIGN LOADS

(continued from page 33)

Occupancy or Use	Live Load, (psf)
Manufacturing:	
Light	125
Heavy	250
Marquees	75
Office buildings:	
Offices	50
Lobbies	100
Corridors, above first floor	80
File and computer rooms require heavier loads based upon anticipated occupancy	
Penal institutions:	
Cell blocks	40
Corridors	100
Residential:	
Multifamily houses:	
Private apartments	40
Public rooms	100
Corridors	80
Dwellings:	
First floor	40
Second floor and habitable attics	30
Uninhabitable attics	20
Hotels:	
Guest rooms	40
Public rooms	100
Corridors serving public rooms	100
Corridors	80
Reviewing stands and bleachers†	100
Schools:	
Classrooms	40
Corridors	80
Sidewalks, vehicular driveways, and yards, subject to trucking	250
Skating rinks	100
Stairs and exitways	100
Storage warehouse:	
Light	125
Heavy	250
Stores:	
Retail:	
First floor, rooms	100
Upper floors	75
Wholesale	125
Theaters:	
Aisles, corridors, and lobbies	100
Orchestra floors	60
Balconies	60
Stage floors	150
Yards and terraces, pedestrians	100

*American Association of State Highway Officials.

†For detailed recommendations, see American National Standard for Tents, Grandstands, and Air-Supported Structures Used for Places of Assembly, Z20.3-1967 (NFPA No. 102-1967).

Table 5.5
CONCENTRATED LOADS[a]

Location	Load lbs.
Elevator machine room grating (on area of 4 sq in)	300
Finish light floor plate construction (on area of 1 sq in)	200
Garages	*
Office floors	2000
Scuttles, skylight ribs, and accessible ceilings	200
Sidewalks	8000
Stair treads (on area of 4 sq in at center of tread)	300

*Floors in garages or portions of buildings used for storage of motor vehicles shall be designed for the uniformly distributed live loads of Table 1 or the following concentrated loads: (1) for passenger cars accommodating not more than nine passengers, 2000 pounds acting on an area of 20 sq in; (2) mechanical parking structures without slab or deck, passenger cars only, 1500 pounds per wheel; (3) for trucks or buses, maximum axle load on an area of 20 sq in.

Table 5.6
WEIGHTS OF CONSTRUCTION MATERIALS

The average figures and ranges given in this table are suitable for general use. Specific products may vary considerably from these values; therefore, where available, actual weights as given in manufacturer's catalogs and in various reference books should be used.

Material	Weight, (psf)
Ceilings	
Acoustical fiber tile	1.0
Channel suspended system	1.0
Plaster and lath (see *Walls and Partitions*)	
Floors	
Hardwood, 1 in. nominal	4.0
Plywood, per inch of thickness	3.0
Asphalt mastic, per inch of thickness	12.0
Cement finish, per inch of thickness	12.0
Ceramic or quarry tile, ¾ in.	10.0
Concrete, per inch of thickness	
Lightweight	6.0 to 10.0
Reinforced	12.5
Stone	12.0
Cork tile, 1/16 in.	0.5
Flexicore, 6 in. slab	46.0
Linoleum, ¼ in.	1.0
Terrazo finish, 1½ in.	19.0
Vinyl tile, ⅛ in.	1.4
Roofs	
Lumber sheathing, 1 in. nominal	2.5
Plywood sheathing, per inch of thickness	3.0

SECTION PROPERTIES AND DESIGN LOADS

Material	Weight, (psf)		
Roofs (continued)			
Timber decking	2 in. nom.	3 in. nom.	4 in. nom.
15% MC			
Douglas Fir—Larch	4.5	7.6	10.6
Douglas Fir South	4.1	6.8	9.5
Hem-Fir	4.0	6.6	9.3
Mountain Hemlock—			
Hem-Fir	4.0	6.6	9.3
Subalpine Fir	2.9	4.9	6.9
Engelmann Spruce	3.1	5.1	7.2
Lodgepole Pine	3.7	6.2	8.6
Ponderosa Pine—Sugar			
Pine	3.7	6.2	8.6
Idaho White Pine	3.5	5.8	8.1
Western Cedars	3.3	5.5	7.7
Western Hemlock	4.0	6.6	9.3

Aluminum (includes laps)	Flat	Corrug. (1½ and 2½ in.)
12 American or B & S ga	1.2	
14 or B & S ga	0.9	1.1
16 or B & S ga	0.7	0.9
18 or B & S ga	0.6	0.7
20 or B & S ga	0.5	0.6
22 or B & S ga		0.4

Galvanized steel (includes laps)	Flat	Corrug. (2½ and 3 in.)
12 U.S. Std. ga	4.5	4.9
14 U.S. Std. ga	3.3	3.6
16 U.S. Std. ga	2.7	2.9
18 U.S. Std. ga	2.2	2.4
20 U.S. Std. ga	1.7	1.8
22 U.S. Std. ga	1.4	1.5
24 U.S. Std. ga	1.2	1.3
26 U.S. Std. ga	0.9	1.0

Other decking, per inch of thickness	Weight (psf)
Concrete plank	6.5
Insulrock	2.7
Petrical	2.7
Porex	2.7
Poured gypsum	6.5
Tectum	2.0
Vermiculite concrete	2.6
Asbestos, corrugated, ¼ in.	3.0
Felt, 3 ply	1.5
Felt, 3 ply with gravel	5.5
Felt, 5 ply	2.5
Felt, 5 ply with gravel	6.5
Insulation, per inch of thickness	
Expanded polystyrene	0.2
Fiberglas, rigid	1.5
Loose	0.5
Roll roofing	1.0
Shingles	
Asphalt, approx. ¼ in.	2.0

Material	Weight, (psf)
Shingles (continued)	
Book tile, 2 in.	12.0
Book tile, 3 in.	20.0
Cement asbestos, approx. ⅜ in.	4.0
Clay tile (for mortar add 10 lb)	9.0 to 14.0
Ludowici	10.0
Roman	12.0
Slate, ¼ in.	10.0
Spanish	19.0
Wood, 1 in.	3.0

Walls and Partitions

Material	Weight, (psf)
Wood paneling, 1 in.	2.5
Wood studs, 2x4	
Douglas Fir and Larch	
12 in. o.c.	1.3
16 in. o.c.	1.0
24 in. o.c.	0.7
Glass block, 4 in.	18.0
Glass, plate, ¼ in.	3.3
Glazed tile	18.0
Marble or marble wainscoting	15.0
Masonry, per 4 inches of thickness	
Brick	38.0
Concrete block	30.0
Cinder concrete block	20.0
Hollow clay tile, load-bearing	23.0
Hollow clay tile, nonbearing	18.0
Hollow gypsum block	13.0
Limestone	55.0
Terra-cotta tile	25.0
Stone	55.0
Plaster, 1 in.	8.0
Plaster, 1 in., on wood lath	10.0
Plaster, 1 in., on metal lath	8.5
Gypsum Wallboard, 1 in.	5.0
Porcelain-enameled steel	3.0
Stucco, ⅞ in.	10.0
Windows, glass, frame, and sash	8.0

Table 5.7
MATERIAL WEIGHTS[a]

Substance	Weight, (pcf)
Earth (Excavated)	
Clay, dry	63
Clay, damp, plastic	110
Clay and gravel, dry	100
Earth, dry	76 to 95
Earth, moist	78 to 96
Mud	108 to 115
Sand and gravel, dry	90 to 120
Sand and gravel, wet	118 to 120

SECTION PROPERTIES AND DESIGN LOADS

Substance	Weight, (pcf)
Liquids	
Gasoline	42
Petroleum	54
Water, fresh	62.4
Water, ice	56
Water, sea	64
Masonry	
Cement, portland	90
Concrete, cinder	111
Concrete, slag	138
Concrete, stone, sand	150
Brick masonry, soft	100
Brick masonry, medium	115
Brick masonry, hard	130
Metals and Alloys	
Aluminum, cast, hammered	165
Brass, cast, rolled	526
Copper, cast, rolled	556
Iron, cast, pig	450
Iron, wrought	480
Lead	710
Steel, rolled	490
Tin, cast, hammered	459
Zinc, rolled, sheet	449
Other Solids	
Asphaltum	81
Glass, common	156
Glass, plate or crown	161
Grain, barley	39
Grain, corn, rye, wheat	48
Grain, oats	32
Pitch	69
Tar, bituminous	75

[a]For timber weights, see Table 1.3

Moving Loads

Vehicles of all sorts, trains, travelling cranes and people, to name a few, are typical moving loads. Their positioning is not fixed and they move frequently on and off of a structure or portions of it. Both the magnitude of individual moving loads and their duration at the loading point vary widely. By properly adjusting the working stresses for wood for these short duration loads, as outlined on Page 21, maximum structural economy is achieved. Forces from moving loads are primarily vertical, but they may induce horizontal forces from acceleration, deceleration, or centrifugal motion. Moving forces may be magnified by impact effect.

Sources of data on moving loads may be obtained from the *Standard Specifications for Highway Bridges,* American Association of State Highway Officials, for highway type traffic; the *Manual Specifications for Steel Railway Bridges,* American Railway Engineering Association, for railway loadings; and from manufacturers for data on special pieces of moving equipment.

Roof Live Loads

The minimum roof live loads should be as required by the governing building code. Roof live loads used in design should represent the designer's determination of the particular service requirements for the structure, but in no case should they be less than the recommended minimum.

Minimum roof live loads for flat, pitched or curved roofs as recommended by the American National Standards Institute are given in Table 5.8. Roofs should be designed to resist either the tabulated minimum loads, applied as either full balanced or full unbalanced or the snow load, whichever produce the greater stress.

The American National Standards Institute also recommends as minimums design vertical live loads of 60 psf for flat roofs used as sundecks or promenades, and of 100 psf for flat roofs used as roof gardens or for assembly uses. These loads are, in effect, floor live loads and may be treated as such. Roofs to be used for other special purposes shall be designed for appropriate loads as approved by the building official.

Table 5.8
Minimum Roof Live Loads[a]
(in psf of horizontal projection)

Roof Slope	Tributary Loaded Area in Square Feet for any Structural Member		
	0 to 200	201 to 600	Over 600
Flat or rise less than 4 inches per foot Arch or dome with rise less than 1/8 of span	20	16	12
Rise 4 inches per foot to less than 12 inches per foot Arch or dome with rise 1/8 of span to less than 3/8 of span	16	14	12
Rise 12 inches per foot and greater Arch or dome with rise 3/8 of span or greater	12	12	12

[a] This material is reproduced with permission from *American National Standard Building Code Requirements for Minimum Design Loads in Buildings and Other Structures* A58.1 copyright 1972 by the American National Standards Institute, copies of which may be purchased from the American National Standards Institute at 1430 Broadway, New York, New York 10018.

SNOW LOADS *
Basic Snow Loads

Snow loads on roofs vary widely throughout the United States. Factors affecting snow load accumulation on roofs include climatic variables or

SECTION PROPERTIES AND DESIGN LOADS

elevation, latitude, wind frequency and duration of snowfall, roof geometry and site exposure. In addition, snowfall varies from year to year and either a mean recurrence interval must be established for design purposes or design should be based on the maximum recorded snow load for which data is available. Snow loads should be as stipulated by the governing building code but in the absence of such a code, snow loading used for design should be based on local investigation, or by the use of accepted snow load maps.

Before discussing roof loads, it is necessary to consider ground snow loads since these form the basis for determining roof loads. Figure 5.1 presents maximum snow loads on the ground based on records of the U.S. Weather Bureau based upon a 50-year mean recurrence interval.

For the Western states, Figure 5.1 indicates that the snow loads for these regions should be established on the basis of local experience. Actual snow pack in these regions of over 700 psf has been recorded and many of the inhabited regions have snow loads of 100, 200 or 300 psf.

*The basic text presented herein for snow loads is as developed by the American Institute of Timber Construction.

Roof Snow Loads

Based on a determination of the ground snow load it is next necessary to determine the actual snow loads to be expected on the roof surface. As indicated, the roof snow load is a function of the geometry of the roof and the exposure to wind forces.

These factors can be accounted for in design by applying appropriate snow load coefficients to the basic ground snow loads.

For the design of both ordinary and multiple series roofs, either flat, pitched or curved, a basic snow load coefficient of 0.8 should be used to convert ground snow load to a roof snow load. This value should then be increased or decreased if necessary due to specific roof geometry conditions such as decreasing for roof slopes exceeding 20°, increasing for roofs having valleys formed by multiple series or other similar geometry conditions. The Uniform Building Code permits snow loads to be reduced for each degree of pitch over 20 degrees by S/40 minus ½, where "S" is the total snow load in psf. Specific coefficients for these roof configurations are given in the *American National Standard Building Code Requirements for Minimum Design Loads in Buildings*

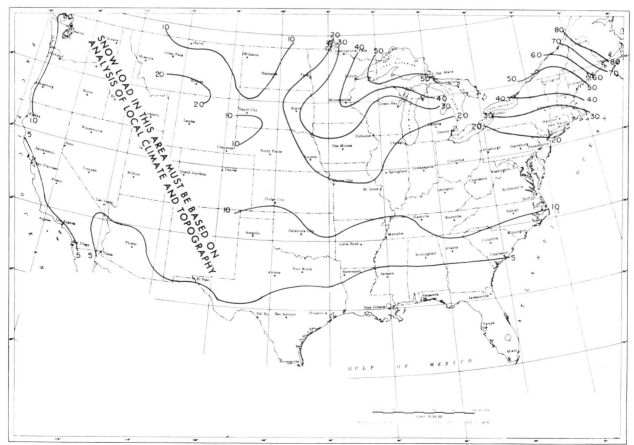

Figure 5.1 Snow Load in psf on the Ground, 50-Year Mean Recurrence Interval*
***(Copy "D")**

SECTION PROPERTIES AND DESIGN LOADS

and Other Structures, A58.1-1972, by the American National Standards Institute.

For roofs exposed to winds of sufficient intensity to blow snow off, the basic snow load coefficient can be reduced to 0.6. This coefficient is only applicable if (a) the roof is not shielded from the wind on any side or is not likely to become shielded by obstructions higher than the roof within a distance of 10h from the building ("h" is the height of the obstruction above the roof level) and (b) the roof does not have any projections, such as parapet walls, which may prevent the snow from being blown off by the wind.

Since unbalanced loading can occur due to drifting, sliding, melting and refreezing or physical removal of snow, structural roof members should be designed to resist the full snow load as defined above, distributed on any one portion of the area, and dead load only on the remainder of the area, depending on whichever one produces the greatest stress on the member considered. With respect to duration of load, snow load duration is the cumulative time during which the full maximum design load is on the structure over its entire life. A *2 month* duration is generally recognized as the proper design level for snow loads. Although some snow remains on roofs for periods exceeding 2 months in a single year, such snow loads seldom approach the design load.

While the analysis of roofs for snow loading is complex due to the many variables involved, recent technical data developed as discussed in the preceding paragraphs has provided the engineer with sufficient information to make a realistic analysis.

WIND LOADS*

Designing structures to resist wind loadings is, like the analysis for snow loading, a very complex engineering problem. Considerable research has been conducted to evaluate wind effects on various structures that has resulted in the establishment of design pressure coefficients which account for building shape and wind direction. In addition, extensive studies of basic wind velocities related to geographical location have resulted in the development of detailed wind velocity maps for the United States. Other studies of surface resistance relative to the degree of land development and gust characteristics at a given location have provided a method for a further refinement of the basic wind velocity and its effect on structures. However, much work remains to be done to further relate the dynamic behavior of structures to wind forces which are attributable to gusting and turbulence.

The wind load analysis information presented herein is intended to provide the engineer with a design procedure which accounts for the basic parameters affecting wind loading of structures. The material has been compiled from a variety of sources, including the *American National Standard Building Code Requirements for Mini-* *mum Design Loads in Buildings and Other Structures,* American National Standards Institute; *Wind Forces on Structures,* Paper No. 3269, Final Report of the Task Committee on Wind Forces of the Committee on Loads and Stresses of the Structural Division, ASCE; *New Distributions of Extreme Winds in the United States* by H.C.S. Thom, Vol. 94, ST 7, July 1968, Journal of the Structural Division, ASCE; *Strength of Houses,* Building Materials and Structures, Report 109, National Bureau of Standards, U.S. Department of Commerce; and *Structural Information for Building Design in Canada,* 1965, Supplement No. 3 to the National Building Code of Canada.

*The basic test presented herein for wind loads is as developed by the American Institute of Timber Construction.

Basic Wind Velocities

Figure 5.2 is a wind probability map for a 50-year mean recurrence interval. This figure provides basic wind velocities for observed air flows in open, level country at a height of 30 ft. above the ground. For the design of most permanent structures, a basic wind speed with a 50-year mean recurrence interval should be applied. However, if in the judgment of the engineer or authority having jurisdiction, the structure presents an unusually high degree of hazard to life and property in case of failure, a 100-year mean recurrence interval wind velocity should be used for design. Similarly, for temporary structures or structures having negligible risk of human life in case of failure, a design wind velocity based on a 25-year mean recurrence interval may be used. A wind probability map for a 100-year or 25-year mean recurrence interval may be found in *American National Standard Building Code Requirements for Minimum Design Loads in Buildings and Other Structures,* American National Standards Institute.

Since the wind velocities given in Figure 5.2 is for a height of 30 feet, it is necessary to modify this value for other design heights. An accepted procedure is to apply the following equation:

$$V_h = V_{30} (h/30)^{1/7}$$

This is commonly referred to as the 1/7th power law for determining wind velocities.

In addition to adjusting the basic wind velocities for height and site exposure conditions, it is possible to also apply a gust response factor in the determination of design velocity pressures. The concept of determining gust response factors is very complex and the engineer is referred to the following ASCE papers for a detailed analysis of gust loading of structures. *Gust Loading Factors* by Davenport, Vol. 93, ST 3, June 1967, Journal of the Structural Division; and *Gust Response Factors* by Vellozzi and Cohen, Vol. 94, ST 6, June 1968, Journal of the Structural Division.

SECTION PROPERTIES AND DESIGN LOADS

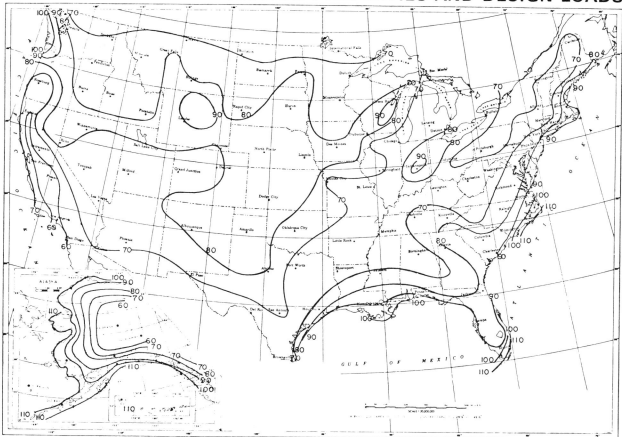

Fig. 5.2*
Basic Wind Speed in Miles per Hour
Annual Extreme Fastest-Mile Speed 30 Feet Above Ground, 50-Year Mean Recurrence Interval

As a general guide, the gust response factor is primarily a function of the size and height of the structure and the surface roughness and obstructions existing in the surrounding area. For small to medium size structures located in open relatively level terrain and ranging in height up to approximately 100 feet, a gust response factor of 1.3 is commonly assumed. Similarly, for taller buildings of approximately 400 feet in height, a gust response factor of 1.1 can be used for design purposes.

It is recommended that the designer use a dynamic analysis accounting for wind turbulence and the size and natural frequency of the structure to determine gusting effects on structures greater than 400 feet in height. Therefore, a design wind velocity is determined by modifying the basic wind velocity obtained from Figure 5.2 for height, site exposure and the gust effect. For additional information related to the effect of site exposure on wind velocity, the engineer is referred to the *American National Standard Building Code Requirements for Minimum Design Loads in Buildings and Other Structures,* ANSI A58.1-1972 American National Standards Institute.

Velocity Pressures

For standard air (0.07651 pcf, corresponding to 15°C at 760 mm of mercury) and velocity of wind, V, expressed in miles per hour, the velocity (dynamic) pressure, q, in psf, is given by:

$$q = 0.00256 \ V^2$$

Thus, the dynamic pressure for any given combination of geographic location, height of structure, and basic wind velocity can be determined by using the design wind velocity in the above equation. The gust response factor can easily be accounted for in a separate calculation by multiplying the calculated values by the applicable gust response factor.

Therefore, for general design purposes, the effective velocity pressure for any height, h, may be determined from the relationship:

$$q_h = (.00256) \ (V_{30})^2 \ (h/30)^{2/7} \ (G_F)$$

where V_{30} = basic wind velocity obtained from Figure 5.2.

   h = height of building

   G_F = gust response factor

SECTION PROPERTIES AND DESIGN LOADS

Example:

Calculate the effective velocity pressure acting on a permanent structure to be located in relatively open, level terrain near Cheyenne, Wyoming. Assume the design height to be 100 ft. and that a 50-year mean recurrence interval wind velocity is applicable.

From Figure 5.2, a basic wind velocity of 80 mph for a height of 30 ft. is applicable for Cheyenne, Wyoming.

Since the height of the structure is 100 ft. and the structure is to be located in relatively open, level terrain, a gust response factor of 1.3 is applied.

The effective velocity pressure for this condition is thus:

$$q_{100} = 0.00256 \, (80)^2 \left(\frac{100}{30}\right)^{2/7} \times (1.3)$$

$$q_{100} = 30.0 \text{ psf}$$

Wind Pressures

To determine the design wind pressure distribution acting on a building or structural element thereof, the calculated velocity pressure is multiplied by an appropriate pressure coefficient, C_p. These pressure coefficients thus define the wind pressure acting normally on the surface of a building or element thereof and are dependent upon the external shape of the structure and its orientation with the wind. Pressure coefficients are considered to be either positive, representing a pressure, or negative, indicating a suction force on the structural element being analyzed. Therefore, depending upon orientation to the wind and existence of openings, a building or element thereof may be subjected to a pressure difference between opposite sides or faces and it is thus the total resultant wind pressure which must be accounted for in design.

General Pressure Coefficients

For typical rectangular buildings and other enclosed structures having vertical walls which may have openings such as for doors, operable windows, etc., design pressure coefficients have been established. These are as given in the following sections.

Internal Pressure Coefficients

The determination of the internal wind pressures acting on a structure or element thereof can be made by applying the following equation:

$$P_i = q_{hi} \, C_{pi}$$

where p_i = internal wind pressure, psf

$\quad q_{hi}$ = internal effective velocity pressure in psf at height h

$\quad C_{pi}$ = internal pressure coefficient

It is important to note that the internal effective velocity pressure, q_{hi}, as used in this equation differs from the basic effective velocity pressure, q_h, as previously discussed in that the gust response factor, G_F, need not be applied. This is due primarily to the fact that the damping provided by restricted exterior openings, as occur in most buildings, causes the internal pressures to be less sensitive to gust effects. As a conservative approach, the designer can apply the effective velocity pressure, q_h, in the determination of internal wind pressure values.

Internal pressure coefficients, C_{pi}, for walls and roofs having various percentages of wall openings may be determined as follows:

Positive C_{pi} (acts out): For windward openings, C_{pi} varies uniformly from 0.3 at 0% wall openings to 0.8 for wall openings of 30%. For wall openings exceeding 30%, C_{pi} is 0.8.

Negative C_{pi} (acts in): For leeward and parallel openings, C_{pi} varies uniformly from 0.3 at 0% wall openings to 0.6 for wall openings of 30%. For wall openings exceeding 30%, C_{pi} is 0.6.

For structures with uniformly distributed openings, a value of ± 0.3 for C_{pi} should be used for all percentages of wall openings.

The pressure as determined by using these coefficients is assumed to be uniform on all internal surfaces at a given building height and is assumed applicable to flat, pitched or arched roof configurations.

External Pressure Coefficients

To calculate the external wind pressures acting on a building or structural element thereof, use is made of the equation:

$$P_e = q_h \, C_{pe}$$

where P_e = external wind pressure, psf

$\quad q_h$ = effective velocity pressure in psf at height h

$\quad C_{pe}$ = external pressure coefficient

Walls

Average external pressure coefficients as given below should be used for calculating external pressures on wall surfaces of buildings:

Wall location with respect to wind direction	External pressure coefficient C_{pe}
Windward Wall	+0.8
Leeward Wall	
Height to width and height to length ratio $=2.5$	−0.6
Other dimensional configurations	−0.5
Parallel Wall	−0.7

Roofs

For structures having a flat, pitched or arched roof, external suction pressure, p_e, based on wind parallel to the surface of the roof can be computed by applying the following external pressure coefficients:

SECTION PROPERTIES AND DESIGN LOADS

Building configuration (roof parallel to wind direction)	External pressure coefficient Cpe
Wall height to least width dimension < 2.5	−0.7
Wall height to least width dimension ≥ 2.5	−0.8

The computed external wind pressure as determined by applying the above pressure coefficients is assumed to be uniform over the entire roof surface.

For structures having a pitched or sloping roof with the direction of wind acting perpendicular to the ridge of the roof, average external pressure coefficients may be obtained from Figure 5.3 for various roof slopes.

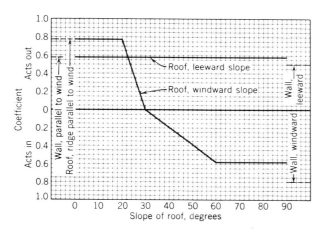

Figure 5.3 ADJUSTMENT FACTORS FOR EXTERNAL WIND LOADS ON ROOFS. The note on the left ("wall, parallel to wind") refers to either an end or a side wall. The notes on the right ("wall, windward" and "wall, leeward") refer to walls, either end or side, normal to the direction of the wind.

For arched roofs with the wind direction perpendicular to the axis of the arch, the external pressure coefficients as indicated for Figure 5.4 are applicable. In the figure shown, N is the ratio of rise to span, h/L.

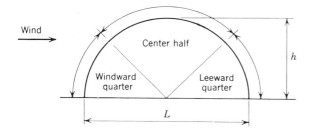

Figure 5.4 ROUNDED OR ARCHED ROOF.

Roof Section	External Pressure Coefficient Cpe
Roof on elevated supports:	
Windward quarter where:	
N < 0.2	−0.9
0.2 ≤ N < 0.3	6N −2.1
0.3 ≤ N ≤ 0.6	2.8N −0.7
Center half:	−N −0.7
Leeward quarter:	−0.5
Roofs supported at ground elevation: N ≤ 0.6	
Windward quarter:	1.4N
Center half:	−N −0.7
Leeward quarter:	−0.5

Local Pressure Coefficients

In determining the local wind pressure acting on ridges, eaves, cornices and 90° corners or roofs, the external pressure coefficients as given below are applicable:

Roof Pitch, θ	Local External Pressure Coefficients for Roofs	
	Ridges and Eaves	Corners
0 to 30°	−2.4	0.1 θ −5.0
> 30°	−1.7	−2.0

The pressure determined by applying these coefficients is assumed to act on a strip of width 0.1 w where w is the least width of the building normal to the ridge. This local pressure is assumed to be applied perpendicularly outward at these locations along the ridges, eaves and cornices but is not included with the net external pressure when computing total wind loads.

Other Structures

For design information concerning net pressure coefficients to be applied in the wind analysis of special structures such as (a) roofs over non-enclosed areas (flat plates), (b) chimneys and tanks, (c) signs and outdoor display structures, (d) trussed towers and (e) tower guys, the designer is referred to *American National Standard Building Code Requirements for Minimum Design Loads in Buildings and Other Structures*, American National Standards Institute.

Bridges and Trestles

The recommendations on wind pressures of the American Association of State Highway Officials for highway bridges or of the American Railway Engineering Association for railroad bridges and trestles should be applied for the wind analysis of these types of structures.

Shielding

No allowance for reductions in those pressures obtained by applying the preceding analyses should be made for the effects of shielding which may be afforded by other buildings, structures or terrain features. The shielding of one element of a structure on another element of the same structure, however, is applicable (see *Wind Forces on Structures*, ASCE paper No. 3269).

Anchorage

Adequate anchorage of the roof and columns, and

SECTION PROPERTIES AND DESIGN LOADS

of wall and columns to the foundation to resist overturning, uplift, and sliding, should be provided in all cases.

Wind Pressure Coefficients

The preceding recommendations are of limited use because they do not take into account oblique wind directions, the variation of pressure over the surfaces, or buildings of unusual shape. The *Timber Construction Manual,* by the American Institute of Timber Construction, provides tabular data and methods which properly account for these factors and their use is highly recommended for critical structures.

EARTHQUAKE LOADS

The lateral force provisions herein are generally based on the recommendations of the 1970 Edition of the *Uniform Building Code* and are intended to provide minimum standards as design criteria for making buildings and other structures earthquake-resistive. These provisions apply to the structure as a unit and also to all parts thereof, including the structural frame or walls, floor and roof systems, and other structural features. The recommendations are general, and, in specific cases, the governing building code regulations should be met.

In areas subject to earthquake shocks, every building or structure and every portion thereof should be so designed and constructed as to resist stresses produced by lateral forces, as provided in these recommendations. Stresses should be calculated as the effect of a force applied horizontally at each floor or roof level above the foundation. The force should be assumed to come from any horizontal direction.

Definitions

The following definitions apply to the recommendations on earthquake loads.

Box System. A structural system without a complete vertical load-carrying space frame. In this system, the required lateral forces are resisted by shear walls.

Shear Wall. A wall designed to resist lateral forces parallel to the wall. Braced frames subjected primarily to axial stresses are considered shear walls for the purpose of this definition.

Space Frame. A three-dimensional structural system composed of interconnected members, other than shear or bearing walls, laterally supported so as to function as a complete self-contained unit with or without the aid of horizontal diaphragms or floor bracing systems.

Space Frame, Moment-Resisting. A vertical load-carrying space frame in which the members and joints are capable of resisting design lateral forces by bending moments.

Space Frame, Vertical Load-Carrying. A space frame designed to carry all vertical loads.

Minimum Earthquake Forces for Buildings
Total lateral force and distribution of lateral force

Every building should be designed and constructed to withstand minimum total lateral seismic forces assumed to act nonconcurrently in the direction of each of the main axes of the building in accordance with the formula (*Note:* The following symbols apply to the recommendations on earthquake loads only):

$$V = ZKCW$$

V = total lateral load or shear at base, lb

$$V = F_t + \sum_{i=1}^{n} F_i$$

where F_t = that portion of V considered concentrated at the top of the structure, at the level n. The remaining portion of the total base shear V shall be distributed over the height of the structure including level n according to the equation for F_x given on page 43.

F_i, F_n, F_x = lateral force applied to level i, n, or x, respectively

W = total dead load, lb. except in storage and warehouse occupancies, where W = total dead load plus 25% of floor live load

K = numerical coefficient as given in Table 5.9.

Z = numerical coefficient dependent on the zone as determined from Figure 5.5.

C = numerical coefficient for base shear:

$C = 0.10$ for all one-and two-story buildings

$C = \dfrac{0.05}{\sqrt[3]{T}}$ for all other buildings

where T = fundamental period of vibration of the building or structure in the direction under consideration, seconds.

Properly substantiated technical data for establishing the period T for the contemplated structure may be used. In the absence of such data, the value of T should be determined by the formulae:

SECTION PROPERTIES AND DESIGN LOADS

$T = 0.10N$ in all buildings in which the lateral resisting system consists of a moment-resisting space frame which resists 100% of the required lateral forces and whose frame is not enclosed by or adjoined by more rigid elements which would tend to prevent the frame from resisting lateral forces; or:

$$T = \frac{0.05H}{\sqrt{D}} \text{ in all other buildings}$$

where N = total number of stories above exterior grade

H = height of the main portion of the building above the base, ft

D = dimension of the building in a direction parallel to the applied forces, ft

The lateral force, V, should be distributed over the height of the structure in the following manner:

(a) $F_t = .004 \ V\left(\dfrac{H}{D_s}\right)^2$

where D_s = the plan dimensions of the vertical lateral force-resisting system, ft.

F_t need not exceed 0.15 V and may be considered as 0 for values $\left(\dfrac{H}{D_s}\right) \leq 3$

(b) $F_x = \dfrac{(V - F_t) \ w_x \ h_x}{\displaystyle\sum_{i=1}^{n} w_i h_i}$

Where w_i, w_x = that portion of w which is located at or is assigned to level i or x respectively, ft.

h_i, h_x = height above the base to level i or x respectively, ft.

At each level designated as x, the force F_x should be applied over the area of the building in accordance with the mass distribution on that level.

(c) One- and two-story buildings shall have uniform distribution.

Lateral force on parts or portions of buildings or other structures

Parts or portions of buildings or structures and their anchorage should be designed for lateral forces in accordance with the formula

$$F_p = ZC_pW_p$$

with the additional notation:

W_p = weight of a part or portion of the structure, lb

C_p = numerical coefficient as defined and tabulated in Table 5.10.

Table 5.9 Horizontal Force Factor K for Buildings or Other Structures[a]

Type or Arrangement of Resisting Elements	Value[b] of K
All building framing systems except as classified below.	1.00
Buildings with a box system as defined in definitions.	1.33
Buildings with a dual bracing system consisting of a ductile moment-resisting space frame and shear walls, designed in accordance with the following criteria: (1) The frames and shear walls shall resist the total lateral force in accordance with their relative rigidities, considering the interaction of the shear walls and frames. (2) The shear walls acting independently of the ductile moment-resisting space frame shall resist the total required lateral force. (3) The ductile moment-resisting space frame shall have the capacity to resist not less than 25% of the required lateral force.	0.80
Buildings with a ductile moment-resisting space frame, designed in accordance with the following criteria: The ductile moment-resisting space frame shall have the capacity to resist the total required lateral force.	0.67
Elevated tanks, plus full contents, on four or more cross-braced legs and not supported by a building.[c][d][e]	3.00
Structures other than buildings and other than those set forth in Table 5.10.	2.00

[a] Where prescribed wind loads produce higher stresses, these loads shall be used in lieu of the loads resulting from earthquake forces.

[b] See Fig. 5.5 for seismic probability zones and values of Z.

[c] The minimum value of KC shall be 0.12 and the maximum value of KC need not exceed 0.25

[d] For overturning, the factor J shall be 1.00.

[e] The tower shall be designed for an accidental torsion of 5% as determined under Horizontal Torsional Moments on page 44.

From 1970 *Uniform Building Code*

Pile foundations

Individual pile or caisson footings of every building or structure should be interconnected by ties each of which can carry by tension and compression a horizontal force equal to 10% of the larger pile cap loading, unless it can be demonstrated that equivalent restraint can be provided by other approved methods.

Distribution of Horizontal Shear

Total shear in any horizontal plane should be distributed to the various resisting elements in proportion to their rigidities, the rigidity of the horizontal bracing system of diaphragm as well as the rigidities of the vertical resisting elements

SECTION PROPERTIES AND DESIGN LOADS

being taken into consideration. Rigid elements that are assumed not to be part of the lateral force resisting system may be incorporated into buildings provided that their effect on the action of the system is considered and provided for in the design.

Drift
Lateral deflections or drift of a story relative to its adjacent stories should be considered in accordance with accepted engineering practice.

Horizontal Torsional Moments
Provisions should be made for the increase in shear resulting from the horizontal torsion due to an eccentricity between the center of mass and the center of rigidity. Negative torsional shears should be neglected. In addition, if the vertical resisting elements depend on diaphragm action for shear distribution at any level, the shear resisting elements should be capable of resisting a torsional moment assumed to be equivalent to the story shear acting with an eccentricity of not less than 5% of the maximum building dimension at that level.

Overturning
Every building or structure should be designed to resist the overturning effects caused by wind forces or by earthquake forces as specified in these recommendations on earthquake loads, whichever govern; with the exception that the axial loads from earthquake forces on vertical elements and footings in every building or structure may be modified in accordance with the following provisions.

1. The overturning moment, *M,* at the base of the building or structure should be determined in accordance with the formula

$$M = J(F_t H + \sum_{i=1}^{n} F_i\, h_i)$$

   where $J = \dfrac{0.6}{T^{2/3}}$

The value of J need not be more than 1.00. For structures other than buildings, the value of J shall be not less than 0.45.

2. The overturning moment, M_x, at any level designated *x* should be determined in accordance with the formula

$$M_x = J_x[F_t\,(H\text{-}h_x) + \sum_{i=x}^{n} F_i(h_i\text{-}h_x]$$

   where $J_x = J + (1\text{-}J)\left(\dfrac{hx}{H}\right)^3$

At any level, the overturning moments should be distributed to the various resisting elements in the same proportion as the distribution of the

shears in the resisting system. Where other vertical members, which are capable of partially resisting the overturning moments, are provided, a redistribution may be made to these members if framing systems of sufficient strength and stiffness to transmit the required loads are provided.

When a vertical resisting element is discontinuous, the overturning moment carried by the lowest story of that element should be carried down as loads to the foundation.

Table 5.10 Horizontal Force Factor *Cp* for Parts or Portions of Buildings or Other Structures

Part or Portion of Buildings	Direction of Force	Value of C_p
Exterior bearing and nonbearing walls, interior bearing walls and partitions, interior nonbearing walls and partitions over 10 ft in height, masonry fences over 6 ft in height	Normal to flat surface	0.20
Cantilever parapet and other cantilever walls, except retaining walls	Normal to flat surface	1.00
Exterior and interior ornamentations and appendages	Any direction	1.00
When connected to or a part of a building: towers, tanks, towers and tanks plus contents, chimneys, smokestacks, and penthouses	Any direction	0.20 [a]
When resting on the ground: tank plus effective mass of its contents	Any direction	0.10
Floors and roofs acting as diaphragms [b]	Any direction	0.10
Connections for exterior panels	Any direction	2.00
Connections for pre-fabricated structural elements other than walls, with force applied at center of gravity of assembly [c]	Any direction	0.30

[a] When *H/D* of any building is equal to or greater than 5 to 1, increase value by 50%.

[b] Floors and roofs acting as diaphragms shall be designed for a minimum value of *Cp* of 10% applied to loads tributary from that story, unless a greater value of *Cp* is required by the basic seismic formula *V = ZKCW.*

[c] *Wp* shall be equal to the total dead load plus 25% of the floor live load in warehouse occupancies.

SECTION PROPERTIES AND DESIGN LOADS

DESIGN REQUIREMENTS
Combined axial and bending stresses in columns forming a part of a space frame
Maximum allowable extreme fiber stress in columns at intersection of columns with floor beams or girders for combined axial and bending stresses should be the allowable bending stress for the material used. Within the center half of the unsupported length of the column, the combined axial and bending stresses should be such that

$$\frac{f_c}{F_c} + \frac{f_b}{F_b} \leq 1$$

where f_c = computed axial stress, psi
F_c = allowable axial stress, psi
f_b = computed bending stress, psi
F_b = allowable bending stress, psi

When stresses are due to a combination of vertical and lateral loads, the allowable unit stresses may be increased one-third.

Building Separations
All portions of structures should be designed and constructed to act as an integral unit in resisting horizontal forces unless separated structurally by a distance sufficient to avoid contact under deflection from seismic action or wind forces.

Minor Alterations
Minor structural alterations may be made in existing buildings and other structures, but the resistance to lateral forces should be not less than that before such alterations were made, unless the building as altered meets the requirements of the governing building code.

Combined Vertical and Horizontal Forces
In computing the effect of seismic force in combination with vertical loads, gravity load stresses induced in members by dead load plus design live load, except roof live load, should be considered.

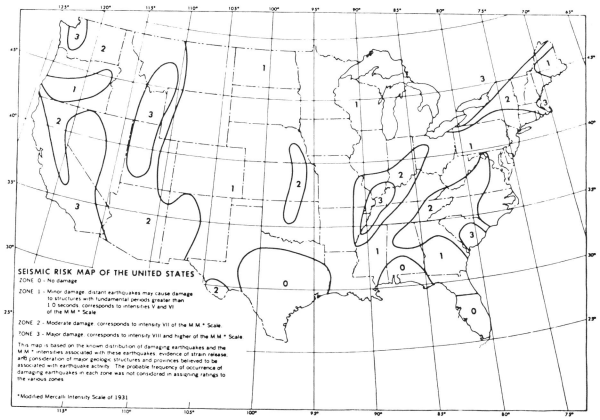

SEISMIC RISK MAP OF THE UNITED STATES
ZONE 0 - No damage
ZONE 1 - Minor damage: distant earthquakes may cause damage to structures with fundamental periods greater than 1 0 seconds; corresponds to intensities V and VI of the M M.* Scale
ZONE 2 - Moderate damage: corresponds to intensity VII of the M.M.* Scale.
ZONE 3 - Major damage: corresponds to intensity VIII and higher of the M.M.* Scale.
This map is based on the known distribution of damaging earthquakes and the M M.* intensities associated with these earthquakes; evidence of strain release; and consideration of major geologic structures and provinces believed to be associated with earthquake activity. The probable frequency of occurrence of damaging earthquakes in each zone was not considered in assigning ratings to the various zones.
*Modified Mercalli Intensity Scale of 1931

Figure 5.5. ZONES OF APPROXIMATELY EQUAL SEISMIC PROBABILITY. Recommended by the International Conference of Building Officials.

CHAPTER VI

Structural Glued Laminated Timber

STRUCTURAL GLUED LAMINATED TIMBER

Structural glued laminated timber, often referred to as "glulam", differs from sawn lumber in that it may be fabricated to curved shapes and to unusually large sizes and long lengths. Fabricators' shop facilities and treating procedures can accommodate almost any size, shape or length, but transportation facilities may be a limitation.

Glued laminated members manufactured and fabricated in accordance with *Voluntary Product Standard PS 56-73,* will meet all structural and service requirements. The use of seasoned lumber, which is required for proper gluing, and the dispersion of growth characteristics, results in higher allowable unit stresses than for sawn lumber. The use of seasoned laminations also provides dimensional stability not expected of large sawn timbers.

Gluing

As laminated members may be pressure impregnated with chemicals either before or after gluing, the time of treatment should be left to the option of the fabricator, as the overall size of a member and size of treating retort often govern the choice. When treatment is to be done after gluing, a wet-use adhesive must be used and oil borne treatments are normally used, especially for large members subjected to severe exposure conditions.

Wet-use adhesives should be used whenever the moisture content of the member in use will exceed 16%. Design details should avoid pockets where moisture can collect, provide protection from damp walls, and eliminate direct contact with the earth. Whenever high moisture content conditions may occur, the use of a pressure impregnated preservative is recommended.

Mill Type or Heavy Timber Construction

Glued laminated members of the nominal sizes required meet the standards of *Heavy Timber Construction* as they have all of the durability necessary under exposure to fire. Although pressure impregnation with fire retardants reduces the spread of flame across the surface of wood, it does not significantly increase the inherent fire resistance of heavy timber. However, it may be used when required by the job specifications or the applicable building code.

Thickness of Laminations

The maximum net thickness of individual laminations shall not exceed two inches. Industry recommended practice uses lumber of nominal 1-inch and 2-inch thickness for laminating. Lumber of nominal 1-inch thickness is generally dressed to ¾″ and is primarily used for curved structural members. Laminations of 2-inch nominal thickness are generally surfaced to 1½″ and are used for straight structural members and for curved members with a radius of curvature not exceeding 125 times the lamination thickness for Douglas Fir-Larch.

Special thinner laminations required for sharp radii are more expensive than standard thickness laminations. Often the saving in head room is offset by the larger size member required because of the unit stress reduction and greater moment in the haunch.

Where special care is taken in selecting the lumber and special precaution is used in bending the individual laminates, it is possible to decrease the radius of curvature over those tabulated without resorting to the use of thinner laminations.

Selection of Material

It is preferable for the designer to specify required stress values and appearance grades only and permit the laminator to select such stock as best meets structural and appearance requirements. Lumber in glued laminated members should conform with grade, manufacture, moisture content and other requirements of the laminating standards for the species. Service conditions should also be specified by the designer. Dry condition of service occurs when the moisture content of the member will be at or below 16% in service. Wet condition of service occurs when the moisture content of the member will be above 16% in service.

Camber

Camber is built into a structural member by introducing a curvature, either circular or parabolic, opposite to the anticipated deflection movement. Camber requirements vary with design criteria for various conditions of use and, in addition, are dependent on whether the member is of simple, continuous or cantilever span; whether roof drainage is to be provided by the camber; and other related factors. Reverse camber may be required in continuous and cantilever spans to permit adequate drainage. For roof and floor beams, it is recommended that glued laminated members have a minimum camber of 1½ times the dead load deflection. Additional camber is recommended to provide necessary roof drainage for roof beams and may be desirable to improve appearance.

Tapered Beams

Glued laminated beams are often tapered to meet architectural requirements, to provide pitched roofs, or to provide a minimum depth of beam at its bearing. The most commonly used tapered beams are simple span and may be of any of the following configurations: (a) single tapered-straight, (b) double tapered-straight, (c) double tapered-pitched or (d) double tapered-curved.

The design of pitched and curved beams must provide for horizontal deflection at their supports. If it does not, that is, if the supports are designed to resist horizontal movement, the member must be designed as a two-hinged arch. It is usually preferable to provide for the relatively small amount of horizontal movement which occurs at the supports by providing slotted or roller connections.

In the design of tapered beams, consideration must be given to the interaction of stresses at the tapered edge. Due to the relative complexity of this analysis, the designer is referred to the

STRUCTURAL GLUED LAMINATED TIMBER

Timber Construction Manual, published by the American Institute of Timber Construction, for the detailed design procedure for tapered beams.

Arches

There are two main categories of arches; first, the haunched, gothic, or boomerang, usually of 3-hinged construction in which bending moment is the most critical consideration; and second, constant radius arches of 2 or 3-hinged construction in which compression is the critical consideration. As in tapered beams, the designer is referred to the *Timber Construction Manual,* published by the American Institute of Timber Construction, for detailed design procedures.

CHAPTER VII

Design

DESIGN — COLUMNS

Theoretically, the Euler formula would suffice for the design of all columns, short or long, provided the ultimate axial compressive strength of a material was of infinite value. However, wood like other materials, has an ultimate strength value that is less than indicated by the Euler formula for columns in the lower range of slenderness ratios.

Tests at the Forest Products Laboratory show that at ultimate values the strength of wood in axial compression decreases approximately as indicated by a fourth power parabolic formula to a value about equal to the proportional limit strength of a species, and thereafter the decrease is equal to that indicated by the Euler formula. These behavior characteristics have led to the following three column classifications:

1. Short columns — where the slenderness ratio is eleven or less.

2. Intermediate columns — between a slenderness ratio of eleven and a slenderness ratio where the strength has decreased to a value of two-thirds the maximum axial compressive strength.

3. Long columns — where the slenderness ratio is greater than that of the intermediate range.

In the short column classification, strength is dependent upon the axial crushing strength of wood and it follows that the unit working strength for compression parallel to grain, "Fc", is used in the design of columns in this range.

In the long column classification, the stiffness of wood governs the buckling strength of the column and in determining the unit working strength the Euler formula is used with an appropriate reduction factor introduced to provide safety. The modulus of elasticity of the species and grade determines the strength of long columns.

In the intermediate column classification, strength is dependent upon a combination of crushing and lateral buckling.

Type of Columns

The shape or the method of assembly has an effect on the design of columns. The most frequently used wood columns are the "simple solid" pieces of square or rectangular cross-section. The column of round cross-section is a type of simple solid column that is less frequently encountered. The "spaced column", an assembly of pieces, is most often used in trusses and similar structural frames. "Built-up" columns are less frequently used as they lack efficiency in total load capacity. In the design of columns of all types, the load capacity depends upon the slenderness ratio.

Slenderness Ratio

The slenderness ratio is the relationship of the unsupported length of the column to the cross-sectional dimension of the face under consideration. This ratio is expressed as

$$l/d = \text{slenderness ratio,}$$

in which d = net dimension in inches of the face under consideration.

The slenderness ratio for simple solid columns is limited to
$$l/d = 50$$
and for spaced columns, the limiting ratio is
$$l/d = 80$$

When columns are firmly stayed laterally on one or more faces or at different points intermediate in the length of the column piece, the slenderness ratio in each plane of lateral support must be determined and the greater ratio used in computing allowable loads. The greater ratio is the controlling condition as its use produces the lesser allowable load.

The formula for determining the unit load in pounds per square inch of cross-sectional area, P/A, for simple solid columns in the short column range is:

$$P/A = F_c$$

P = the axial load on the column, pounds,

A = the net cross-sectional area, square inches,

F_c = the allowable unit stress in compression parallel to grain for the grades of lumber used, pounds per square inch,

and for those in the long column range is a development of the Euler formula for axially loaded members.

With a reduction factor to provide structural adequacy and an adjustment for normal loading conditions applied to the values derived from test data of axially loaded pin ended specimens, the general Euler formula for a column of any cross-section becomes:

$$P/A = \frac{3.619E}{(l/r)^2}$$

in which E = modulus of elasticity,

l = unsupported length in inches,

r = least radius of gyration.

For columns of square or rectangular cross-section this formula becomes:

$$P/A = \frac{0.3E}{(l/d)^2}$$

in which l/d = slenderness ratio

E = Modulus of Elasticity

The formula is conservative as it applies to restrained and square end columns as well as to the pin ended condition from which it was derived.

Maximum Simple Solid Column Capacity

When the P/A value from the Euler formula is equal to the allowable compression parallel to grain value "F_C" for the grade of lumber used, the maximum unit working stress capacity of the column is attained. The slenderness ratio at which this condition occurs varies depending on the "F_C" and "E" values and can be expressed as:

$$l/\text{d} = \sqrt{\frac{0.3E}{F_C}}$$

For slenderness ratios equal to or less than given by the formula, the allowable unit stress in compression parallel to grain, "F_C" is used, and for greater slenderness ratios, the P/A value obtained by the Euler formula is used.

To obtain the maximum load capacity of a column, the net cross-sectional area of the column is multiplied by the values of "P/A" obtained from the appropriate formula, whichever governs. The load capacity of a simple solid column is subject to adjustment for duration of load as outlined on page 21 and for condition of service as specified on page 20.

Spaced Columns

Parallel compression members, separated by spacer blocks and effectively joined at their ends through the spacer blocks, are called "spaced-columns". See Figure 7.1. As the axial strength of any column cannot be greater than the compression parallel to grain value, "F_C" for the species and grade of lumber used, it follows that the efficiency of spaced columns, with a fixity factor that affects the buckling strength, is only obtained in the larger slenderness ratios of the long column classification. Spaced column action is the result of joining the ends of the compression members, through the spacer blocks, with connectors. This restrains differential movement between the ends of the members and introduces some end rigidity. The degree of rigidity is related to the location of the timber connector from the ends of the column. Where the connectors are close to the ends, the factor of rigidity is 2½ and further from the ends the factor increases to 3. Hence, location of connectors from the ends is described as "condition a" and "condition b." The design of spaced columns is essentially the same as the design of simple solid columns with the factor of rigidity introduced in the Euler column formula as follows:

Condition "a":

For end condition "a", the required connectors in end blocks are between the ends of the column and $l/20$ from the ends. With a factor of 2½ for this condition the allowable load for the individual pieces is determined by the formula—

$$\text{P/A} = 2.5 \; \frac{0.3E}{(l/\text{d})^2} \; = \; \frac{0.75E}{(l/\text{d})^2}$$

Condition "b":

For end condition "b", the required connectors in end blocks are between a distance of $l/20$ to $l/10$ from the ends. The factor for end condition "b" is 3, and the allowable load for the individual pieces is determined by the formula—

$$\text{P/A} = 3.0 \; \frac{0.3E}{(l/\text{d})^2} \; = \; \frac{0.9E}{(l/\text{d})^2}$$

If there are two or more connectors in a contact face, the position of the center of gravity of the group of connectors is used in measuring the distance from connectors in the end blocks to the end of the column for determining end conditions "a" or "b".

Maximum Spaced Column Capacity

Spaced column action is only obtained when the individual column pieces of the assembly have a slenderness ratio, "l/d", greater than:

$$\sqrt{\frac{0.3E}{F_C}}$$

For an assembly of members having a lesser slenderness ratio, the individual members are designed as simple columns using the compression parallel to grain value "F_C". Because of the rigidity factor, the compression parallel to grain value "F_C" is also applicable to spaced columns where the range of slenderness ratio of a column piece is

between $\sqrt{\dfrac{0.3E}{F_C}}$, and for

condition "a" $\sqrt{\dfrac{2.5 \times 0.3E}{F_C}}$, or

$\sqrt{\dfrac{3.0 \times 0.3E}{F_C}}$ for condition "b".

The slenderness ratio of a spaced column is always determined by the ratio of the unsupported length of the column, "l", to the thickness of an individual column leg, "d", measured parallel to the buckling direction of the spaced column. See Figure 7.1. The width of the column leg in the other direction is related to the slenderness ratio of the assembly acting as a simple solid column except when spaced column action is developed in both directions by a more elaborate assembly of pieces. Spaced columns should be investigated for the minimum load capacity, which is also the governing capacity, determined from the slenderness ratio of both the thickness and width of a leg in the column assembly.

DESIGN — COLUMNS

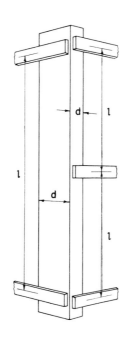

Simple Solid Column

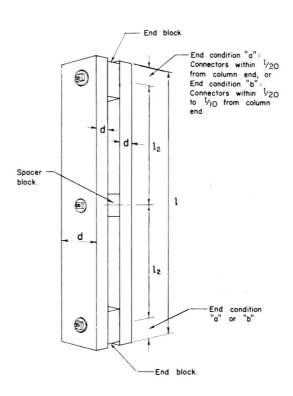

Spaced Column

Figure 7.1 — Column Types

The total axial load "P" for a spaced column assembly is the unit load "P/A" obtained by the formulas for condition "a" or condition "b", whichever is applicable, multiplied by the sum of the cross-sectional areas of the individual column pieces. The axial load for spaced columns is subject to adjustment for duration of load as outlined on page 21 and for condition of service as specified on page 20.

Though the spaced column has advantages, quite often a simple solid column having an equal cross-section to that of the sum of the areas of the spaced column pieces will be more practical and economical. This is because the slenderness ratio of the simple solid column will be about half of that for the spaced column giving greater load capacity for the simple solid column piece. The economics of fabrication and extra hardware required for a spaced column as compared to a simple solid column should be considered in choosing which is most suited to design requirements.

Spacer and End Blocks

The thickness of spacer and end blocks must not be less than that of the individual members of the spaced column, except that spacer and end blocks to one-half that thickness may be used, provided the length of the block is made inversely proportional to the thickness in relation to required length of a full thickness block. Blocks

thicker than a side member do not increase the load capacity.

The thickness, length and width of end blocks must be sufficient to give the necessary margins and spacing for the number of timber connectors required for spaced column effect. Intermediate in the length of a spaced column, a spacer block or blocks must be used in addition to those at the ends. If a single intermediate spacer block is located within the middle one-tenth of the column length "*l*", connectors are not required for this block. If there are two or more intermediate spacer blocks, the distance between any two should not exceed one-half of the distance between centers of connectors in the two end blocks. The requirements for connectors in spacer blocks are the same as for end blocks when two or more blocks are located outside of the middle one-fourth of the length of the column.

For spaced columns used as compression chords of a truss, a panel point which is stayed laterally is considered as the end of the spaced column and the portion of the member between the individual members making up a spaced column may be considered as the end block. For compression web members designed as spaced columns, joints at the tension chord may be considered stayed laterally by the tautness of the tension chord or by lateral bracing generally used between trusses in the plane of the tension chord.

Connector Requirements at Ends of Spaced Columns

To obtain spaced column action, timber connectors, as well as end blocks are required at the ends of the column pieces to resist differential movement between the pieces.

Theoretical considerations, coupled with limited test data, indicate that for spaced column action the timber connector requirements in the end blocks between each connecting face is zero when the slenderness ratio of the individual column piece is

$$\sqrt{\frac{0.3E}{F_c}}$$

or less and is maximum at a slenderness ratio of 60. Maximum timber connector requirements for each connecting face are equal to one-fourth of the clear wood working strength in compression parallel to grain for the species being used, times the required cross-sectional area of the column piece.

To obtain spaced-column action the connectors in each mutually contacting surface of end block and individual member at each end of a spaced column must be of a size and number to provide a load capacity in pounds equal to the required cross-sectional area in square inches of one of the individual members times the appropriate endspacer block constant in Table 7.1.

If spaced columns are a part of a truss system or other similar framing, the connectors required by joint design may be sufficient for end block connectors but should be checked against Table 7.1.

For connector load grouping of species see Table 7.2.

Table 7.1 — End spacer block constants for connector joined spaced columns.

| l/d ratio of individual member in the spaced column[1] | End spacer block constant | | | |
	Group A connector loads	Group B connector loads	Group C connector loads	Group D connector loads
0 to 11	0	0	0	0
15	38	33	27	21
20	86	73	61	48
25	134	114	94	75
30	181	155	128	101
35	229	195	162	128
40	277	236	195	154
45	325	277	229	181
50	372	318	263	208
55	420	358	296	234
60 to 80	468	399	330	261

[1]Constants for intermediate l/d ratios may be obtained by straight line interpolation.

Table 7.2 Connector Load Grouping of Species.

Connector Load Grouping	Species
Group A	Douglas Fir-Larch (Dense)
Group B	Douglas Fir-Larch
Group C	Douglas Fir South Hem-Fir Western Hemlock Mountain Hemlock Lodgepole Pine Ponderosa Pine- Sugar Pine Idaho White Pine
Group D	Engelmann Spruce Subalpine Fir Western Cedars

Round Columns

Round columns are essentially simple solid columns. The effect of the cross-sectional shape, in determining the capacity load for such columns when they are in the Euler Column range of slenderness ratios, results in the formula:

$$P/A = \frac{3.619E}{(l/r)^2}$$

where r = the least radius of gyration.

As round and square columns of the same cross-sectional area, other conditions being equal, will carry the same loads and have equal stiffness, the design of round columns can be simplified by assuming a square column for analytical purposes and then using a round column of the same cross-sectional area.

Tapered Columns

Columns that are tapered to one or to both ends are designed as simple solid columns using as the least dimension "d", in determining the slenderness ratio, "l/d", the sum of the minimum width and one-third the difference between the minimum and maximum width for the face under consideration, but in no case should it be assumed as more than one and one-half times the minimum dimension. If the column is round, the minimum and maximum diameters are substituted for the face width in the preceding rule. The bearing stress on the small end of a tapered column should be investigated to be sure there is no overstress at this point.

End-Bearing of Compression Members

For end-bearing or end-to-end bearing of columns see page 78.

Axial Compression and Bending Combined

The design of a column subject to combined loads is a trial and error procedure. By this method a tentative size is assumed and then analyzed to

DESIGN — COLUMNS

determine if it is over-stressed or under-stressed. Based on the results of the preliminary analysis, the size is adjusted to obtain a more refined design and the procedure repeated until the most economical size is obtained.

When a column is loaded eccentrically on its end or when it supports a side load, both axial compression and flexural stresses are induced in the member. The usual formulas for combined loading are difficult to apply and are further complicated by the difference in stress values for bending and compression in wood. Design formulas for combined stresses, desirably simplified yet within the needed range of accuracy, are presented herein.

Columns Having a Slenderness Ratio of $\sqrt{\dfrac{0.3E}{F_c}}$ **or Less**

For columns that support side loads as well as concentric end loads and are within this range of slenderness ratios, there is no additive flexural stress due to deflection and the formula for the combined loads is:

$$\frac{M/S}{F_b} + \frac{P/A}{F_c{}'} = 1 \text{ or less.}$$

When the bending stress in a column is induced by an eccentric end load and there is no side load the above formula takes the form:

$$\frac{P/A\left(\dfrac{6e}{d}\right)}{F_b} + \frac{P/A}{F_c{}'} = 1 \text{ or less.}$$

A combination of concentric end loads, side loads, and eccentricity results in the addition of another term to the preceding formula for the flexural stress caused by the side loads. The formula then becomes:

$$\frac{M/S + P/A\left(\dfrac{6e}{d}\right)}{F_b} + \frac{P/A}{F_c{}'} = 1 \text{ or less.}$$

Columns Having a Slenderness Ratio Greater Than

$$\sqrt{\frac{0.3E}{F_c}}$$

In this range of slenderness ratios, bending stresses are induced by the deflection of the column from eccentric or side loads and the derivation of a formula for combined stresses must include the effect of the stresses caused by deflection. The formula for a column subject to concentric end load, side load, and stress caused by deflection is:

$$\frac{M/S}{F_b - P/A} + \frac{P/A}{F_c{}'} = 1 \text{ or less.}$$

When there are no side loads and bending stresses are induced by an eccentric end load the formula becomes:

$$\frac{P/A\left(\dfrac{15e}{2d}\right)}{F_b - P/A} + \frac{P/A}{F_c{}'} = 1 \text{ or less.}$$

The preceding formula can be expanded to include combined end load, side loads and eccentricity by adding the bending stress caused by the side load. The formula for such a combination takes the form:

$$\frac{M/S + P/A\left(\dfrac{15e}{2d}\right)}{F_b - P/A} + \frac{P/A}{F_c{}'} = 1 \text{ or less}$$

in which
M	=	total bending moment, inch pounds,
S	=	section modulus of member,
e	=	eccentricity in inches,
d	=	side in inches of a rectangular column measured in the direction of side loads.

All other terms are as previously defined.

Columns with Side Brackets

The formulas given for eccentric end loads are for loads applied at the ends of the column. When an eccentric load is applied by a bracket at a distance below the upper end of the column, conditions of stress and deflection are more favorable. The exact formula for this condition is complex and difficult to solve, hence, the following procedure, which is conservative and quite accurate for brackets in the upper one-fourth of the length of the column. The load thus determined may be substituted in the formulas for columns having combined axial compression and bending from side loads.

1. Assume that the bracket load P is acting as a concentric end load at the top of the column and that a side load P_1 is acting at mid-height of the column in Figure 7.2.
2. The side load P_1 can be determined by the following empirical formula:

$$P_1 = \frac{3al_1P}{l^2}$$

where P_1 = assumed horizontal side load in pounds,

         P = actual load on bracket in pounds,

         a = horizontal distance from load on bracket to center of column in inches,

         l = total length of column in inches,

         l_1 = distance from point of application of load on the bracket to the base of the column in inches.

3. The assumed concentric end load P may then be added to other column loads and with the assumed side load P_1 substituted in the appropriate combined load formula.

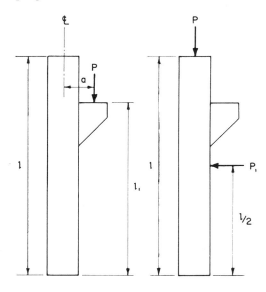

Figure 7.2 — Columns with Side Brackets.

Tables of Safe Unit Axial Loads for Columns
Tables for safe unit axial loads for simple solid columns, spaced columns with end condition "a" and spaced columns with end condition "b" are provided in this section.

Use of Tables
The tabular data included herein for safe unit axial stresses provides a simplified and accurate method for calculating allowable loads on columns. Safe unit axial stresses are tabulated for unsupported lengths from 3 feet through 30 feet and for critical dimensions yielding slenderness

DESIGN — COLUMNS

ratios (l/d) between those required for the short and the long column ranges. The allowable column load is determined by multiplying the appropriate tabular unit stress by the cross-sectional area of the member, based on net dimensions. If it is necessary to refine the design further, the weight of the column should be deducted to determine the allowable applied total load.

Modulus of Elasticity
The recommended modulus of elasticity, E, for the species and grade of lumber to be used should be determined from the building code, the *National Design Specification for Stress-Grade Lumber and Its Fastenings,* or on page 22 of this book. Tabular values for F'_c are provided for a range of E values from 800,000 to 2,400,000 psi.

Maximum Allowable F'_c
When calculating the total load on a column, the F'_c value obtained from the tabular data may not exceed the compression parallel to grain, F_c, for the species and grade of lumber to be used. For example, the tabular F'_c value may be listed as 1439 but the allowable F_c value for the species and grade may be only 1150, in which case the 1150 psi controls in calculating the total allowable load for the column.

Adjustment for Load Duration
The tabular values for F'_c and the allowable values of F_c for the species and grade of lumber used should be multiplied by the following factors:

For permanent loading 0.90
For normal loading 1.00
For snow loading 1.15
For loading of 7 day duration 1.25
For wind or earthquake loads 1.33
For impact 2.00

Example:

Known:
Simple column:
Unsupported length: 14'-0"
Size: 6 x 8 (Cross sectional area = 5½ x 7½ = 41.25 in.²)
Grade and Species: No. 1 Douglas Fir-Larch, Post and Timber
    Fc = 1000 psi, E = 1,600,000 psi
Duration of loading adjustment: 1.15 for snow loading
Critical Dimension: 7½" (Assuming adequate support in the 5½" direction).

Find: Allowable load on column.
From Table for Simple-Solid Columns find F'_c of 957 psi. Since the F'_c of 957 is less than the allowable Fc of 1000, the Fc value of 957 psi must be used.

Allowable total load on column is
957x1.15x41.25 = 45,398 pounds.

DESIGN — SIMPLE SOLID COLUMNS
SAFE UNIT AXIAL LOADS

See instructions for use of tables.
Obtain allowable E Value from building code or Pages 22-27.
Value of Fc' from table may not exceed Fc value for species and grade of lumber used.
Total allowable load on column equals cross sectional area in square inches times Fc' value.

CRITICAL DIMENSION Inches Nominal	Net	L/D	MODULUS OF ELASTICITY (1,000,000 psi)														
			.8	.9	1.0	1.1	1.2	1.3	1.4	1.5	1.6	1.7	1.8	1.9	2.0	2.2	2.4
3 FEET UNSUPPORTED LENGTH																	
2	1½	24.0	417	469	521	573	625	677	729	781	833	885	937	990	1042	1146	1250
3	2½	14.4	1157	1302	1447	1591	1736	1881	2025	2170	2315	2459	2604	2749	2894	3183	3472
4	3½	10.3	2269	2552	2836	3119	3403	3686	3970	4253	4537	4821	5104	5388	5671	6238	6806
4 FEET UNSUPPORTED LENGTH																	
2	1½	32.0	234	264	293	322	352	381	410	439	469	498	527	557	586	645	703
3	2½	19.2	651	732	814	895	977	1058	1139	1221	1302	1383	1465	1546	1628	1790	1953
4	3½	13.7	1276	1436	1595	1755	1914	2074	2233	2393	2552	2712	2871	3031	3190	3509	3828
5 FEET UNSUPPORTED LENGTH																	
2	1½	40.0	150	169	188	206	225	244	263	281	300	319	338	356	375	413	450
3	2½	24.0	417	469	521	573	625	677	729	781	833	885	937	990	1042	1146	1250
4	3½	17.1	817	919	1021	1123	1225	1327	1429	1531	1633	1735	1837	1940	2042	2246	2450
6 FEET UNSUPPORTED LENGTH																	
2	1½	48.0	104	117	130	143	156	169	182	195	208	221	234	247	260	286	312
3	2½	28.8	289	326	362	398	434	470	506	543	579	615	651	687	723	796	868
4	3½	20.6	567	638	709	780	851	922	992	1063	1134	1205	1276	1347	1418	1560	1701
6	5½	13.1	1400	1576	1751	1926	2101	2276	2451	2626	2801	2976	3151	3326	3501	3851	4201
7 FEET UNSUPPORTED LENGTH																	
3	2½	33.6	213	239	266	292	319	345	372	399	425	452	478	505	531	585	638
4	3½	24.0	417	469	521	573	625	677	729	781	833	885	937	990	1042	1146	1250
6	5½	15.3	1029	1158	1286	1415	1543	1672	1801	1929	2058	2186	2315	2444	2572	2830	3087
8 FEET UNSUPPORTED LENGTH																	
3	2½	38.4	163	183	203	224	244	264	285	305	326	346	366	387	407	448	488
4	3½	27.4	319	359	399	439	479	518	558	598	638	678	718	758	798	877	957
6	5½	17.5	788	886	985	1083	1182	1280	1379	1477	1576	1674	1772	1871	1969	2166	2363
9 FEET UNSUPPORTED LENGTH																	
3	2½	43.2	129	145	161	177	193	209	225	241	257	273	289	305	322	354	386
4	3½	30.9	252	284	315	347	378	410	441	473	504	536	567	599	630	693	756
6	5½	19.6	622	700	778	856	934	1011	1089	1167	1245	1323	1400	1478	1556	1712	1867
10 FEET UNSUPPORTED LENGTH																	
3	2½	48.0	104	117	130	143	156	169	182	195	208	221	234	247	260	286	312
4	3½	34.3	204	230	255	281	306	332	357	383	408	434	459	485	510	561	613
6	5½	21.8	504	567	630	693	756	819	882	945	1008	1071	1134	1197	1260	1386	1512
8	7¼	16.6	876	986	1095	1205	1314	1424	1533	1643	1752	1862	1971	2081	2190	2409	2628
8	7½	16.0	938	1055	1172	1289	1406	1523	1641	1758	1875	1992	2109	2227	2344	2578	2813
11 FEET UNSUPPORTED LENGTH																	
4	3½	37.7	169	190	211	232	253	274	295	316	337	359	380	401	422	464	506
6	5½	24.0	417	469	521	573	625	677	729	781	833	885	937	990	1042	1146	1250
8	7¼	18.2	724	815	905	996	1086	1177	1267	1358	1448	1539	1629	1720	1810	1991	2172
8	7½	17.6	775	872	968	1065	1162	1259	1356	1453	1550	1646	1743	1840	1937	2131	2324
12 FEET UNSUPPORTED LENGTH																	
4	3½	41.1	142	160	177	195	213	230	248	266	284	301	319	337	354	390	425
6	5½	26.2	350	394	438	481	525	569	613	656	700	744	788	832	875	963	1050
8	7¼	19.9	608	684	760	836	913	989	1065	1141	1217	1293	1369	1445	1521	1673	1825
8	7½	19.2	651	732	814	895	977	1058	1139	1221	1302	1383	1465	1546	1628	1790	1953
10	9¼	15.6	990	1114	1238	1362	1485	1609	1733	1857	1981	2104	2228	2352	2476	2723	2971
10	9½	15.2	1045	1175	1306	1436	1567	1697	1828	1959	2089	2220	2350	2481	2611	2873	3134
13 FEET UNSUPPORTED LENGTH																	
4	3½	44.6	121	136	151	166	181	196	211	227	242	257	272	287	302	332	362
6	5½	28.4	298	336	373	410	447	485	522	559	597	634	671	709	746	820	895
8	7¼	21.5	518	583	648	713	778	842	907	972	1037	1102	1166	1231	1296	1426	1555
8	7½	20.8	555	624	693	763	832	901	971	1040	1109	1179	1248	1317	1387	1526	1664
10	9¼	16.9	844	949	1055	1160	1266	1371	1477	1582	1688	1793	1899	2004	2110	2320	2531
10	9½	16.4	890	1001	1113	1224	1335	1446	1558	1669	1780	1891	2003	2114	2225	2448	2670

DESIGN — SIMPLE SOLID COLUMNS
SAFE UNIT AXIAL LOADS

See instructions for use of tables.
Obtain allowable E Value from building code or Pages 22-27.
Value of Fc′ from table may not exceed Fc value for species and grade of lumber used.
Total allowable load on column equals cross sectional area in square inches times Fc′ value.

CRITICAL DIMENSION Inches Nominal	Net	L/D	.8	.9	1.0	1.1	1.2	1.3	1.4	1.5	1.6	1.7	1.8	1.9	2.0	2.2	2.4
MODULUS OF ELASTICITY (1,000,000 psi)																	
14 FEET UNSUPPORTED LENGTH																	
4	3½	48.0	104	117	130	143	156	169	182	195	208	221	234	247	260	286	312
6	5½	30.5	257	289	322	354	386	418	450	482	514	547	579	611	643	707	772
8	7¼	23.2	447	503	559	615	670	726	782	838	894	950	1006	1062	1117	1229	1341
8	7½	22.4	478	538	598	658	717	777	837	897	957	1016	1076	1136	1196	1315	1435
10	9¼	18.2	728	819	909	1000	1091	1182	1273	1364	1455	1546	1637	1728	1819	2001	2183
10	9½	17.7	767	863	959	1055	1151	1247	1343	1439	1535	1631	1727	1823	1919	2110	2302
12	11¼	14.9	1076	1211	1345	1480	1614	1749	1883	2018	2152	2287	2421	2556	2691	2960	3229
12	11½	14.6	1125	1265	1406	1546	1687	1827	1968	2109	2249	2390	2530	2671	2811	3093	3374
15 FEET UNSUPPORTED LENGTH																	
6	5½	32.7	224	252	280	308	336	364	392	420	448	476	504	532	560	616	672
8	7¼	24.8	389	438	487	535	584	633	681	730	779	827	876	925	973	1071	1168
8	7½	24.0	417	469	521	573	625	677	729	781	833	885	937	990	1042	1146	1250
10	9¼	19.5	634	713	792	871	951	1030	1109	1188	1268	1347	1426	1505	1584	1743	1901
10	9½	18.9	669	752	836	919	1003	1086	1170	1253	1337	1421	1504	1588	1671	1838	2006
12	11¼	16.0	938	1055	1172	1289	1406	1523	1641	1758	1875	1992	2109	2227	2344	2578	2813
12	11½	15.7	980	1102	1225	1347	1469	1592	1714	1837	1959	2082	2204	2327	2449	2694	2939
16 FEET UNSUPPORTED LENGTH																	
6	5½	34.9	197	222	246	271	295	320	345	369	394	418	443	468	492	542	591
8	7¼	26.5	342	385	428	471	513	556	599	642	684	727	770	813	856	941	1027
8	7½	25.6	366	412	458	504	549	595	641	687	732	778	824	870	916	1007	1099
10	9¼	20.8	557	627	696	766	836	905	975	1044	1114	1184	1253	1323	1393	1532	1671
10	9½	20.2	588	661	734	808	881	955	1028	1102	1175	1249	1322	1395	1469	1616	1763
12	11¼	17.1	824	927	1030	1133	1236	1339	1442	1545	1648	1751	1854	1957	2060	2266	2472
12	11½	16.7	861	969	1076	1184	1291	1399	1507	1614	1722	1830	1937	2045	2152	2368	2583
14	13¼	14.5	1143	1286	1429	1572	1714	1857	2000	2143	2286	2429	2572	2715	2857	3143	3429
14	13½	14.2	1187	1335	1483	1631	1780	1928	2076	2225	2373	2521	2670	2818	2966	3263	3560
17 FEET UNSUPPORTED LENGTH																	
6	5½	37.1	174	196	218	240	262	283	305	327	349	371	393	414	436	480	523
8	7¼	28.1	303	341	379	417	455	493	530	568	606	644	682	720	758	834	909
8	7½	27.2	324	365	405	446	487	527	568	608	649	689	730	770	811	892	973
10	9¼	22.1	493	555	617	678	740	802	864	925	987	1049	1110	1172	1234	1357	1480
10	9½	21.5	520	586	651	716	781	846	911	976	1041	1106	1171	1236	1301	1431	1561
12	11¼	18.1	730	821	912	1004	1095	1186	1277	1369	1460	1551	1642	1733	1825	2007	2190
12	11½	17.7	763	858	953	1049	1144	1239	1335	1430	1525	1621	1716	1811	1907	2097	2288
14	13¼	15.4	1012	1139	1266	1392	1519	1645	1772	1898	2025	2152	2278	2405	2531	2784	3037
14	13½	15.1	1051	1182	1314	1445	1577	1708	1839	1971	2102	2233	2365	2496	2628	2890	3153
18 FEET UNSUPPORTED LENGTH																	
6	5½	39.3	156	175	195	214	233	253	272	292	311	331	350	370	389	428	467
8	7¼	29.8	270	304	338	372	406	439	473	507	541	575	608	642	676	744	811
8	7½	28.8	289	326	362	398	434	470	506	543	579	615	651	687	723	796	868
10	9¼	23.4	440	495	550	605	660	715	770	825	880	935	990	1045	1100	1210	1320
10	9½	22.7	464	522	580	638	696	754	812	870	929	987	1045	1103	1161	1277	1393
12	11¼	19.2	651	732	814	895	977	1058	1139	1221	1302	1383	1465	1546	1628	1790	1953
12	11½	18.8	680	765	850	935	1020	1105	1191	1276	1361	1446	1531	1616	1701	1871	2041
14	13¼	16.3	903	1016	1129	1242	1355	1468	1580	1693	1806	1919	2032	2145	2258	2484	2709
14	13½	16.0	938	1055	1172	1289	1406	1523	1641	1758	1875	1992	2109	2227	2344	2578	2813
19 FEET UNSUPPORTED LENGTH																	
6	5½	41.5	140	157	175	192	209	227	244	262	279	297	314	332	349	384	419
8	7¼	31.4	243	273	303	334	364	394	425	455	485	516	546	576	607	667	728
8	7½	30.4	260	292	325	357	390	422	454	487	519	552	584	617	649	714	779
10	9¼	24.6	395	444	494	543	593	642	691	741	790	839	889	938	988	1086	1185
10	9½	24.0	417	469	521	573	625	677	729	781	833	885	937	990	1042	1146	1250
12	11¼	20.3	584	657	730	803	876	950	1023	1096	1169	1242	1315	1388	1461	1607	1753
12	11½	19.8	611	687	763	840	916	992	1069	1145	1221	1297	1374	1450	1526	1679	1832
14	13¼	17.2	811	912	1013	1114	1216	1317	1418	1520	1621	1722	1824	1925	2026	2229	2432
14	13½	16.9	841	947	1052	1157	1262	1367	1472	1578	1683	1788	1893	1998	2104	2314	2524
16	15¼	15.0	1074	1208	1342	1476	1611	1745	1879	2013	2147	2282	2416	2550	2684	2953	3221
16	15½	14.7	1109	1248	1386	1525	1664	1802	1941	2080	2218	2357	2496	2634	2773	3050	3328

DESIGN — SIMPLE SOLID COLUMNS
SAFE UNIT AXIAL LOADS

See instructions for use of tables.
Obtain allowable E Value from building code or Pages 22-27.
Value of Fc' from table may not exceed Fc value for species and grade of lumber used.
Total allowable load on column equals cross sectional area in square inches times Fc' value.

CRITICAL DIMENSION Inches Nominal	Net	L/D	MODULUS OF ELASTICITY (1,000,000 psi) .8	.9	1.0	1.1	1.2	1.3	1.4	1.5	1.6	1.7	1.8	1.9	2.0	2.2	2.4
20 FEET UNSUPPORTED LENGTH																	
6	5½	43.6	126	142	158	173	189	205	221	236	252	268	284	299	315	347	378
8	7¼	33.1	219	246	274	301	329	356	383	411	438	465	493	520	548	602	657
8	7½	32.0	234	264	293	322	352	381	410	439	469	498	527	557	586	645	703
10	9¼	25.9	357	401	446	490	535	579	624	668	713	758	802	847	891	980	1070
10	9½	25.3	376	423	470	517	564	611	658	705	752	799	846	893	940	1034	1128
12	11¼	21.3	527	593	659	725	791	857	923	989	1055	1121	1187	1252	1318	1450	1582
12	11½	20.9	551	620	689	758	827	895	964	1033	1102	1171	1240	1309	1378	1515	1653
14	13¼	18.1	732	823	914	1006	1097	1189	1280	1372	1463	1554	1646	1737	1829	2012	2195
14	13½	17.8	759	854	949	1044	1139	1234	1329	1424	1519	1614	1709	1804	1898	2088	2278
16	15¼	15.7	969	1090	1211	1332	1454	1575	1696	1817	1938	2059	2180	2301	2423	2665	2907
16	15½	15.5	1001	1126	1251	1376	1502	1627	1752	1877	2002	2127	2252	2377	2503	2753	3003
21 FEET UNSUPPORTED LENGTH																	
6	5½	45.8	114	129	143	157	171	186	200	214	229	243	257	272	286	314	343
8	7¼	34.8	199	223	248	273	298	323	348	372	397	422	447	472	497	546	596
8	7½	33.6	213	239	266	292	319	345	372	399	425	452	478	505	531	585	638
10	9¼	27.2	323	364	404	445	485	525	566	606	647	687	728	768	808	889	970
10	9½	26.5	341	384	426	469	512	554	597	640	682	725	767	810	853	938	1023
12	11¼	22.4	478	538	598	658	717	777	837	897	957	1016	1076	1136	1196	1315	1435
12	11½	21.9	500	562	625	687	750	812	875	937	1000	1062	1125	1187	1250	1374	1499
14	13¼	19.0	663	746	829	912	995	1078	1161	1244	1327	1410	1493	1576	1659	1825	1990
14	13½	18.7	689	775	861	947	1033	1119	1205	1291	1378	1464	1550	1636	1722	1894	2066
16	15¼	16.5	879	989	1099	1209	1318	1428	1538	1648	1758	1868	1978	2087	2197	2417	2637
16	15½	16.3	908	1021	1135	1248	1362	1475	1589	1702	1816	1929	2043	2156	2270	2497	2724
18	17½	14.4	1157	1302	1447	1591	1736	1881	2025	2170	2315	2459	2604	2749	2894	3183	3472
22 FEET UNSUPPORTED LENGTH																	
6	5½	48.0	104	117	130	143	156	169	182	195	208	221	234	247	260	286	312
8	7¼	36.4	181	204	226	249	272	294	317	339	362	385	407	430	453	498	543
8	7½	35.2	194	218	242	266	291	315	339	363	387	412	436	460	484	533	581
10	9¼	28.5	295	331	368	405	442	479	516	552	589	626	663	700	737	810	884
10	9½	27.8	311	350	388	427	466	505	544	583	622	660	699	738	777	855	932
12	11¼	23.5	436	490	545	599	654	708	763	817	872	926	981	1035	1090	1199	1307
12	11½	23.0	455	512	569	626	683	740	797	854	911	968	1025	1082	1139	1252	1366
14	13¼	19.9	605	680	756	831	907	982	1058	1134	1209	1285	1360	1436	1511	1663	1814
14	13½	19.6	628	706	784	863	941	1020	1098	1177	1255	1334	1412	1491	1569	1726	1883
16	15¼	17.3	801	901	1001	1101	1201	1301	1401	1502	1602	1702	1802	1902	2002	2202	2402
16	15½	17.0	827	931	1034	1138	1241	1344	1448	1551	1655	1758	1861	1965	2068	2275	2482
18	17½	15.1	1055	1186	1318	1450	1582	1714	1846	1977	2109	2241	2373	2505	2636	2900	3164
23 FEET UNSUPPORTED LENGTH																	
8	7¼	38.1	166	186	207	228	248	269	290	311	331	352	373	393	414	455	497
8	7½	36.8	177	199	222	244	266	288	310	332	354	377	399	421	443	487	532
10	9¼	29.8	270	303	337	371	404	438	472	505	539	573	607	640	674	741	809
10	9½	29.1	284	320	355	391	427	462	498	533	569	604	640	675	711	782	853
12	11¼	24.5	399	449	498	548	598	648	698	748	797	847	897	947	997	1097	1196
12	11½	24.0	417	469	521	573	625	677	729	781	833	885	937	990	1042	1146	1250
14	13¼	20.8	553	622	691	761	830	899	968	1037	1106	1175	1245	1314	1383	1521	1659
14	13½	20.4	574	646	718	790	861	933	1005	1077	1148	1220	1292	1364	1435	1579	1723
16	15¼	18.1	733	824	916	1007	1099	1191	1282	1374	1465	1557	1649	1740	1832	2015	2198
16	15½	17.8	757	852	946	1041	1135	1230	1325	1419	1514	1608	1703	1798	1892	2082	2271
18	17½	15.8	965	1085	1206	1327	1447	1568	1689	1809	1930	2050	2171	2292	2412	2653	2895
20	19½	14.2	1198	1348	1498	1647	1797	1947	2097	2246	2396	2546	2696	2845	2995	3295	3594
24 FEET UNSUPPORTED LENGTH																	
8	7¼	39.7	152	171	190	209	228	247	266	285	304	323	342	361	380	418	456
8	7½	38.4	163	183	203	224	244	264	285	305	326	346	366	387	407	448	488
10	9¼	31.1	248	279	309	340	371	402	433	464	495	526	557	588	619	681	743
10	9½	30.3	261	294	326	359	392	424	457	490	522	555	588	620	653	718	783
12	11¼	25.6	366	412	458	504	549	595	641	687	732	778	824	870	916	1007	1099
12	11½	25.0	383	431	478	526	574	622	670	718	765	813	861	909	957	1052	1148
14	13¼	21.7	508	571	635	698	762	825	889	952	1016	1079	1143	1206	1270	1397	1524
14	13½	21.3	527	593	659	725	791	857	923	989	1055	1121	1187	1252	1318	1450	1582

DESIGN — SIMPLE SOLID COLUMNS
SAFE UNIT AXIAL LOADS

See instructions for use of tables.
Obtain allowable E Value from building code or Pages 22-27.
Value of Fc' from table may not exceed Fc value for species and grade of lumber used.
Total allowable load on column equals cross sectional area in square inches times Fc' value.

Nominal	Net	L/D	.8	.9	1.0	1.1	1.2	1.3	1.4	1.5	1.6	1.7	1.8	1.9	2.0	2.2	2.4
CRITICAL DIMENSION Inches			**MODULUS OF ELASTICITY (1,000,000 psi)**														
24 FEET UNSUPPORTED LENGTH (CONTINUED)																
16	15¼	18.9	673	757	841	925	1009	1094	1178	1262	1346	1430	1514	1598	1682	1851	2019
16	15½	18.6	695	782	869	956	1043	1130	1217	1303	1390	1477	1564	1651	1738	1912	2086
18	17½	16.5	886	997	1108	1218	1329	1440	1551	1662	1772	1883	1994	2105	2215	2437	2658
20	19½	14.8	1100	1238	1375	1513	1650	1788	1925	2063	2201	2338	2476	2613	2751	3036	3301
25 FEET UNSUPPORTED LENGTH																
8	7¼	41.4	140	158	175	193	210	228	245	263	280	298	315	333	350	385	421
8	7½	40.0	150	169	188	206	225	244	263	281	300	319	338	356	375	413	450
10	9¼	32.4	228	257	285	314	342	371	399	428	456	485	513	542	570	627	685
10	9½	31.6	241	271	301	331	361	391	421	451	481	511	542	572	602	662	722
12	11¼	26.7	337	380	422	464	506	548	591	633	675	717	759	802	844	928	1012
12	11½	26.1	353	397	441	485	529	573	617	661	705	749	793	838	882	970	1058
14	13¼	22.6	468	527	585	644	702	761	819	878	936	995	1053	1112	1170	1287	1405
14	13½	22.2	486	547	608	668	729	790	851	911	972	1033	1094	1154	1215	1337	1458
16	15¼	19.7	620	698	775	853	930	1008	1085	1163	1240	1318	1395	1473	1550	1705	1861
16	15½	19.4	641	721	801	881	961	1041	1121	1201	1281	1361	1442	1522	1602	1762	1922
18	17½	17.1	817	919	1021	1123	1225	1327	1429	1531	1633	1735	1837	1940	2042	2246	2450
20	19½	15.4	1014	1141	1268	1394	1521	1648	1775	1901	2028	2155	2282	2408	2535	2789	3042
26 FEET UNSUPPORTED LENGTH																
8	7¼	43.0	130	146	162	178	194	211	227	243	259	275	292	308	324	356	389
8	7½	41.6	139	156	173	191	208	225	243	260	277	295	312	329	347	381	416
10	9¼	33.7	211	237	264	290	316	343	369	396	422	448	475	501	527	580	633
10	9½	32.8	223	250	278	306	334	362	389	417	445	473	501	528	556	612	668
12	11¼	27.7	312	351	390	429	468	507	546	585	624	663	702	741	780	858	936
12	11½	27.1	326	367	408	448	489	530	571	611	652	693	734	774	815	897	978
14	13¼	23.5	433	487	541	595	649	703	757	812	866	920	974	1028	1082	1190	1299
14	13½	23.1	449	506	562	618	674	730	786	843	899	955	1011	1067	1123	1236	1348
16	15¼	20.5	573	645	717	788	860	932	1003	1075	1147	1218	1290	1362	1433	1577	1720
16	15½	20.1	592	666	740	814	889	963	1037	1111	1185	1259	1333	1407	1481	1629	1777
18	17½	17.8	755	849	944	1038	1133	1227	1321	1416	1510	1604	1699	1793	1888	2076	2265
20	19½	16.0	938	1055	1172	1289	1406	1523	1641	1758	1875	1992	2109	2227	2344	2578	2813
22	21½	14.5	1140	1282	1425	1567	1710	1852	1994	2137	2279	2422	2564	2707	2849	3134	3419
27 FEET UNSUPPORTED LENGTH																
8	7¼	44.7	120	135	150	165	180	195	210	225	240	255	270	285	300	330	361
8	7½	43.2	129	145	161	177	193	209	225	241	257	273	289	305	322	354	386
10	9¼	35.0	196	220	245	269	293	318	342	367	391	416	440	465	489	538	587
10	9½	34.1	206	232	258	284	309	335	361	387	413	438	464	490	516	567	619
12	11¼	28.8	289	326	362	398	434	470	506	543	579	615	651	687	723	796	868
12	11½	28.2	302	340	378	416	454	491	529	567	605	643	680	718	756	831	907
14	13¼	24.5	401	452	502	552	602	652	702	753	803	853	903	953	1003	1104	1204
14	13½	24.0	417	469	521	573	625	677	729	781	833	885	937	990	1042	1146	1250
16	15¼	21.2	532	598	665	731	798	864	930	997	1063	1130	1196	1263	1329	1462	1595
16	15½	20.9	549	618	687	755	824	893	961	1030	1099	1167	1236	1305	1373	1510	1648
18	17½	18.5	700	788	875	963	1050	1138	1225	1313	1400	1488	1575	1663	1750	1925	2100
20	19½	16.6	869	978	1087	1195	1304	1413	1521	1630	1739	1847	1956	2065	2173	2391	2608
22	21½	15.1	1057	1189	1321	1453	1585	1717	1849	1982	2114	2246	2378	2510	2642	2906	3170
28 FEET UNSUPPORTED LENGTH																
8	7¼	46.3	112	126	140	154	168	182	196	210	223	237	251	265	279	307	335
8	7½	44.8	120	135	149	164	179	194	209	224	239	254	269	284	299	329	359
10	9¼	36.3	182	205	227	250	273	296	318	341	364	387	409	432	455	500	546
10	9½	35.4	192	216	240	264	288	312	336	360	384	408	432	456	480	528	576
12	11¼	29.9	269	303	336	370	404	437	471	504	538	572	605	639	673	740	807
12	11½	29.2	281	316	351	387	422	457	492	527	562	597	633	668	703	773	843
14	13¼	25.4	373	420	467	513	560	606	653	700	746	793	840	886	933	1026	1120
14	13½	24.9	387	436	484	533	581	630	678	726	775	823	872	920	969	1065	1162
16	15¼	22.0	494	556	618	680	742	803	865	927	989	1051	1112	1174	1236	1360	1483
16	15½	21.7	511	575	638	702	766	830	894	958	1021	1085	1149	1213	1277	1405	1532
18	17½	19.2	651	732	814	895	977	1058	1139	1221	1302	1383	1465	1546	1628	1790	1953
20	19½	17.2	808	909	1010	1111	1213	1314	1415	1516	1617	1718	1819	1920	2021	2223	2425
22	21½	15.6	983	1106	1228	1351	1474	1597	1720	1843	1965	2088	2211	2334	2457	2702	2948

DESIGN — SIMPLE SOLID COLUMNS
SAFE UNIT AXIAL LOADS

See instructions for use of tables.

Obtain allowable E Value from building code or Pages 22-27.

Value of Fc' from table may not exceed Fc value for species and grade of lumber used.

Total allowable load on column equals cross sectional area in square inches times Fc' value.

Nominal	Net	L/D	.8	.9	1.0	1.1	1.2	1.3	1.4	1.5	1.6	1.7	1.8	1.9	2.0	2.2	2.4
CRITICAL DIMENSION Inches			**MODULUS OF ELASTICITY (1,000,000 psi)**														
29 FEET UNSUPPORTED LENGTH																	
8	7¼	48.0	104	117	130	143	156	169	182	195	208	221	234	247	260	286	312
8	7½	46.4	111	125	139	153	167	181	195	209	223	237	251	265	279	307	334
10	9¼	37.6	170	191	212	233	254	276	297	318	339	360	382	403	424	466	509
10	9½	36.6	179	201	224	246	268	291	313	335	358	380	402	425	447	492	537
12	11¼	30.9	251	282	314	345	376	408	439	470	502	533	564	596	627	690	752
12	11½	30.3	262	295	328	360	393	426	459	491	524	557	590	622	655	721	786
14	13¼	26.3	348	391	435	478	522	565	609	652	696	739	783	826	870	957	1044
14	13½	25.8	361	406	451	497	542	587	632	677	722	768	813	858	903	993	1084
16	15¼	22.8	461	518	576	634	691	749	807	864	922	979	1037	1095	1152	1267	1383
16	15½	22.5	476	536	595	655	714	774	833	893	952	1012	1071	1131	1190	1309	1428
18	17½	19.9	607	683	759	835	910	986	1062	1138	1214	1290	1366	1441	1517	1669	1821
20	19½	17.8	754	848	942	1036	1130	1225	1319	1413	1507	1601	1696	1790	1884	2072	2261
22	21½	16.2	916	1031	1145	1260	1374	1489	1603	1718	1832	1947	2061	2176	2290	2519	2748
24	23½	14.8	1094	1231	1368	1505	1642	1778	1915	2052	2189	2326	2462	2599	2736	3010	3283
30 FEET UNSUPPORTED LENGTH																	
8	7¼	49.7	97	110	122	134	146	158	170	183	195	207	219	231	243	268	292
8	7½	48.0	104	117	130	143	156	169	182	195	208	221	234	247	260	286	312
10	9¼	38.9	158	178	198	218	238	257	277	297	317	337	357	376	396	436	475
10	9½	37.9	167	188	209	230	251	272	292	313	334	355	376	397	418	460	501
12	11¼	32.0	234	264	293	322	352	381	410	439	469	498	527	557	586	645	703
12	11½	31.3	245	276	306	337	367	398	429	459	490	520	551	582	612	673	735
14	13¼	27.2	325	366	406	447	488	528	569	610	650	691	732	772	813	894	975
14	13½	26.7	337	380	422	464	506	548	591	633	675	717	759	802	844	928	1012
16	15¼	23.6	431	485	538	592	646	700	754	808	861	915	969	1023	1077	1184	1292
16	15½	23.2	445	501	556	612	667	723	779	834	890	945	1001	1057	1112	1223	1335
18	17½	20.6	567	638	709	780	851	922	992	1063	1134	1205	1276	1347	1418	1560	1701
20	19½	18.5	704	792	880	968	1056	1144	1232	1320	1408	1496	1584	1672	1760	1936	2113
22	21½	16.7	856	963	1070	1177	1284	1391	1498	1605	1712	1819	1926	2033	2140	2354	2568
24	23½	15.3	1023	1151	1278	1406	1534	1662	1790	1918	2045	2173	2301	2429	2557	2812	3068

DESIGN — SPACED COLUMNS CONDITION "A"
SAFE UNIT AXIAL LOADS

See instructions for use of tables.
Obtain allowable E Value from building code or Pages 22-27.
Value of Fc' from table may not exceed Fc value for species and grade of lumber used.
Total allowable load on column equals cross sectional area in square inches times Fc' value.

CRITICAL DIMENSION Inches Nominal	Net	L/D	.8	.9	1.0	1.1	1.2	1.3	1.4	1.5	1.6	1.7	1.8	1.9	2.0	2.2	2.4
MODULUS OF ELASTICITY (1,000,000 psi)																	

3 FEET UNSUPPORTED LENGTH

Nominal	Net	L/D	.8	.9	1.0	1.1	1.2	1.3	1.4	1.5	1.6	1.7	1.8	1.9	2.0	2.2	2.4
2	1½	24.0	1042	1172	1302	1432	1562	1693	1823	1953	2083	2214	2344	2474	2604	2865	3125

4 FEET UNSUPPORTED LENGTH

Nominal	Net	L/D	.8	.9	1.0	1.1	1.2	1.3	1.4	1.5	1.6	1.7	1.8	1.9	2.0	2.2	2.4
2	1½	32.0	586	659	732	806	879	952	1025	1099	1172	1245	1318	1392	1465	1611	1758
3	2½	19.2	1628	1831	2035	2238	2441	2645	2848	3052	3255	3459	3662	3866	4069	4476	4883

5 FEET UNSUPPORTED LENGTH

Nominal	Net	L/D	.8	.9	1.0	1.1	1.2	1.3	1.4	1.5	1.6	1.7	1.8	1.9	2.0	2.2	2.4
2	1½	40.0	375	422	469	516	563	609	656	703	750	797	844	891	938	1031	1125
3	2½	24.0	1042	1172	1302	1432	1562	1693	1823	1953	2083	2214	2344	2474	2604	2865	3125

6 FEET UNSUPPORTED LENGTH

Nominal	Net	L/D	.8	.9	1.0	1.1	1.2	1.3	1.4	1.5	1.6	1.7	1.8	1.9	2.0	2.2	2.4
2	1½	48.0	260	293	326	358	391	423	456	488	521	553	586	618	651	716	781
3	2½	28.8	723	814	904	995	1085	1175	1266	1356	1447	1537	1628	1718	1808	1989	2170
4	3½	20.6	1418	1595	1772	1950	2127	2304	2481	2658	2836	3013	3190	3367	3545	3899	4253

7 FEET UNSUPPORTED LENGTH

Nominal	Net	L/D	.8	.9	1.0	1.1	1.2	1.3	1.4	1.5	1.6	1.7	1.8	1.9	2.0	2.2	2.4
2	1½	56.0	191	215	239	263	287	311	335	359	383	407	430	454	478	526	574
3	2½	33.6	531	598	664	731	797	864	930	996	1063	1129	1196	1262	1329	1462	1594
4	3½	24.0	1042	1172	1302	1432	1562	1693	1823	1953	2083	2214	2344	2474	2604	2865	3125

8 FEET UNSUPPORTED LENGTH

Nominal	Net	L/D	.8	.9	1.0	1.1	1.2	1.3	1.4	1.5	1.6	1.7	1.8	1.9	2.0	2.2	2.4
2	1½	64.0	146	165	183	201	220	238	256	275	293	311	330	348	366	403	439
3	2½	38.4	407	458	509	559	610	661	712	763	814	865	916	966	1017	1119	1221
4	3½	27.4	798	897	997	1097	1196	1296	1396	1495	1595	1695	1794	1894	1994	2193	2393
6	5½	17.5	1969	2216	2462	2708	2954	3200	3446	3693	3939	4185	4431	4677	4924	5416	5908

9 FEET UNSUPPORTED LENGTH

Nominal	Net	L/D	.8	.9	1.0	1.1	1.2	1.3	1.4	1.5	1.6	1.7	1.8	1.9	2.0	2.2	2.4
2	1½	72.0	116	130	145	159	174	188	203	217	231	246	260	275	289	318	347
3	2½	43.2	322	362	402	442	482	522	563	603	643	683	723	764	804	884	965
4	3½	30.9	630	709	788	866	945	1024	1103	1182	1260	1339	1418	1497	1575	1733	1890
6	5½	19.6	1556	1751	1945	2140	2334	2529	2723	2918	3112	3307	3501	3696	3890	4279	4668

10 FEET UNSUPPORTED LENGTH

Nominal	Net	L/D	.8	.9	1.0	1.1	1.2	1.3	1.4	1.5	1.6	1.7	1.8	1.9	2.0	2.2	2.4
2	1½	80.0	94	105	117	129	141	152	164	176	188	199	211	223	234	258	281
3	2½	48.0	260	293	326	358	391	423	456	488	521	553	586	618	651	716	781
4	3½	34.3	510	574	638	702	766	829	893	957	1021	1085	1148	1212	1276	1404	1531
6	5½	21.8	1260	1418	1576	1733	1891	2048	2206	2363	2521	2678	2836	2993	3151	3466	3781

11 FEET UNSUPPORTED LENGTH

Nominal	Net	L/D	.8	.9	1.0	1.1	1.2	1.3	1.4	1.5	1.6	1.7	1.8	1.9	2.0	2.2	2.4
3	2½	52.8	215	242	269	296	323	350	377	404	430	457	484	511	538	592	646
4	3½	37.7	422	475	527	580	633	685	738	791	844	896	949	1002	1055	1160	1265
6	5½	24.0	1042	1172	1302	1432	1562	1693	1823	1953	2083	2214	2344	2474	2604	2865	3125

12 FEET UNSUPPORTED LENGTH

Nominal	Net	L/D	.8	.9	1.0	1.1	1.2	1.3	1.4	1.5	1.6	1.7	1.8	1.9	2.0	2.2	2.4
3	2½	57.6	181	203	226	249	271	294	316	339	362	384	407	430	452	497	543
4	3½	41.1	354	399	443	487	532	576	620	665	709	753	798	842	886	975	1063
6	5½	26.2	875	985	1094	1204	1313	1422	1532	1641	1751	1860	1969	2079	2188	2407	2626
8	7¼	19.9	1521	1711	1901	2091	2281	2471	2662	2852	3042	3232	3422	3612	3802	4182	4563
8	7½	19.2	1628	1831	2035	2238	2441	2645	2848	3052	3255	3459	3662	3866	4069	4476	4883

13 FEET UNSUPPORTED LENGTH

Nominal	Net	L/D	.8	.9	1.0	1.1	1.2	1.3	1.4	1.5	1.6	1.7	1.8	1.9	2.0	2.2	2.4
3	2½	62.4	154	173	193	212	231	250	270	289	308	327	347	366	385	424	462
4	3½	44.6	302	340	378	415	453	491	529	566	604	642	680	717	755	831	906
6	5½	28.4	746	839	932	1025	1119	1212	1305	1398	1492	1585	1678	1771	1865	2051	2237
8	7¼	21.5	1296	1458	1620	1782	1944	2106	2268	2430	2592	2754	2916	3078	3240	3564	3888
8	7½	20.8	1387	1560	1734	1907	2080	2254	2427	2600	2774	2947	3120	3294	3467	3814	4161

14 FEET UNSUPPORTED LENGTH

Nominal	Net	L/D	.8	.9	1.0	1.1	1.2	1.3	1.4	1.5	1.6	1.7	1.8	1.9	2.0	2.2	2.4
3	2½	67.2	133	149	166	183	199	216	233	249	266	282	299	316	332	365	399
4	3½	48.0	260	293	326	358	391	423	456	488	521	553	586	618	651	716	781
6	5½	30.5	643	723	804	884	965	1045	1125	1206	1286	1367	1447	1527	1608	1768	1929
8	7¼	23.2	1117	1257	1397	1536	1676	1816	1955	2095	2235	2374	2514	2654	2794	3073	3352
8	7½	22.4	1196	1345	1495	1644	1794	1943	2093	2242	2392	2541	2691	2840	2989	3288	3587

WESTERN WOODS USE BOOK
DESIGN — SPACED COLUMNS CONDITION "A"
SAFE UNIT AXIAL LOADS

See instructions for use of tables.
Obtain allowable E Value from building code or Pages 22-27.
Value of Fc' from table may not exceed Fc value for species and grade of lumber used.
Total allowable load on column equals cross sectional area in square inches times Fc' value.

MODULUS OF ELASTICITY (1,000,000 psi)

Nominal	Net	L/D	.8	.9	1.0	1.1	1.2	1.3	1.4	1.5	1.6	1.7	1.8	1.9	2.0	2.2	2.4
15 FEET UNSUPPORTED LENGTH																	
3	2½	72.0	116	130	145	159	174	188	203	217	231	246	260	275	289	318	347
4	3½	51.4	227	255	284	312	340	369	397	425	454	482	510	539	567	624	681
6	5½	32.7	560	630	700	770	840	910	980	1050	1120	1190	1260	1330	1400	1541	1681
8	7¼	24.8	973	1095	1217	1338	1460	1582	1703	1825	1947	2068	2190	2312	2433	2677	2920
8	7½	24.0	1042	1172	1302	1432	1562	1693	1823	1953	2083	2214	2344	2474	2604	2865	3125
16 FEET UNSUPPORTED LENGTH																	
3	2½	76.8	102	114	127	140	153	165	178	191	203	216	229	242	254	280	305
4	3½	54.9	199	224	249	274	299	324	349	374	399	424	449	474	498	548	598
6	5½	34.9	492	554	615	677	739	800	862	923	985	1046	1108	1169	1231	1354	1477
8	7¼	26.5	856	962	1069	1176	1283	1390	1497	1604	1711	1818	1925	2032	2139	2353	2567
8	7½	25.6	916	1030	1144	1259	1373	1488	1602	1717	1831	1945	2060	2174	2289	2518	2747
10	9¼	20.8	1393	1567	1741	1915	2089	2263	2437	2611	2785	2959	3133	3307	3482	3830	4178
10	9½	20.2	1469	1653	1836	2020	2203	2387	2571	2754	2938	3121	3305	3489	3672	4040	4407
17 FEET UNSUPPORTED LENGTH																	
4	3½	58.3	177	199	221	243	265	287	309	331	353	375	397	419	442	486	530
6	5½	37.1	436	491	545	600	654	709	763	818	872	927	981	1036	1090	1199	1308
8	7¼	28.1	758	853	947	1042	1137	1231	1326	1421	1516	1610	1705	1800	1895	2084	2273
8	7½	27.2	811	912	1014	1115	1216	1318	1419	1521	1622	1723	1825	1926	2027	2230	2433
10	9¼	22.1	1234	1388	1542	1696	1850	2005	2159	2313	2467	2621	2776	2930	3084	3392	3701
10	9½	21.5	1301	1464	1626	1789	1952	2114	2277	2440	2602	2765	2928	3090	3253	3578	3904
18 FEET UNSUPPORTED LENGTH																	
4	3½	61.7	158	177	197	217	236	256	276	295	315	335	354	374	394	433	473
6	5½	39.3	389	438	486	535	584	632	681	729	778	827	875	924	973	1070	1167
8	7¼	29.8	676	760	845	929	1014	1098	1183	1267	1352	1436	1521	1605	1690	1859	2028
8	7½	28.8	723	814	904	995	1085	1175	1266	1356	1447	1537	1628	1718	1808	1989	2170
10	9¼	23.4	1100	1238	1375	1513	1651	1788	1926	2063	2201	2338	2476	2613	2751	3026	3301
10	9½	22.7	1161	1306	1451	1596	1741	1886	2031	2176	2321	2466	2611	2756	2902	3192	3482
19 FEET UNSUPPORTED LENGTH																	
4	3½	65.1	141	159	177	194	212	230	247	265	283	300	318	336	353	389	424
6	5½	41.5	349	393	436	480	524	567	611	655	698	742	786	829	873	960	1047
8	7¼	31.4	607	683	758	834	910	986	1062	1138	1213	1289	1365	1441	1517	1668	1820
8	7½	30.4	649	730	812	893	974	1055	1136	1217	1298	1380	1461	1542	1623	1785	1948
10	9¼	24.6	988	1111	1234	1358	1481	1605	1728	1852	1975	2099	2222	2345	2469	2716	2963
10	9½	24.0	1042	1172	1302	1432	1562	1693	1823	1953	2083	2214	2344	2474	2604	2865	3125
20 FEET UNSUPPORTED LENGTH																	
4	3½	68.6	128	144	160	175	191	207	223	239	255	271	287	303	319	351	383
6	5½	43.6	315	354	394	433	473	512	551	591	630	670	709	748	788	867	945
8	7¼	33.1	548	616	684	753	821	890	958	1027	1095	1163	1232	1300	1369	1506	1643
8	7½	32.0	586	659	732	806	879	952	1025	1099	1172	1245	1318	1392	1465	1611	1758
10	9¼	25.9	891	1003	1114	1226	1337	1448	1560	1671	1783	1894	2005	2117	2228	2451	2674
10	9½	25.3	940	1058	1175	1293	1410	1528	1645	1763	1880	1998	2115	2233	2350	2585	2820
12	11¼	21.3	1318	1483	1648	1813	1978	2142	2307	2472	2637	2802	2966	3131	3296	3625	3955
12	11½	20.9	1378	1550	1722	1894	2066	2239	2411	2583	2755	2927	3100	3272	3444	3788	4133
21 FEET UNSUPPORTED LENGTH																	
4	3½	72.0	116	130	145	159	174	188	203	217	231	246	260	275	289	318	347
6	5½	45.8	286	322	357	393	429	464	500	536	572	607	643	679	715	786	857
8	7¼	34.8	497	559	621	683	745	807	869	931	993	1055	1117	1179	1242	1366	1490
8	7½	33.6	531	598	664	731	797	864	930	996	1063	1129	1196	1262	1329	1462	1594
10	9¼	27.2	808	909	1011	1112	1213	1314	1415	1516	1617	1718	1819	1920	2021	2223	2425
10	9½	26.5	853	959	1066	1172	1279	1386	1492	1599	1705	1812	1919	2025	2132	2345	2558
12	11¼	22.4	1196	1345	1495	1644	1794	1943	2093	2242	2392	2541	2691	2840	2989	3288	3587
12	11½	21.9	1250	1406	1562	1718	1874	2030	2187	2343	2499	2655	2811	2968	3124	3436	3749
22 FEET UNSUPPORTED LENGTH																	
4	3½	75.4	105	119	132	145	158	171	185	198	211	224	237	250	264	290	316
6	5½	48.0	260	293	326	358	391	423	456	488	521	553	586	618	651	716	781
8	7¼	36.4	453	509	566	622	679	735	792	848	905	962	1018	1075	1131	1244	1358

DESIGN — SPACED COLUMNS CONDITION "A"
SAFE UNIT AXIAL LOADS

See instructions for use of tables.
Obtain allowable E Value from building code or Pages 22-27.
Value of Fc' from table may not exceed Fc value for species and grade of lumber used.
Total allowable load on column equals cross sectional area in square inches times Fc' value.

CRITICAL DIMENSION Inches Nominal	Net	L/D	MODULUS OF ELASTICITY (1,000,000 psi)														
			.8	.9	1.0	1.1	1.2	1.3	1.4	1.5	1.6	1.7	1.8	1.9	2.0	2.2	2.4
22 FEET UNSUPPORTED LENGTH (CONTINUED)																	
8	7½	35.2	484	545	605	666	726	787	847	908	968	1029	1090	1150	1211	1332	1453
10	9¼	28.5	737	829	921	1013	1105	1197	1289	1381	1473	1565	1657	1749	1841	2026	2210
10	9½	27.8	777	874	971	1068	1165	1263	1360	1457	1554	1651	1748	1845	1942	2137	2331
12	11¼	23.5	1090	1226	1362	1498	1634	1771	1907	2043	2179	2315	2451	2588	2724	2996	3269
12	11½	23.0	1139	1281	1423	1565	1708	1850	1992	2135	2277	2419	2562	2704	2846	3131	3416
23 FEET UNSUPPORTED LENGTH																	
4	3½	78.9	96	109	121	133	145	157	169	181	193	205	217	229	241	265	289
6	5½	50.2	238	268	298	328	357	387	417	447	477	506	536	566	596	655	715
8	7¼	38.1	414	466	518	569	621	673	725	776	828	880	932	983	1035	1139	1242
8	7½	36.8	443	498	554	609	665	720	775	831	886	941	997	1052	1108	1218	1329
10	9¼	29.8	674	758	842	927	1011	1095	1179	1264	1348	1432	1516	1601	1685	1853	2022
10	9½	29.1	711	800	889	977	1066	1155	1244	1333	1422	1511	1599	1688	1777	1955	2133
12	11¼	24.5	997	1121	1246	1371	1495	1620	1745	1869	1994	2118	2243	2368	2492	2741	2991
12	11½	24.0	1042	1172	1302	1432	1562	1693	1823	1953	2083	2214	2344	2474	2604	2865	3125
24 FEET UNSUPPORTED LENGTH																	
6	5½	52.4	219	246	274	301	328	356	383	410	438	465	492	520	547	602	656
8	7¼	39.7	380	428	475	523	570	618	665	713	760	808	856	903	951	1046	1141
8	7½	38.4	407	458	509	559	610	661	712	763	814	865	916	966	1017	1119	1221
10	9¼	31.1	619	696	774	851	928	1006	1083	1161	1238	1315	1393	1470	1547	1702	1857
10	9½	30.3	653	734	816	898	979	1061	1142	1224	1306	1387	1469	1551	1632	1795	1959
12	11¼	25.6	916	1030	1144	1259	1373	1488	1602	1717	1831	1945	2060	2174	2289	2518	2747
12	11½	25.0	957	1076	1196	1315	1435	1555	1674	1794	1913	2033	2153	2272	2392	2631	2870
14	13¼	21.7	1270	1429	1587	1746	1905	2064	2222	2381	2540	2699	2857	3016	3175	3492	3810
14	13½	21.3	1318	1483	1648	1813	1978	2142	2307	2472	2637	2802	2966	3131	3296	3625	3955
25 FEET UNSUPPORTED LENGTH																	
6	5½	54.5	202	227	252	277	302	328	353	378	403	429	454	479	504	555	605
8	7¼	41.4	350	394	438	482	526	569	613	657	701	745	788	832	876	964	1051
8	7½	40.0	375	422	469	516	563	609	656	703	750	797	844	891	938	1031	1125
10	9¼	32.4	570	642	713	784	856	927	998	1070	1141	1212	1283	1355	1426	1569	1711
10	9½	31.6	602	677	752	827	903	978	1053	1128	1203	1279	1354	1429	1504	1655	1805
12	11¼	26.7	844	949	1055	1160	1266	1371	1477	1582	1687	1793	1898	2004	2109	2320	2531
12	11½	26.1	882	992	1102	1212	1322	1433	1543	1653	1763	1874	1984	2094	2204	2425	2645
14	13¼	22.6	1170	1317	1463	1609	1756	1902	2048	2195	2341	2487	2633	2780	2926	3219	3511
14	13½	22.2	1215	1367	1519	1671	1823	1974	2126	2278	2430	2582	2734	2886	3038	3341	3645
26 FEET UNSUPPORTED LENGTH																	
6	5½	56.7	186	210	233	256	280	303	326	350	373	396	420	443	466	513	559
8	7¼	43.0	324	364	405	445	486	526	567	607	648	688	729	769	810	891	972
8	7½	41.6	347	390	433	477	520	563	607	650	693	737	780	823	867	953	1040
10	9¼	33.7	527	593	659	725	791	857	923	989	1055	1121	1187	1253	1318	1450	1582
10	9½	32.8	556	626	695	765	834	904	973	1043	1113	1182	1252	1321	1391	1530	1669
12	11¼	27.7	780	878	975	1073	1170	1268	1365	1463	1560	1658	1755	1853	1950	2145	2340
12	11½	27.1	815	917	1019	1121 ·	1223	1325	1427	1528	1630	1732	1834	1936	2038	2242	2445
14	13¼	23.5	1082	1217	1353	1488	1623	1758	1894	2029	2164	2299	2435	2570	2705	2976	3246
14	13½	23.1	1123	1264	1404	1545	1685	1825	1966	2106	2247	2387	2528	2668	2808	3089	3370
27 FEET UNSUPPORTED LENGTH																	
6	5½	58.9	173	195	216	238	259	281	303	324	346	367	389	411	432	475	519
8	7¼	44.7	300	338	376	413	451	488	526	563	601	638	676	714	751	826	901
8	7½	43.2	322	362	402	442	482	522	563	603	643	683	723	764	804	884	965
10	9¼	35.0	489	550	611	672	734	795	856	917	978	1039	1100	1161	1223	1345	1467
10	9½	34.1	516	580	645	709	774	838	903	967	1032	1096	1161	1225	1290	1419	1547
12	11¼	28.8	723	814	904	995	1085	1175	1266	1356	1447	1537	1628	1718	1808	1989	2170
12	11½	28.2	756	850	945	1039	1134	1228	1323	1417	1512	1606	1701	1795	1890	2079	2268
14	13¼	24.5	1003	1129	1254	1380	1505	1631	1756	1881	2007	2132	2258	2383	2509	2759	3010
14	13½	24.0	1042	1172	1302	1432	1562	1693	1823	1953	2083	2214	2344	2474	2604	2865	3125
28 FEET UNSUPPORTED LENGTH																	
6	5½	61.1	161	181	201	221	241	261	281	301	322	342	362	382	402	442	482
8	7¼	46.3	279	314	349	384	419	454	489	524	559	594	629	663	698	768	838

DESIGN — SPACED COLUMNS CONDITION "A"
SAFE UNIT AXIAL LOADS

See instructions for use of tables.
Obtain allowable E Value from building code or Pages 22-27.
Value of Fc' from table may not exceed Fc value for species and grade of lumber used.
Total allowable load on column equals cross sectional area in square inches times Fc' value.

Nominal	Net	L/D	.8	.9	1.0	1.1	1.2	1.3	1.4	1.5	1.6	1.7	1.8	1.9	2.0	2.2	2.4
CRITICAL DIMENSION (Inches)			**MODULUS OF ELASTICITY (1,000,000 psi)**														
28 FEET UNSUPPORTED LENGTH (CONTINUED)																	
8	7½	44.8	299	336	374	411	448	486	523	561	598	635	673	710	747	822	897
10	9¼	36.3	455	512	568	625	682	739	796	853	909	966	1023	1080	1137	1251	1364
10	9½	35.4	480	540	600	660	719	779	839	899	959	1019	1079	1139	1199	1319	1439
12	11¼	29.9	673	757	841	925	1009	1093	1177	1261	1345	1429	1513	1597	1682	1850	2018
12	11½	29.2	703	791	879	966	1054	1142	1230	1318	1406	1494	1581	1669	1757	1933	2109
14	13¼	25.4	933	1050	1166	1283	1400	1516	1633	1749	1866	1983	2099	2216	2333	2566	2799
14	13½	24.9	969	1090	1211	1332	1453	1574	1695	1816	1937	2058	2179	2300	2421	2664	2906
29 FEET UNSUPPORTED LENGTH																	
6	5½	63.3	150	169	187	206	225	244	262	281	300	318	337	356	375	412	450
8	7¼	48.0	260	293	326	358	391	423	456	488	521	553	586	618	651	716	781
8	7½	46.4	279	314	348	383	418	453	488	523	557	592	627	662	697	766	836
10	9¼	37.6	424	477	530	583	636	689	742	795	848	901	954	1007	1060	1166	1272
10	9½	36.6	447	503	559	615	671	727	782	838	894	950	1006	1062	1118	1230	1341
12	11¼	30.9	627	705	784	862	941	1019	1097	1176	1254	1332	1411	1489	1568	1724	1881
12	11½	30.3	655	737	819	901	983	1065	1147	1229	1310	1392	1474	1556	1638	1802	1966
14	13¼	26.3	870	979	1087	1196	1305	1413	1522	1631	1740	1848	1957	2066	2175	2392	2609
14	13½	25.8	903	1016	1129	1242	1354	1467	1580	1693	1806	1919	2032	2144	2257	2483	2709
16	15¼	22.8	1152	1296	1440	1584	1728	1872	2016	2160	2304	2448	2592	2736	2881	3169	3457
16	15½	22.5	1190	1339	1488	1637	1785	1934	2083	2232	2381	2529	2678	2827	2976	3273	3571
30 FEET UNSUPPORTED LENGTH																	
6	5½	65.5	140	158	175	193	210	228	245	263	280	298	315	333	350	385	420
8	7¼	49.7	243	274	304	335	365	395	426	456	487	517	548	578	608	669	730
8	7½	48.0	260	293	326	358	391	423	456	488	521	553	586	618	651	716	781
10	9¼	38.9	396	446	495	545	594	644	693	743	792	842	891	941	990	1089	1188
10	9½	37.9	418	470	522	575	627	679	731	783	836	888	940	992	1045	1149	1253
12	11¼	32.0	586	659	732	806	879	952	1025	1099	1172	1245	1318	1392	1465	1611	1758
12	11½	31.3	612	689	765	842	918	995	1071	1148	1225	1301	1378	1454	1531	1684	1837
14	13¼	27.2	813	914	1016	1118	1219	1321	1422	1524	1626	1727	1829	1930	2032	2235	2438
14	13½	26.7	844	949	1055	1160	1266	1371	1477	1582	1687	1793	1898	2004	2109	2320	2531
16	15¼	23.6	1077	1211	1346	1480	1615	1750	1884	2019	2153	2288	2423	2557	2692	2961	3230
16	15½	23.2	1112	1251	1390	1529	1668	1807	1946	2086	2225	2364	2503	2642	2781	3059	3337

DESIGN — SPACED COLUMNS CONDITION "B"
SAFE UNIT AXIAL LOADS

See instructions for use of tables.
Obtain allowable E Value from building code or Pages 22-27.
Value of Fc' from table may not exceed Fc value for species and grade of lumber used.
Total allowable load on column equals cross sectional area in square inches times Fc' value.

CRITICAL DIMENSION Inches Nominal	Net	L/D	.8	.9	1.0	1.1	1.2	1.3	1.4	1.5	1.6	1.7	1.8	1.9	2.0	2.2	2.4
							MODULUS OF ELASTICITY (1,000,000 psi)										
3 FEET UNSUPPORTED LENGTH																	
2	1½	24.0	1250	1406	1563	1719	1875	2031	2188	2344	2500	2656	2813	2969	3125	3438	3750
4 FEET UNSUPPORTED LENGTH																	
2	1½	32.0	703	791	879	967	1055	1143	1230	1318	1406	1494	1582	1670	1758	1934	2109
3	2½	19.2	1953	2197	2441	2686	2930	3174	3418	3662	3906	4150	4395	4639	4883	5371	5859
5 FEET UNSUPPORTED LENGTH																	
2	1½	40.0	450	506	563	619	675	731	788	844	900	956	1013	1069	1125	1238	1350
3	2½	24.0	1250	1406	1563	1719	1875	2031	2188	2344	2500	2656	2813	2969	3125	3438	3750
6 FEET UNSUPPORTED LENGTH																	
2	1½	48.0	313	352	391	430	469	508	547	586	625	664	703	742	781	859	938
3	2½	28.8	868	977	1085	1194	1302	1411	1519	1628	1736	1845	1953	2062	2170	2387	2604
4	3½	20.6	1701	1914	2127	2339	2552	2765	2977	3190	3403	3615	3828	4041	4253	4679	5104
7 FEET UNSUPPORTED LENGTH																	
2	1½	56.0	230	258	287	316	344	373	402	430	459	488	517	545	574	631	689
3	2½	33.6	638	717	797	877	957	1036	1116	1196	1276	1355	1435	1515	1594	1754	1913
4	3½	24.0	1250	1406	1563	1719	1875	2031	2188	2344	2500	2656	2813	2969	3125	3438	3750
8 FEET UNSUPPORTED LENGTH																	
2	1½	64.0	176	198	220	242	264	286	308	330	352	374	396	417	439	483	527
3	2½	38.4	488	549	610	671	732	793	854	916	977	1038	1099	1160	1221	1343	1465
4	3½	27.4	957	1077	1196	1316	1436	1555	1675	1794	1914	2034	2153	2273	2393	2632	2871
9 FEET UNSUPPORTED LENGTH																	
2	1½	72.0	139	156	174	191	208	226	243	260	278	295	312	330	347	382	417
3	2½	43.2	386	434	482	530	579	627	675	723	772	820	868	916	965	1061	1157
4	3½	30.9	756	851	945	1040	1134	1229	1323	1418	1512	1607	1701	1796	1890	2079	2269
6	5½	19.6	1867	2101	2334	2568	2801	3034	3268	3501	3735	3968	4201	4435	4668	5135	5602
10 FEET UNSUPPORTED LENGTH																	
2	1½	80.0	113	127	141	155	169	183	197	211	225	239	253	267	281	309	338
3	2½	48.0	313	352	391	430	469	508	547	586	625	664	703	742	781	859	938
4	3½	34.3	613	689	766	842	919	995	1072	1148	1225	1302	1378	1455	1531	1684	1838
6	5½	21.8	1512	1702	1891	2080	2269	2458	2647	2836	3025	3214	3403	3592	3781	4159	4537
11 FEET UNSUPPORTED LENGTH																	
3	2½	52.8	258	291	323	355	387	420	452	484	517	549	581	613	646	710	775
4	3½	37.7	506	569	633	696	759	823	886	949	1012	1076	1139	1202	1265	1392	1519
6	5½	24.0	1250	1406	1563	1719	1875	2031	2188	2344	2500	2656	2813	2969	3125	3438	3750
12 FEET UNSUPPORTED LENGTH																	
3	2½	57.6	217	244	271	298	326	353	380	407	434	461	488	515	543	597	651
4	3½	41.1	425	479	532	585	638	691	744	798	851	904	957	1010	1063	1170	1276
6	5½	26.2	1050	1182	1313	1444	1576	1707	1838	1969	2101	2232	2363	2495	2626	2888	3151
13 FEET UNSUPPORTED LENGTH																	
3	2½	62.4	185	208	231	254	277	300	324	347	370	393	416	439	462	509	555
4	3½	44.6	362	408	453	498	544	589	634	680	725	770	815	861	906	997	1087
6	5½	28.4	895	1007	1119	1231	1342	1454	1566	1678	1790	1902	2014	2126	2237	2461	2685
8	7¼	21.5	1555	1749	1944	2138	2333	2527	2721	2916	3110	3305	3499	3693	3888	4277	4665
8	7½	20.8	1664	1872	2080	2288	2496	2704	2912	3120	3328	3536	3744	3952	4161	4577	4993
14 FEET UNSUPPORTED LENGTH																	
3	2½	67.2	159	179	199	219	239	259	279	299	319	339	359	379	399	438	478
4	3½	48.0	313	352	391	430	469	508	547	586	625	664	703	742	781	859	938
6	5½	30.5	772	868	965	1061	1158	1254	1350	1447	1543	1640	1736	1833	1929	2122	2315
8	7¼	23.2	1341	1508	1676	1844	2011	2179	2347	2514	2682	2849	3017	3185	3352	3687	4023
8	7½	22.4	1435	1614	1794	1973	2152	2332	2511	2691	2870	3049	3229	3408	3587	3946	4305
15 FEET UNSUPPORTED LENGTH																	
3	2½	72.0	139	156	174	191	208	226	243	260	278	295	312	330	347	382	417
4	3½	51.4	272	306	340	374	408	442	476	510	544	578	612	647	681	749	817

DESIGN — SPACED COLUMNS CONDITION "B"
SAFE UNIT AXIAL LOADS

See instructions for use of tables.
Obtain allowable E Value from building code or Pages 22-27.
Value of Fc′ from table may not exceed Fc value for species and grade of lumber used.
Total allowable load on column equals cross sectional area in square inches times Fc′ value.

CRITICAL DIMENSION Inches Nominal	Net	L/D	MODULUS OF ELASTICITY (1,000,000 psi)														
			.8	.9	1.0	1.1	1.2	1.3	1.4	1.5	1.6	1.7	1.8	1.9	2.0	2.2	2.4
15 FEET UNSUPPORTED LENGTH (CONTINUED)																	
6	5½	32.7	672	756	840	924	1008	1092	1176	1260	1344	1428	1512	1597	1681	1849	2017
8	7¼	24.8	1168	1314	1460	1606	1752	1898	2044	2190	2336	2482	2628	2774	2920	3212	3504
8	7½	24.0	1250	1406	1563	1719	1875	2031	2188	2344	2500	2656	2813	2969	3125	3438	3750
16 FEET UNSUPPORTED LENGTH																	
3	2½	76.8	122	137	153	168	183	198	214	229	244	259	275	290	305	336	366
4	3½	54.9	239	269	299	329	359	389	419	449	479	508	538	568	598	658	718
6	5½	34.9	591	665	739	812	886	960	1034	1108	1182	1255	1329	1403	1477	1625	1772
8	7¼	26.5	1027	1155	1283	1412	1540	1668	1797	1925	2053	2182	2310	2438	2567	2823	3080
8	7½	25.6	1099	1236	1373	1511	1648	1785	1923	2060	2197	2335	2472	2609	2747	3021	3296
17 FEET UNSUPPORTED LENGTH																	
4	3½	58.3	212	238	265	291	318	344	371	397	424	450	477	503	530	583	636
6	5½	37.1	523	589	654	720	785	850	916	981	1047	1112	1178	1243	1308	1439	1570
8	7¼	28.1	909	1023	1137	1250	1364	1478	1591	1705	1819	1932	2046	2160	2273	2501	2728
8	7½	27.2	973	1095	1216	1338	1460	1581	1703	1825	1946	2068	2190	2311	2433	2676	2920
10	9¼	22.1	1480	1665	1850	2035	2220	2406	2591	2776	2961	3146	3331	3516	3701	4071	4441
10	9½	21.5	1561	1757	1952	2147	2342	2537	2732	2928	3123	3318	3513	3708	3904	4294	4684
18 FEET UNSUPPORTED LENGTH																	
4	3½	61.7	189	213	236	260	284	307	331	354	378	402	425	449	473	520	567
6	5½	39.3	467	525	584	642	700	759	817	875	934	992	1050	1109	1167	1284	1400
8	7¼	29.8	811	913	1014	1115	1217	1318	1420	1521	1622	1724	1825	1926	2028	2231	2433
8	7½	28.8	868	977	1085	1194	1302	1411	1519	1628	1736	1845	1953	2062	2170	2387	2604
10	9¼	23.4	1320	1485	1651	1816	1981	2146	2311	2476	2641	2806	2971	3136	3301	3631	3961
10	9½	22.7	1393	1567	1741	1915	2089	2263	2437	2611	2786	2960	3134	3308	3482	3830	4178
19 FEET UNSUPPORTED LENGTH																	
4	3½	65.1	170	191	212	233	255	276	297	318	339	361	382	403	424	467	509
6	5½	41.5	419	471	524	576	628	681	733	786	838	890	943	995	1047	1152	1257
8	7¼	31.4	728	819	910	1001	1092	1183	1274	1365	1456	1547	1638	1729	1820	2002	2184
8	7½	30.4	779	876	974	1071	1169	1266	1363	1461	1558	1656	1753	1850	1948	2142	2337
10	9¼	24.6	1185	1333	1481	1629	1778	1926	2074	2222	2370	2518	2666	2815	2963	3259	3555
10	9½	24.0	1250	1406	1563	1719	1875	2031	2188	2344	2500	2656	2813	2969	3125	3438	3750
20 FEET UNSUPPORTED LENGTH																	
4	3½	68.6	153	172	191	211	230	249	268	287	306	325	345	364	383	421	459
6	5½	43.6	378	425	473	520	567	614	662	709	756	804	851	898	945	1040	1134
8	7¼	33.1	657	739	821	903	986	1068	1150	1232	1314	1396	1478	1560	1643	1807	1971
8	7½	32.0	703	791	879	967	1055	1143	1230	1318	1406	1494	1582	1670	1758	1934	2109
10	9¼	25.9	1070	1203	1337	1471	1604	1738	1872	2005	2139	2273	2406	2540	2674	2941	3209
10	9½	25.3	1128	1269	1410	1551	1692	1833	1974	2115	2256	2397	2538	2679·	2820	3102	3384
21 FEET UNSUPPORTED LENGTH																	
4	3½	72.0	139	156	174	191	208	226	243	260	278	295	312	330	347	382	417
6	5½	45.8	343	386	429	472	514	557	600	643	686	729	772	815	857	943	1029
8	7¼	34.8	596	670	745	819	894	968	1043	1117	1192	1266	1341	1415	1490	1639	1788
8	7½	33.6	638	717	797	877	957	1036	1116	1196	1276	1355	1435	1515	1594	1754	1913
10	9¼	27.2	970	1091	1213	1334	1455	1576	1698	1819	1940	2061	2183	2304	2425	2668	2910
10	9½	26.5	1023	1151	1279	1407	1535	1663	1791	1919	2046	2174	2302	2430	2558	2814	3070
22 FEET UNSUPPORTED LENGTH																	
4	3½	75.4	127	142	158	174	190	206	221	237	253	269	285	301	316	348	380
6	5½	48.0	313	352	391	430	469	508	547	586	625	664	703	742	781	859	938
8	7¼	36.4	543	611	679	747	815	882	950	1018	1086	1154	1222	1290	1358	1493	1629
8	7½	35.2	581	654	726	799	872	944	1017	1090	1162	1235	1307	1380	1453	1598	1743
10	9¼	28.5	884	994	1105	1215	1326	1436	1547	1657	1768	1878	1989	2099	2210	2431	2652
10	9½	27.8	932	1049	1165	1282	1398	1515	1632	1748	1865	1981	2098	2214	2331	2564	2797
12	11¼	23.5	1307	1471	1634	1798	1961	2125	2288	2451	2615	2778	2942	3105	3269	3596	3922
12	11½	23.0	1366	1537	1708	1879	2049	2220	2391	2562	2732	2903	3074	3245	3416	3757	4099

DESIGN — SPACED COLUMNS CONDITION "B"
SAFE UNIT AXIAL LOADS

See instructions for use of tables.
Obtain allowable E Value from building code or Pages 22-27.
Value of Fc' from table may not exceed Fc value for species and grade of lumber used.
Total allowable load on column equals cross sectional area in square inches times Fc' value.

MODULUS OF ELASTICITY (1,000,000 psi)

Nominal	Net	L/D	.8	.9	1.0	1.1	1.2	1.3	1.4	1.5	1.6	1.7	1.8	1.9	2.0	2.2	2.4
						23 FEET UNSUPPORTED LENGTH											
4	3½	78.9	116	130	145	159	174	188	203	217	232	246	261	275	289	318	347
6	5½	50.2	286	322	357	393	429	465	500	536	572	608	643	679	715	786	858
8	7¼	38.1	497	559	621	683	745	807	869	932	994	1056	1118	1180	1242	1366	1490
8	7½	36.8	532	598	665	731	797	864	930	997	1063	1130	1196	1263	1329	1462	1595
10	9¼	29.8	809	910	1011	1112	1213	1314	1415	1516	1617	1719	1820	1921	2022	2224	2426
10	9½	29.1	853	960	1066	1173	1280	1386	1493	1599	1706	1813	1919	2026	2133	2346	2559
12	11¼	24.5	1196	1346	1495	1645	1794	1944	2093	2243	2392	2542	2692	2841	2991	3290	3589
12	11½	24.0	1250	1406	1563	1719	1875	2031	2188	2344	2500	2656	2813	2969	3125	3438	3750
						24 FEET UNSUPPORTED LENGTH											
6	5½	52.4	263	295	328	361	394	427	460	492	525	558	591	624	656	722	788
8	7¼	39.7	456	513	570	627	684	741	798	856	913	970	1027	1084	1141	1255	1369
8	7½	38.4	488	549	610	671	732	793	854	916	977	1038	1099	1160	1221	1343	1465
10	9¼	31.1	743	836	928	1021	1114	1207	1300	1393	1485	1578	1671	1764	1857	2043	2228
10	9½	30.3	783	881	979	1077	1175	1273	1371	1469	1567	1665	1763	1861	1959	2154	2350
12	11¼	25.6	1099	1236	1373	1511	1648	1785	1923	2060	2197	2335	2472	2609	2747	3021	3296
12	11½	25.0	1148	1292	1435	1579	1722	1866	2009	2153	2296	2440	2583	2727	2870	3157	3444
						25 FEET UNSUPPORTED LENGTH											
6	5½	54.5	242	272	302	333	363	393	423	454	484	514	544	575	605	665	726
8	7¼	41.4	421	473	526	578	631	683	736	788	841	894	946	999	1051	1156	1262
8	7½	40.0	450	506	563	619	675	731	788	844	900	956	1013	1069	1125	1238	1350
10	9¼	32.4	685	770	856	941	1027	1112	1198	1283	1369	1455	1540	1626	1711	1882	2054
10	9½	31.6	722	812	903	993	1083	1173	1264	1354	1444	1534	1625	1715	1805	1986	2166
12	11¼	26.7	1012	1139	1266	1392	1519	1645	1772	1898	2025	2152	2278	2405	2531	2784	3037
12	11½	26.1	1058	1190	1322	1455	1587	1719	1851	1984	2116	2248	2380	2513	2645	2909	3174
						26 FEET UNSUPPORTED LENGTH											
6	5½	56.7	224	252	280	308	336	364	392	420	447	475	503	531	559	615	671
8	7¼	43.0	389	437	486	535	583	632	680	729	778	826	875	923	972	1069	1166
8	7½	41.6	416	468	520	572	624	676	728	780	832	884	936	988	1040	1144	1248
10	9¼	33.7	633	712	791	870	949	1028	1108	1187	1266	1345	1424	1503	1582	1740	1899
10	9½	32.8	668	751	834	918	1001	1085	1168	1252	1335	1419	1502	1585	1669	1836	2003
12	11¼	27.7	936	1053	1170	1287	1404	1521	1638	1755	1872	1989	2106	2223	2340	2574	2808
12	11½	27.1	978	1100	1223	1345	1467	1590	1712	1834	1956	2079	2201	2323	2445	2690	2935
						27 FEET UNSUPPORTED LENGTH											
6	5½	58.9	207	233	259	285	311	337	363	389	415	441	467	493	519	571	622
8	7¼	44.7	361	406	451	496	541	586	631	676	721	766	811	856	901	991	1082
8	7½	43.2	386	434	482	530	579	627	675	723	772	820	868	916	965	1061	1157
10	9¼	35.0	587	660	734	807	880	954	1027	1100	1174	1247	1320	1394	1467	1614	1761
10	9½	34.1	619	696	774	851	928	1006	1083	1161	1238	1315	1393	1470	1547	1702	1857
12	11¼	28.8	868	977	1085	1194	1302	1411	1519	1628	1736	1845	1953	2062	2170	2387	2604
12	11½	28.2	907	1020	1134	1247	1361	1474	1587	1701	1814	1928	2041	2154	2268	2494	2721
14	13¼	24.5	1204	1355	1505	1656	1806	1957	2107	2258	2408	2559	2709	2860	3010	3311	3612
14	13½	24.0	1250	1406	1563	1719	1875	2031	2188	2344	2500	2656	2813	2969	3125	3438	3750
						28 FEET UNSUPPORTED LENGTH											
6	5½	61.1	193	217	241	265	289	313	338	362	386	410	434	458	482	531	579
8	7¼	46.3	335	377	419	461	503	545	587	629	670	712	754	796	838	922	1006
8	7½	44.8	359	404	448	493	538	583	628	673	717	762	807	852	897	987	1076
10	9¼	36.3	546	614	682	750	819	887	955	1023	1091	1160	1228	1296	1364	1501	1637
10	9½	35.4	576	648	719	791	863	935	1007	1079	1151	1223	1295	1367	1439	1583	1727
12	11¼	29.9	807	908	1009	1110	1211	1312	1413	1513	1614	1715	1816	1917	2018	2220	2421
12	11½	29.2	843	949	1054	1160	1265	1371	1476	1581	1687	1792	1898	2003	2109	2319	2530
14	13¼	25.4	1120	1260	1400	1540	1679	1819	1959	2099	2239	2379	2519	2659	2799	3079	3359
14	13½	24.9	1162	1308	1453	1598	1743	1889	2034	2179	2325	2470	2615	2760	2906	3196	3487
						29 FEET UNSUPPORTED LENGTH											
6	5½	63.3	180	202	225	247	270	292	315	337	360	382	405	427	450	495	540
8	7¼	48.0	313	352	391	430	469	508	547	586	625	664	703	742	781	859	938
8	7½	46.4	334	376	418	460	502	543	585	627	669	711	752	794	836	920	1003
10	9¼	37.6	509	572	636	699	763	827	890	954	1017	1081	1145	1208	1272	1399	1526

DESIGN — SPACED COLUMNS CONDITION "B"
SAFE UNIT AXIAL LOADS

See instructions for use of tables.
Obtain allowable E Value from building code or Pages 22-27.
Value of Fc' from table may not exceed Fc value for species and grade of lumber used.
Total allowable load on column equals cross sectional area in square inches times Fc' value.

CRITICAL DIMENSION Inches Nominal	Net	L/D	MODULUS OF ELASTICITY (1,000,000 psi)														
			.8	.9	1.0	1.1	1.2	1.3	1.4	1.5	1.6	1.7	1.8	1.9	2.0	2.2	2.4
29 FEET UNSUPPORTED LENGTH (CONTINUED)																	
10	9½	36.6	537	604	671	738	805	872	939	1006	1073	1140	1207	1274	1341	1476	1610
12	11¼	30.9	752	847	941	1035	1129	1223	1317	1411	1505	1599	1693	1787	1881	2069	2257
12	11½	30.3	786	885	983	1081	1179	1278	1376	1474	1573	1671	1769	1867	1966	2162	2359
14	13¼	26.3	1044	1174	1305	1435	1566	1696	1827	1957	2088	2218	2348	2479	2609	2870	3131
14	13½	25.8	1084	1219	1354	1490	1625	1761	1896	2032	2167	2303	2438	2573	2709	2980	3251
30 FEET UNSUPPORTED LENGTH																	
6	5½	65.5	168	189	210	231	252	273	294	315	336	357	378	399	420	462	504
8	7¼	49.7	292	329	365	402	438	475	511	548	584	621	657	694	730	803	876
8	7½	48.0	313	352	391	430	469	508	547	586	625	664	703	742	781	859	938
10	9¼	38.9	475	535	594	654	713	772	832	891	951	1010	1070	1129	1188	1307	1426
10	9½	37.9	501	564	627	689	752	815	877	940	1003	1065	1128	1191	1253	1379	1504
12	11¼	32.0	703	791	879	967	1055	1143	1230	1318	1406	1494	1582	1670	1758	1934	2109
12	11½	31.3	735	827	918	1010	1102	1194	1286	1378	1469	1561	1653	1745	1837	2020	2204
14	13¼	27.2	975	1097	1219	1341	1463	1585	1707	1829	1951	2073	2195	2316	2438	2682	2926
14	13½	26.7	1012	1139	1266	1392	1519	1645	1772	1898	2025	2152	2278	2405	2531	2784	3037

General Design Information

In the design of members stressed primarily in bending, proper consideration must be given to a number of factors:
1. Bending stresses induced by the load
   a. Combined bending and axial loading stresses
   b. Lateral stability
   c. Depth effect of deep beams
2. Deflection or deformation caused by the load
3. Horizontal shear at the supports
4. Bearing on supporting members

Any of the above major factors may control the design and all must be satisfied to insure adequate structural stability and safety.

Design Loads

Bending members should be designed and constructed to support safely all anticipated loads. Minimum design loads depend upon the code under which the structure is designed, or if no code governs, the designer's estimate of the particular service requirements of the structure.

Design loads may include any, or a combination, of the following loads or forces: dead, live, snow, wind, earthquake, erection and other static and dynamic forces. The most severe distribution, concentration and combination of design loads and forces should be taken into consideration.

Span

For simple beams, the span is taken as the distance from face to face of supports, plus one-half the required length of bearing at each end. For continuous beams, the span is the distance between centers of bearings on supports over which the beam is continuous.

Net Sizes

Computations to determine the required sizes of members shall be based on the net dimensions (actual sizes) and not the nominal sizes customarily specified.

Beam Diagrams And Formulas

Pages 80 through 99 provide a series of shear and moment diagrams with accompanying formulas for beams under various conditions of static loading.

Allowable Stresses

The allowable unit stresses for design of wood beams are given in Tables 4.1 through 4.8 for visually graded lumber, and in Table 4.10 for machine stress rated lumber. For structural glued laminated timbers the allowable unit stresses are shown in the National Design Specification for Stress Grade Lumber and its Fastenings and in the *AITC Timber Construction Manual*.

Notations

Except where otherwise noted, the following symbols are used in the formulas for beam design:

b = thickness or breadth of rectangular member, inches
E = modulus of elasticity
F_b = allowable unit stress in extreme fiber in bending

DESIGN — BENDING MEMBERS

F_c = allowable unit stress in compression parallel to grain
$F_{c'}$ = allowable unit stress in compression parallel to grain adjusted for l/d ratio
$F_{c\perp}$ = allowable unit stress in compression perpendicular to grain
d = depth of rectangular member, inches
F_t = allowable unit stress in tension parallel to grain
F_v = allowable unit stress in horizontal shear
I = moment of inertia of the section
M = moment or resisting moment
Δ = deflection due to load
P = total concentrated load, pounds
L = span in feet
l = span in inches
S = section modulus
V = total vertical end shear or reaction, pounds
W = total uniformly distributed load, pounds
w = load per linear foot of beam, pounds
Q = statical moment of an area about the neutral axis

Design For Bending Moment

To maintain static equilibrium, the allowable internal resisting moment of the beam must be at least equal to the external bending moment induced by the live and dead loads supported by the beam.

The external bending moment is determined for the specific conditions of loading and span for the beam under consideration. The beam diagrams and formulas on pages 80 through 99 apply to most situations encountered. However, span and loading conditions not specifically covered herein should be analyzed by a competent designer.

For a simple span rectangular beam supporting a uniformly distributed load the external bending moment is:

$$M = \frac{WL}{8} \text{ in pound-feet.}$$

When converted to pound-inches, the formula becomes:

$$M = \frac{wL^2 (12)}{8} = \frac{3wL^2}{2}$$

The internal resisting moment of a beam is the product of the allowable extreme fiber stress in bending, F_b, for the particular grade and species of lumber, and the section modulus, S, of the beam. The formula is:

$$M = F_bS$$

in which S for a rectangular section $= \dfrac{bh^2}{6}$.

Since the internal resisting moment must be at least equal to the external bending moment, the two formulas may be equated as follows:

$$F_bS = \frac{3wL^2}{2}$$

DESIGN — BENDING MEMBERS

To determine the required section modulus of a beam, and thus its size, the formula may be rearranged as follows:

$$S = \frac{3wL^2}{2F_b}$$

To determine the allowable span for a given size beam, load per lineal foot and allowable extreme fiber stress in bending, F_b, the formula is:

$$L = \sqrt{\frac{2F_bS}{3w}}$$

To determine the allowable load per linear foot for a given span, size grade and species of beam, the formula is written:

$$w = \frac{2F_bS}{3L^2}$$

Combined Bending And Axial Loading Stresses

Structural members, such as upper and lower chords in trusses, are often subjected to a combination of bending and axial tension or compression loading. When such conditions exist, the member must be designed to resist the combined forces without exceeding the allowable unit stresses.

For bending and tension:

$$\frac{P/A}{F_t} + \frac{M/S}{F_b} \leq 1$$

For bending and compression:

$$\frac{P/A}{F_{c'}} + \frac{M/S}{F_b} \leq 1$$

Lateral Stability Of Beams

Beams which are relatively deep in comparison to width may be unstable under the application of loads. Such instability is due to the tendency of the compression edge of the beam to buckle, causing the beam to deflect laterally. The following general rules, based on nominal dimensions, may be applied in providing lateral restraint:

a. If the ratio of depth to width, or thickness, is 2 to 1, no lateral support is needed.

b. If the ratio is 3 to 1 or 4 to 1, the ends should be held in position, as when nailed or bolted to a vertical member, or laterally supported by blocking.

c. If the ratio is 5 to 1, one edge should be held in line for its entire length.

d. If the ratio is 6 to 1 or more, the beam should be supported laterally at intervals of 8 feet by bridging or transverse beams.

Design To Prevent Lateral Buckling

Although the design procedures for the prevention of lateral buckling recommended by the American Institute of Timber Construction are believed to be ultra-conservative, they are presented here to provide the best available procedures. Research is continuing in this field and future recommendations will reflect improved procedures.

Beams of square section, or with breadth greater then depth, require no lateral support in pure bending.

Beams with the compression side supported against lateral movement do not require modification of F_b, inasmuch as the compression side cannot buckle.

When beam depth exceeds breadth, the beam must be secured against lateral rotation at points of bearing, and the allowable bending stress must be limited in accordance with the formulas for short, intermediate and long beams.

Short Beams

When the slenderness factor, C_s, does not exceed 10, the full allowable unit stress in bending, F_b, adjusted for various conditions such as load duration and moisture content in service, but excluding depth effect factor, is used for beam strength design.

$$C_s = \sqrt{\frac{l_e h}{b^2}}$$

where

C_s = slenderness factor

l_e = effective length in inches (see Table 7.3)

h = depth of beam, inches

b = breadth of beam, inches

TABLE 7.3 EFFECTIVE BEAM LENGTH

Type of Beam Span and Nature of Load	Value of Effective Length, l_e
Single span beam, load concentrated at center	$1.61l$*
Single span beam, uniformly distributed load	$1.92l$
Single span beam, equal end moments	$1.84l$
Cantilever beam, load concentrated at unsupported end	$1.69l$
Cantilever beam, uniformly distributed load	$1.06l$
Single span or cantilever beam, any load (conservative value)	$1.92l$

*l = unsupported length

Intermediate beams

Where C_s exceeds 10, but does not exceed C_k, the allowable bending stress, $F_{b'}$ is:

$$F_b^1 = F_b \left[1 + \frac{1}{3} \left(\frac{C_s}{C_k} \right)^4 \right]$$

where: $C_k = 0.775 \sqrt{E/F_b}$

Long Beams

In cases where slenderness ratio exceeds C_k, but is not greater than 50:

$$F_{b'} = 0.40 \, E/C_s^2$$

Unsupported length

For beams with ends supported against lateral rotation, and the compression edge supported against lateral deflection throughout its entire length, the unsupported length, l, is zero.

If support at ends prevents lateral rotation but no restraint is provided for the compression edge, the full length of the member is the unsupported length, l.

With support against lateral rotation and lateral displacement at the ends and at intermediate points along the length, the distance between points of support is the unsupported length.

If, at the intermediate points, the restraint prevents lateral rotation but does not prevent lateral deflection, (as with vertical bridging), the unsupported length is the full length between bearing points of the member.

The provision of adequate lateral support should be given careful attention by the designer to insure that the decking sway bracing, bridging or tie stringers are properly anchored and fixed.

Depth Effect For Deep Rectangular Wood Beams

As the depth of a beam increases there is a slight decrease in the unit bending strength. Since laboratory test values for clear wood are determined on the basis of a beam 2 inches (net) in depth, it is customary practice to adjust the clear wood values for a depth of beam of 4 inches (nominal) for Light Framing, Structural Light Framing and Decking. The allowable stresses in extreme fiber in bending for Structural Joists and Planks incorporate the depth factor along with the strength ratio of all grades and sizes so adjustments for depth effect need not be made. For Beams and Stringers deeper than 12 inches (nominal) the depth factor may be determined from the following formula; however, as noted on page 101 the effect of depth has been incorporated in the beam design tables:

$$C_d = \left(\frac{12}{d}\right)^{\frac{1}{9}}$$

in which,
C_d = depth factor
d = actual depth of beam, inches

Values for C_d for solid-sawn beams having various depths are as follows:

when d equals:	C_d equals:
13.5	.987
15.5	.972
17.5	.959
19.5	.947
21.5	.937
23.5	.928
25.5	.920
27.5	.912

DESIGN — BENDING MEMBERS

To calculate the resisting moment of a beam deeper than 12 inches, the depth factor is inserted in the standard formula as follows:

$$M = C_d F_b S$$

For stress rated boards and dimension 2" to 4" in thickness when used flatwise, the recommended design values for fiber stress in bending may be multiplied by the factors shown in the following table:

ADJUSTMENT FACTORS FOR DEPTH EFFECT
Apply to Design Values for Extreme Fiber in Bending (Fb)

Lumber Width	Nominal Thickness When used as a plank			
	1"	2"	3"	4"
2" to 4"	1.19	1.10	1.04	1.00
6" and wider	1.32	1.22	1.16	1.11

For all widths of Decking and Scaffold Plank, use factors listed above for 2″ to 4″ widths.

Design For Deflection

Structural members deflect or bend under load. The greater the load the greater the deflection. Thus, the deflection of a beam is a measure of the deformation which occurs as the beam resists bending under applied load. When the induced bending stress does not exceed the allowable unit stress used in design, this deformation does not seriously affect the endurance of the beam.

Limits are placed on deflection for a number of reasons, all of which are related to the satisfaction of the occupant or user.

Excessive deflection may cause unsightly cracking of brittle finishes such as plaster. Limitations on deflection are a means of controlling the vibrational properties of floor structures. Excessive sag in flat roofs may interfere with roof drainage causing ponding and a potential dangerous build up of applied load due to water. Excessive sag in beams can interfere with the operation of doors and windows and in certain instances the sag of beams under dead load can be unattractive and denote a shoddy quality of construction or design. Deflection limits, then, arise out of requirements for structural performance, aesthetics, and function.

It is generally considered good practice to limit deflection to some proportion of the span length. The following proportions are those most widely required by building codes for deflection due to live loads:

	Deflection Limitation As Fraction of Span
Floor Comfort	1/360th
Plastered ceilings	1/360th
Ceilings of other materials	1/240th
Roofs, slope 3 in 12 or less	1/240th
Roofs, slope more than 3 in 12	1/180th
Industrial buildings (no appearance factor)	1/180th

DESIGN — BENDING MEMBERS

Deflection Under Long-Time Loads

Wood beams usually sag in time; that is, the deflection increases beyond what it was immediately after the load was first applied. Unseasoned timbers, especially, will sag if allowed to season under load, although partially seasoned material will also sag to some extent. In thoroughly seasoned beams, there are small changes in deflection with changes in moisture content but little permanent increase in deflection. The increase in deflection of a wood beam due to dead loads beyond what it was immediately after the load was first applied is called creep and does not endanger the safety of the beam. Where it is necessary to limit the deflection under such long-continued loading, extra stiffness can be provided in the design stage by increasing any dead or longtime loads, by setting an initial deflection limit at less than the acceptable long-time limit or by using less than the recommended value of modulus of elasticity in calculating the initial deflection. In any case, it should be understood that the recommended values for modulus of elasticity will give the initial deflection of a beam and that this will increase under sustained, full dead load.

If the cumulative long time deflection under permanent load needs to be limited, it is recommended, for unseasoned material, that the amount of the permanent load be multiplied by two in designing the structural element to the limited deflection, or the amount of the permanent load may be used with one-half of the published value for modulus of elasticity. For seasoned lumber designated as DRY or MC-15, it is recommended that the amount of the permanent load be multiplied by 1.5 in designing the structural element to the limited deflection, or the amount of the permanent load may be used with two-thirds of the published value for modulus of elasticity.

In all of the span tables that are a part of this book, the required modulus of elasticity for a given span and deflection limitation have been determined on the basis of the initial deflection caused by the load. When deflection under long time loading needs to be limited, the load capacity or the span must be calculated for the effect of permanent load.

Camber

Glued laminated timber beams are usually cambered to counteract the effects of plastic deformation under long-time loading. Camber is built into a structural member by introducing a curvature, either circular or parabolic, opposite to the anticipated deflection movement. Camber recommendations vary with design criteria for various conditions of use and, in addition, are dependent on: whether the member is of simple, continuous, or cantilever span; whether roof drainage is to be provided by the camber; and other factors. Reverse camber may be required in continuous and cantilever spans to permit adequate drainage. In general, the AITC recommends that roof and floor beams be cambered to 1½ times the dead load deflection; however, more detailed information may be found in the *AITC Timber Construction Manual*.

Ponding

When there is the possibility of water ponding, which may cause excessive loads and additional and progressive deflection, each component of the roof system, including decking, purlins, beams, girders, or other principal structural supports, should be designed with sufficient slope or camber to assure adequate drainage after the long-time deflection from dead load, or should be designed to support maximum loads including possible ponding of water due to deflection. For more detailed recommendations on the design of beams for ponding, the reader is referred to the *AITC Timber Construction Manual*.

DESIGN FOR HORIZONTAL SHEAR

Horizontal shear strength of a wood joist or beam is a function of that strength property of the species and the extent of seasoning checks, splits or shake when present. As a stress concentration occurs at the base of checks, splits or shake, and as checking occurs to some extent in practically all structural sizes of lumber, the allowable clear unit stress for horizontal shear is determined by reducing horizontal shear strength unseasoned clear-wood values by a factor of 4.1. This is a combined factor which incorporates an adjustment to normal loading, a stress concentration factor and a factor of safety. It has long been recognized, however, that horizontal shear stress in members with checks, etc., present is not distributed as indicated by the customary shear formula for a rectangular piece, and that this formula indicates a greater stress than is normally present, particularly with moving or concentrated loads.

Studies at the United States Forest Products Laboratory, supported by tests, show that the upper and lower half of a checked joist or beam resist a portion of the horizontal shear load independently of that at the neutral plane and in increasing proportion as the load approaches the support. As a consequence of this "two-beam" action, a concentrated or moving load will induce a "maximum" horizontal shear stress at a support when the load is at some distance from the support. This distance has been found to be between 3 and 4 beam depths for a simple span in the range of the most frequently occurring beam depth to span length relationships. This information has led to empirical rules for calculating the vertical end shear for a simple span from a single concentrated or moving load or a uniformly distributed load. The vertical end shear thus obtained is conservative when used in the customary horizontal shear formula:

$$F_V = \frac{3\,V}{2\,bh}$$

where

F_V = unit stress in horizontal shear, lbs. per sq. in

DESIGN — BENDING MEMBERS

V = vertical end shear, pounds,
b = width of member, inches,
h = depth of member, inches.

Rules For Calculating Vertical End Shear

In calculating the vertical end shear the rules are:

(a) Take into account any relief to the beam under consideration resulting from the moving or concentrated load being distributed to adjacent parallel beams by flooring or other members.

(b) Neglect all loads within the height of the beam from both supports.

(c) If there are any moving loads, place the largest one at three times the height of the beam from the support or at the quarter point, whichever is closer.

(d) Treat all other loads in the usual manner.

Accurate Method Of Evaluating Vertical End Shear

More accurate vertical end shears can be calculated, including shears for other than simple spans and for combinations of concentrated or moving loads, from the Forest Products Laboratory data. Their tests show that the effect of size of member and the degree of checking, from moderate to severe, is practically a constant so that a simple formula can express algebraically the "two beam" division of the horizontal shear stress between that at the neutral plane and the upper and lower half as

$$\frac{r_1}{r_2} = \frac{x^2}{2} \qquad (1)$$

where

r_1 = shear stress in neutral plane,
r_2 = shear stress in upper and lower halves,
x = number of beam depths from support to load.

Curve A in Figure 7.3 shows the proportional division by this formula of shear stress between the neutral plane and the upper and lower halves of a checked beam for any position of load along the beam. An ordinate measured below the curve is the portion of shear on the neutral plane and that above is the portion on the upper and lower part of the member.

With a concentrated load "P" and the sum of r_1 and r_2 being equivalent to the end reaction, then

$$r^1 + r^2 = \frac{P(L - x)}{L} \qquad (2)$$

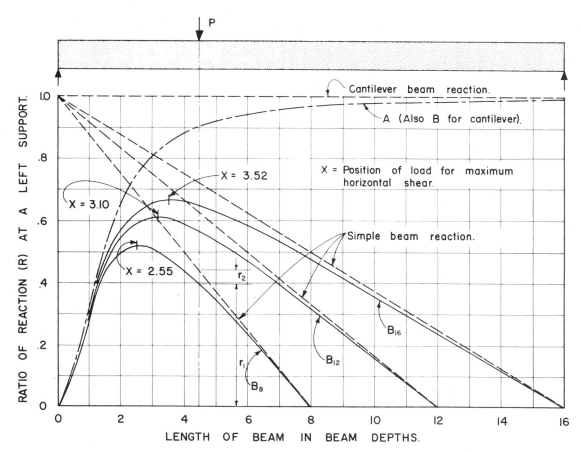

Figure 7.3 — Ratios of Simple Beam Reactions to Vertical End Shears, r_1 and r_2, for a Concentrated or Moving Load.

DESIGN — BENDING MEMBERS

where

$$L = \text{length of beam expressed as beam depths.}$$

By combining the two preceding formulas

$$r_1 = \frac{P(L-x)\,x^2}{L(2+x^2)} \qquad (3)$$

This gives the ratio of the vertical end shear, r_1, at the neutral plane to the simple beam reaction. On Figure 7.3 curves B_8, B_{12} and B_{16} illustrate the ratios and the proportional division of the two-beam end shears for simple beams of 8, 12 and 16 beam-depths in length respectively, and for any position of the load on the beam. The length of the ordinate from the base to curve B is the ratio of the shear, r_1, from the simple beam reaction that is distributed to the neutral plane, to the total end shear, and the length of the ordinate from curve B to the line representing the simple beam reaction is the ratio of the end shear, r_2, that is distributed to the upper and lower halves of the beam, to the total end shear. Both r_1 and r_2 increase as the load P moves to the left to a maximum when P is at the distances x that are shown in Figure 7.3.

Equating to zero the first derivative of r_1, with respect to x in formula (3) yields the equation

$$x^3 + 6x = 4L \qquad (4)$$

the solution of which will give the position of a single load on a simple beam for the vertical end shear, r_1, that induces maximum horizontal shear on the neutral plane. This positioning of the single load is illustrated in Figure 7.4 and for comparison, the empirical rule method is also plotted.

A factor of 10/9 is introduced in formula (5) as a reducing adjustment for recommended unit working stresses for horizontal shear. This adjustment was indicated by the tests.

Formulas For Accurately Calculating Vertical End Shears

By similar analysis, formulas for determining the vertical end shear for uniformly distributed loads on simple beams and loads on cantilever beams are derived. Converting these formulas from a beam depth to a dimensional relationship gives usable formulas for

Simple Beam Spans:

Concentrated load—

$$r_1 = \frac{10\,P(l-x)\,(x/h)^2}{9l\,[2+(x/h)^2]} \qquad (5)$$

Uniformly distributed load—

$$r_1 = \frac{W}{2}\left(1 - \frac{2h}{l}\right) \qquad (6)$$

Cantilever Beam:

Concentrated load—

$$r_1 = \frac{10\,P(x/h)^2}{9[2+(x/h)^2]} \qquad (7)$$

Uniformly distributed load—

$$r_1 = W\,(1 - h/l) \qquad (8)$$

in which

r_1 = vertical end shear at neutral plane. Substitute r_1 for V in customary horizontal shear formula.

h = depth of beam in inches,

l = span in inches,

P = concentrated load in pounds,

W = total uniform load in pounds,

x = distance in inches from center of bearing to load.

Where horizontal shears appear to be critical by the ordinary computation of reactions at supports, or even by following the rules previously outlined, a less conservative joist or beam size may be found satisfactory if vertical end shears are more accurately determined for the two-beam action.

Calculating Shear — Multiple Concentrated Or Moving Loads

Where there are fixed, concentrated loads on a span, any load within one beam depth from the support can be neglected as its effect on shear stress is slight. Other concentrated loads produce a horizontal shear stress equal to the sum of the vertical end shears, r_1, as calculated by formula (5) for the loads at their respective locations.

Where there are moving loads, the largest load is positioned to produce maximum vertical end shear by formula (4) or from Figure 7.4. The other loads, in their relative positions to the largest one, are similarly evaluated for vertical end shear and the total vertical end shear from moving loads is the sum of the r_1 values from all loads.

Calculating Shear — Simple Beam With Cantilever

If there are a number of concentrated or moving loads on a simple beam span with a cantilever, it is recommended that the maximum horizontal shear be determined by plotting graphically the summations of the vertical end shears for each load above the uniform dead load shear of the member. The highest peak of the summation of the r_1 values for the range of load movement will be the maximum vertical end shear. The vertical end shears from the moving and dead loads on the cantilever are computed as normal reactions and are included in the summation of loads on the simple span.

DESIGN — BENDING MEMBERS

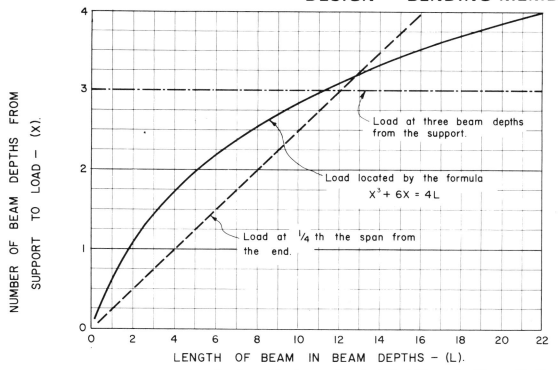

Figure 7.4 Locating Single Load to Produce Maximum Vertical End Shear by Three Methods.

Shear In Members Supported By Connectors Or Bolts

Joists or beams that are supported by timber connectors, bolts or other devices are considered as having a reduced effective depth and the horizontal shear strength of the member is determined by using the reduced depth in the customary shear formula. The shear stresses in eccentric joints, such as timber connector or bolted joints in trusses, are similarly determined. Figure 7.5 illustrates these conditions and the customary shear formula is revised as follows:

$$F_v = \frac{3V}{2bh_e}$$

Where the joint is at least 5 times the depth of the member from its end, Fv may be increased

h_e = (with connectors) = the depth of the member less the distance from the unloaded edge of the member to the nearest edge of the nearest connector.

h_e = (with bolt only) = the depth of the member less the distance from the unloaded edge of the member to the center of the nearest bolt.

50 percent, provided the allowable horizontal shear, without increase, on the full cross section is not exceeded.

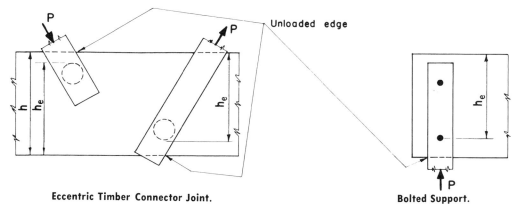

Eccentric Timber Connector Joint.   **Bolted Support.**

Figure 7.5 Reduced Effective Depth of Members Supported by Various Devices.

DESIGN — BENDING MEMBERS

Notched Beams

Beams are often notched at the ends to improve clearance or to bring the top surfaces level with adjacent beams or girders. Occasionally they are also notched at intermediate points, either bottom or top, in order to clear other parts of a structure.

Effect Of Notches On Shear

When notched on the lower side at the ends, the horizontal shearing strength of a short relatively deep joist or beam is decreased by an amount depending upon the shape of the notch and the relation of the depth of the notch to the depth of the beam. When designing such a member the horizontal shear stress is obtained by the formula:

$$F_v = \frac{3Vh}{2bh_e^2}$$

where F_v =   allowable unit shear stress, lb. per sq. in.

V =   vertical shear, pounds,

h =   total net depth of the beam, inches,

b =   net width of the beam, inches,

h_e =   actual end depth above the notch, inches.

A gradual change in cross section compared with a square notch increases the shearing strength nearly to that computed for the actual depth above the notch.

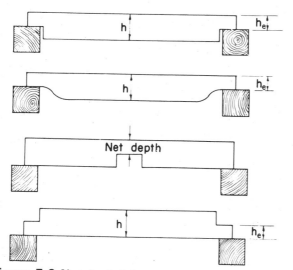

Figure 7.6 Notched Joists or Beams.

When a beam is notched or beveled on its upper side at the ends, a less severe condition of stress concentration exists. The reader is referred to the *Timber Construction Manual* by the American Institute of Timber Construction for methods of design.

Design For Bearing On Supports

The load on a wood beam tends to compress the wood fibers at points where the beam rests on supporting members. Thus, the area of bearing on such supports must be large enough to transfer the load without damage to the wood fibers. Such required bearing area is determined by dividing the reaction, V, by the allowable unit stress in compression perpendicular to grain, $F_{c\perp}$, for the species and grade of lumber to be used.

For bearings less than 6 inches in length, located away from the ends of a wood beam, higher stresses in compression perpendicular to grain may be used safely. For bearings shorter than 6 inches, located 3 inches or more from the end of a beam, the allowable unit stresses in compression perpendicular to grain may be increased in accordance with the following factors:

Length of Bearing	½"	1"	1½"	2"	3"	4"	6"or more
Factor	1.75	1.38	1.25	1.19	1.13	1.10	1.00

For stress under a washer, the same factor may be taken as for a bearing whose length equals the diameter of the washer.

End Bearing Of Wood On Wood And Wood On Metal

When wood compression members are squared and butted end-to end, the contacting areas of the narrow bands of the stronger summer wood are small in comparison with the total area of the cross section and become overstressed before the remainder of the wood fibers in the piece reach the allowable stress. For this reason, the ends tend to bed themselves into each other and the maximum capacity will be less than the compressive strength of clear wood. However, for end-to-end bearing of wood compression members the full allowable compression stress parallel to grain for clear wood may be used when a metal plate of a minimum of 20 gauge is inserted with a snug fit between the ends. End cuts must be accurately squared and parallel and the pieces must be restrained laterally. When the metal plate is not used the bearing stress must not exceed 75 per cent of the clear wood value for compression parallel to grain. The full, clear wood value for compression parallel to grain may also be used where the end grain of wood bears on a metal plate or strap as at the heel joint of a truss or on other durable and rigid homogeneous material of adequate structural strength.

As end grain bearing values are based on compression parallel to grain for clear wood, the rate of growth, (dense or medium grain), and the condition of use, (whether continuously dry or at or above the fiber saturation point), are considered in selecting the value to use in calculating end bearing.

Where there are combinations of grades in glued laminated members that will combine different rates of growth, the weighted value for the combinations applies.

DESIGN — BENDING MEMBERS

Bearing At Angles To The Grain

The compressive strength of wood varies between loading parallel to the grain and perpendicular to the grain. The value is highest when the load is parallel, and lowest when the load is perpendicular to the grain. The rate of growth and the condition of use affect the allowable unit working stress for loading from parallel to perpendicular to the grain.

When the load is at an angle to the grain, between parallel and perpendicular to the grain, the allowable unit design stress in bearing is determined by the Hankinson formula:

$$N = \frac{c \times c\perp}{c \, \text{sine}^2 \, \theta \, + \, c\perp \, \text{cosine}^2 \, \theta}$$

Where

N = Allowable unit compression stress at inclination θ with the direction of grain.

c = Allowable unit stress in compression parallel to grain for clear wood.

$c\perp$ = Allowable unit stress in compression perpendicular to grain for clear wood.

θ = Angle between direction of grain and direction of load normal to the face being considered.

The strength values used in this formula are always for clear wood. Figure 7.7 is a nomographic chart of the Hankinson formula for rapid solution of bearing at angle to grain values.

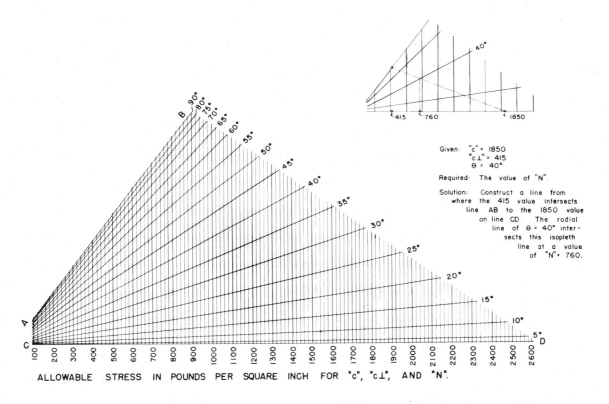

Given: "c" = 1850
        "c⊥" = 415
        θ = 40°

Required: The value of "N".

Solution: Construct a line from where the 415 value intersects line AB to the 1850 value on line CD. The radial line of θ = 40° intersects this isopleth line at a value of "N" = 760.

ALLOWABLE STRESS IN POUNDS PER SQUARE INCH FOR "c", "c⊥", AND "N".

Figure 7.7 Chart for Determining Bearing Strength of Wood at Angles to the Grain.

DESIGN — BENDING MEMBERS

Simple Beam—Uniformly Distributed Load

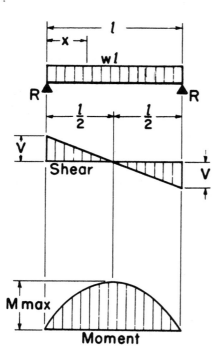

$$R = V \quad \ldots \ldots \ldots \ldots = \frac{wl}{2}$$

$$V_x \quad \ldots \ldots \ldots \ldots = w\left(\frac{l}{2} - x\right)$$

$$M \text{ max.} \left(\text{at center}\right) \ldots \ldots = \frac{wl^2}{8}$$

$$M_x \quad \ldots \ldots \ldots \ldots = \frac{wx}{2}(l - x)$$

$$\triangle \text{max.} \left(\text{at center}\right) \ldots \ldots = \frac{5\,wl^4}{384\,EI}$$

$$\triangle_x \quad \ldots \ldots \ldots \ldots = \frac{wx}{24EI}(l^3 - 2lx^2 + x^3)$$

Simple Beam—Uniform Load Partially Distributed

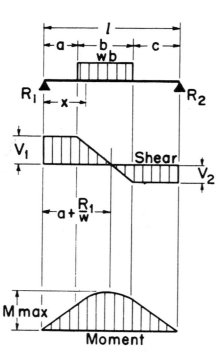

$$R_1 = V_1 \left(\text{max. when } a < c\right) \ldots \ldots = \frac{wb}{2l}(2c + b)$$

$$R_2 = V_2 \left(\text{max. when } a > c\right) \ldots \ldots = \frac{wb}{2l}(2a + b)$$

$$V_x \quad \left(\text{when } x < a \text{ and } > (a + b)\right) = R_1 - w(x-a)$$

$$M \text{ max.} \left(\text{at } x = a + \frac{R_1}{w}\right) \ldots \ldots = R_1\left(a + \frac{R_1}{2w}\right)$$

$$M_x \quad \left(\text{when } x < a\right) \ldots \ldots \ldots = R_1 x$$

$$M_x \quad \left(\text{when } x > a \text{ and } < (a + b)\right) = R_1 x - \frac{w}{2}(x-a)^2$$

$$M_x \quad \left(\text{when } x > (a + b)\right) \ldots \ldots = R_2(l-x)$$

DESIGN — BENDING MEMBERS

Simple Beam—Uniform Load Partially Distributed at One End

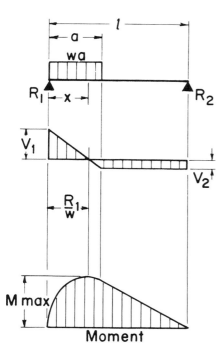

$$R_1 = V_1 \text{ max.} \quad \ldots \ldots \ldots \quad = \frac{wa}{2l}(2l-a)$$

$$R_2 = V_2 \quad \ldots \ldots \ldots \ldots \quad = \frac{wa^2}{2l}$$

$$V_x \quad \left(\text{when } x < a\right) \quad \ldots \ldots \quad = R_1 - wx$$

$$M \text{ max.} \quad \left(\text{at } x = \frac{R_1}{w}\right) \quad \ldots \ldots \quad = \frac{R_1^2}{2w}$$

$$M_x \quad \left(\text{when } x < a\right) \quad \ldots \ldots \quad = R_1 x - \frac{wx^2}{2}$$

$$M_x \quad \left(\text{when } x > a\right) \quad \ldots \ldots \quad = R_2(l-x)$$

$$\triangle_x \quad \left(\text{when } x < a\right) \quad \ldots \ldots \quad = \frac{wx}{24EIl}\left(a^2(2l-a)^2 - 2ax^2(2l-a) + lx^3\right)$$

$$\triangle_x \quad \left(\text{when } x > a\right) \quad \ldots \ldots \quad = \frac{wa^2(l-x)}{24EIl}(4xl - 2x^2 - a^2)$$

Simple Beam—Uniform Load Partially Distributed at Each End

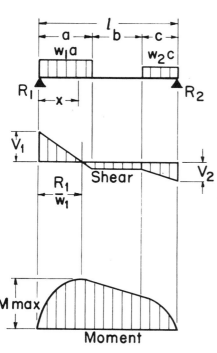

$$R_1 = V_1 \quad \ldots \ldots \ldots \quad = \frac{w_1a(2l-a) + w_2c^2}{2l}$$

$$R_2 = V_2 \quad \ldots \ldots \ldots \ldots \quad = \frac{w_2c(2l-c) + w_1a^2}{2l}$$

$$V_x \quad \left(\text{when } x < a\right) \quad \ldots \ldots \quad = R_1 - w_1x$$

$$V_x \quad \left(\text{when } x > a \text{ and } < (a+b)\right) \quad = R_1 - R_2$$

$$V_x \quad \left(\text{when } x > (a+b)\right) \quad \ldots \quad = R_2 - w_2(l-x)$$

$$M \text{ max.} \quad \left(\text{at } x = \frac{R_1}{w_1} \text{ when } R_1 < w_1a\right) \quad = \frac{R_1^2}{2w_1}$$

$$M \text{ max.} \quad \left(\text{at } x = l - \frac{R_2}{w_2} \text{ when } R_2 < w_2c\right) \quad = \frac{R_2^2}{2w_2}$$

$$M_x \quad \left(\text{when } x < a\right) \quad \ldots \ldots \quad = R_1 x - \frac{w_1x^2}{2}$$

$$M_x \quad \left(\text{when } x > a \text{ and } < (a+b)\right) \quad = R_1 x - \frac{w_1a}{2}(2x-a)$$

$$M_x \quad \left(\text{when } x > (a+b)\right) \quad \ldots \quad = R_2(l-x) - \frac{w_2(l-x)^2}{2}$$

DESIGN — BENDING MEMBERS

Simple Beam—Load Increasing Uniformly to One End

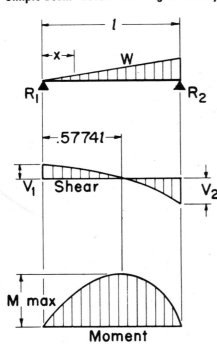

$$R_1 = V_1 \ldots \ldots \ldots = \frac{W}{3}$$

$$R_2 = V_2 \text{ max.} \ldots \ldots = \frac{2W}{3}$$

$$V_x \ldots \ldots \ldots = \frac{W}{3} - \frac{Wx^2}{l^2}$$

$$M \text{ max.} \left(\text{at } x = \frac{l}{\sqrt{3}} = .5774l \right) \ldots = \frac{2Wl}{9\sqrt{3}} = .1283\, Wl$$

$$M_x \ldots \ldots \ldots = \frac{Wx}{3l^2} (l^2 - x^2)$$

$$\Delta \text{max.} \left(\text{at } x = l\sqrt{1 - \sqrt{\frac{8}{15}}} = .5193l \right) = .01304 \frac{Wl^3}{EI}$$

$$\Delta_x \ldots \ldots \ldots = \frac{Wx}{180 EI\, l^2} (3x^4 - 10l^2 x^2 + 7l^4)$$

Simple Beam—Load Increasing Uniformly to Center

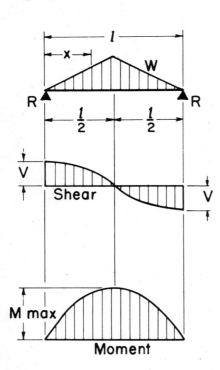

$$R = V \ldots \ldots \ldots = \frac{W}{2}$$

$$V_x \quad \left(\text{when } x < \frac{l}{2} \right) \ldots \ldots = \frac{W}{2l^2} (l^2 - 4x^2)$$

$$M \text{ max.} \left(\text{at center} \right) \ldots \ldots = \frac{Wl}{6}$$

$$M_x \quad \left(\text{when } x < \frac{l}{2} \right) \ldots \ldots = Wx \left(\frac{1}{2} - \frac{2x^2}{3l^2} \right)$$

$$\Delta \text{max.} \left(\text{at center} \right) \ldots \ldots = \frac{Wl^3}{60 EI}$$

$$\Delta_x \ldots \ldots \ldots = \frac{Wx}{480 EI\, l^2} (5l^2 - 4x^2)^2$$

DESIGN — BENDING MEMBERS

Simple Beam—Concentrated Load at Center

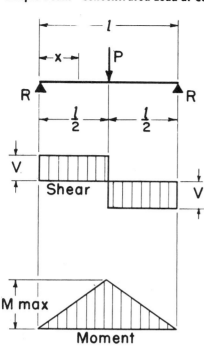

$$R = V \quad \cdots \cdots \cdots \cdots \cdots = \frac{P}{2}$$

$$M \text{ max.} \left(\text{at point of load} \right) \cdots \cdots = \frac{Pl}{4}$$

$$M_x \quad \left(\text{when } x < \frac{l}{2} \right) \cdots \cdots = \frac{Px}{2}$$

$$\triangle \text{max.} \left(\text{at point of load} \right) \cdots \cdots = \frac{Pl^3}{48EI}$$

$$\triangle_x \quad \left(\text{when } x < \frac{l}{2} \right) \cdots \cdots = \frac{Px}{48EI} (3l^2 - 4x^2)$$

Simple Beam—Concentrated Load at Any Point

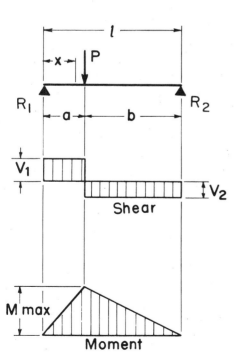

$$R_1 = V_1 \left(\text{max. when } a < b \right) \cdots \cdots = \frac{Pb}{l}$$

$$R_2 = V_2 \left(\text{max. when } a > b \right) \cdots \cdots = \frac{Pa}{l}$$

$$M \text{ max.} \left(\text{at point of load} \right) \cdots \cdots = \frac{Pab}{l}$$

$$M_x \left(\text{when } x < a \right) \cdots \cdots = \frac{Pbx}{l}$$

$$\triangle \text{max.} \left(\text{at } x = \sqrt{\frac{a(a+2b)}{3}} \text{ when } a > b \right) = \frac{Pab(a+2b)\sqrt{3a(a+2b)}}{27\,EI\,l}$$

$$\triangle_a \left(\text{at point of load} \right) \cdots \cdots = \frac{Pa^2b^2}{3EI\,l}$$

$$\triangle_x \left(\text{when } x < a \right) \cdots \cdots = \frac{Pbx}{6EI\,l}(l^2 - b^2 - x^2)$$

$$\triangle_x \left(\text{when } x > a \right) \cdots \cdots = \frac{Pa(l-x)}{6EI\,l}(2lx - x^2 - a^2)$$

DESIGN — BENDING MEMBERS

Simple Beam—Two Equal Concentrated Loads Symmetrically Placed

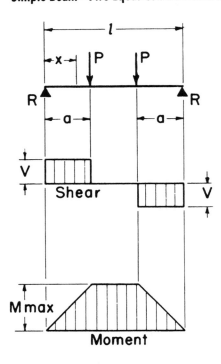

$R = V$ . . . . $= P$

$M \text{ max.} \left(\text{between loads} \right)$ . . . . . $= Pa$

$M_x \quad \left(\text{when } x < a \right)$ . . . . . . $= Px$

$\triangle \text{max.} \left(\text{at center} \right)$ . . . . . . $= \dfrac{Pa}{24EI} (3l^2 - 4a^2)$

$\triangle_x \quad \left(\text{when } x < a \right)$ . . . . $= \dfrac{Px}{6EI} (3la - 3a^2 - x^2)$

$\triangle_x \quad \left(\text{when } x > a \text{ and } < (l - a) \right)$. $= \dfrac{Pa}{6EI} (3lx - 3x^2 - a^2)$

Simple Beam—Two Equal Concentrated Loads Unsymmetrically Placed

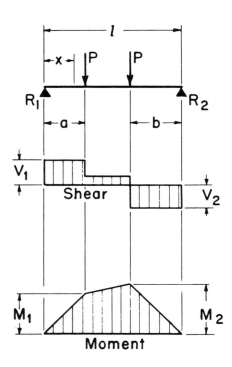

$R_1 = V_1 \left(\text{max. when } a < b \right)$ . . . . . $= \dfrac{P}{l} (l - a + b)$

$R_2 = V_2 \left(\text{max. when } a > b \right)$ . . . . . $= \dfrac{P}{l} (l - b + a)$

$V_x \quad \left(\text{when } x > a \text{ and } < (l - b) \right)$. $= \dfrac{P}{l} (b - a)$

$M_1 \quad \left(\text{max. when } a > b \right)$ . . . . . $= R_1 a$

$M_2 \quad \left(\text{max. when } a < b \right)$ . . . . . $= R_2 b$

$M_x \quad \left(\text{when } x < a \right)$ . . . . . . $= R_1 x$

$M_x \quad \left(\text{when } x > a \text{ and } < (l - b) \right)$. $= R_1 x - P (x - a)$

DESIGN — BENDING MEMBERS

Simple Beam—Two Unequal Concentrated Loads Unsymmetrically Placed

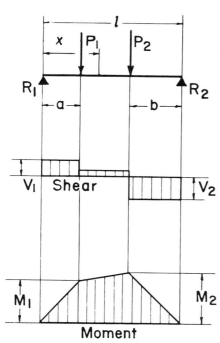

$$R_1 = V_1 \quad \ldots \ldots \ldots \ldots \ldots = \frac{P_1(l-a) + P_2 b}{l}$$

$$R_2 = V_2 \quad \ldots \ldots \ldots \ldots \ldots = \frac{P_1 a + P_2(l-b)}{l}$$

$$V_x \quad \left(\text{when } x > a \text{ and} < (l-b)\right) . \quad = R_1 - P_1$$

$$M_1 \quad \left(\text{max. when } R_1 < P_1\right) \ldots \ldots = R_1 a$$

$$M_2 \quad \left(\text{max. when } R_2 < P_2\right) \ldots \ldots = R_2 b$$

$$M_x \quad \left(\text{when } x < a\right) \ldots \ldots \ldots = R_1 x$$

$$M_x \quad \left(\text{when } x > a \text{ and} < (l-b)\right) . \quad = R_1 x - P_1(x-a)$$

Cantilever Beam—Uniformly Distributed Load

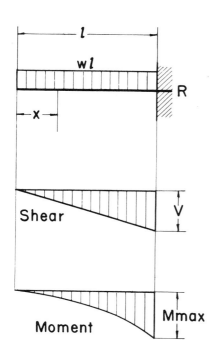

$$R = V \quad \ldots \ldots \ldots \ldots \ldots \ldots = wl$$

$$V_x \quad \ldots \ldots \ldots \ldots \ldots \ldots = wx$$

$$M \text{ max.} \left(\text{at fixed end}\right) \ldots \ldots \ldots = \frac{wl^2}{2}$$

$$M_x \quad \ldots \ldots \ldots \ldots \ldots \ldots = \frac{wx^2}{2}$$

$$\triangle \text{max.} \left(\text{at free end}\right) \ldots \ldots \ldots = \frac{wl^4}{8EI}$$

$$\triangle_x \quad \ldots \ldots \ldots \ldots \ldots = \frac{w}{24EI}(x^4 - 4l^3 x + 3l^4)$$

DESIGN — BENDING MEMBERS

Cantilever Beam—Concentrated Load at Free End

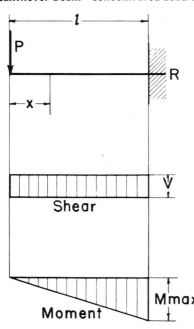

$R = V$ . . . . $= P$

$M \text{ max.} \left(\text{at fixed end} \right)$ . . . . . $= Pl$

Mx . . . . $= Px$

$\triangle \text{max.} \left(\text{at free end} \right)$ . . . . . . $= \dfrac{Pl^3}{3EI}$

$\triangle x$ . . . . $= \dfrac{P}{6EI} (2l^3 - 3l^2x + x^3)$

Cantilever Beam—Concentrated Load at Any Point

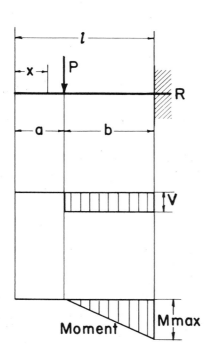

$R = V \left(\text{when } x < a \right)$ . . . . . . $= P$

$M \text{ max.} \left(\text{at fixed end} \right)$ . . . . . . $= Pb$

$Mx \left(\text{when } x > a \right)$ . . . . . $= P (x - a)$

$\triangle \text{max.} \left(\text{at free end} \right)$ . . . . . $= \dfrac{Pb^2}{6EI} (3l - b)$

$\triangle a \left(\text{at point of load} \right)$ . . . . . $= \dfrac{Pb^3}{3EI}$

$\triangle x \left(\text{when } x < a \right)$ . . . . . . $= \dfrac{Pb^2}{6EI} (3l - 3x - b)$

$\triangle x \left(\text{when } x > a \right)$ . . . . . . $= \dfrac{P (l - x)^2}{6EI} (3b - l + x)$

DESIGN — BENDING MEMBERS

Beam Fixed at One End, Supported at Other—Uniformly Distributed Load

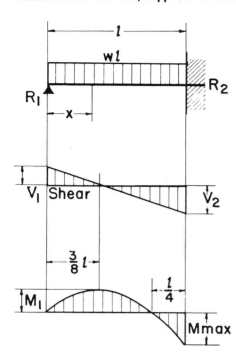

$$R_1 = V_1 \quad \ldots \ldots \ldots \quad = \frac{3wl}{8}$$

$$R_2 = V_2 \text{ max.} \quad \ldots \ldots \quad = \frac{5wl}{8}$$

$$V_x \quad \ldots \ldots \ldots \ldots \quad = R_1 - wx$$

$$M \text{ max.} \quad \ldots \ldots \ldots \quad = \frac{wl^2}{8}$$

$$M_1 \quad \left(\text{at } x = \frac{3}{8}l\right) \ldots \ldots \quad = \frac{9}{128}wl^2$$

$$M_x \quad \ldots \ldots \ldots \ldots \quad = R_1 x - \frac{wx^2}{2}$$

$$\triangle \text{max.} \left(\text{at } x = \frac{l}{16}(1 + \sqrt{33}) = .4215l\right) = \frac{wl^4}{185EI}$$

$$\triangle_x \quad \ldots \ldots \ldots \ldots \quad = \frac{wx}{48EI}(l^3 - 3lx^2 + 2x^3)$$

Beam Fixed at One End, Supported at Other—Concentrated Load at Center

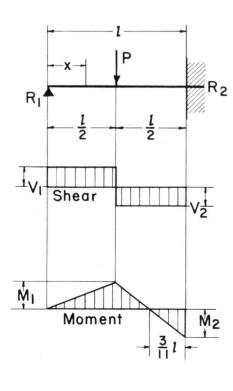

$$R_1 = V_1 \ldots \ldots \ldots \ldots \quad = \frac{5P}{16}$$

$$R_2 = V_2 \text{ max.} \ldots \ldots \ldots \quad = \frac{11P}{16}$$

$$M \text{ max.} \left(\text{at fixed end}\right) \ldots \ldots \quad = \frac{3Pl}{16}$$

$$M_1 \left(\text{at point of load}\right) \ldots \ldots \quad = \frac{5Pl}{32}$$

$$M_x \left(\text{when } x < \frac{l}{2}\right) \ldots \ldots \quad = \frac{5Px}{16}$$

$$M_x \left(\text{when } x > \frac{l}{2}\right) \ldots \ldots \quad = P\left(\frac{l}{2} - \frac{11x}{.16}\right)$$

$$\triangle \text{max.} \left(\text{at } x = l\sqrt{\frac{1}{5}} = .4472l\right) \ldots = \frac{Pl^3}{48EI\sqrt{5}} = .009317\frac{Pl^3}{EI}$$

$$\triangle_x \left(\text{at point of load}\right) \ldots \ldots \quad = \frac{7Pl^3}{768EI}$$

$$\triangle_x \left(\text{when } x < \frac{l}{2}\right) \ldots \ldots \quad = \frac{Px}{96EI}(3l^2 - 5x^2)$$

$$\triangle_x \left(\text{when } x > \frac{l}{2}\right) \ldots \ldots \quad = \frac{P}{96EI}(x - l)^2(11x - 2l)$$

DESIGN — BENDING MEMBERS

Beam Fixed at One End, Supported at Other—Concentrated Load at Any Point

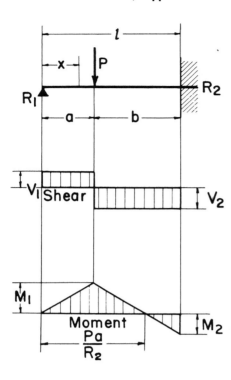

$R_1 = V_1 \quad \ldots \quad = \dfrac{Pb^2}{2l^3}(a + 2l)$

$R_2 = V_2 \quad \ldots \quad = \dfrac{Pa}{2l^3}(3l^2 - a^2)$

$M_1 \left(\text{at point of load}\right) \ldots = R_1 a$

$M_2 \left(\text{at fixed end}\right) \ldots = \dfrac{Pab}{2l^2}(a + l)$

$M_x \left(\text{when } x < a\right) \ldots = R_1 x$

$M_x \left(\text{when } x > a\right) \ldots = R_1 x - P(x - a)$

$\triangle\text{max.} \left(\text{when } a < .414l \text{ at } x = l\dfrac{l^2 + a^2}{3l^2 - a^2}\right) = \dfrac{Pa}{3EI}\dfrac{(l^2 - a^2)^3}{(3l^2 - a^2)^2}$

$\triangle\text{max.} \left(\text{when } a > .414l \text{ at } x = l\sqrt{\dfrac{a}{2l + a}}\right) = \dfrac{Pab^2}{6EI}\sqrt{\dfrac{a}{2l + a}}$

$\triangle a \left(\text{at point of load}\right) \ldots = \dfrac{Pa^2 b^3}{12EIl^3}(3l + a)$

$\triangle x \left(\text{when } x < a\right) \ldots = \dfrac{Pb^2 x}{12EIl^3}(3al^2 - 2lx^2 - ax^2)$

$\triangle x \left(\text{when } x > a\right) \ldots = \dfrac{Pa}{12EIl^3}(l - x)^2(3l^2 x - a^2 x - 2a^2 l)$

Beam Overhanging One Support—Uniformly Distributed Load

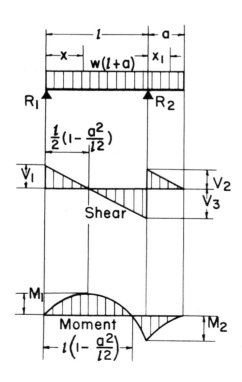

$R_1 = V_1 \quad \ldots \quad = \dfrac{w}{2l}(l^2 - a^2)$

$R_2 = V_2 + V_3 \quad \ldots \quad = \dfrac{w}{2l}(l + a)^2$

$V_2 \quad \ldots \quad = wa$

$V_3 \quad \ldots \quad = \dfrac{w}{2l}(l^2 + a^2)$

$V_x \left(\text{between supports}\right) \ldots = R_1 - wx$

$V_{x_1} \left(\text{for overhang}\right) \ldots = w(a - x_1)$

$M_1 \left(\text{at } x = \dfrac{l}{2}\left[1 - \dfrac{a^2}{l^2}\right]\right) \ldots = \dfrac{w}{8l^2}(l + a)^2(l - a)^2$

$M_2 \left(\text{at } R_2\right) \ldots = \dfrac{wa^2}{2}$

$M_x \left(\text{between supports}\right) \ldots = \dfrac{wx}{2l}(l^2 - a^2 - xl)$

$M_{x_1} \left(\text{for overhang}\right) \ldots = \dfrac{w}{2}(a - x_1)^2$

$\triangle x \left(\text{between supports}\right) \ldots = \dfrac{wx}{24EIl}(l^4 - 2l^2 x^2 + lx^3 - 2a^2 l^2 + 2a^2 x^2)$

$\triangle x_1 \left(\text{for overhang}\right) \ldots = \dfrac{wx_1}{24EI}(4a^2 l - l^3 + 6a^2 x_1 - 4ax_1^2 + x_1^3)$

DESIGN — BENDING MEMBERS

Beam Overhanging One Support—Uniformly Distributed Load on Overhang

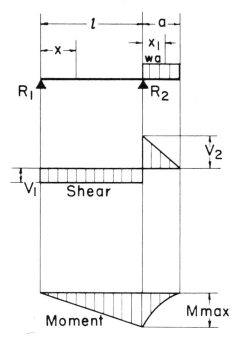

$$R_1 = V_1 \quad \ldots \ldots \ldots \ldots \quad = \frac{wa^2}{2l}$$

$$R_2 = V_1 + V_2 \quad \ldots \ldots \ldots \quad = \frac{wa}{2l}(2l + a)$$

$$V_2 \quad \ldots \ldots \ldots \ldots \ldots \quad = wa$$

$$V_{x_1} \quad \left(\text{for overhang}\right) \ldots \ldots \quad = w(a - x_1)$$

$$M \text{ max.} \left(\text{at } R_2\right) \ldots \ldots \ldots \quad = \frac{wa^2}{2}$$

$$M_x \quad \left(\text{between supports}\right) \ldots \ldots \quad = \frac{wa^2 x}{2l}$$

$$M_{x_1} \quad \left(\text{for overhang}\right) \ldots \ldots \quad = \frac{w}{2}(a - x_1)^2$$

$$\triangle \text{max.} \left(\text{between supports at } x = \frac{l}{\sqrt{3}}\right) = \frac{wa^2 l^2}{18\sqrt{3}EI} = .03208\frac{wa^2 l^2}{EI}$$

$$\triangle \text{max.} \left(\text{for overhang at } x_1 = a\right) \ldots = \frac{wa^3}{24EI}(4l + 3a)$$

$$\triangle_x \quad \left(\text{between supports}\right) \ldots \ldots \quad = \frac{wa^2 x}{12EI l}(l^2 - x^2)$$

$$\triangle_{x_1} \quad \left(\text{for overhang}\right) \ldots \ldots \quad = \frac{wx_1}{24EI}(4a^2 l + 6a^2 x_1 - 4ax_1^2 + x_1^3)$$

Beam Overhanging One Support—Concentrated Load at End of Overhang

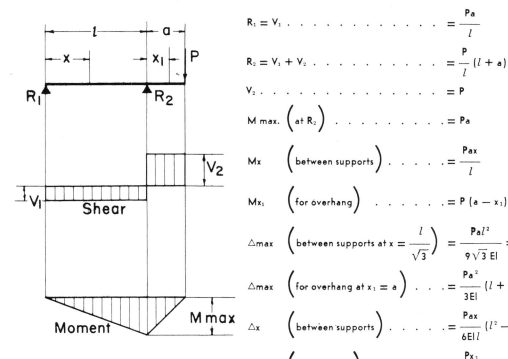

$$R_1 = V_1 \quad \ldots \ldots \ldots \ldots \quad = \frac{Pa}{l}$$

$$R_2 = V_1 + V_2 \quad \ldots \ldots \ldots \quad = \frac{P}{l}(l + a)$$

$$V_2 \quad \ldots \ldots \ldots \ldots \ldots \quad = P$$

$$M \text{ max.} \left(\text{at } R_2\right) \ldots \ldots \ldots \quad = Pa$$

$$M_x \quad \left(\text{between supports}\right) \ldots \ldots \quad = \frac{Pax}{l}$$

$$M_{x_1} \quad \left(\text{for overhang}\right) \ldots \ldots \quad = P(a - x_1)$$

$$\triangle \text{max} \left(\text{between supports at } x = \frac{l}{\sqrt{3}}\right) = \frac{Pal^2}{9\sqrt{3}EI} = .06415\frac{Pal^2}{EI}$$

$$\triangle \text{max} \left(\text{for overhang at } x_1 = a\right) \ldots = \frac{Pa^2}{3EI}(l + a)$$

$$\triangle_x \quad \left(\text{between supports}\right) \ldots \ldots \quad = \frac{Pax}{6EI l}(l^2 - x^2)$$

$$\triangle_{x_1} \quad \left(\text{for overhang}\right) \ldots \ldots \quad = \frac{Px_1}{6EI}(2al + 3ax_1 - x_1^2)$$

DESIGN — BENDING MEMBERS

Beam Overhanging One Support—Concentrated Load at Any Point Between Supports

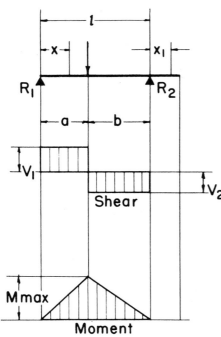

$$R_1 = V_1 \left(\text{max. when } a < b \right) \ldots \ldots = \frac{Pb}{l}$$

$$R_2 = V_2 \left(\text{max. when } a > b \right) \ldots \ldots = \frac{Pa}{l}$$

$$M \text{ max.} \left(\text{at point of load} \right) \ldots \ldots \ldots = \frac{Pab}{l}$$

$$M_x \quad \left(\text{when } x < a \right) \ldots \ldots \ldots = \frac{Pbx}{l}$$

$$\triangle \text{max.} \left(\text{at } x = \sqrt{\frac{a(a + 2b)}{3}} \text{ when } a > b \right) = \frac{Pab (a + 2b) \sqrt{3a (a + 2b)}}{27EI \, l}$$

$$\triangle_a \quad \left(\text{at point of load} \right) \ldots \ldots = \frac{Pa^2 b^2}{3EI \, l}$$

$$\triangle_x \quad \left(\text{when } x < a \right) \ldots \ldots \ldots = \frac{Pbx}{6EI \, l} (l^2 - b^2 - x^2)$$

$$\triangle_x \quad \left(\text{when } x > a \right) \ldots \ldots \ldots = \frac{Pa (l - x)}{6EI \, l} (2lx - x^2 - a^2)$$

$$\triangle_{x_1} \ldots \ldots \ldots \ldots \ldots = \frac{Pabx_1}{6EI \, l} (l + a)$$

Beam Overhanging Both Supports—Unequal Overhangs—Uniformly Distributed Load

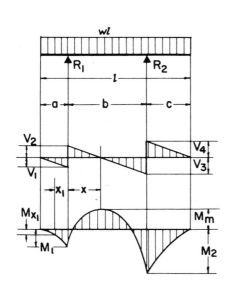

$$R_1 \ldots \ldots \ldots \ldots = \frac{wl (l - 2c)}{2b}$$

$$R_2 \ldots \ldots \ldots \ldots = \frac{wl (l - 2a)}{2b}$$

$$V_1 \ldots \ldots \ldots \ldots \ldots = wa$$

$$V_2 \ldots \ldots \ldots \ldots \ldots = R_1 - V_1$$

$$V_3 \ldots \ldots \ldots \ldots \ldots = R_2 - V_4$$

$$V_4 \ldots \ldots \ldots \ldots \ldots = wc$$

$$V_{x_1} \ldots \ldots \ldots \ldots \ldots = V_1 - wx_1$$

$$V_x \quad \left(\text{when } x < l \right) \ldots \ldots = R_1 - w (a + x_1)$$

$$V_m \quad \left(\text{when } a < c \right) \ldots \ldots = R_2 - wc$$

$$M_1 \ldots \ldots \ldots \ldots = -\frac{wa^2}{2}$$

$$M_2 \ldots \ldots \ldots \ldots = -\frac{wc^2}{2}$$

$$M_m \ldots \ldots \ldots \ldots = R_1 \left(\frac{R_1}{2w} - a \right)$$

$$M_x \quad \left(\text{max. when } x = \frac{R_1}{w} - a \right) \ldots = R_1 x - \frac{w (a + x)^2}{2}$$

DESIGN — BENDING MEMBERS

Beam Fixed at Both Ends—Uniformly Distributed Load

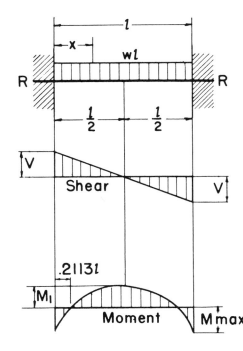

$$R = V \quad . . . . = \frac{wl}{2}$$

$$V_x \quad . . . . = w\left(\frac{l}{2} - x\right)$$

$$M \text{ max.} \left(\text{at ends}\right) . . . . = \frac{wl^2}{12}$$

$$M_1 \quad \left(\text{at center}\right) . . . . . . = \frac{wl^2}{24}$$

$$M_x \quad . . . . = \frac{w}{12}(6lx - l^2 - 6x^2)$$

$$\triangle \text{max.} \left(\text{at center}\right) . . . . . . = \frac{wl^4}{384EI}$$

$$\triangle_x \quad . . . . = \frac{wx^2}{24EI}(l - x)^2$$

Beam Fixed at Both Ends—Concentrated Load at Center

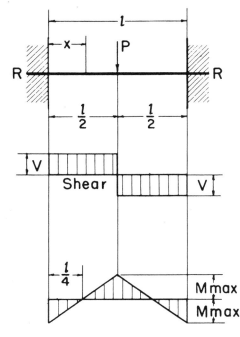

$$R = V \quad . . . . = \frac{P}{2}$$

$$M \text{ max.} \left(\text{at center and ends}\right) . . . . = \frac{Pl}{8}$$

$$M_x \quad \left(\text{when } x < \frac{l}{2}\right) . . . . . . = \frac{P}{8}(4x - l)$$

$$\triangle \text{max.} \left(\text{at center}\right) . . . . . . = \frac{Pl^3}{192EI}$$

$$\triangle_x \quad . . . . = \frac{Px^2}{48EI}(3l - 4x)$$

DESIGN — BENDING MEMBERS

Beam Fixed at Both Ends—Concentrated Load at Any Point

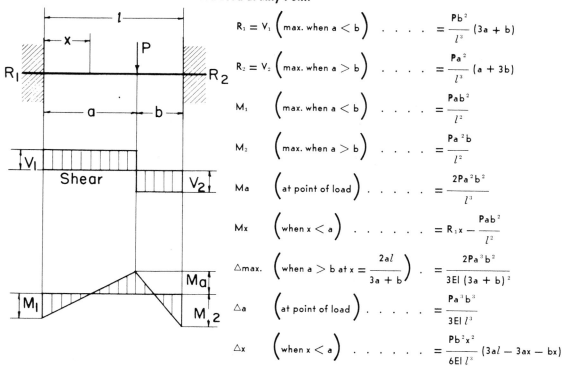

$$R_1 = V_1 \left(\text{max. when } a < b \right) \; \ldots \; = \frac{Pb^2}{l^3}(3a + b)$$

$$R_2 = V_2 \left(\text{max. when } a > b \right) \; \ldots \; = \frac{Pa^2}{l^3}(a + 3b)$$

$$M_1 \left(\text{max. when } a < b \right) \; \ldots \; = \frac{Pab^2}{l^2}$$

$$M_2 \left(\text{max. when } a > b \right) \; \ldots \; = \frac{Pa^2b}{l^2}$$

$$Ma \left(\text{at point of load} \right) \; \ldots \; = \frac{2Pa^2b^2}{l^3}$$

$$Mx \left(\text{when } x < a \right) \; \ldots \; = R_1 x - \frac{Pab^2}{l^2}$$

$$\triangle \text{max.} \left(\text{when } a > b \text{ at } x = \frac{2al}{3a + b} \right) . \; = \frac{2Pa^3b^2}{3EI(3a + b)^2}$$

$$\triangle a \left(\text{at point of load} \right) \; \ldots \; = \frac{Pa^3b^3}{3EI\,l^3}$$

$$\triangle x \left(\text{when } x < a \right) \; \ldots \; = \frac{Pb^2x^2}{6EI\,l^3}(3al - 3ax - bx)$$

Continuous Beam—Two Equal Spans—Uniform Load on One Span

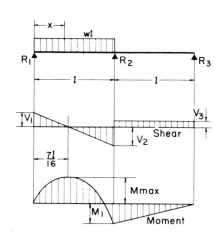

$$R_1 = V_1 \; \ldots \; = \frac{7}{16}wl$$

$$R_2 = V_2 + V_3 \; \ldots \; = \frac{5}{8}wl$$

$$R_3 = V_3 \; \ldots \; = \frac{1}{16}wl$$

$$V_2 \; \ldots \; = \frac{9}{16}wl$$

$$M \text{ max.} \left(\text{at } x = \frac{7}{16}l \right) \; \ldots \; = \frac{49}{512}wl^2$$

$$M_1 \left(\text{at support } R_2 \right) \; \ldots \; = \frac{1}{16}wl^2$$

$$Mx \left(\text{when } x < l \right) \; \ldots \; = \frac{wx}{16}(7l - 8x)$$

DESIGN — BENDING MEMBERS

Continuous Beam—Two Equal Spans—Concentrated Load at Center of One Span

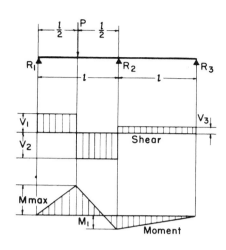

$$R_1 = V_1 \quad . \quad . \quad . \quad . \quad . \quad . \quad . \quad . \quad . \quad . \quad = \frac{13}{32} P$$

$$R_2 = V_2 + V_3 \quad . \quad . \quad . \quad . \quad . \quad . \quad . \quad . \quad = \frac{11}{16} P$$

$$R_3 = V_3 \quad . \quad . \quad . \quad . \quad . \quad . \quad . \quad . \quad . \quad . \quad = -\frac{3}{32} P$$

$$V_2 \quad . \quad . \quad . \quad . \quad . \quad . \quad . \quad . \quad . \quad . \quad . \quad . \quad = \frac{19}{32} P$$

$$M \text{ max.} \left(\text{at point of load} \right) \quad . \quad . \quad . \quad . \quad = \frac{13}{64} Pl$$

$$M_1 \quad \left(\text{at support } R_2 \right) \quad . \quad . \quad . \quad . \quad . \quad = \frac{3}{32} Pl$$

Continuous Beam—Two Equal Spans—Concentrated Load at Any Point

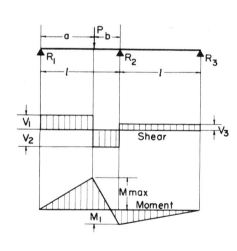

$$R_1 = V_1 \quad . \quad . \quad . \quad . \quad . \quad . \quad . \quad . \quad . \quad = \frac{Pb}{4l^3} \left(4l^2 - a \, (l + a) \right)$$

$$R_2 = V_2 + V_3 \quad . \quad . \quad . \quad . \quad . \quad . \quad . \quad = \frac{Pa}{2l^3} \left(2l^2 + b \, (l + a) \right)$$

$$R_3 = V_3 \quad . \quad . \quad . \quad . \quad . \quad . \quad . \quad . \quad . \quad = \frac{Pab}{4l^3} \, (l + a)$$

$$V_2 \quad . \quad . \quad . \quad . \quad . \quad . \quad . \quad . \quad . \quad . \quad . \quad = \frac{Pa}{4l^3} \left(4l^2 + b \, (l + a) \right)$$

$$M \text{ max.} \left(\text{at point of load} \right) \quad . \quad . \quad . \quad . \quad = \frac{Pab}{4l^3} \left(4l^2 - a \, (l + a) \right)$$

$$M_1 \quad \left(\text{at support } R_2 \right) \quad . \quad . \quad . \quad . \quad . \quad = \frac{Pab}{4l^2} \, (l + a)$$

DESIGN — BENDING MEMBERS

Continues Beam — Two Equal Spans — Uniformly Distributed Load

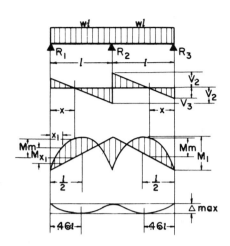

$$R_1 = V_1 = R_3 = V_3 \quad \ldots \ldots \ldots = \frac{3wl}{8}$$

$$R_2 \quad \ldots \ldots \ldots \ldots \ldots \ldots = \frac{10wl}{8}$$

$$V_2 = V_{max} \quad \ldots \ldots \ldots \ldots \ldots = \frac{5wl}{8}$$

$$M_1 \quad \ldots \ldots \ldots \ldots \ldots \ldots = -\frac{wl^2}{8}$$

$$M_m \quad \left(at \frac{3l}{8}\right) \ldots \ldots \ldots = \frac{9wl^2}{128}$$

$$\triangle max. \left(at\ 0.46l,\ approx,\ from\ R_1\ and\ R_3\right) = \frac{wl^4}{185EI}$$

Continuous Bear—Two Equal Spans—Two Equal Concentrated Loads Symmetrically Placed

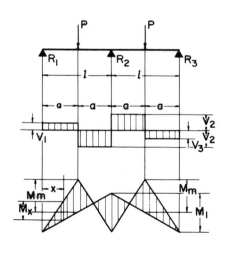

$$R_1 = V_1 = R_3 = V_3 \quad \ldots \ldots \ldots = \frac{5P}{16}$$

$$R_2 = 2V_2 \quad \ldots \ldots \ldots \ldots = \frac{11P}{8}$$

$$V_2 = P - R_1 \quad \ldots \ldots \ldots \ldots = \frac{11P}{16}$$

$$V_{max.} \quad \ldots \ldots \ldots \ldots \ldots = V_2$$

$$M_1 \quad \ldots \ldots \ldots \ldots \ldots \ldots = -\frac{3Pl}{16}$$

$$M_m \quad \ldots \ldots \ldots \ldots \ldots \ldots = \frac{5Pl}{32}$$

$$M_x \quad \left(when\ x < a\right) \ldots \ldots \ldots = R_1x$$

DESIGN — BENDING MEMBERS

Continuous Beam—Two Unequal Spans—Uniformly Distributed Load

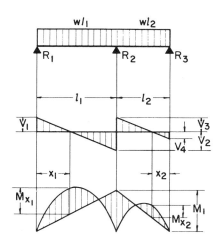

$$R_1 \ldots\ldots\ldots\ldots = \frac{M_1}{l_1} + \frac{wl_1}{2}$$

$$R_2 \ldots\ldots\ldots\ldots = wl_1 + wl_2 - R_1 - R_3$$

$$R_3 = V_4 \ldots\ldots\ldots = \frac{M_1}{l_2} + \frac{wl_2}{2}$$

$$V_1 \ldots\ldots\ldots\ldots = R_1$$

$$V_2 \ldots\ldots\ldots\ldots = wl_1 - R_1$$

$$V_3 \ldots\ldots\ldots\ldots = wl_2 - R_3$$

$$V_4 \ldots\ldots\ldots\ldots = R_3$$

$$M_1 \ldots\ldots\ldots\ldots = -\frac{wl_2^3 + wl_1^3}{8(l_1 + l_2)}$$

$$M_{x_1} \left(\text{when } x_1 = \frac{R_1}{w}\right) \ldots = R_1 x_1 - \frac{wx_1^2}{2}$$

$$M_{x_2} \left(\text{when } x_2 = \frac{R_3}{w}\right) \ldots = R_3 x_2 - \frac{wx_2^2}{2}$$

Continuous Beam—Two Unequal Spans—Concentrated Load on Each Span Symmetrically Placed

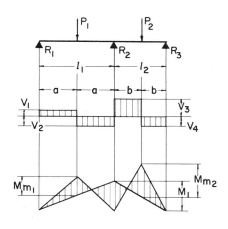

$$R_1 \ldots\ldots\ldots\ldots = \frac{M_1}{l_1} + \frac{P_1}{2}$$

$$R_2 \ldots\ldots\ldots\ldots = P_1 + P_2 - R_1 - R_3$$

$$R_3 \ldots\ldots\ldots\ldots = \frac{M_1}{l_2} + \frac{P_2}{2}$$

$$V_1 \ldots\ldots\ldots\ldots = R_1$$

$$V_2 \ldots\ldots\ldots\ldots = P_1 - R_1$$

$$V_3 \ldots\ldots\ldots\ldots = P_2 - R_3$$

$$V_4 \ldots\ldots\ldots\ldots = R_3$$

$$M_1 \ldots\ldots\ldots\ldots = -\frac{3}{16}\left(\frac{P_1 l_1^2 + P_2 l_2^2}{l_1 + l_2}\right)$$

$$M_{m_1} \ldots\ldots\ldots\ldots = R_1 a$$

$$M_{m_2} \ldots\ldots\ldots\ldots = R_3 b$$

DESIGN — BENDING MEMBERS

Continuous Beam—Three Equal Spans—Uniformly Distributed Load

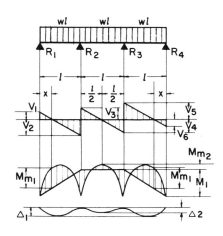

$$R_1 = R_1 = V_1 = V_6 \ldots \ldots \ldots = \frac{4wl}{10}$$

$$R_2 = R_3 \ldots \ldots \ldots \ldots = \frac{11wl}{10}$$

$$V_2 = V_5 \ldots \ldots \ldots \ldots = \frac{6wl}{10}$$

$$V_3 = V_4 \ldots \ldots \ldots \ldots = \frac{wl}{2}$$

$$M_1 \ldots \ldots \ldots \ldots = -\frac{wl^2}{10}$$

$$Mm_1 \quad \left(at\ x = \frac{4l}{10} \right) \ldots \ldots = \frac{2wl^2}{25}$$

$$Mm_2 \ldots \ldots \ldots \ldots = \frac{wl^2}{40}$$

$$\triangle_1 \ldots \ldots \ldots \ldots = \frac{4wl^4}{581EI}$$

$$\triangle_2 \ldots \ldots \ldots \ldots = \frac{wl^4}{1920EI}$$

Continuous Beam—Three Equal Spans—Concentrated Load on Each Span Unsymmetrically Placed

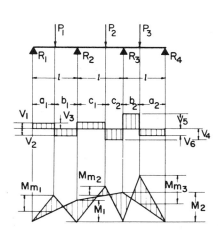

$$R_1 \ldots \ldots \ldots = \frac{M_1 + P_1b_1}{l}$$

$$R_2 \ldots \ldots \ldots = \frac{M_2 - 2R_1l + P_2c_2 + P_1\,(l + b_1)}{l}$$

$$R_3 \ldots \ldots \ldots = \frac{M_1 - 2R_4l + P_2c_1 + P_3\,(l + b_2)}{l}$$

$$R_4 \ldots \ldots \ldots = \frac{M_2 + P_3b_2}{l}$$

$$V_1 \ldots \ldots \ldots \ldots = R_1$$

$$V_2 \ldots \ldots \ldots \ldots = R_1 - P_1$$

$$V_3 \ldots \ldots \ldots \ldots = R_2 - V_2$$

$$V_4 \ldots \ldots \ldots \ldots = R_3 - V_5$$

$$V_5 \ldots \ldots \ldots \ldots = R_4 - P_3$$

$$V_6 \ldots \ldots \ldots \ldots = R_4$$

$$M_1 \ldots \ldots \ldots = \frac{-4P_1a_1b_1\,(l + a_1) - P_2c_1c_2\,(7l - 5c_1) + P_3b_2a_2\,(l + a_2)}{15l^2}$$

$$M_2 \ldots \ldots \ldots = \frac{P_1a_1b_1\,(l - a_1) - P_2c_1c_2\,(2l - 5c_1) - 4P_3b_2c_2\,(l + a_2)}{15l^2}$$

$$Mm_1 \ldots \ldots \ldots = R_1a_1$$

$$Mm_2 \ldots \ldots \ldots = M_1 + V_3c_1$$

$$Mm_3 \ldots \ldots \ldots = R_4a_2$$

DESIGN — BENDING MEMBERS

Three Hinged Arch—Vertical Concentrated Load at Any Point

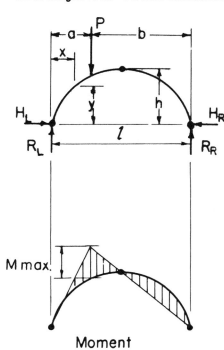

Moment

$$R_L \quad \ldots \quad = \frac{Pb}{l}$$

$$R_R \quad \ldots \quad = \frac{Pa}{l}$$

$$H_L = H_R \quad \ldots \quad = \frac{P}{h}\left(\frac{b}{2} - \frac{l}{2} + a\right)$$

$$M_{max.} \quad \ldots \quad = \frac{Pab}{l} - \frac{Py}{h}\left(\frac{b}{2} - \frac{l}{2} + a\right)$$

$$M_x \quad \ldots \quad = \frac{Pbx}{l} - \frac{Py}{h}\left(\frac{b}{2} - \frac{l}{2} + a\right)$$

$$M_{x_1} \quad \ldots \quad = \frac{Pax_1}{l} - \frac{Py_1}{h}\left(\frac{b}{2} - \frac{l}{2} + a\right)$$

Three Hinged Arch—Horizontal Concentrated Load at Any Point

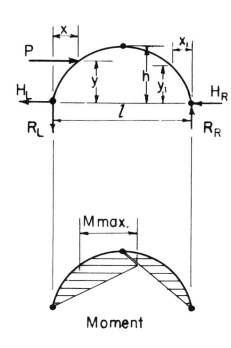

Moment

$$R_L \quad \ldots \quad = -\frac{Py}{l}$$

$$R_R \quad \ldots \quad = \frac{Py}{l}$$

$$H_L \quad \ldots \quad = \frac{P}{h}\left(h - \frac{y}{2}\right)$$

$$H_R \quad \ldots \quad = \frac{Py}{2h}$$

$$M_{max.} \quad \ldots \quad = Py\left(1 - \frac{y}{2h} - \frac{x}{l}\right)$$

$$M_x \quad \ldots \quad = Py\left(1 - \frac{y}{2h} - \frac{x}{l}\right)$$

$$M_{x_1} \quad \ldots \quad = Py\left(\frac{y_1}{2h} - \frac{x_1}{l}\right)$$

DESIGN — BENDING MEMBERS

Three Hinged Arch—Vertical Uniformly Distributed Load

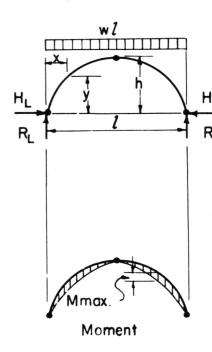

$$R_L = R_R \quad \ldots \ldots \ldots \ldots \ldots = \frac{wl}{2}$$

$$H_L = H_R \quad \ldots \ldots \ldots \ldots \ldots = \frac{wl^2}{8h}$$

$$M_x \left(\text{max. when } x = \frac{l}{2} - \frac{1}{2} \sqrt{\frac{l^2}{2} - h^2} \right) = \frac{w}{2} \left(lx - x^2 - \frac{l^2 y}{4h} \right)$$

Moment

Three Hinged Arch—Vertical Uniform Load Distributed on One Half the Span

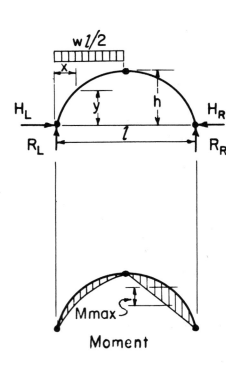

$$R_L \quad \ldots \ldots \ldots \ldots \ldots \ldots = \frac{3wl}{8}$$

$$R_R \quad \ldots \ldots \ldots \ldots \ldots \ldots = \frac{wl}{8}$$

$$H_L = H_R \quad \ldots \ldots \ldots \ldots \ldots = \frac{wl^2}{16h}$$

$$M_{max} \quad \ldots \ldots \ldots \ldots \ldots = \frac{wl^2}{16} \left(\frac{1}{2} - \frac{y}{h} \right)$$

$$M_x \quad \ldots \ldots \ldots \ldots \ldots \ldots = \frac{w}{2} \left(\frac{3}{4} lx - x^2 - \frac{l^2 y}{8h} \right)$$

Moment

DESIGN — BENDING MEMBERS

Three Hinged Arch—Horizontal Uniformly Distributed Load

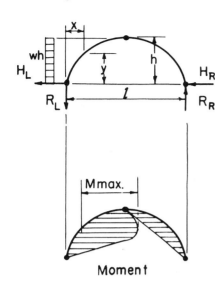

Moment

$$R_L \quad \ldots \ldots \ldots \ldots \ldots \quad = -\frac{wh^2}{2l}$$

$$R_R \quad \ldots \ldots \ldots \ldots \ldots \quad = \frac{wh^2}{2l}$$

$$H_L \quad \ldots \ldots \ldots \ldots \ldots \quad = \frac{3wh}{4}$$

$$H_R \quad \ldots \ldots \ldots \ldots \ldots \quad = \frac{wh}{4}$$

$$M_{max} \quad \ldots \ldots \ldots \ldots \quad = \frac{wh^2}{8}$$

$$M_x \quad \ldots \ldots \ldots \ldots \quad = \frac{w}{2}\left(y^2 + \frac{h^2 x}{l} - \frac{3hy}{2}\right)$$

Symbols

$\triangle_{max}$	=	Maximum deflection, inches.
$\triangle_a$	=	Deflection, inches, at point of load.
$\triangle_x$	=	Deflection inches, at distance x from support.
h	=	Rise of arch, feet or inches.
H_L, H_R	=	Horizontal thrust at arch abutments, pounds.
l	=	Span of beam or arch, feet or inches.
M_{max}	=	Maximum moment, foot pounds or inch pounds.
M_x	=	Moment, foot pounds or inch pounds, at distance x from support.
M_1, M_2 etc.	=	Moment, foot pounds or inch pounds, at designated point.
P	=	Concentrated load, pounds.
R_1, R_2 etc.	=	Vertical reactions of beams, pounds.
R_L, R_R	=	Vertical reactions of arches, pounds.
V_{max}	=	Maximum vertical end shear, pounds.
V_1, V_2 etc.	=	Vertical shear, pounds, at designated points.
w	=	Uniformly distributed load, pounds per lineal foot.
x	=	Horizontal distance from reaction to point on beam or arch rib, feet or inches.
y	=	Vertical distance from spring line to point on arch rib, feet or inches.

BEAM DESIGN TABLES FOR DIMENSION AND TIMBERS

The information presented here is pertinent to the use of Beam Design Tables for Dimension and Timbers.

The tables which follow are applicable to all sizes from 2 x 3 through 12 x 24; to any uniformly distributed load on simple spans; to any grade and species of lumber; and to any span from 3 feet through 32 feet. Tabulated values are also shown for some of the more commonly encountered concentrated loading conditions.

The span is usually known when a beam size is wanted; hence the tables are arranged in order of increasing span lengths rather than by sizes. Sizes are shown for each span in ascending order of their section modulus, but are not necessarily in order of resistance to shear and deflection.

All tabulated values are based on a simply supported single span beam with the load applied to the narrow face of the member. The span length is the distance from center to center of bearings.

Since it is the usual practice to refer to lumber by its nominal dimensions, this has been done in listing the member sizes, though design factors are computed for net finished lumber sizes in accordance with American Lumber Standards for Softwood Lumber. For dimension lumber 2" to 4" in thickness and 2" and wider, computations are based upon the net seasoned sizes. For lumber 6" and thicker and 6" and wider, computations are based upon the net unseasoned sizes.

For a given size, the total beam weight and the beam weight per foot of length are shown for each span. The required strength and stiffness properties (design factors) for a given loading and beam size are indicated as "F_b" (extreme fiber stress in bending), "F_v" (horizontal shear) and "E" (modulus of elasticity) for a deflection limitation of 1/360 of the span in inches.

The design factors for uniform loading are calculated on the basis of one (1) pound per linear foot along the beam. These design factors are related to a unit load; thus any amount of uniform load may be easily accommodated. In like manner, the design factors for concentrated loading conditions shown are calculated on the basis of a total concentrated load on the beam of one (1) pound, and may be used for any amount of total concentrated load on the beam.

The tabulated F_b, F_v and E factors are those required for uniform loading including the weight of the beam; hence to obtain the uniform load which the beam can support in addition to its own weight, its weight must be subtracted from the tabulated loading. Similarly, the factors for concentrated loading conditions do not include the weight of the beam and such weight must be separately considered.

The factors shown for F_b or F_v are directly proportional to the stresses induced in extreme fiber

DESIGN — BENDING MEMBERS

in bending or horizontal shear and care must be taken not to exceed those stresses permitted by the grade and species of lumber used. Duration of loading increases may be applied to F_b and F_v recommended design values prior to entering the table. For duration of load effect see page 21.

Standard timber design procedure has been followed in computing the induced horizontal shear values (F_v). This neglects all load within a distance from either support equal to the depth of the beam. The procedure is explained in detail on page 74.

It is unnecessary to check the strength of beams in vertical shear.

The factors shown for "E" are the modulus of elasticity values required to limit beam deflection to 1/360 of the span in inches due to the imposed load. Where less restrictive deflection limits are acceptable, the tabular values may be adjusted by multiplying by the following factors:

For limit of 1/300 — .833
For limit of 1/240 — .667
For limit of 1/180 — .500

In the design of Beams and Stringers deeper than 12" nominal, consideration must be given to the depth effect factor. A discussion of depth effect and appropriate factors for adjustment of F_b values may be found on page 73. In order to eliminate this additional step in selecting appropriate beam sizes, the effect of depth has been incorporated in the values for F_b tabulated in the tables. Thus, do not apply a depth effect factor to the F_b factors shown in the Beam Design Tables for Dimension and Timbers, as it has already been included.

Beam Design Procedure — General

In the design of beams it is necessary to proceed in an orderly manner — listing the known conditions first and then the properties or factors which are needed, such as size, strength and stiffness properties or loading. In most cases the known conditions consist of the beam span and spacing and the type and thickness of materials supported by the beam.

In addition to construction materials, the beam must also support a live load, such as snow, and these loads are normally specified by building codes.

In order to convert these loads to a form useful in design, it is necessary to calculate the loads in terms of uniform load along the beam, usually expressed in pounds per linear foot (plf).

Dead load is the weight of materials supported by the beam, including the weight of the beam itself. Surface materials such as roofing, flooring, decking and ceiling usually have weights expressed in terms of pounds per square foot and are converted to pounds per linear foot along the beam by multiplying pounds per square foot by the beam spacing in feet.

Live loads are normally given in units of pounds

DESIGN — BENDING MEMBERS

per square foot and are converted to pounds per linear foot along the beam by multiplying pounds per square foot by the beam spacing in feet.

In some cases beams may be required to support concentrated loads in addition to a uniform load. And in other cases, perhaps the beams may be supporting only concentrated loads. Concentrated loads may occur on a beam due to permanently attached machinery such as air-conditioning units, or due to the reaction of other beams or columns in the structure.

Deflection limitations are usually specified (such as 1/360 or 1/240 of the span in inches) and most often apply to the condition of live load only.

Strength calculations for extreme fiber stress in bending and horizontal shear must include the full live and dead loads which the beam is required to support.

An example of a typical situation follows:

Known:

Span: 20'-0"
Spacing: 10'-0"
Loading: Dead Load:

Tar and gravel roofing:	6.0 psf
1/2" plywood sheathing:	1.5 psf
2 x 10 joists at 24" o.c.:	2.0 psf
Beam (estimate):	2.5 psf
	12.0 psf

Total Dead Load:	12.0 psf
Live Load:	40.0 psf
Total Load:	52.0 psf

For Stiffness: 40 psf x 10' = 400 plf
For Strength: 52 psf x 10' = 520 plf

USE OF TABLES

The Beam Design Tables for Dimension and Timbers can be used in determining:

    I. A **member size** when the grade, species, span length and uniformly distributed loads are known;
    II. The **uniformly distributed load** when the size, span, grade and species are known;
    III. The **grade and species** when the size, span and uniformly distributed load are known;

The tables also work equally well for concentrated loading conditions where the conditions are identical to those specified in the table. For a given combination of uniformly distributed and concentrated loads and a given size of beam, the tables are convenient to determine the induced fiber stress in bending and horizontal shear and also the required modulus of elasticity (E) value. Thus, the tables can be used to determine the grade and species needed for a given or trial size and a combination of uniform and concentrated loads.

The following notations are used in the Beam Design Tables and the formulas which follow:
    F_b: Recommended design value for extreme fiber in bending, psi.
    F_v: Recommended design value for horizontal shear, psi.

E: Recommended modulus of elasticity value, psi.
w: Uniformly distributed load applied or carrying capacity of beam, in pounds per linear foot, plf.
P: Total concentrated load applied; or carrying capacity of beam, pounds.
F_b factor: Extreme fiber stress in bending induced by a uniform load of 1 (one) plf or by a total concentrated load of 1 (one) pound, psi.
F_v factor: Horizontal shear stress induced by a uniform load of 1 (one) plf or by a total concentrated load of 1 (one) pound, psi.
E factor: Modulus of elasticity value needed to limit deflection to a specified ratio (such as 1/360 or 1/240 of the span) for a uniform load of 1 (one) plf or a total concentrated load of 1 (one) pound, psi.

I. DETERMINATION OF SIZE
Uniformly Distributed Loading

To determine the size needed for a given grade and species, span and uniformly distributed loading condition, calculate the design factors required by dividing the recommended property values used for design by the uniform load to be applied to the beam. The factors thus found are the **maximum** which may be used.

$$F_b \text{ factor} = \frac{F_b}{w}$$

$$F_v \text{ factor} = \frac{F_v}{w}$$

$$E \text{ factor} = \frac{E}{w}$$

EXAMPLE (1)
Known:
Span: 20'-0"
Spacing: 10'-0"
Loading: Dead Load:

Tar and gravel roofing:	6.0 psf
1/2" plywood sheathing:	1.5 psf
2 x 10 joists at 24" o.c.:	2.0 psf
Beam (estimate)	2.5 psf
	12.0 psf

Total Dead Load:	12.0 psf
Live Load:	40.0 psf
Total Load:	52.0 psf

For Stiffness: 40 psf x 10' = 400 plf
For Strength: 52 psf x 10' = 520 plf

Assume: Grade and species: Douglas Fir and Larch, No. 1, Beam and Stringer
    F_b = 1350 x 1.15 = 1553 psi (adjusted for duration of load)
    F_v = 85 x 1.15 = 98 psi (adjusted for duration of load)
    E = 1,600,000 psi

Find: Size
Size needed for bending:

$$F_b \text{ factor} = \frac{F_b}{w} = \frac{1553}{520} = 2.99 \text{ psi}$$

In the table for a span of 20 feet find an F_b factor equal to or less than 2.99 in the uniform load column. The smallest size that qualifies is 10 x 12 with an F_b factor of 2.865. All sizes listed below the 10 x 12 will qualify, but none above will.

Choose the lightest weight beam that qualifies, for most economy. **A 6 x 16 is most economical.** Note that a 6 x 16 weighs 450 pounds and a 10 x 12 weighs 577 pounds.

Size needed for horizontal shear:

$$F_v \text{ factor} = \frac{F_v}{w} = \frac{98}{520} = .188 \text{ psi}$$

In the table for a 20 foot span, note that the following beam sizes qualify for horizontal shear but are not adequate for bending: 10 x 10, 8 x 12 and 6 x 14.

A 6 x 16, adequate for bending, has an F_v factor of .153, which is less than .188 and therefore is adequate. **A 6 x 16 is most economical for bending and shear.**

Size needed for deflection:

$$E \text{ factor} = \frac{E}{w} = \frac{1,600,000}{400} = 4000 \text{ psi}$$

In the table for 20 foot span, note that a 6 x 16 is the smallest size which qualifies. A 6 x 16 has an E factor of 3164 which is less than 4000 and therefore is adequate for a deflection limitation of 1/360 of the span. **A 6 x 16 is most economical for bending, shear and deflection.**

Concentrated Loading
To determine the size needed for a given grade and species, span and concentrated loading condition, calculate the design factors needed by dividing the recommended property values used for design by the total amount of concentrated loads to be applied to the beam.

$$F_b \text{ factor} = \frac{F_b}{P}$$

$$F_v \text{ factor} = \frac{F_v}{P}$$

$$E \text{ factor} = \frac{E}{P}$$

EXAMPLE (2)
Known:
Span: 20'-0"
Loading: Single concentrated load applied at center of span.

Concentrated load due to live load:	8000 lbs. (for stiffness)
Concentrated load due to dead load:	2000 lbs.
Total concentrated load = P =	10000 lbs. (for strength)

Assume: Grade and species: Douglas Fir and Larch, No. 1, Beam and Stringer

$F_b = 1350 \times 1.15 = 1553$ psi (adjusted for duration of load)

DESIGN — BENDING MEMBERS

$F_v = 85 \times 1.15 = 98$ psi (adjusted for duration of load)

$E = 1,600,000$ psi

Find: Size.
Size needed for bending:

$$F_b \text{ factor} = \frac{F_b}{P} = \frac{1553}{10000} = .1553 \text{ psi}$$

In the table for a span of 20 feet find an F_b factor equal to or less than .1553 in the column for single load at center of span. The smallest size that qualifies is 12 x 16 with an F_b factor of .1341. All sizes listed below 12 x 16 will qualify, but none above will.

Choose the lightest weight beam that qualifies, for most economy. **An 8 x 20 is most economical.** Note that an 8 x 20 weighs 772 pounds and a 12 x 16 weighs 941 pounds.

Size needed for horizontal shear:

$$F_v \text{ factor} = \frac{F_v}{P} = \frac{98}{10000} = .0098 \text{ psi}$$

Note that an 8 x 20 has an F_v factor of .0051 which qualifies. It can be easily determined by inspection that all sizes larger than 6 x 14 are adequate in horizontal shear because the F_v factors are less than .0098. **An 8 x 20 is most economical for bending and shear.**

Size needed for deflection:

$$E \text{ factor} = \frac{E}{P} = \frac{1,600,000}{8000} = 200 \text{ psi}$$

Note that a 6 x 18 has an E factor of 176 which qualifies for deflection but is not adequate for bending. An 8 x 20 has an E factor of 93 which is significantly less than the 200 needed. **An 8 x 20 is the most economical for bending, shear and deflection.**

II. DETERMINATION OF ALLOWABLE LOAD
Uniformly Distributed Loading
To determine the allowable uniform load which a beam can safely support for a given size, span, grade and species, divide the recommended property values used for design by the design factors for each property: F_b, F_v and E.

$$w = \frac{F_b}{F_b \text{ factor}}$$

$$w = \frac{F_v}{F_v \text{ factor}}$$

$$w = \frac{E}{E \text{ factor}}$$

The smallest value of "w" applies.

EXAMPLE (3)
Known:
Span: 20'-0"
Uniformly distributed load.

DESIGN — BENDING MEMBERS

Deflection limit: 1/240 of the span.
Size: 6 x 18
Grade and species: Douglas Fir-Larch, Select Structural, Beam and Stringer

$F_b = 1600 \times 1.25 = 2000$ psi (adjusted for duration of load)

$F_v = 85 \times 1.25 = 106$ psi (adjusted for duration of load)

$E = 1,600,000$ psi

Find: Allowable uniform load.

Allowable uniform load:
From the table, for a span of 20 feet and a size of 6 x 18, the F_b factor is 2.229.

$$w = \frac{F_b}{F_b \text{ factor}} = \frac{2000}{2.229} = 897 \text{ plf for bending.}$$

The F_v factor is .133.

$$w = \frac{F_v}{F_v \text{ factor}} = \frac{106}{.133}$$
$$= 797 \text{ plf for horizontal shear.}$$

The E factor is 2198.

$$w = \frac{E}{E \text{ factor}} = \frac{1,600,000}{2198 \times .667}$$
$$= 1091 \text{ plf for deflection.}$$

(Note: Factor of .667 is adjustment from 1/360 to 1/240 deflection limit) see page 101.

Maximum safe load is 797 plf, controlled by horizontal shear.

Concentrated Loading

To determine the allowable concentrated load which a beam can safely support for a given size, span, grade and species, divide the recommended property values used for design by the design factors for each property: F_b, F_v and E.

"P" in the following formulas is the **sum** of all concentrated loads on the span. If the loading condition is two equal concentrated loads, divide "P" by 2 (two) to determine the amount of each load. If the loading condition is three equal concentrated loads, divide "P" by 3 (three) to determine the amount of each load.

$$P = \frac{F_b}{F_b \text{ factor}}$$

$$P = \frac{F_v}{F_v \text{ factor}}$$

$$P = \frac{E}{E \text{ factor}}$$

The smallest value of "P" applies

EXAMPLE (4)
Known:
Span: 20'-0"
Two equal concentrated loads at third points.

Duration of load adjustment factor: 1.25
Deflection limit: 1/240 of the span
Size: 6 x 18
Grade and species: Douglas Fir-Larch, Select Structural, Beam and Stringer

$F_b = 1600 \times 1.25 = 2000$ psi (adjusted for duration of load)

$F_v = 85 \times 1.25 = 106$ psi (adjusted for duration of load)

$E = 1,600,000$ psi

Find: Maximum safe concentrated load.

Allowable concentrated load for bending:
From the table, for a span of 20 feet, two equal concentrated loads at third points and a size of 6 x 18, the F_b factor is .1486.

$$P = \frac{F_b}{F_b \text{ factor}} = \frac{2000}{.1486} = 13,460 \text{ lbs.}$$

The F_v factor is .0078.

$$P = \frac{F_v}{F_v \text{ factor}} = \frac{106}{.0078} = 13,590 \text{ lbs.}$$

The E factor is 150.

$$P = \frac{E}{E \text{ factor}} = \frac{1,600,000}{150 \times .667} = 16,000 \text{ lbs.}$$

(Note: Factor of .667 is the adjustment from 1/360 to 1/240 deflection limit.) see page 101.

The maximum safe total load is 13,460 pounds, controlled by the allowable extreme fiber stress in bending.

Each of the two concentrated loads is limited to 13,460 ÷ 2 = 6,730 lbs.

III. DETERMINATION OF GRADE AND SPECIES
Uniformly Distributed Loading

To determine the grade and species needed for a given size, span and uniformly distributed loading condition, multiply the design factor for the property under consideration by the uniform load, w, to be applied to the beam.

$$F_b = w \, (F_b \text{ factor}),$$
$$F_v = w \, (F_v \text{ factor}),$$
$$E = w \, (E \text{ factor})$$

With the required property values, choose a grade and species from recommended design value tables.

EXAMPLE (5)
Known:
Span: 20'-0"
Spacing: 10'-0"
Loading: See example (1) on page 102.

Dead Load:	12.0 psf
Live Load:	40.0 psf
Total Load:	52.0 psf

For Stiffness: 40 psf x 10' = 400 plf
For Strength: 52 psf x 10' = 520 plf

Duration of load adjustment factor: 1.15
Size: 6 x 16

Find: Grade and species needed.

In the table for 20 foot span, uniform load and 6 x 16 find:

$$F_b \text{ factor} = 2.803$$

$$F_v \text{ factor} = .153$$

$$E \text{ factor} = 3,164$$

$$F_b = \frac{w\,(F_b \text{ factor})}{1.15} = \frac{520 \times 2.803}{1.15} = 1267 \text{ psi}$$

$$F_v = \frac{w\,(F_v \text{ factor})}{1.15} = \frac{520 \times .153}{1.15} = 69.2 \text{ psi}$$

E = w (E factor) = 400 x 3164 = 1,266,000 psi

For the above required property values, the lowest grade and species which qualifies is Douglas Fir-Larch, No. 1, Beam and Stringer with an F_b of 1350 psi, an F_v of 85 psi and an E value of 1,600,000 psi.

In the same example, assume a size of 6 x 18 and determine grade and species:

$$F_b \text{ factor} = 2.229$$

$$F_v \text{ factor} = .133$$

$$E \text{ factor} = 2,198$$

$$F_b = \frac{w\,(F_b \text{ factor})}{1.15} = \frac{520 \times 2.229}{1.15} = 1008 \text{ psi}$$

$$F_v = \frac{w\,(F_v \text{ factor})}{1.15} = \frac{520 \times .133}{1.15} = 60 \text{ psi}$$

E = w (E factor) = 400 x 2,198 = 879,200 psi

For the above required property values the following grades and species qualify:

Select Structural and No. 1: Douglas Fir-Larch, Douglas Fir South, Hem-Fir, Western Hemlock, Mountain Hemlock, and Mountain Hemlock-Hem-Fir.

Select Structural: Engelmann Spruce, Lodgepole Pine, Ponderosa Pine-Sugar Pine, Idaho White Pine and Western Cedars.

Thus, an increase of 2" in depth of beam provides a much wider choice of lumber grades and species.

Concentrated Loading

To determine the grade and species needed for a given size, span and concentrated loading condition, multiply the design factor for the property under consideration by the sum of all concentrated loads, "P", to be applied to the beam.

$$F_b = P\,(F_b \text{ factor}),$$

$$F_v = P\,(F_v \text{ factor})$$

$$E = P\,(E \text{ factor})$$

DESIGN — BENDING MEMBERS

EXAMPLE (6)
Known:
Span: 20'-0"
Two equal concentrated loads at third points: 6,730 lbs. each: P = 13,460 lbs.
Duration of load adjustment factor: 1.25
Deflection limit: 1/240 of the span.
Size: 6 x 18

Find: Grade and species needed.

In the table for 20 foot span, two equal concentrated loads at third points and 6 x 18 find:

$$F_b \text{ factor} = .1486$$

$$F_v \text{ factor} = .0078$$

$$E \text{ factor} = 150$$

$$F_b = \frac{P\,(F_b \text{ factor})}{1.25} = \frac{13,460 \times .1486}{1.25} = 1600 \text{ psi}$$

$$F_v = \frac{P\,(F_v \text{ factor})}{1.25} = \frac{13,460 \times .0078}{1.25} = 84 \text{ psi}$$

$$E = P\,(E \text{ factor})\, .667 =$$

$$13,460 \times 150 \times .667 =$$

$$1,347,000 \text{ psi}$$

For the above required property values, the only grade and species which qualifies is Douglas Fir-Larch, Select Structural, Beam and Stringer with an F_b of 1600 psi, an F_v of 85 psi and an E value of 1,600,000 psi.

Determination of Grade and Species for a Combination of Uniformly Distributed and Concentrated Loading

To determine the grade and species needed for a given size, span and combination of uniformly distributed and concentrated loading:

1. Multiply the F_b, F_v and E design factors for uniform loading by uniform load "w."
2. Multiply the F_b, F_v and E design factors for concentrated loading by the total concentrated load "P."
3. For each property, add the products from (1) and (2) above to obtain required F_b, F_v and E values.
4. Choose a grade and species which has the required recommended design values.

EXAMPLE (7)
Known:

Span: 20'-0"

Spacing: 10'0"

Loading:

Uniformly Distributed:

Dead Load:	12.0 psf
Live Load:	40.0 psf
Total Load:	52.0 psf

For Stiffness: 40 psf x 10' = 400 plf
For Strength: 52 psf x 10' = 520 plf

DESIGN — BENDING MEMBERS

Concentrated (Sum of two equal loads at third points):

Dead Load:	1000 lbs.
Live Load:	4000 lbs.
Total Load:	5000 lbs.
For Stiffness:	4000 lbs.
For Strength:	5000 lbs.

Size: 8 x 20
Find: Grade and species needed.

In the table for 20 foot span, uniform load and 8 x 20, find:

$$F_b \text{ factor} = 1.333$$

$$F_v \text{ factor} = .086$$

$$E \text{ factor} = 1,165$$

$F_b = w (F_b \text{ factor}) = 520 (1.333) = 693$ psi

$F_v = w (F_v \text{ factor}) = 520 (.086) = 45$ psi

$E = w (E \text{ factor}) = 400 (1,165) = 466,000$ psi

In the table for 20 foot span, sum of two equal concentrated loads at third points and 8 x 20, find:

$$F_b \text{ factor} = .0889$$

$$F_v \text{ factor} = .0051$$

$$E \text{ factor} = 79$$

$F_b = P (F_b \text{ factor}) = 5000 (.0889) = 445$ psi

$F_v = P (F_v \text{ factor}) = 5000 (.0051) = 26$ psi

$E = P (E \text{ factor}) = 4000 (79) = 316,000$ psi

The sum of property value requirements for uniform plus concentrated loading conditions are:
$F_b = 693 + 445 = 1138$ psi
$F_v = 45 + 26 = 71$ psi
$E = 466,000 + 316,000 = 782,000$ psi

For the above required property values the following grades and species qualify:
   Select Structural and No. 1: Douglas Fir-Larch, Douglas Fir South and Western Hemlock.
   Select Structural: Mountain Hemlock

WWPA SPAN COMPUTER

The WWPA Span Computer has been developed to assist architects, engineers, code officials, builders and retail and wholesale lumbermen in the selection of spans and lumber requirements for joists, rafters and light beams in dimension sizes. It is a precise engineering tool which may be easily used to determine grade and species, size, spacing, span, loading and deflection requirements. It has no provision for the determination of the shear properties of a member, therefore, when it is considered necessary or desirable to check the shear capabilities of a member the designer may refer to the Beam Design Tables for Dimension and Timbers on Page 108. A WWPA Span Computer is supplied with this book. Additional copies may be obtained for $1.00 each from the Western Wood Products Association.

Span Limitation—Stiffness

Structural members deflect or bend under load. The greater the load the greater the deflection. Deflection is limited for appearance purposes so noticeable sag will not be apparent in ceilings, for instance. Deflection is limited to control comfort, such as in floors and decks.

In joisted construction, where appearance and stiffness are important, deflection may often be the controlling factor in the determination of the size, grade and species that may be used. Deflection is usually limited to some proportion of the span length as shown on the outside flap of the Span Computer. For example, floor joist deflection is limited to 1" in every 360" of span.

The Modulus of Elasticity of a material is a measure of stiffness and is used in conjunction with the deflection limitation and live load in controlling maximum spans. Lumber has assigned E values as shown under the **Stiffness** heading on the inside flap, and the slide rule reads E values on the Δ (delta) scales of the **Stiffness** slides. A reading of 1.5 means 1,500,000 pounds per square inch. When any given size of lumber on the slide is set against the live load requirement, the E value needed for any span is shown. Regulatory agencies usually specify that live loads only be used for limiting spans by deflection because it is the performance of the structure when loaded that is important.

Span Limitation—Strength

When designing for strength, the total load (dead load plus live load) is used. For example, floor joists supporting a live load of 40 psf and a dead load of 10 psf are designed for strength on the basis of a total load of 50 psf.

When loads are applied, structural members bend, producing tension in the fibers along the face farthest from the applied load and compression in the fibers along the face nearest to the applied load. These induced stresses in the fibers are designated as "extreme fiber stress in bending" or (F_b).

Lumber has assigned F_b values as shown under the **Strength** heading on the inside flap, and the slide rule reads F_b values on the F_b scales of the **Strength** slides. When any given size of lumber on the slide is set against the total load required, the F_b needed for any span is shown. The "F_b Repetitive" values are usually used when three or more load sharing members such as joists, rafters or beams are spaced no more than 24" apart and are joined by flooring, sheathing or other load distributing elements. Single F_b values are used when spacing is greater than 24".

The **Normal** scale on the **Strength** slide is used for floor and ceiling joists where long-term loads are anticipated. Only occasional loads, such as construction or snow loads, are anticipated on rafters, hence, values are increased because long-term loads are not applied. The increases are built into the **Snow And 7 Day** scales and should be used in conformance with the local code requirements.

The computer will most often be used with the loading criteria shown on the front flap. But, it can also be used for a greater range of load, span and deflection criteria not usually covered by span tables. The joist and rafter loading scales make provisions for abnormal loadings up to 80 psf for deflection and 100 psf for strength. The beam loading scales provide for loadings up to 400 lb./ft. for both deflection and strength.

EXAMPLES

I. To find what grade in what species can be used to span 14' when 2x10's are used on 16" centers as floor joists in living areas:
1. From outside flap opposite "Floor Joists (Living Areas)," find loading and deflection criteria:
    Stiffness: 40 psf and L/360
    Strength: 50 psf and normal
2. On **Stiffness** portion of computer, set 2x10/16" at live load (40 psf).
3. Read required (E) value opposite 14'-0" on Δ = L/360 scale:
    1.0 "E" required (1,000,000 psi)
4. On **Strength** portion of computer, set 2x10/16" at total load (50 psf).
5. Read required (F_b) value opposite 14'-0" on normal scale:
    920 "F_b" Repetitive required.
6. Use required (E) and (F_b) values obtained above to select minimum grade and species on inside flap:

For (E): No. 2 Western Cedars or above qualifies.

For (F_b Repetitive): No. 2 Engelmann Spruce or above qualifies.

II. To find the span for a No. 2 grade Douglas Fir and Larch 2x6 on 24" centers for a low slope rafter with no finished ceiling and a 30 psf live load:

1. From outside flap opposite "Low Slope Rafters, No Finished Ceiling" and 30 psf find:
    Stiffness 30 psf and L/240
    Strength: 40 psf and snow

DESIGN — BENDING MEMBERS

2. On Stiffness portion of computer, set 2x6/24" at live load (30 psf).
3. Read span opposite (E) of 1.7x10⁶ on Δ = L/240 scale:
    10'-11"
4. On **Strength** portion of computer, set 2x6/24" at total load (40 psf).
5. Read **span** opposite (F_b) of 1450 psi on snow scale:
    10'-3"
    The maximum span permitted for this condition is 10'-3" as controlled by (F_b).

III. Beam Computer
    The Beam Computer works in an identical fashion to the Joist and Rafter Computer except that the loading scale is in pounds per linear foot (lb./ft.) and the spacing is not included with the beam size. The Beam Calculator covers all dimension lumber sizes from 2x4 through 4x14 and will be most useful in determining spans or grade and species for unusual loading conditions, wider spacings and larger sizes than those covered by the Joist and Rafter Span Computer.

    To find the grade and species required for a 4x14 having a span of 20', a spacing of 8', a live load of 20 psf, a dead load of 10 psf, a deflection limitation of L/180 and a 7 day duration of loading:
    For stiffness, obtain lb./ft. by multiplying 8' spacing by 20 psf live load: 8'x20 = **160 lb./ft.**
    For strength, obtain lb./ft. by multiplying 8' spacing by total load (20 + 10): 8'x30 = **240 lb./ft.**
    1. On **Stiffness** portion of computer, set 4x14 at 160 lb./ft.
    2. Read (E) value opposite 20'-0" on

    $\Delta = $ L/180 scale:
        0.64 (E) required. (0.64x 10⁶).
    3. On **Strength** portion of computer, set 4x14 at 240 lb./ft.
    4. Read (F_b) value opposite 20'-0" on "7 day" scale:
        1125 psi (F_b Single) required.
    5. Use required (E) and (F_b) values obtained above to select minimum grade and species on inside flap:
For (E): No. 3 Western Woods or above qualifies.
For (F_b Single): Select Structural Engelmann Spruce or above qualifies.

STRENGTH AND STIFFNESS REQUIREMENTS FOR BEAMS

See instructions for use of tables on page 101. Symbols used in the tables are as follows: Tabulated values are based on net size.

F_b = Extreme fiber stress in bending induced by a uniform load of 1 (one) plf or by a concentrated load of 1 (one) pound, psi

F_v = Horizontal shear stress induced by a uniform load of 1 (one) plf or a total concentrated load of 1 (one) pound. psi.

E = Modulus of elasticity value needed to limit deflection to 1/360 of the span for a uniform load of 1 (one) plf or a total concentrated load of 1 (one) pound, psi.

3 FOOT SPAN

Nominal Size (Inches)	Property	UNIFORM	Single Load — At Center of Span	Single Load — At Third Point	Single Load — At Quarter Point	Sum of Two Equal Loads — At Third Point	Sum of Two Equal Loads — At Quarter Points From Reactions	Sum of 3 Equal Loads — At Quarter Points and Center of Span
2x3 3 lb/beam 1.0 lb/ft	F_b / F_v / E	8.640 / .517 / 9,331	5.7600 / .2000 / 4,977	5.1200 / .2667 / 4,241	4.3200 / .3000 / 3,421	3.8400 / .2000 / 4,241	2.8800 / .2000 / 3,421	3.8400 / .2000 / 3,940
2x4 4 lb/beam 1.4 lb/ft	F_b / F_v / E	4.408 / .345 / 3,401	2.9388 / .1429 / 1,814	2.6122 / .1905 / 1,546	2.2041 / .2143 / 1,247	1.9592 / .1429 / 1,546	1.4694 / .1429 / 1,247	1.9592 / .1429 / 1,436
3x4 7 lb/beam 2.3 lb/ft	F_b / F_v / E	2.645 / .207 / 2,040	1.7633 / .0857 / 1,088	1.5674 / .1143 / 927	1.3225 / .1286 / 748	1.1755 / .0857 / 927	.8816 / .0857 / 748	1.1755 / .0857 / 861
2x6 7 lb/beam 2.2 lb/ft	F_b / F_v / E	1.785 / .189 / 876	1.1901 / .0909 / 467	1.0579 / .1212 / 398	.8926 / .1364 / 321	.7934 / .0909 / 398	.5950 / .0909 / 321	.7934 / .0909 / 370
3x6 11 lb/beam 3.6 lb/ft	F_b / F_v / E	1.071 / .114 / 526	.7140 / .0545 / 280	.6347 / .0727 / 239	.5355 / .0818 / 193	.4760 / .0545 / 239	.3570 / .0545 / 193	.4760 / .0545 / 222
2x8 9 lb/beam 2.9 lb/ft	F_b / F_v / E	1.027 / .124 / 383	.6849 / .0690 / 204	.6088 / .0920 / 174	.5137 / .1034 / 140	.4566 / .0690 / 174	.3425 / .0690 / 140	.4566 / .0690 / 162
4x6 15 lb/beam 5.1 lb/ft	F_b / F_v / E	.765 / .081 / 376	.5100 / .0390 / 200	.4534 / .0519 / 171	.3825 / .0584 / 138	.3400 / .0390 / 171	.2550 / .0390 / 138	.3400 / .0390 / 159
2x10 11 lb/beam 3.7 lb/ft	F_b / F_v / E	.631 / .079 / 184	.4207 / .0541 / 98	.3740 / .0721 / 84	.3156 / .0811 / 68	.2805 / .0541 / 84	.2104 / .0541 / 68	.2805 / .0541 / 78
3x8 14 lb/beam 4.8 lb/ft	F_b / F_v / E	.616 / .074 / 230	.4109 / .0414 / 122	.3653 / .0552 / 104	.3082 / .0621 / 84	.2740 / .0414 / 104	.2055 / .0414 / 84	.2740 / .0414 / 97
6x6 24 lb/beam 8.0 lb/ft	F_b / F_v / E	.487 / .052 / 239	.3246 / .0248 / 127	.2885 / .0331 / 109	.2434 / .0372 / 88	.2164 / .0248 / 109	.1623 / .0248 / 88	.2164 / .0248 / 101

4 FOOT SPAN

Nominal Size (Inches)	Property	UNIFORM	Single Load — At Center of Span	Single Load — At Third Point	Single Load — At Quarter Point	Sum of Two Equal Loads — At Third Point	Sum of Two Equal Loads — At Quarter Points From Reactions	Sum of 3 Equal Loads — At Quarter Points and Center of Span
4x8 20 lb/beam 6.7 lb/ft	F_b / F_v / E	.440 / .053 / 164	.2935 / .0296 / 87	.2609 / .0394 / 75	.2201 / .0443 / 60	.1957 / .0296 / 75	.1468 / .0296 / 60	.1957 / .0296 / 69
2x12 13 lb/beam 4.5 lb/ft	F_b / F_v / E	.427 / .050 / 102	.2844 / .0444 / 55	.2528 / .0593 / 47	.2133 / .0667 / 38	.1896 / .0444 / 47	.1422 / .0444 / 38	.1896 / .0444 / 43
2x3 4 lb/beam 1.0 lb/ft	F_b / F_v / E	15.360 / .717 / 22,118	7.6800 / .2000 / 8,847	6.8267 / .2667 / 7,540	5.7600 / .3000 / 6,083	5.1200 / .2000 / 7,540	3.8400 / .2000 / 6,083	5.1200 / .2000 / 7,004
2x4 6 lb/beam 1.4 lb/ft	F_b / F_v / E	7.837 / .488 / 8,061	3.9184 / .1429 / 3,224	3.4830 / .1905 / 2,748	2.9388 / .2143 / 2,217	2.6122 / .1429 / 2,748	1.9592 / .1429 / 2,217	2.6122 / .1429 / 2,553
3x4 9 lb/beam 2.3 lb/ft	F_b / F_v / E	4.702 / .293 / 4,836	2.3510 / .0857 / 1,935	2.0898 / .1143 / 1,649	1.7633 / .1286 / 1,330	1.5673 / .0857 / 1,649	1.1755 / .0857 / 1,330	1.5673 / .0857 / 1,532
2x6 9 lb/beam 2.2 lb/ft	F_b / F_v / E	3.174 / .280 / 2,077	1.5868 / .0909 / 831	1.4105 / .1212 / 708	1.1901 / .1364 / 571	1.0579 / .0909 / 708	.7934 / .0909 / 571	1.0579 / .0909 / 658
3x6 15 lb/beam 3.6 lb/ft	F_b / F_v / E	1.904 / .168 / 1,246	.9521 / .0545 / 499	.8463 / .0727 / 425	.7141 / .0818 / 343	.6347 / .0545 / 425	.4760 / .0545 / 343	.6347 / .0545 / 395
2x8 11 lb/beam 2.9 lb/ft	F_b / F_v / E	1.826 / .193 / 907	.9132 / .0690 / 363	.8117 / .0920 / 309	.6849 / .1034 / 249	.6088 / .0690 / 309	.4566 / .0690 / 249	.6088 / .0690 / 287
4x6 20 lb/beam 5.1 lb/ft	F_b / F_v / E	1.360 / .120 / 890	.6800 / .0390 / 356	.6045 / .0519 / 303	.5100 / .0584 / 245	.4534 / .0390 / 303	.3400 / .0390 / 245	.4534 / .0390 / 282
2x10 15 lb/beam 3.7 lb/ft	F_b / F_v / E	1.122 / .133 / 437	.5610 / .0541 / 175	.4987 / .0721 / 149	.4207 / .0811 / 120	.3740 / .0541 / 149	.2805 / .0541 / 120	.3740 / .0541 / 138

STRENGTH AND STIFFNESS REQUIREMENTS FOR BEAMS

See instructions for use of tables on page 101. Symbols used in the tables are as follows: Tabulated values are based on net size.

F_b = Extreme fiber stress in bending induced by a uniform load of 1 (one) plf or by a concentrated load of 1 (one) pound, psi

F_v = Horizontal shear stress induced by a uniform load of 1 (one) plf or a total concentrated load of 1 (one) pound, psi

E = Modulus of elasticity value needed to limit deflection to 1/360 of the span for a uniform load of 1 (one) plf or a total concentrated load of 1 (one) pound, psi.

4 FOOT SPAN

Nominal Size (Inches)	Property	UNIFORM	CONCENTRATED — Single Load — At Center of Span	Single Load — At Third Point	Single Load — At Quarter Point	Sum of Two Equal Loads — At Third Point	Sum of Two Equal Loads — At Quarter Points From Reactions	Sum of 3 Equal Loads — At Quarter Points and Center of Span
3x14 (Continued) 35 lb/beam 8.7 lb/ft	F_b	.328	.1640	.1458	.1230	.1094	.0820	.1094
	F_v	.041	.0226	.0302	.0340	.0226	.0226	.0226
	E	89	36	30	25	30	25	28
3x8 19 lb/beam 4.8 lb/ft	F_b	1.096	.5479	.4870	.4109	.3653	.2740	.3653
	F_v	.116	.0414	.0552	.0621	.0414	.0414	.0414
	E	544	218	186	150	186	150	172
6x6 32 lb/beam 8.0 lb/ft	F_b	.866	.4328	.3847	.3246	.2885	.2164	.2885
	F_v	.076	.0248	.0331	.0372	.0248	.0248	.0248
	E	567	227	193	156	193	156	179
4x8 27 lb/beam 6.7 lb/ft	F_b	.783	.3914	.3479	.2935	.2609	.1957	.2609
	F_v	.083	.0296	.0394	.0443	.0296	.0296	.0296
	E	389	155	133	107	133	107	123
2x12 18 lb/beam 4.5 lb/ft	F_b	.759	.3793	.3371	.2844	.2528	.1896	.2528
	F_v	.094	.0444	.0593	.0667	.0444	.0444	.0444
	E	243	97	83	67	83	67	77
3x10 24 lb/beam 6.1 lb/ft	F_b	.673	.3366	.2992	.2524	.2244	.1683	.2244
	F_v	.080	.0324	.0432	.0486	.0324	.0324	.0324
	E	262	105	89	72	89	72	83
2x14 21 lb/beam 5.2 lb/ft	F_b	.547	.2734	.2430	.2051	.1823	.1367	.1823
	F_v	.068	.0377	.0503	.0566	.0377	.0377	.0377
	E	149	59	51	41	51	41	47
4x10 34 lb/beam 8.5 lb/ft	F_b	.481	.2404	.2137	.1803	.1603	.1202	.1603
	F_v	.057	.0232	.0309	.0347	.0232	.0232	.0232
	E	187	75	64	51	64	51	59
6x8 44 lb/beam 10.9 lb/ft	F_b	.465	.2327	.2069	.1745	.1552	.1164	.1552
	F_v	.050	.0182	.0242	.0273	.0182	.0182	.0182
	E	223	89	76	61	76	61	71
3x12 30 lb/beam 7.4 lb/ft	F_b	.455	.2276	.2023	.1707	.1517	.1138	.1517
	F_v	.057	.0267	.0356	.0400	.0267	.0267	.0267
	E	146	58	50	40	50	40	46
8x8 59 lb/beam 14.8 lb/ft	F_b	.341	.1707	.1517	.1280	.1138	.0853	.1138
	F_v	.037	.0133	.0178	.0200	.0133	.0133	.0133
	E	164	66	56	45	56	45	52

5 FOOT SPAN

Nominal Size (Inches)	Property	UNIFORM	CONCENTRATED — Single Load — At Center of Span	Single Load — At Third Point	Single Load — At Quarter Point	Sum of Two Equal Loads — At Third Point	Sum of Two Equal Loads — At Quarter Points From Reactions	Sum of 3 Equal Loads — At Quarter Points and Center of Span
2x3 5 lb/beam 1.0 lb/ft	F_b	24.000	9.6000	8.5333	7.2000	6.4000	4.8000	6.4000
	F_v	.917	.2000	.2667	.3000	.2000	.2000	.2000
	E	43,200	13,824	11,782	9,504	11,782	9,504	10,944
2x4 7 lb/beam 1.4 lb/ft	F_b	12.245	4.8980	4.3537	3.6735	3.2653	2.4490	3.2653
	F_v	.631	.1429	.1905	.2143	.1429	.1429	.1429
	E	15,743	5,038	4,294	3,464	4,294	3,464	3,988
3x4 12 lb/beam 2.3 lb/ft	F_b	7.347	2.9388	2.6122	2.2041	1.9592	1.4694	1.9592
	F_v	.379	.0857	.1143	.1286	.0857	.0857	.0857
	E	9,446	3,023	2,576	2,078	2,576	2,078	2,393
2x6 11 lb/beam 2.2 lb/ft	F_b	4.959	1.9835	1.7631	1.4876	1.3223	.9917	1.3223
	F_v	.371	.0909	.1212	.1364	.0909	.0909	.0909
	E	4,057	1,298	1,106	893	1,106	893	1,028
3x6 18 lb/beam 3.6 lb/ft	F_b	2.975	1.1901	1.0579	.8926	.7934	.5950	.7934
	F_v	.223	.0545	.0727	.0818	.0545	.0545	.0545
	E	2,434	779	664	536	664	536	617
2x8 14 lb/beam 2.9 lb/ft	F_b	2.854	1.1415	1.0147	.8561	.7610	.5707	.7610
	F_v	.261	.0690	.0920	.1034	.0690	.0690	.0690
	E	1,771	567	483	390	483	390	449
4x6 25 lb/beam 5.1 lb/ft	F_b	2.125	.8501	.7556	.6375	.5667	.4250	.5667
	F_v	.159	.0390	.0519	.0584	.0390	.0390	.0390
	E	1,739	556	474	383	474	383	440
2x10 18 lb/beam 3.7 lb/ft	F_b	1.753	.7012	.6233	.5259	.4675	.3506	.4675
	F_v	.187	.0541	.0721	.0811	.0541	.0541	.0541
	E	853	273	233	188	233	188	216
3x8 24 lb/beam 4.8 lb/ft	F_b	1.712	.6849	.6088	.5137	.4566	.3425	.4566
	F_v	.157	.0414	.0552	.0621	.0414	.0414	.0414
	E	1,063	340	290	234	290	234	269

STRENGTH AND STIFFNESS REQUIREMENTS FOR BEAMS

See instructions for use of tables on page 101. Symbols used in the tables are as follows: Tabulated values are based on net size.

F_b = Extreme fiber stress in bending induced by a uniform load of 1 (one) plf or by a concentrated load of 1 (one) pound, psi

F_v = Horizontal shear stress induced by a uniform load of 1 (one) plf or a total concentrated load of 1 (one) pound, psi.

E = Modulus of elasticity value needed to limit deflection to 1/360 of the span for a uniform load of 1 (one) plf or a total concentrated load of 1 (one) pound, psi.

5 FOOT SPAN (Continued)

Nominal Size (Inches)	Property	UNIFORM	CONCENTRATED Single Load At Center of Span	At Third Point	At Quarter Point	Sum of Two Equal Loads At Third Point	At Quarter Points From Reactions	Sum of 3 Equal Loads At Quarter Points and Center of Span
6x6 40 lb/beam 8.0 lb/ft	F_b F_v E	1.352 .101 1,106	.5409 .0248 354	.4808 .0331 302	.4057 .0372 243	.3606 .0248 302	.2705 .0248 243	.3606 .0248 280
4x8 33 lb/beam 6.7 lb/ft	F_b F_v E	1.223 .112 759	.4892 .0296 243	.4349 .0394 207	.3669 .0443 167	.3261 .0296 207	.2446 .0296 167	.3261 .0296 192
2x12 22 lb/beam 4.5 lb/ft	F_b F_v E	1.185 .139 474	.4741 .0444 152	.4214 .0593 129	.3556 .0667 104	.3160 .0444 129	.2370 .0444 104	.3160 .0444 120
3x10 31 lb/beam 6.1 lb/ft	F_b F_v E	1.052 .112 512	.4207 .0324 164	.3740 .0432 140	.3156 .0486 113	.2805 .0324 140	.2104 .0324 113	.2805 .0324 130
2x14 26 lb/beam 5.2 lb/ft	F_b F_v E	.854 .105 290	.3418 .0377 93	.3038 .0503 79	.2563 .0566 64	.2278 .0377 79	.1709 .0377 64	.2278 .0377 74
4x10 43 lb/beam 8.5 lb/ft	F_b F_v E	.751 .080 366	.3005 .0232 117	.2671 .0309 100	.2254 .0347 80	.2004 .0232 100	.1503 .0232 80	.2004 .0232 93
6x8 54 lb/beam 10.9 lb/ft	F_b F_v E	.727 .068 436	.2909 .0182 140	.2586 .0242 119	.2182 .0273 96	.1939 .0182 119	.1455 .0182 96	.1939 .0182 111
3x12 37 lb/beam 7.4 lb/ft	F_b F_v E	.711 .083 284	.2844 .0267 91	.2528 .0356 78	.2133 .0400 63	.1896 .0267 78	.1422 .0267 63	.1896 .0267 72
8x8 74 lb/beam 14.8 lb/ft	F_b F_v E	.533 .050 320	.2133 .0133 102	.1896 .0178 87	.1600 .0200 70	.1422 .0133 87	.1067 .0133 70	.1422 .0133 81
3x14 44 lb/beam 8.7 lb/ft	F_b F_v E	.513 .063 174	.2051 .0226 56	.1823 .0302 47	.1538 .0340 38	.1367 .0226 47	.1025 .0226 38	.1367 .0226 44

(5 FOOT SPAN, upper portion) / 6 FOOT SPAN

Nominal Size (Inches)	Property	UNIFORM	CONCENTRATED Single Load At Center of Span	At Third Point	At Quarter Point	Sum of Two Equal Loads At Third Point	At Quarter Points From Reactions	Sum of 3 Equal Loads At Quarter Points and Center of Span
4x12 52 lb/beam 10.4 lb/ft	F_b F_v E	.508 .060 203	.2032 .0190 65	.1806 .0254 55	.1524 .0286 45	.1355 .0190 55	.1016 .0190 45	.1355 .0190 51
6x10 69 lb/beam 13.8 lb/ft	F_b F_v E	.453 .049 215	.1813 .0144 69	.1612 .0191 59	.1360 .0215 47	.1209 .0144 59	.0907 .0144 47	.1209 .0144 54
3x16 50 lb/beam 10.1 lb/ft	F_b F_v E	.397 .048 114	.1589 .0197 37	.1413 .0262 31	.1192 .0295 25	.1060 .0197 31	.0795 .0197 25	.1060 .0197 29

6 FOOT SPAN

Nominal Size (Inches)	Property	UNIFORM	CONCENTRATED Single Load At Center of Span	At Third Point	At Quarter Point	Sum of Two Equal Loads At Third Point	At Quarter Points From Reactions	Sum of 3 Equal Loads At Quarter Points and Center of Span
2x3 6 lb/beam 1.0 lb/ft	F_b F_v E	34.560 1.117 74,650	11.5200 .2000 19,907	10.2400 .2667 16,966	8.6400 .3000 13,686	7.6800 .2000 16,966	5.7600 .2000 13,686	7.6800 .2000 15,759
2x4 8 lb/beam 1.4 lb/ft	F_b F_v E	17.633 .774 27,205	5.8776 .1429 7,255	5.2245 .1905 6,183	4.4082 .2143 4,988	3.9184 .1429 6,183	2.9388 .1429 4,988	3.9184 .1429 5,743
3x4 14 lb/beam 2.3 lb/ft	F_b F_v E	10.580 .464 16,323	3.5265 .0857 4,353	3.1347 .1143 3,710	2.6449 .1286 2,993	2.3510 .0857 3,710	1.7633 .0857 2,993	2.3510 .0857 3,446
2x6 13 lb/beam 2.2 lb/ft	F_b F_v E	7.141 .462 7,011	2.3802 .0909 1,870	2.1157 .1212 1,593	1.7851 .1364 1,285	1.5868 .0909 1,593	1.1901 .0909 1,285	1.5868 .0909 1,480
3x6 22 lb/beam 3.6 lb/ft	F_b F_v E	4.284 .277 4,206	1.4281 .0545 1,122	1.2694 .0727 956	1.0711 .0818 771	.9521 .0545 956	.7141 .0545 771	.9521 .0545 888
2x8 17 lb/beam 2.9 lb/ft	F_b F_v E	4.109 .330 3,061	1.3698 .0690 816	1.2176 .0920 696	1.0273 .1034 561	.9132 .0690 696	.6849 .0690 561	.9132 .0690 646
4x6 30 lb/beam 5.1 lb/ft	F_b F_v E	3.060 .198 3,005	1.0201 .0390 801	.9067 .0519 683	.7651 .0584 551	.6800 .0390 683	.5100 .0390 551	.6800 .0390 634

STRENGTH AND STIFFNESS REQUIREMENTS FOR BEAMS

See instructions for use of tables on page 101. Symbols used in the tables are as follows: Tabulated values are based on net size.

F_b = Extreme fiber stress in bending induced by a uniform load of 1 (one) plf or by a concentrated load of 1 (one) pound, psi

F_v = Horizontal shear stress induced by a uniform load of 1 (one) plf or a total concentrated load of 1 (one) pound, psi.

E = Modulus of elasticity value needed to limit deflection to 1/360 of the span for a uniform load of 1 (one) plf or a total concentrated load of 1 (one) pound, psi.

6 FOOT SPAN (Continued)

Nominal Size (Inches)	Property	UNIFORM	Single Load — At Center of Span	Single Load — At Third Point	Single Load — At Quarter Point	Sum of Two Equal Loads — At Third Point	Sum of Two Equal Loads — At Quarter Points From Reactions	Sum of 3 Equal Loads — At Quarter Points and Center of Span
2x10 22 lb/beam 3.7 lb/ft	F_b	2.524	.8415	.7480	.6311	.5610	.4207	.5610
	F_v	.241	.0541	.0721	.0811	.0541	.0541	.0541
	E	1,474	393	335	270	335	270	311
3x8 29 lb/beam 4.8 lb/ft	F_b	2.466	.8219	.7306	.6164	.5479	.4109	.5479
	F_v	.198	.0414	.0552	.0621	.0414	.0414	.0414
	E	1,836	490	417	337	417	337	388
6x6 48 lb/beam 8.0 lb/ft	F_b	1.947	.6491	.5770	.4869	.4328	.3246	.4328
	F_v	.126	.0248	.0331	.0372	.0248	.0248	.0248
	E	1,912	510	435	351	435	351	404
4x8 40 lb/beam 6.7 lb/ft	F_b	1.761	.5871	.5218	.4403	.3914	.2935	.3914
	F_v	.142	.0296	.0394	.0443	.0296	.0296	.0296
	E	1,312	350	298	240	298	240	277
2x12 27 lb/beam 4.5 lb/ft	F_b	1.707	.5689	.5057	.4267	.3793	.2844	.3793
	F_v	.183	.0444	.0593	.0667	.0444	.0444	.0444
	E	819	218	186	150	186	150	173
3x10 37 lb/beam 6.1 lb/ft	F_b	1.515	.5049	.4488	.3787	.3366	.2524	.3366
	F_v	.145	.0324	.0432	.0486	.0324	.0324	.0324
	E	884	236	201	162	201	162	187
2x14 31 lb/beam 5.2 lb/ft	F_b	1.230	.4101	.3645	.3076	.2734	.2051	.2734
	F_v	.143	.0377	.0503	.0566	.0377	.0377	.0377
	E	501	134	114	92	114	92	106
4x10 51 lb/beam 8.5 lb/ft	F_b	1.082	.3606	.3206	.2705	.2404	.1803	.2404
	F_v	.103	.0232	.0309	.0347	.0232	.0232	.0232
	E	632	168	144	116	144	116	133
6x8 65 lb/beam 10.9 lb/ft	F_b	1.047	.3491	.3103	.2618	.2327	.1745	.2327
	F_v	.086	.0182	.0242	.0273	.0182	.0182	.0182
	E	754	201	171	138	171	138	159
3x12 45 lb/beam 7.4 lb/ft	F_b	1.024	.3413	.3034	.2560	.2276	.1707	.2276
	F_v	.110	.0267	.0356	.0400	.0267	.0267	.0267
	E	492	131	112	90	112	90	104
8x8 89 lb/beam 14.8 lb/ft	F_b	.768	.2560	.2276	.1920	.1707	.1280	.1707
	F_v	.063	.0133	.0178	.0200	.0133	.0133	.0133
	E	553	147	126	101	126	101	117
3x14 52 lb/beam 8.7 lb/ft	F_b	.738	.2461	.2187	.1846	.1640	.1230	.1640
	F_v	.086	.0226	.0302	.0340	.0226	.0226	.0226
	E	301	80	68	55	68	55	64
4x12 62 lb/beam 10.4 lb/ft	F_b	.731	.2438	.2167	.1829	.1625	.1219	.1625
	F_v	.079	.0190	.0254	.0286	.0190	.0190	.0190
	E	351	94	80	64	80	64	74
6x10 83 lb/beam 13.8 lb/ft	F_b	.653	.2176	.1934	.1632	.1451	.1088	.1451
	F_v	.063	.0144	.0191	.0215	.0144	.0144	.0144
	E	371	99	84	68	84	68	78
3x16 60 lb/beam 10.1 lb/ft	F_b	.572	.1907	.1695	.1430	.1271	.0954	.1271
	F_v	.068	.0197	.0262	.0295	.0197	.0197	.0197
	E	197	53	45	36	45	36	42
4x14 73 lb/beam 12.2 lb/ft	F_b	.527	.1758	.1562	.1318	.1172	.0879	.1172
	F_v	.061	.0162	.0216	.0243	.0162	.0162	.0162
	E	215	57	49	39	49	39	45
8x10 113 lb/beam 18.8 lb/ft	F_b	.479	.1596	.1418	.1197	.1064	.0798	.1064
	F_v	.046	.0105	.0140	.0158	.0105	.0105	.0105
	E	272	73	62	50	62	50	57
6x12 100 lb/beam 16.7 lb/ft	F_b	.445	.1485	.1320	.1114	.0990	.0742	.0990
	F_v	.048	.0119	.0158	.0178	.0119	.0119	.0119
	E	209	56	48	38	48	38	44
4x16 85 lb/beam 14.1 lb/ft	F_b	.409	.1362	.1211	.1022	.0908	.0681	.0908
	F_v	.049	.0141	.0187	.0211	.0141	.0141	.0141
	E	141	38	32	26	32	26	30

7 FOOT SPAN

Nominal Size (Inches)	Property	UNIFORM	Single Load — At Center of Span	Single Load — At Third Point	Single Load — At Quarter Point	Sum of Two Equal Loads — At Third Point	Sum of Two Equal Loads — At Quarter Points From Reactions	Sum of 3 Equal Loads — At Quarter Points and Center of Span
2x3 7 lb/beam 1.0 lb/ft	F_b	47.040	13.4400	11.9467	10.0800	8.9600	6.7200	8.9600
	F_v	1.317	.2000	.2667	.3000	.2000	.2000	.2000
	E	118.541	27,095	23,092	18,628	23,092	18,628	21,450

STRENGTH AND STIFFNESS REQUIREMENTS FOR BEAMS

See instructions for use of tables on page 101. Symbols used in the tables are as follows: Tabulated values are based on net size.

F_b = Extreme fiber stress in bending induced by a uniform load of 1 (one) plf or by a concentrated load of 1 (one) pound, psi

F_v = Horizontal shear stress induced by a uniform load of 1 (one) plf or a total concentrated load of 1 (one) pound, psi.

E = Modulus of elasticity value needed to limit deflection to 1/360 of the span for a uniform load of 1 (one) plf or a total concentrated load of 1 (one) pound, psi.

7 FOOT SPAN

Nominal Size (Inches)	Property	UNIFORM	CONCENTRATED — Single Load — At Center of Span	At Third Point	At Quarter Point	Sum of Two Equal Loads — At Third Point	At Quarter Points From Reactions	Sum of 3 Equal Loads — At Quarter Points and Center of Span
2x4 10 lb/beam 1.4 lb/ft	F_b F_v E	24.000 .917 43,200	6.8571 .1429 9,874	6.0952 .1905 8,416	5.1429 .2143 6,789	4.5714 .1429 8,416	3.4286 .1429 6,789	4.5714 .1429 7,817
3x4 16 lb/beam 2.3 lb/ft	F_b F_v E	14.400 .550 25,920	4.1143 .0857 5,925	3.6571 .1143 5,049	3.0857 .1286 4,073	2.7429 .0857 5,049	2.0571 .0857 4,073	2.7429 .0857 4,690
2x6 15 lb/beam 2.2 lb/ft	F_b F_v E	9.719 .553 11,133	2.7769 .0909 2,545	2.4683 .1212 2,169	2.0826 .1364 1,749	1.8512 .0909 2,169	1.3884 .0909 1,749	1.8512 .0909 2,014
3x6 25 lb/beam 3.6 lb/ft	F_b F_v E	5.831 .332 6,680	1.6661 .0545 1,527	1.4810 .0727 1,301	1.2496 .0818 1,050	1.1107 .0545 1,301	.8331 .0545 1,050	1.1107 .0545 1,209
2x8 20 lb/beam 2.9 lb/ft	F_b F_v E	5.593 .399 4,860	1.5981 .0690 1,111	1.4205 .0920 947	1.1986 .1034 764	1.0654 .0690 947	.7990 .0690 764	1.0654 .0690 880
4x6 36 lb/beam 5.1 lb/ft	F_b F_v E	4.165 .237 4,771	1.1901 .0390 1,091	1.0579 .0519 929	.8926 .0584 750	.7934 .0390 929	.5950 .0390 750	.7934 .0390 863
2x10 26 lb/beam 3.7 lb/ft	F_b F_v E	3.436 .295 2,340	.9817 .0541 535	.8727 .0721 456	.7363 .0811 368	.6545 .0541 456	.4909 .0541 368	.6545 .0541 423
3x8 33 lb/beam 4.8 lb/ft	F_b F_v E	3.356 .240 2,916	.9589 .0414 667	.8523 .0552 568	.7191 .0621 458	.6392 .0414 568	.4794 .0414 458	.6392 .0414 528
6x6 56 lb/beam 8.0 lb/ft	F_b F_v E	2.651 .151 3,036	.7573 .0248 694	.6732 .0331 591	.5680 .0372 477	.5049 .0248 591	.3787 .0248 477	.5049 .0248 549
4x8 47 lb/beam 6.7 lb/ft	F_b F_v E	2.397 .171 2,083	.6849 .0296 476	.6068 .0394 406	.5137 .0443 327	.4566 .0296 406	.3425 .0296 327	.4566 .0296 377

7 FOOT SPAN (Continued)

Nominal Size (Inches)	Property	UNIFORM	CONCENTRATED — Single Load — At Center of Span	At Third Point	At Quarter Point	Sum of Two Equal Loads — At Third Point	At Quarter Points From Reactions	Sum of 3 Equal Loads — At Quarter Points and Center of Span
2x12 31 lb/beam 4.5 lb/ft	F_b F_v E	2.323 .228 1,301	.6637 .0444 297	.5900 .0593 253	.4978 .0667 204	.4425 .0444 253	.3319 .0444 204	.4425 .0444 235
3x10 43 lb/beam 6.1 lb/ft	F_b F_v E	2.062 .177 1,404	.5890 .0324 321	.5236 .0432 274	.4418 .0486 221	.3927 .0324 274	.2945 .0324 221	.3927 .0324 254
2x14 37 lb/beam 5.2 lb/ft	F_b F_v E	1.675 .181 796	.4785 .0377 182	.4253 .0503 155	.3588 .0566 125	.3190 .0377 155	.2392 .0377 125	.3190 .0377 144
4x10 60 lb/beam 8.5 lb/ft	F_b F_v E	1.473 .126 1,003	.4207 .0232 229	.3740 .0309 195	.3156 .0347 158	.2805 .0232 195	.2104 .0232 158	.2805 .0232 181
6x8 76 lb/beam 10.9 lb/ft	F_b F_v E	1.425 .105 1,197	.4073 .0182 274	.3620 .0242 233	.3055 .0273 188	.2715 .0182 233	.2036 .0182 188	.2715 .0182 217
3x12 52 lb/beam 7.4 lb/ft	F_b F_v E	1.394 .137 781	.3982 .0267 178	.3540 .0356 152	.2987 .0400 123	.2655 .0267 152	.1991 .0267 123	.2655 .0267 141
8x8 104 lb/beam 14.8 lb/ft	F_b F_v E	1.045 .077 878	.2987 .0133 201	.2655 .0178 171	.2240 .0200 138	.1991 .0133 171	.1493 .0133 138	.1991 .0133 159
3x14 61 lb/beam 8.7 lb/ft	F_b F_v E	1.005 .108 478	.2871 .0226 109	.2552 .0302 93	.2153 .0340 75	.1914 .0226 93	.1435 .0226 75	.1914 .0226 86
4x12 73 lb/beam 10.4 lb/ft	F_b F_v E	.996 .098 558	.2844 .0190 127	.2528 .0254 109	.2133 .0286 88	.1896 .0190 109	.1422 .0190 88	.1896 .0190 101
6x10 97 lb/beam 13.8 lb/ft	F_b F_v E	.888 .078 589	.2538 .0144 135	.2256 .0191 115	.1904 .0215 93	.1692 .0144 115	.1269 .0144 93	.1692 .0144 107
3x16 70 lb/beam 10.1 lb/ft	F_b F_v E	.779 .088 313	.2225 .0197 72	.1978 .0262 61	.1669 .0295 49	.1483 .0197 61	.1113 .0197 49	.1483 .0197 57

STRENGTH AND STIFFNESS REQUIREMENTS FOR BEAMS

See instructions for use of tables on page 101. Symbols used in the tables are as follows: Tabulated values are based on net size.

F_b = Extreme fiber stress in bending induced by a uniform load of 1 (one) plf or by a concentrated load of 1 (one) pound, psi

F_v = Horizontal shear stress induced by a uniform load of 1 (one) plf or a total concentrated load of 1 (one) pound, psi.

E = Modulus of elasticity value needed to limit deflection to 1/360 of the span for a uniform load of 1 (one) plf or a total concentrated load of 1 (one) pound, psi.

7 FOOT SPAN

Nominal Size (Inches)	Property	UNIFORM	CONCENTRATED Single Load — At Center of Span	Single Load — At Third Point	Single Load — At Quarter Point	Sum of Two Equal Loads — At Third Point	Sum of Two Equal Loads — At Quarter Points From Reactions	Sum of 3 Equal Loads — At Quarter Points and Center of Span
2x6 — 17 lb/beam — 2.2 lb/ft	F_b / F_v / E	12.694 / .644 / 16.618	3.1736 / .0909 / 3,324	2.8209 / .1212 / 2,833	2.3802 / .1364 / 2,285	2.1157 / .0909 / 2,833	1.5868 / .0909 / 2,285	2.1157 / .0909 / 2,631
3x6 — 29 lb/beam — 3.6 lb/ft	F_b / F_v / E	7.617 / .386 / 9.971	1.9041 / .0545 / 1,994	1.6926 / .0727 / 1,700	1.4281 / .0818 / 1,371	1.2694 / .0545 / 1,700	.9521 / .0545 / 1,371	1.2694 / .0545 / 1,579
2x8 — 23 lb/beam — 2.9 lb/ft	F_b / F_v / E	7.306 / .468 / 7.255	1.8264 / .0690 / 1,451	1.6235 / .0920 / 1,237	1.3698 / .1034 / 998	1.2176 / .0690 / 1,237	.9132 / .0690 / 998	1.2176 / .0690 / 1,149
4x6 — 41 lb/beam — 5.1 lb/ft	F_b / F_v / E	5.440 / .276 / 7.122	1.3601 / .0390 / 1,424	1.2090 / .0519 / 1,214	1.0201 / .0584 / 979	.9067 / .0390 / 1,214	.6800 / .0390 / 979	.9067 / .0390 / 1,128
2x10 — 29 lb/beam — 3.7 lb/ft	F_b / F_v / E	4.488 / .349 / 3.493	1.1220 / .0541 / 699	.9973 / .0721 / 595	.8415 / .0811 / 480	.7480 / .0541 / 595	.5610 / .0541 / 480	.7480 / .0541 / 553
3x8 — 38 lb/beam — 4.8 lb/ft	F_b / F_v / E	4.383 / .281 / 4.353	1.0958 / .0414 / 871	.9741 / .0552 / 742	.8219 / .0621 / 599	.7306 / .0414 / 742	.5479 / .0414 / 599	.7306 / .0414 / 689
6x6 — 64 lb/beam — 8.0 lb/ft	F_b / F_v / E	3.462 / .176 / 4.532	.8655 / .0248 / 906	.7693 / .0331 / 773	.6491 / .0372 / 623	.5770 / .0248 / 773	.4328 / .0248 / 623	.5770 / .0248 / 718
4x8 — 54 lb/beam — 6.7 lb/ft	F_b / F_v / E	3.131 / .201 / 3.109	.7827 / .0296 / 622	.6958 / .0394 / 530	.5871 / .0443 / 428	.5218 / .0296 / 530	.3914 / .0296 / 428	.5218 / .0296 / 492
2x12 — 36 lb/beam — 4.5 lb/ft	F_b / F_v / E	3.034 / .272 / 1.942	.7585 / .0444 / 388	.6742 / .0593 / 331	.5689 / .0667 / 267	.5057 / .0444 / 331	.3793 / .0444 / 267	.5057 / .0444 / 307
3x10 — 49 lb/beam — 6.1 lb/ft	F_b / F_v / E	2.693 / .209 / 2.096	.6732 / .0324 / 419	.5984 / .0432 / 357	.5049 / .0486 / 288	.4488 / .0324 / 357	.3366 / .0324 / 288	.4488 / .0324 / 332
2x14 — 42 lb/beam — 5.2 lb/ft	F_b / F_v / E	2.187 / .219 / 1.189	.5468 / .0377 / 238	.4861 / .0503 / 203	.4101 / .0566 / 163	.3645 / .0377 / 203	.2734 / .0377 / 163	.3645 / .0377 / 188

7 FOOT SPAN (Continued)

Nominal Size (Inches)	Property	UNIFORM	Single Load — At Center of Span	Single Load — At Third Point	Single Load — At Quarter Point	Sum of Two Equal Loads — At Third Point	Sum of Two Equal Loads — At Quarter Points From Reactions	Sum of 3 Equal Loads — At Quarter Points and Center of Span
4x14 — 86 lb/beam — 12.2 lb/ft	F_b / F_v / E	.718 / .077 / 341	.2051 / .0162 / 78	.1823 / .0216 / 66	.1538 / .0243 / 54	.1367 / .0162 / 66	.1025 / .0162 / 54	.1367 / .0162 / 62
8x10 — 132 lb/beam — 18.8 lb/ft	F_b / F_v / E	.652 / .057 / 432	.1861 / .0105 / 99	.1655 / .0140 / 84	.1396 / .0158 / 68	.1241 / .0105 / 84	.0931 / .0105 / 68	.1241 / .0105 / 78
6x12 — 117 lb/beam — 16.7 lb/ft	F_b / F_v / E	.606 / .060 / 332	.1732 / .0119 / 76	.1540 / .0158 / 65	.1299 / .0178 / 52	.1155 / .0119 / 65	.0866 / .0119 / 52	.1155 / .0119 / 60
4x16 — 99 lb/beam — 14.1 lb/ft	F_b / F_v / E	.556 / .063 / 224	.1589 / .0141 / 51	.1413 / .0187 / 44	.1192 / .0211 / 35	.1060 / .0141 / 44	.0795 / .0141 / 35	.1060 / .0141 / 41
10x10 — 167 lb/beam — 23.8 lb/ft	F_b / F_v / E	.514 / .045 / 341	.1470 / .0083 / 78	.1306 / .0111 / 66	.1102 / .0125 / 54	.0980 / .0083 / 66	.0735 / .0083 / 54	.0980 / .0083 / 62
8x12 — 159 lb/beam — 22.8 lb/ft	F_b / F_v / E	.445 / .044 / 244	.1270 / .0087 / 56	.1129 / .0116 / 47	.0953 / .0130 / 38	.0847 / .0087 / 47	.0635 / .0087 / 38	.0847 / .0087 / 44
6x14 — 137 lb/beam — 19.6 lb/ft	F_b / F_v / E	.446 / .048 / 205	.1274 / .0101 / 47	.1132 / .0135 / 40	.0955 / .0152 / 32	.0849 / .0101 / 40	.0637 / .0101 / 32	.0849 / .0101 / 37

8 FOOT SPAN

Nominal Size (Inches)	Property	UNIFORM	Single Load — At Center of Span	Single Load — At Third Point	Single Load — At Quarter Point	Sum of Two Equal Loads — At Third Point	Sum of Two Equal Loads — At Quarter Points From Reactions	Sum of 3 Equal Loads — At Quarter Points and Center of Span
2x4 — 11 lb/beam — 1.4 lb/ft	F_b / F_v / E	31.347 / 1.060 / 64.485	7.8367 / .1429 / 12.897	6.9660 / .1905 / 10.992	5.8776 / .2143 / 8.867	5.2245 / .1429 / 10.992	3.9184 / .1429 / 8.867	5.2245 / .1429 / 10.210
3x4 — 18 lb/beam — 2.3 lb/ft	F_b / F_v / E	18.808 / .636 / 38.691	4.7020 / .0857 / 7.738	4.1796 / .1143 / 6.595	3.5265 / .1286 / 5.320	3.1347 / .0857 / 6.595	2.3510 / .0857 / 5.320	3.1347 / .0857 / 6.126

STRENGTH AND STIFFNESS REQUIREMENTS FOR BEAMS

See instructions for use of tables on page 101. Symbols used in the tables are as follows: Tabulated values are based on net size.

F_b = Extreme fiber stress in bending induced by a uniform load of 1 (one) plf or by a concentrated load of 1 (one) pound, psi

F_v = Horizontal shear stress induced by a uniform load of 1 (one) plf or a total concentrated load of 1 (one) pound, psi.

E = Modulus of elasticity value needed to limit deflection to 1/360 of the span for a uniform load of 1 (one) plf or a total concentrated load of 1 (one) pound, psi.

8 FOOT SPAN

Nominal Size (Inches)	Property	UNIFORM	Single Load — At Center of Span	Single Load — At Third Point	Single Load — At Quarter Point	Sum of Two Equal Loads — At Third Point	Sum of Two Equal Loads — At Quarter Points From Reactions	Sum of 3 Equal Loads — At Quarter Points and Center of Span
4x10 — 68 lb/beam — 8.5 lb/ft	F_b	1.923	.4809	.4274	.3606	.3206	.2404	.3206
	F_v	.150	.0232	.0309	.0347	.0232	.0232	.0232
	E	1,497	299	255	206	255	206	237
6x8 — 87 lb/beam — 10.9 lb/ft	F_b	1.862	.4655	.4137	.3491	.3103	.2327	.3103
	F_v	.123	.0182	.0242	.0273	.0182	.0182	.0182
	E	1,787	357	305	246	305	246	283
3x12 — 59 lb/beam — 7.4 lb/ft	F_b	1.820	.4551	.4045	.3413	.3034	.2276	.3034
	F_v	.163	.0267	.0356	.0400	.0267	.0267	.0267
	E	1,165	233	199	160	199	160	184
8x8 — 119 lb/beam — 14.8 lb/ft	F_b	1.365	.3413	.3034	.2560	.2276	.1707	.2276
	F_v	.090	.0133	.0178	.0200	.0133	.0133	.0133
	E	1,311	262	223	180	223	180	208
3x14 — 70 lb/beam — 8.7 lb/ft	F_b	1.312	.3281	.2916	.2461	.2187	.1640	.2187
	F_v	.131	.0226	.0302	.0340	.0226	.0226	.0226
	E	713	143	122	98	122	98	113
4x12 — 83 lb/beam — 10.4 lb/ft	F_b	1.300	.3251	.2890	.2438	.2167	.1625	.2167
	F_v	.117	.0190	.0254	.0286	.0190	.0190	.0190
	E	832	166	142	114	142	114	132
6x10 — 110 lb/beam — 13.8 lb/ft	F_b	1.160	.2901	.2579	.2176	.1934	.1451	.1934
	F_v	.092	.0144	.0191	.0215	.0144	.0144	.0144
	E	879	176	150	121	150	121	139
3x16 — 80 lb/beam — 10.1 lb/ft	F_b	1.017	.2543	.2260	.1907	.1695	.1271	.1695
	F_v	.107	.0197	.0262	.0295	.0197	.0197	.0197
	E	468	94	80	64	80	64	74
4x14 — 98 lb/beam — 12.2 lb/ft	F_b	.937	.2344	.2083	.1758	.1562	.1172	.1562
	F_v	.094	.0162	.0216	.0243	.0162	.0162	.0162
	E	509	102	87	70	87	70	81
8x10 — 150 lb/beam — 18.8 lb/ft	F_b	.851	.2127	.1891	.1596	.1418	.1064	.1418
	F_v	.068	.0105	.0140	.0158	.0105	.0105	.0105
	E	645	129	110	89	110	89	102

8 FOOT SPAN (Continued)

Nominal Size (Inches)	Property	UNIFORM	Single Load — At Center of Span	Single Load — At Third Point	Single Load — At Quarter Point	Sum of Two Equal Loads — At Third Point	Sum of Two Equal Loads — At Quarter Points From Reactions	Sum of 3 Equal Loads — At Quarter Points and Center of Span
6x12 — 134 lb/beam — 16.7 lb/ft	F_b	.792	.1980	.1760	.1485	.1320	.0990	.1320
	F_v	.072	.0119	.0158	.0178	.0119	.0119	.0119
	E	496	99	85	68	85	68	79
4x16 — 113 lb/beam — 14.1 lb/ft	F_b	.727	.1816	.1615	.1362	.1211	.0908	.1211
	F_v	.077	.0141	.0187	.0211	.0141	.0141	.0141
	E	334	67	57	46	57	46	53
10x10 — 191 lb/beam — 23.8 lb/ft	F_b	.672	.1680	.1493	.1260	.1120	.0840	.1120
	F_v	.053	.0083	.0111	.0125	.0083	.0083	.0083
	E	509	102	87	70	87	70	81
8x12 — 182 lb/beam — 22.8 lb/ft	F_b	.581	.1452	.1290	.1089	.0968	.0726	.0968
	F_v	.053	.0087	.0116	.0130	.0087	.0087	.0087
	E	364	73	62	50	62	50	58
6x14 — 157 lb/beam — 19.6 lb/ft	F_b	.582	.1456	.1294	.1092	.0970	.0728	.0970
	F_v	.058	.0101	.0135	.0152	.0101	.0101	.0101
	E	306	61	52	42	52	42	49
10x12 — 231 lb/beam — 28.8 lb/ft	F_b	.458	.1146	.1019	.0860	.0764	.0573	.0764
	F_v	.042	.0069	.0092	.0103	.0069	.0069	.0069
	E	287	57	49	39	49	39	45
6x16 — 180 lb/beam — 22.5 lb/ft	F_b	.448	.1121	.0997	.0841	.0747	.0561	.0747
	F_v	.048	.0088	.0117	.0132	.0088	.0088	.0088
	E	202	40	35	28	35	28	32

9 FOOT SPAN

Nominal Size (Inches)	Property	UNIFORM	Single Load — At Center of Span	Single Load — At Third Point	Single Load — At Quarter Point	Sum of Two Equal Loads — At Third Point	Sum of Two Equal Loads — At Quarter Points From Reactions	Sum of 3 Equal Loads — At Quarter Points and Center of Span
2x4 — 12 lb/beam — 1.4 lb/ft	F_b	39.673	8.8163	7.8367	6.6122	5.8776	4.4082	5.8776
	F_v	1.202	.1429	.1905	.2143	.1429	.1429	.1429
	E	91,816	16,323	13,911	11,222	13,911	11,222	12,922
3x4 — 21 lb/beam — 2.3 lb/ft	F_b	23.804	5.2898	4.7020	3.9673	3.5265	2.6449	3.5265
	F_v	.721	.0857	.1143	.1286	.0857	.0857	.0857
	E	55,089	9,794	8,347	6,733	8,347	6,733	7,753
2x6 — 20 lb/beam — 2.2 lb/ft	F_b	16.066	3.5702	3.1736	2.6777	2.3802	1.7851	2.3802
	F_v	.735	.0909	.1212	.1364	.0909	.0909	.0909
	E	23,661	4,206	3,585	2,892	3,585	2,892	3,330

STRENGTH AND STIFFNESS REQUIREMENTS FOR BEAMS

See instructions for use of tables on page 101. Symbols used in the tables are as follows: Tabulated values are based on net size.

F_b = Extreme fiber stress in bending induced by a uniform load of 1 (one) plf or by a concentrated load of 1 (one) pound, psi

F_v = Horizontal shear stress induced by a uniform load of 1 (one) plf or a total concentrated load of 1 (one) pound, psi.

E = Modulus of elasticity value needed to limit deflection to 1/360 of the span for a uniform load of 1 (one) plf or a total concentrated load of 1 (one) pound, psi.

9 FOOT SPAN (Continued)

Nominal Size (Inches)	Property	UNIFORM	Single Load — At Center of Span	Single Load — At Third Point	Single Load — At Quarter Point	Sum of Two Equal Loads — At Third Point	Sum of Two Equal Loads — At Quarter Points From Reactions	Sum of 3 Equal Loads — At Quarter Points and Center of Span
4x10 77 lb/beam 8.5 lb/ft	F_b	2.434	.5410	.4809	.4057	.3606	.2705	.3606
	F_v	.173	.0232	.0309	.0347	.0232	.0232	.0232
	E	2,132	379	323	261	323	261	300
6x8 98 lb/beam 10.9 lb/ft	F_b	2.356	.5236	.4655	.3927	.3491	.2618	.3491
	F_v	.141	.0182	.0242	.0273	.0182	.0182	.0182
	E	2,545	452	386	311	386	311	358
3x12 67 lb/beam 7.4 lb/ft	F_b	2.304	.5120	.4551	.3840	.3413	.2560	.3413
	F_v	.190	.0267	.0356	.0400	.0267	.0267	.0267
	E	1,659	295	251	203	251	203	233
8x8 134 lb/beam 14.8 lb/ft	F_b	1.728	.3840	.3413	.2880	.2560	.1920	.2560
	F_v	.103	.0133	.0178	.0200	.0133	.0133	.0133
	E	1,866	332	283	228	283	228	263
3x14 79 lb/beam 8.7 lb/ft	F_b	1.661	.3691	.3281	.2768	.2461	.1846	.2461
	F_v	.154	.0226	.0302	.0340	.0226	.0226	.0226
	E	1,015	181	154	124	154	124	143
4x12 94 lb/beam 10.4 lb/ft	F_b	1.646	.3657	.3251	.2743	.2438	.1829	.2438
	F_v	.136	.0190	.0254	.0286	.0190	.0190	.0190
	E	1,185	211	180	145	180	145	167
6x10 124 lb/beam 13.8 lb/ft	F_b	1.469	.3264	.2901	.2448	.2176	.1632	.2176
	F_v	.106	.0144	.0191	.0215	.0144	.0144	.0144
	E	1,252	223	190	153	190	153	176
3x16 91 lb/beam 10.1 lb/ft	F_b	1.287	.2861	.2543	.2146	.1907	.1430	.1907
	F_v	.127	.0197	.0262	.0295	.0197	.0197	.0197
	E	666	118	101	81	101	81	94
4x14 110 lb/beam 12.2 lb/ft	F_b	1.186	.2636	.2343	.1977	.1758	.1318	.1758
	F_v	.110	.0162	.0216	.0243	.0162	.0162	.0162
	E	725	129	110	89	110	89	102
8x10 169 lb/beam 18.8 lb/ft	F_b	1.077	.2393	.2127	.1795	.1596	.1197	.1596
	F_v	.078	.0105	.0140	.0158	.0105	.0105	.0105
	E	918	163	139	112	139	112	129
6x12 150 lb/beam 16.7 lb/ft	F_b	1.002	.2227	.1980	.1670	.1485	.1114	.1485
	F_v	.084	.0119	.0158	.0178	.0119	.0119	.0119
	E	706	125	107	86	107	86	99

9 FOOT SPAN (Continued)

Nominal Size (Inches)	Property	UNIFORM	Single Load — At Center of Span	Single Load — At Third Point	Single Load — At Quarter Point	Sum of Two Equal Loads — At Third Point	Sum of Two Equal Loads — At Quarter Points From Reactions	Sum of 3 Equal Loads — At Quarter Points and Center of Span
3x6 33 lb/beam 3.6 lb/ft	F_b	9.640	2.1421	1.9041	1.6066	1.4281	1.0711	1.4281
	F_v	.441	.0545	.0727	.0818	.0545	.0545	.0545
	E	14,197	2,524	2,151	1,735	2,151	1,735	1,998
2x8 26 lb/beam 2.9 lb/ft	F_b	9.246	2.0547	1.8264	1.5410	1.3698	1.0273	1.3698
	F_v	.537	.0690	.0920	.1034	.0690	.0690	.0690
	E	10,330	1,836	1,565	1,263	1,565	1,263	1,454
4x6 46 lb/beam 5.1 lb/ft	F_b	6.885	1.5301	1.3601	1.1476	1.0201	.7651	1.0201
	F_v	.315	.0390	.0519	.0584	.0390	.0390	.0390
	E	10,140	1,803	1,536	1,239	1,536	1,239	1,427
2x10 33 lb/beam 3.7 lb/ft	F_b	5.680	1.2622	1.1220	.9467	.8415	.6311	.8415
	F_v	.403	.0541	.0721	.0811	.0541	.0541	.0541
	E	4,974	884	754	608	754	608	700
3x8 43 lb/beam 4.8 lb/ft	F_b	5.548	1.2328	1.0958	.9246	.8219	.6164	.8219
	F_v	.322	.0414	.0552	.0621	.0414	.0414	.0414
	E	6,198	1,102	939	758	939	758	872
6x6 72 lb/beam 8.0 lb/ft	F_b	4.382	.9737	.8655	.7303	.6491	.4869	.6491
	F_v	.200	.0248	.0331	.0372	.0248	.0248	.0248
	E	6,453	1,147	978	789	978	789	908
4x8 60 lb/beam 6.7 lb/ft	F_b	3.963	.8806	.7827	.6604	.5871	.4403	.5871
	F_v	.230	.0296	.0394	.0443	.0296	.0296	.0296
	E	4,427	787	671	541	671	541	623
2x12 40 lb/beam 4.5 lb/ft	F_b	3.840	.8533	.7585	.6400	.5689	.4267	.5689
	F_v	.317	.0444	.0593	.0667	.0444	.0444	.0444
	E	2,765	492	419	338	419	338	389
3x10 55 lb/beam 6.1 lb/ft	F_b	3.408	.7573	.6732	.5680	.5049	.3787	.5049
	F_v	.242	.0324	.0432	.0486	.0324	.0324	.0324
	E	2,984	531	452	365	452	365	420
2x14 47 lb/beam 5.2 lb/ft	F_b	2.768	.6152	.5468	.4614	.4101	.3076	.4101
	F_v	.256	.0377	.0503	.0566	.0377	.0377	.0377
	E	1,692	301	256	207	256	207	238

STRENGTH AND STIFFNESS REQUIREMENTS FOR BEAMS

See instructions for use of tables on page 101. Symbols used in the tables are as follows: Tabulated values are based on net size.

F_b = Extreme fiber stress in bending induced by a uniform load of 1 (one) plf or by a concentrated load of 1 (one) pound, psi.

F_v = Horizontal shear stress induced by a uniform load of 1 (one) plf or a total concentrated load of 1 (one) pound, psi.

E = Modulus of elasticity value needed to limit deflection to 1/360 of the span for a uniform load of 1 (one) plf or a total concentrated load of 1 (one) pound, psi.

9 FOOT SPAN (Continued)

Nominal Size (Inches)	Property	UNIFORM	Single Load – At Center of Span	Single Load – At Third Point	Single Load – At Quarter Point	Sum of Two Equal Loads – At Third Point	Sum of Two Equal Loads – At Quarter Points From Reactions	Sum of 3 Equal Loads – At Quarter Points and Center of Span
4x16 127 lb/beam 14.1 lb/ft	F_b F_v E	.920 .091 476	.2043 .0141 85	.1816 .0187 72	.1533 .0211 58	.1362 .0141 72	.1022 .0141 58	.1362 .0141 67
10x10 214 lb/beam 23.8 lb/ft	F_b F_v E	.850 .062 725	.1889 .0083 129	.1680 .0111 110	.1417 .0125 89	.1260 .0083 110	.0945 .0083 89	.1260 .0083 102
8x12 205 lb/beam 22.8 lb/ft	F_b F_v E	.735 .062 518	.1633 .0087 92	.1452 .0116 78	.1225 .0130 63	.1089 .0087 78	.0817 .0087 63	.1089 .0087 73
6x14 176 lb/beam 19.6 lb/ft	F_b F_v E	.737 .068 436	.1637 .0101 78	.1456 .0135 66	.1228 .0152 53	.1092 .0101 66	.0819 .0101 53	.1092 .0101 61
10x12 259 lb/beam 28.8 lb/ft	F_b F_v E	.580 .049 409	.1289 .0069 73	.1146 .0092 62	.0967 .0103 50	.0860 .0069 62	.0645 .0069 50	.0860 .0069 58
6x16 202 lb/beam 22.5 lb/ft	F_b F_v E	.568 .056 288	.1261 .0088 51	.1121 .0117 44	.0946 .0132 35	.0841 .0088 44	.0631 .0088 35	.0841 .0088 41
8x14 240 lb/beam 26.7 lb/ft	F_b F_v E	.540 .050 320	.1201 .0074 57	.1067 .0099 48	.0901 .0111 39	.0801 .0074 48	.0600 .0074 39	.0801 .0074 45
12x12 314 lb/beam 34.9 lb/ft	F_b F_v E	.479 .040 338	.1065 .0057 60	.0947 .0076 51	.0799 .0085 41	.0710 .0057 51	.0533 .0057 41	.0710 .0057 48
6x18 229 lb/beam 25.4 lb/ft	F_b F_v E	.451 .047 200	.1003 .0078 36	.0891 .0104 30	.0752 .0117 24	.0669 .0078 30	.0501 .0078 24	.0669 .0078 28

10 FOOT SPAN

Nominal Size (Inches)	Property	UNIFORM	Single Load – At Center of Span	Single Load – At Third Point	Single Load – At Quarter Point	Sum of Two Equal Loads – At Third Point	Sum of Two Equal Loads – At Quarter Points From Reactions	Sum of 3 Equal Loads – At Quarter Points and Center of Span
2x4 14 lb/beam 1.4 lb/ft	F_b F_v E	48.980 1.345 125,948	9.7959 .1429 20,152	8.7075 .1905 17,175	7.3469 .2143 13,854	6.5306 .1429 17,175	4.8980 .1429 13,854	6.5306 .1429 15,953
3x4 23 lb/beam 2.3 lb/ft	F_b F_v E	29.388 .807 75,569	5.8776 .0857 12,091	5.2245 .1143 10,305	4.4082 .1286 8,313	3.9184 .0857 10,305	2.9388 .0857 8,313	3.9184 .0857 9,572
2x6 22 lb/beam 2.2 lb/ft	F_b F_v E	19.835 .826 32,457	3.9669 .0909 5,193	3.5262 .1212 4,426	2.9752 .1364 3,570	2.6446 .0909 4,426	1.9835 .0909 3,570	2.6446 .0909 4,111
3x6 36 lb/beam 3.6 lb/ft	F_b F_v E	11.901 .495 19,474	2.3802 .0545 3,116	2.1157 .0727 2,656	1.7851 .0818 2,142	1.5868 .0545 2,656	1.1901 .0545 2,142	1.5868 .0545 2,467
2x8 29 lb/beam 2.9 lb/ft	F_b F_v E	11.415 .606 14,170	2.2830 .0690 2,267	2.0293 .0920 1,932	1.7122 .1034 1,559	1.5220 .0690 1,932	1.1415 .0690 1,559	1.5220 .0690 1,795
4x6 51 lb/beam 5.1 lb/ft	F_b F_v E	8.501 .354 13,910	1.7001 .0390 2,226	1.5112 .0519 1,897	1.2751 .0584 1,530	1.1334 .0390 1,897	.8501 .0390 1,530	1.1334 .0390 1,762
2x10 37 lb/beam 3.7 lb/ft	F_b F_v E	7.012 .457 6,823	1.4025 .0541 1,092	1.2467 .0721 930	1.0519 .0811 751	.9350 .0541 930	.7012 .0541 751	.9350 .0541 864
3x8 48 lb/beam 4.8 lb/ft	F_b F_v E	6.849 .364 8,502	1.3698 .0414 1,360	1.2176 .0552 1,159	1.0273 .0621 935	.9132 .0414 1,159	.6849 .0414 935	.9132 .0414 1,077
6x6 80 lb/beam 8.0 lb/ft	F_b F_v E	5.409 .225 8,852	1.0819 .0248 1,416	.9617 .0331 1,207	.8114 .0372 974	.7213 .0248 1,207	.5409 .0248 974	.7213 .0248 1,121

STRENGTH AND STIFFNESS REQUIREMENTS FOR BEAMS

See instructions for use of tables on page 101. Symbols used in the tables are as follows: Tabulated values are based on net size.

F_b = Extreme fiber stress in bending induced by a uniform load of 1 (one) plf or by a concentrated load of 1 (one) pound, psi
F_v = Horizontal shear stress induced by a uniform load of 1 (one) plf or a total concentrated load of 1 (one) pound, psi.
E = Modulus of elasticity value needed to limit deflection to 1/360 of the span for a uniform load of 1 (one) plf or a total concentrated load of 1 (one) pound, psi.

10 FOOT SPAN (Continued)

Nominal Size (Inches)	Property	UNIFORM	CONCENTRATED — Single Load — At Center of Span	At Third Point	At Quarter Point	Sum of Two Equal Loads — At Third Point	At Quarter Points From Reactions	Sum of 3 Equal Loads — At Quarter Points and Center of Span
4x8 67 lb/beam 6.7 lb/ft	F_b F_v E	4.892 .260 6,073	.9784 .0296 972	.8697 .0394 828	.7338 .0443 668	.6523 .0296 828	.4892 .0296 668	.6523 .0296 769
2x12 45 lb/beam 4.5 lb/ft	F_b F_v E	4.741 .361 3,793	.9481 .0444 607	.8428 .0593 517	.7111 .0667 417	.6321 .0444 517	.4741 .0444 417	.6321 .0444 480
3x10 61 lb/beam 6.1 lb/ft	F_b F_v E	4.207 .274 4,094	.8415 .0324 655	.7480 .0432 558	.6311 .0486 450	.5610 .0324 558	.4207 .0324 450	.5610 .0324 519
2x14 52 lb/beam 5.2 lb/ft	F_b F_v E	3.418 .294 2,321	.6835 .0377 371	.6076 .0503 317	.5126 .0566 255	.4557 .0377 317	.3418 .0377 255	.4557 .0377 294
4x10 85 lb/beam 8.5 lb/ft	F_b F_v E	3.005 .196 2,924	.6011 .0232 468	.5343 .0309 399	.4508 .0347 322	.4007 .0232 399	.3005 .0232 322	.4007 .0232 370
6x8 109 lb/beam 10.9 lb/ft	F_b F_v E	2.909 .159 3,491	.5818 .0182 559	.5172 .0242 476	.4364 .0273 384	.3879 .0182 476	.2909 .0182 384	.3879 .0182 442
3x12 74 lb/beam 7.4 lb/ft	F_b F_v E	2.844 .217 2,276	.5689 .0267 364	.5057 .0356 310	.4267 .0400 250	.3793 .0267 310	.2844 .0267 250	.3793 .0267 288
8x8 148 lb/beam 14.8 lb/ft	F_b F_v E	2.133 .117 2,560	.4267 .0133 410	.3793 .0178 349	.3200 .0200 282	.2844 .0133 349	.2133 .0133 282	.2844 .0133 324
3x14 87 lb/beam 8.7 lb/ft	F_b F_v E	2.051 .176 1,393	.4101 .0226 223	.3645 .0302 190	.3076 .0340 153	.2734 .0226 190	.2051 .0226 153	.2734 .0226 176
4x12 104 lb/beam 10.4 lb/ft	F_b F_v E	2.032 .155 1,625	.4064 .0190 260	.3612 .0254 222	.3048 .0286 179	.2709 .0190 222	.2032 .0190 179	.2709 .0190 206

10 FOOT SPAN (Continued)

Nominal Size (Inches)	Property	UNIFORM	CONCENTRATED — Single Load — At Center of Span	At Third Point	At Quarter Point	Sum of Two Equal Loads — At Third Point	At Quarter Points From Reactions	Sum of 3 Equal Loads — At Quarter Points and Center of Span
6x10 138 lb/beam 13.8 lb/ft	F_b F_v E	1.813 .121 1,718	.3626 .0144 275	.3223 .0191 234	.2720 .0215 189	.2418 .0144 234	.1813 .0144 189	.2418 .0144 218
3x16 101 lb/beam 10.1 lb/ft	F_b F_v E	1.589 .147 914	.3179 .0197 146	.2825 .0262 125	.2384 .0295 100	.2119 .0197 125	.1589 .0197 100	.2119 .0197 116
4x14 122 lb/beam 12.2 lb/ft	F_b F_v E	1.465 .126 995	.2929 .0162 159	.2604 .0216 136	.2197 .0243 109	.1953 .0162 136	.1465 .0162 109	.1953 .0162 126
8x10 188 lb/beam 18.8 lb/ft	F_b F_v E	1.330 .089 1,260	.2659 .0105 202	.2364 .0140 172	.1994 .0158 139	.1773 .0105 172	.1330 .0105 139	.1773 .0105 160
6x12 167 lb/beam 16.7 lb/ft	F_b F_v E	1.237 .096 968	.2475 .0119 155	.2200 .0158 132	.1856 .0178 107	.1650 .0119 132	.1237 .0119 107	.1650 .0119 123
4x16 141 lb/beam 14.1 lb/ft	F_b F_v E	1.135 .105 653	.2270 .0141 104	.2018 .0187 89	.1703 .0211 72	.1514 .0141 89	.1135 .0141 72	.1514 .0141 83
10x10 238 lb/beam 23.8 lb/ft	F_b F_v E	1.050 .070 994	.2099 .0083 159	.1866 .0111 136	.1575 .0125 109	.1400 .0083 136	.1050 .0083 109	.1400 .0083 126
8x12 228 lb/beam 22.8 lb/ft	F_b F_v E	.907 .070 710	.1815 .0087 114	.1613 .0116 97	.1361 .0130 78	.1210 .0087 97	.0907 .0087 78	.1210 .0087 90
6x14 196 lb/beam 19.6 lb/ft	F_b F_v E	.910 .078 599	.1819 .0101 96	.1617 .0135 82	.1365 .0152 66	.1213 .0101 82	.0910 .0101 66	.1213 .0101 76
10x12 288 lb/beam 28.8 lb/ft	F_b F_v E	.716 .055 561	.1433 .0069 90	.1274 .0092 76	.1075 .0103 62	.0955 .0069 76	.0716 .0069 62	.0955 .0069 71

STRENGTH AND STIFFNESS REQUIREMENTS FOR BEAMS

See instructions for use of tables on page 101. Symbols used in the tables are as follows: Tabulated values are based on net size.

F_b = Extreme fiber stress in bending induced by a uniform load of 1 (one) plf or by a concentrated load of 1 (one) pound, psi

F_v = Horizontal shear stress induced by a uniform load of 1 (one) plf or a total concentrated load of 1 (one) pound, psi.

E = Modulus of elasticity value needed to limit deflection to 1/360 of the span for a uniform load of 1 (one) plf or a total concentrated load of 1 (one) pound, psi.

10 FOOT SPAN (Continued)

Nominal Size (Inches)	Property	UNIFORM	CONCENTRATED — Single Load — At Center of Span	Single Load — At Third Point	Single Load — At Quarter Point	Sum of Two Equal Loads — At Third Point	Sum of Two Equal Loads — At Quarter Points From Reactions	Sum of 3 Equal Loads — At Quarter Points and Center of Span
2x6 — 24 lb/beam — 2.2 lb/ft	F_b	24.000	4.3636	3.8788	3.2727	2.9091	2.1818	2.9091
	F_v	.917	.0909	.1212	.1364	.0909	.0909	.0909
	E	43,200	6,284	5,355	4,320	5,355	4,320	4,975
3x6 — 40 lb/beam — 3.6 lb/ft	F_b	14.400	2.6182	2.3273	1.9636	1.7455	1.3091	1.7455
	F_v	.550	.0545	.0727	.0818	.0545	.0545	.0545
	E	25,920	3,770	3,213	2,592	3,213	2,592	2,985
2x8 — 32 lb/beam — 2.9 lb/ft	F_b	13.812	2.5113	2.2323	1.8835	1.6742	1.2556	1.6742
	F_v	.675	.0690	.0920	.1034	.0690	.0690	.0690
	E	18,861	2,743	2,338	1,886	2,338	1,886	2,172
4x6 — 56 lb/beam — 5.1 lb/ft	F_b	10.286	1.8701	1.6623	1.4026	1.2468	.9351	1.2468
	F_v	.393	.0390	.0519	.0584	.0390	.0390	.0390
	E	18,514	2,693	2,295	1,851	2,295	1,851	2,132
2x10 — 40 lb/beam — 3.7 lb/ft	F_b	8.485	1.5427	1.3713	1.1570	1.0285	.7714	1.0285
	F_v	.511	.0541	.0721	.0811	.0541	.0541	.0541
	E	9,081	1,321	1,126	908	1,126	908	1,046
3x8 — 53 lb/beam — 4.8 lb/ft	F_b	8.287	1.5068	1.3394	1.1301	1.0045	.7534	1.0045
	F_v	.405	.0414	.0552	.0621	.0414	.0414	.0414
	E	11,316	1,646	1,403	1,132	1,403	1,132	1,303
6x6 — 88 lb/beam — 8.0 lb/ft	F_b	6.545	1.1901	1.0579	.8926	.7934	.5950	.7934
	F_v	.250	.0248	.0331	.0372	.0248	.0248	.0248
	E	11,782	1,714	1,461	1,178	1,461	1,178	1,357
4x8 — 74 lb/beam — 6.7 lb/ft	F_b	5.919	1.0763	.9567	.8072	.7175	.5381	.7175
	F_v	.289	.0296	.0394	.0443	.0296	.0296	.0296
	E	8,083	1,176	1,002	808	1,002	808	931
6x16 — 225 lb/beam — 22.5 lb/ft	F_b	.701	.1401	.1246	.1051	.0934	.0701	.0934
	F_v	.065	.0088	.0117	.0132	.0088	.0088	.0088
	E	395	63	54	44	54	44	50
8x14 — 267 lb/beam — 26.7 lb/ft	F_b	.667	.1334	.1186	.1001	.0889	.0667	.0889
	F_v	.057	.0074	.0099	.0111	.0074	.0074	.0074
	E	439	70	60	48	60	48	56
12x12 — 349 lb/beam — 34.9 lb/ft	F_b	.592	.1184	.1052	.0888	.0789	.0592	.0789
	F_v	.046	.0057	.0076	.0085	.0057	.0057	.0057
	E	463	74	63	51	63	51	59
6x18 — 254 lb/beam — 25.4 lb/ft	F_b	.557	.1114	.0991	.0836	.0743	.0557	.0743
	F_v	.055	.0078	.0104	.0117	.0078	.0078	.0078
	E	275	44	37	30	37	30	35
10x14 — 338 lb/beam — 33.8 lb/ft	F_b	.527	.1053	.0936	.0790	.0702	.0527	.0702
	F_v	.045	.0058	.0078	.0088	.0058	.0058	.0058
	E	347	55	47	38	47	38	44
8x16 — 307 lb/beam — 30.7 lb/ft	F_b	.514	.1028	.0914	.0771	.0685	.0514	.0685
	F_v	.048	.0065	.0086	.0097	.0065	.0065	.0065
	E	290	46	40	32	40	32	37
6x20 — 283 lb/beam — 28.3 lb/ft	F_b	.454	.0909	.0808	.0682	.0606	.0454	.0606
	F_v	.047	.0070	.0093	.0105	.0070	.0070	.0070
	E	199	32	27	22	27	22	25

11 FOOT SPAN

Nominal Size (Inches)	Property	UNIFORM	CONCENTRATED — Single Load — At Center of Span	Single Load — At Third Point	Single Load — At Quarter Point	Sum of Two Equal Loads — At Third Point	Sum of Two Equal Loads — At Quarter Points From Reactions	Sum of 3 Equal Loads — At Quarter Points and Center of Span
2x12 — 49 lb/beam — 4.5 lb/ft	F_b	5.736	1.0430	.9271	.7822	.6953	.5215	.6953
	F_v	.406	.0444	.0593	.0667	.0444	.0444	.0444
	E	5,048	734	626	505	626	505	581
3x10 — 67 lb/beam — 6.1 lb/ft	F_b	5.091	.9256	.8228	.6942	.6171	.4628	.6171
	F_v	.307	.0324	.0432	.0486	.0324	.0324	.0324
	E	5,449	793	675	545	675	545	627
2x14 — 58 lb/beam — 5.2 lb/ft	F_b	4.135	.7519	.6683	.5639	.5012	.3759	.5012
	F_v	.332	.0377	.0503	.0566	.0377	.0377	.0377
	E	3,090	449	383	309	383	309	356
2x4 — 15 lb/beam — 1.4 lb/ft	F_b	59.265	10.7755	9.5782	8.0816	7.1837	5.3878	7.1837
	F_v	1.488	.1429	.1905	.2143	.1429	.1429	.1429
	E	167,636	24,383	20,781	16,764	20,781	16,764	19,304
3x4 — 25 lb/beam — 2.3 lb/ft	F_b	35.559	6.4653	5.7469	4.8490	4.3102	3.2327	4.3102
	F_v	.893	.0857	.1143	.1286	.0857	.0857	.0857
	E	100,582	14,630	12,469	10,058	12,469	10,058	11,582

STRENGTH AND STIFFNESS REQUIREMENTS FOR BEAMS

See instructions for use of tables on page 101. Symbols used in the tables are as follows: Tabulated values are based on net size.

F_b = Extreme fiber stress in bending induced by a uniform load of 1 (one) plf or by a concentrated load of 1 (one) pound, psi

F_v = Horizontal shear stress induced by a uniform load of 1 (one) plf or a total concentrated load of 1 (one) pound, psi.

E = Modulus of elasticity value needed to limit deflection to 1/360 of the span for a uniform load of 1 (one) plf or a total concentrated load of 1 (one) pound, psi.

11 FOOT SPAN (Continued)

Nominal Size (Inches)	Property	UNIFORM	CONCENTRATED Single Load — At Center of Span	At Third Point	At Quarter Point	Sum of Two Equal Loads — At Third Point	At Quarter Points From Reactions	Sum of 3 Equal Loads — At Quarter Points and Center of Span
4x10 — 94 lb/beam — 8.5 lb/ft	F_b	3.636	.6612	.5877	.4959	.4408	.3306	.4408
	F_v	.219	.0232	.0309	.0347	.0232	.0232	.0232
	E	3,892	566	482	389	482	389	448
6x8 — 120 lb/beam — 10.9 lb/ft	F_b	3.520	.6400	.5689	.4800	.4267	.3200	.4267
	F_v	.177	.0182	.0242	.0273	.0182	.0182	.0182
	E	4,646	676	576	465	576	465	535
3x12 — 82 lb/beam — 7.4 lb/ft	F_b	3.442	.6258	.5562	.4693	.4172	.3129	.4172
	F_v	.243	.0267	.0356	.0400	.0267	.0267	.0267
	E	3,029	441	375	303	375	303	349
8x8 — 163 lb/beam — 14.8 lb/ft	F_b	2.581	.4693	.4172	.3520	.3129	.2347	.3129
	F_v	.130	.0133	.0178	.0200	.0133	.0133	.0133
	E	3,407	496	422	341	422	341	392
3x14 — 96 lb/beam — 8.7 lb/ft	F_b	2.481	.4511	.4010	.3383	.3007	.2256	.3007
	F_v	.199	.0226	.0302	.0340	.0226	.0226	.0226
	E	1,854	270	230	185	230	185	213
4x12 — 114 lb/beam — 10.4 lb/ft	F_b	2.458	.4470	.3973	.3352	.2980	.2235	.2980
	F_v	.174	.0190	.0254	.0286	.0190	.0190	.0190
	E	2,163	315	268	216	268	216	249
6x10 — 152 lb/beam — 13.8 lb/ft	F_b	2.194	.3989	.3546	.2992	.2659	.1994	.2659
	F_v	.135	.0144	.0191	.0215	.0144	.0144	.0144
	E	2,286	333	283	229	283	229	263
3x16 — 111 lb/beam — 10.1 lb/ft	F_b	1.923	.3496	.3108	.2622	.2331	.1748	.2331
	F_v	.166	.0197	.0262	.0295	.0197	.0197	.0197
	E	1,216	177	151	122	151	122	140
4x14 — 135 lb/beam — 12.2 lb/ft	F_b	1.772	.3222	.2864	.2417	.2148	.1611	.2148
	F_v	.142	.0162	.0216	.0243	.0162	.0162	.0162
	E	1,324	193	164	132	164	132	152
8x10 — 207 lb/beam — 18.8 lb/ft	F_b	1.609	.2925	.2600	.2194	.1950	.1463	.1950
	F_v	.099	.0105	.0140	.0158	.0105	.0105	.0105
	E	1,677	244	208	168	208	168	193

Nominal Size (Inches)	Property	UNIFORM	CONCENTRATED Single Load — At Center of Span	At Third Point	At Quarter Point	Sum of Two Equal Loads — At Third Point	At Quarter Points From Reactions	Sum of 3 Equal Loads — At Quarter Points and Center of Span
6x12 — 184 lb/beam — 16.7 lb/ft	F_b	1.497	.2722	.2420	.2042	.1815	.1361	.1815
	F_v	.108	.0119	.0158	.0178	.0119	.0119	.0119
	E	1,289	187	160	129	160	129	148
4x16 — 155 lb/beam — 14.1 lb/ft	F_b	1.374	.2497	.2220	.1873	.1665	.1249	.1665
	F_v	.119	.0141	.0187	.0211	.0141	.0141	.0141
	E	869	126	108	87	108	87	100
10x10 — 262 lb/beam — 23.8 lb/ft	F_b	1.270	.2309	.2053	.1732	.1540	.1155	.1540
	F_v	.078	.0083	.0111	.0125	.0083	.0083	.0083
	E	1,324	193	164	132	164	132	152
8x12 — 250 lb/beam — 22.8 lb/ft	F_b	1.098	.1996	.1774	.1497	.1331	.0998	.1331
	F_v	.079	.0087	.0116	.0130	.0087	.0087	.0087
	E	945	137	117	95	117	95	109
6x14 — 216 lb/beam — 19.6 lb/ft	F_b	1.101	.2001	.1779	.1501	.1334	.1001	.1334
	F_v	.088	.0101	.0135	.0152	.0101	.0101	.0101
	E	797	116	99	80	99	80	92
10x12 — 317 lb/beam — 28.8 lb/ft	F_b	.867	.1576	.1401	.1182	.1051	.0788	.1051
	F_v	.062	.0069	.0092	.0103	.0069	.0069	.0069
	E	746	109	93	75	93	75	86
6x16 — 247 lb/beam — 22.5 lb/ft	F_b	.848	.1542	.1370	.1156	.1028	.0771	.1028
	F_v	.074	.0088	.0117	.0132	.0088	.0088	.0088
	E	526	77	65	53	65	53	61
8x14 — 294 lb/beam — 26.7 lb/ft	F_b	.807	.1468	.1305	.1101	.0978	.0734	.0978
	F_v	.065	.0074	.0099	.0111	.0074	.0074	.0074
	E	584	85	72	58	72	58	67
12x12 — 384 lb/beam — 34.9 lb/ft	F_b	.716	.1302	.1157	.0976	.0868	.0651	.0868
	F_v	.052	.0057	.0076	.0085	.0057	.0057	.0057
	E	616	90	76	62	76	62	71
6x18 — 279 lb/beam — 25.4 lb/ft	F_b	.674	.1226	.1090	.0919	.0817	.0613	.0817
	F_v	.063	.0078	.0104	.0117	.0078	.0078	.0078
	E	366	53	45	37	45	37	42
10x14 — 372 lb/beam — 33.8 lb/ft	F_b	.637	.1159	.1030	.0869	.0772	.0579	.0772
	F_v	.051	.0058	.0078	.0088	.0058	.0058	.0058
	E	461	67	57	46	57	46	53

STRENGTH AND STIFFNESS REQUIREMENTS FOR BEAMS

See instructions for use of tables on page 101. Symbols used in the tables are as follows: Tabulated values are based on net size.

F_b = Extreme fiber stress in bending induced by a uniform load of 1 (one) plf or by a concentrated load of 1 (one) pound, psi.

F_v = Horizontal shear stress induced by a uniform load of 1 (one) plf or a total concentrated load of 1 (one) pound, psi.

E = Modulus of elasticity value needed to limit deflection to 1/360 of the span for a uniform load of 1 (one) plf or a total concentrated load of 1 (one) pound, psi.

11 FOOT SPAN (Continued)

Nominal Size (Inches)	Property	UNIFORM	Single Load: At Center of Span	At Third Point	At Quarter Point	Sum of Two Equal Loads: At Third Point	At Quarter Points From Reactions	Sum of 3 Equal Loads: At Quarter Points and Center of Span
2x8 (34 lb/beam, 2.9 lb/ft)	F_b	16.438	2.7396	2.4352	2.0547	1.8264	1.3698	1.8264
	F_v	.744	.0690	.0920	.1034	.0690	.0690	.0690
	E	24.486	3,265	2,783	2,245	2,783	2,245	2,585
4x6 (61 lb/beam, 5.1 lb/ft)	F_b	12.241	2.0401	1.8135	1.5301	1.3601	1.0201	1.3601
	F_v	.432	.0390	.0519	.0584	.0390	.0390	.0390
	E	24.037	3,205	2,731	2,203	2,731	2,203	2,537
2x10 (44 lb/beam, 3.7 lb/ft)	F_b	10.098	1.6830	1.4960	1.2622	1.1220	.8415	1.1220
	F_v	.565	.0541	.0721	.0811	.0541	.0541	.0541
	E	11.790	1,572	1,340	1,081	1,340	1,081	1,244
3x8 (57 lb/beam, 4.8 lb/ft)	F_b	9.863	1.6438	1.4611	1.2328	1.0958	.8219	1.0958
	F_v	.447	.0414	.0552	.0621	.0414	.0414	.0414
	E	14.692	1,959	1,670	1,347	1,670	1,347	1,551
6x6 (96 lb/beam, 8.0 lb/ft)	F_b	7.790	1.2983	1.1540	.9737	.8655	.6491	.8655
	F_v	.275	.0248	.0331	.0372	.0248	.0248	.0248
	E	15.296	2,039	1,738	1,402	1,738	1,402	1,615
4x8 (80 lb/beam, 6.7 lb/ft)	F_b	7.045	1.1741	1.0437	.8806	.7827	.5871	.7827
	F_v	.319	.0296	.0394	.0443	.0296	.0296	.0296
	E	10.494	1,399	1,193	962	1,193	962	1,108
2x12 (53 lb/beam, 4.5 lb/ft)	F_b	6.827	1.1378	1.0114	.8533	.7585	.5689	.7585
	F_v	.450	.0444	.0593	.0667	.0444	.0444	.0444
	E	6.554	874	745	601	745	601	692
3x10 (73 lb/beam, 6.1 lb/ft)	F_b	6.059	1.0098	.8976	.7573	.6732	.5049	.6732
	F_v	.339	.0324	.0432	.0486	.0324	.0324	.0324
	E	7.074	943	804	648	804	648	747
2x14 (63 lb/beam, 5.2 lb/ft)	F_b	4.921	.8202	.7291	.6152	.5468	.4101	.5468
	F_v	.369	.0377	.0503	.0566	.0377	.0377	.0377
	E	4.011	535	456	368	456	368	423
4x10 (103 lb/beam, 8.5 lb/ft)	F_b	4.328	.7213	.6411	.5410	.4809	.3606	.4809
	F_v	.242	.0232	.0309	.0347	.0232	.0232	.0232
	E	5.053	674	574	463	574	463	533
6x8 (131 lb/beam, 10.9 lb/ft)	F_b	4.189	.6982	.6206	.5236	.4655	.3491	.4655
	F_v	.195	.0182	.0242	.0273	.0182	.0182	.0182
	E	6.032	804	685	553	685	553	637

11 FOOT SPAN

Nominal Size (Inches)	Property	UNIFORM	Single Load: At Center of Span	At Third Point	At Quarter Point	Sum of Two Equal Loads: At Third Point	At Quarter Points From Reactions	Sum of 3 Equal Loads: At Quarter Points and Center of Span
8x16 (337 lb/beam, 30.7 lb/ft)	F_b	.622	.1131	.1005	.0848	.0754	.0565	.0754
	F_v	.054	.0065	.0086	.0097	.0065	.0065	.0065
	E	386	56	48	39	48	39	44
6x20 (311 lb/beam, 28.3 lb/ft)	F_b	.550	.1000	.0889	.0750	.0666	.0500	.0666
	F_v	.054	.0070	.0093	.0105	.0070	.0070	.0070
	E	264	38	33	26	33	26	30
12x14 (451 lb/beam, 41.0 lb/ft)	F_b	.526	.0957	.0851	.0718	.0638	.0479	.0638
	F_v	.042	.0048	.0064	.0072	.0048	.0048	.0048
	E	381	55	47	38	47	38	44
10x16 (427 lb/beam, 38.9 lb/ft)	F_b	.491	.0892	.0793	.0669	.0595	.0446	.0595
	F_v	.043	.0051	.0068	.0076	.0051	.0051	.0051
	E	305	44	38	30	38	30	35
8x18 (381 lb/beam, 34.6 lb/ft)	F_b	.494	.0899	.0799	.0674	.0599	.0449	.0599
	F_v	.046	.0057	.0076	.0086	.0057	.0057	.0057
	E	268	39	33	27	33	27	31

12 FOOT SPAN

Nominal Size (Inches)	Property	UNIFORM	Single Load: At Center of Span	At Third Point	At Quarter Point	Sum of Two Equal Loads: At Third Point	At Quarter Points From Reactions	Sum of 3 Equal Loads: At Quarter Points and Center of Span
2x4 (17 lb/beam, 1.4 lb/ft)	F_b	70.531	11.7551	10.4490	8.8163	7.8367	5.8776	7.8367
	F_v	1.631	.1429	.1905	.2143	.1429	.1429	.1429
	E	217.637	29.018	24.732	19.950	24.732	19.950	22.973
3x4 (28 lb/beam, 2.3 lb/ft)	F_b	42.318	7.0531	6.2694	5.2898	4.7020	3.5265	4.7020
	F_v	.979	.0857	.1143	.1286	.0857	.0857	.0857
	E	130.582	17.411	14.839	11.970	14.839	11.970	13.784
2x6 (26 lb/beam, 2.2 lb/ft)	F_b	28.562	4.7603	4.2314	3.5702	3.1736	2.3802	3.1736
	F_v	1.008	.0909	.1212	.1364	.0909	.0909	.0909
	E	56.085	7.478	6.373	5.141	6.373	5.141	5.920
3x6 (44 lb/beam, 3.6 lb/ft)	F_b	17.137	2.8562	2.5388	2.1421	1.9041	1.4281	1.9041
	F_v	.605	.0545	.0727	.0818	.0545	.0545	.0545
	E	33.651	4.487	3.824	3.085	3.824	3.085	3.552

STRENGTH AND STIFFNESS REQUIREMENTS FOR BEAMS

See instructions for use of tables on page 101. Symbols used in the tables are as follows: Tabulated values are based on net size.

F_b = Extreme fiber stress in bending induced by a uniform load of 1 (one) plf or by a concentrated load of 1 (one) pound, psi

F_v = Horizontal shear stress induced by a uniform load of 1 (one) plf or a total concentrated load of 1 (one) pound, psi.

E = Modulus of elasticity value needed to limit deflection to 1/360 of the span for a uniform load of 1 (one) plf or a total concentrated load of 1 (one) pound, psi.

12 FOOT SPAN (Continued) — upper table

Nominal Size (Inches)	Property	UNIFORM	CONCENTRATED Single Load — At Center of Span	Single Load — At Third Point	Single Load — At Quarter Point	Sum of Two Equal Loads — At Third Point	Sum of Two Equal Loads — At Quarter Points From Reactions	Sum of 3 Equal Loads — At Quarter Points and Center of Span
10x10 286 lb/beam 23.8 lb/ft	F_b F_v E	1.512 .087 1,718	.2519 .0083 229	.2239 .0111 195	.1889 .0125 158	.1680 .0083 195	.1260 .0083 158	.1680 .0083 181
8x12 273 lb/beam 22.8 lb/ft	F_b F_v E	1.307 .088 1,227	.2178 .0087 164	.1936 .0116 139	.1633 .0130 112	.1452 .0087 139	.1089 .0087 112	.1452 .0087 130
6x14 235 lb/beam 19.6 lb/ft	F_b F_v E	1.310 .098 1,034	.2183 .0101 138	.1941 .0135 118	.1637 .0152 95	.1456 .0101 118	.1092 .0101 95	.1456 .0101 109
10x12 346 lb/beam 28.8 lb/ft	F_b F_v E	1.032 .069 969	.1719 .0069 129	.1528 .0092 110	.1289 .0103 89	.1146 .0069 110	.0860 .0069 89	.1146 .0069 102
6x16 270 lb/beam 22.5 lb/ft	F_b F_v E	1.009 .083 683	.1682 .0088 91	.1495 .0117 78	.1261 .0132 63	.1121 .0088 78	.0841 .0088 63	.1121 .0088 72
8x14 321 lb/beam 26.7 lb/ft	F_b F_v E	.961 .072 759	.1601 .0074 101	.1423 .0099 86	.1201 .0111 70	.1067 .0074 86	.0801 .0074 70	.1067 .0074 80
12x12 419 lb/beam 34.9 lb/ft	F_b F_v E	.852 .057 800	.1420 .0057 107	.1262 .0076 91	.1065 .0085 73	.0947 .0057 91	.0710 .0057 73	.0947 .0057 84
6x18 305 lb/beam 25.4 lb/ft	F_b F_v E	.802 .071 475	.1337 .0078 63	.1189 .0104 54	.1003 .0117 44	.0891 .0078 54	.0669 .0078 44	.0891 .0078 50
10x14 406 lb/beam 33.8 lb/ft	F_b F_v E	.758 .057 599	.1264 .0058 80	.1124 .0078 68	.0948 .0088 55	.0843 .0058 68	.0632 .0058 55	.0843 .0058 63
8x16 368 lb/beam 30.7 lb/ft	F_b F_v E	.740 .061 501	.1233 .0065 67	.1096 .0086 57	.0925 .0097 46	.0822 .0065 57	.0617 .0065 46	.0822 .0065 53
6x20 340 lb/beam 28.3 lb/ft	F_b F_v E	.654 .061 343	.1091 .0070 46	.0969 .0093 39	.0818 .0105 31	.0727 .0070 39	.0545 .0070 31	.0727 .0070 36

12 FOOT SPAN (Continued) — lower table

Nominal Size (Inches)	Property	UNIFORM	CONCENTRATED Single Load — At Center of Span	Single Load — At Third Point	Single Load — At Quarter Point	Sum of Two Equal Loads — At Third Point	Sum of Two Equal Loads — At Quarter Points From Reactions	Sum of 3 Equal Loads — At Quarter Points and Center of Span
3x12 89 lb/beam 7.4 lb/ft	F_b F_v E	4.096 .270 3,932	.6827 .0267 524	.6068 .0356 447	.5120 .0400 360	.4551 .0267 447	.3413 .0267 360	.4551 .0267 415
8x8 178 lb/beam 14.8 lb/ft	F_b F_v E	3.072 .143 4,424	.5120 .0133 590	.4551 .0178 503	.3840 .0200 406	.3413 .0133 503	.2560 .0133 406	.3413 .0133 467
3x14 105 lb/beam 8.7 lb/ft	F_b F_v E	2.953 .222 2,407	.4921 .0226 321	.4375 .0302 274	.3691 .0340 221	.3281 .0226 274	.2461 .0226 221	.3281 .0226 254
4x12 125 lb/beam 10.4 lb/ft	F_b F_v E	2.926 .193 2,809	.4876 .0190 374	.4334 .0254 319	.3657 .0286 257	.3251 .0190 319	.2438 .0190 257	.3251 .0190 296
6x10 165 lb/beam 13.8 lb/ft	F_b F_v E	2.611 .150 2,968	.4352 .0144 396	.3868 .0191 337	.3264 .0215 272	.2901 .0144 337	.2176 .0144 272	.2901 .0144 313
3x16 121 lb/beam 10.1 lb/ft	F_b F_v E	2.289 .186 1,579	.3814 .0197 210	.3390 .0262 179	.2861 .0295 145	.2543 .0197 179	.1907 .0197 145	.2543 .0197 167
4x14 147 lb/beam 12.2 lb/ft	F_b F_v E	2.109 .158 1,719	.3515 .0162 229	.3125 .0216 195	.2636 .0243 158	.2343 .0162 195	.1758 .0162 158	.2343 .0162 181
8x10 226 lb/beam 18.8 lb/ft	F_b F_v E	1.915 .110 2,177	.3191 .0105 290	.2837 .0140 247	.2393 .0158 200	.2127 .0105 247	.1596 .0105 200	.2127 .0105 230
6x12 200 lb/beam 16.7 lb/ft	F_b F_v E	1.782 .120 1,673	.2970 .0119 223	.2640 .0158 190	.2227 .0178 153	.1980 .0119 190	.1485 .0119 153	.1980 .0119 177
4x16 169 lb/beam 14.1 lb/ft	F_b F_v E	1.635 .133 1,128	.2725 .0141 150	.2422 .0187 128	.2043 .0211 103	.1816 .0141 128	.1362 .0141 103	.1816 .0141 119

STRENGTH AND STIFFNESS REQUIREMENTS FOR BEAMS

See instructions for use of tables on page 101. Symbols used in the tables are as follows: Tabulated values are based on net size.

F_b = Extreme fiber stress in bending induced by a uniform load of 1 (one) plf or by a concentrated load of 1 (one) pound, psi.

F_v = Horizontal shear stress induced by a uniform load of 1 (one) plf or a total concentrated load of 1 (one) pound, psi.

E = Modulus of elasticity value needed to limit deflection to 1/360 of the span for a uniform load of 1 (one) plf or a total concentrated load of 1 (one) pound, psi.

12 FOOT SPAN (Continued)

Nominal Size (Inches)	Property	UNIFORM	Single Load — At Center of Span	Single Load — At Third Point	Single Load — At Quarter Point	Sum of Two Equal Loads — At Third Point	Sum of Two Equal Loads — At Quarter Points From Reactions	Sum of 3 Equal Loads — At Quarter Points and Center of Span
2x10 48 lb/beam 3.7 lb/ft	F_b	11.851	1.8232	1.6206	1.3674	1.2155	.9116	1.2155
	F_v	.619	.0541	.0721	.0811	.0541	.0541	.0541
	E	14.990	1.845	1.572	1.268	1.572	1.268	1.461
3x8 62 lb/beam 4.8 lb/ft	F_b	11.575	1.7807	1.5829	1.3356	1.1872	.8904	1.1872
	F_v	.488	.0414	.0552	.0621	.0414	.0414	.0414
	E	18.679	2.299	1.959	1.581	1.959	1.581	1.820
6x6 104 lb/beam 8.0 lb/ft	F_b	9.142	1.4065	1.2502	1.0548	.9376	.7032	.9376
	F_v	.300	.0248	.0331	.0372	.0248	.0248	.0248
	E	19.448	2.394	2.040	1.646	2.040	1.646	1.895
4x8 87 lb/beam 6.7 lb/ft	F_b	8.268	1.2720	1.1306	.9540	.8480	.6360	.8480
	F_v	.349	.0296	.0394	.0443	.0296	.0296	.0296
	E	13.342	1,642	1,400	1,129	1,400	1,129	1,300
2x12 58 lb/beam 4.5 lb/ft	F_b	8.012	1.2326	1.0956	.9244	.8217	.6163	.8217
	F_v	.494	.0444	.0593	.0667	.0444	.0444	.0444
	E	8.332	1,026	874	705	874	705	812
3x10 79 lb/beam 6.1 lb/ft	F_b	7.111	1.0939	.9724	.8205	.7293	.5470	.7293
	F_v	.372	.0324	.0432	.0486	.0324	.0324	.0324
	E	8.994	1,107	943	761	943	761	876
2x14 68 lb/beam 5.2 lb/ft	F_b	5.776	.8886	.7898	.6664	.5924	.4443	.5924
	F_v	.407	.0377	.0503	.0566	.0377	.0377	.0377
	E	5,100	628	535	432	535	432	497
4x10 111 lb/beam 8.5 lb/ft	F_b	5.079	.7814	.6946	.5860	.5209	.3907	.5209
	F_v	.265	.0232	.0309	.0347	.0232	.0232	.0232
	E	6.424	791	674	544	674	544	626
6x8 142 lb/beam 10.9 lb/ft	F_b	4.916	.7564	.6723	.5673	.5042	.3782	.5042
	F_v	.214	.0182	.0242	.0273	.0182	.0182	.0182
	E	7,670	944	804	649	804	649	747
3x12 96 lb/beam 7.4 lb/ft	F_b	4.807	.7396	.6574	.5547	.4930	.3698	.4930
	F_v	.297	.0267	.0356	.0400	.0267	.0267	.0267
	E	4,999	615	524	423	524	423	487
8x8 193 lb/beam 14.8 lb/ft	F_b	3.605	.5547	.4930	.4160	.3698	.2773	.3698
	F_v	.157	.0133	.0178	.0200	.0133	.0133	.0133
	E	5,624	692	590	476	590	476	548
12x14 492 lb/beam 41.0 lb/ft	F_b	.627	.1044	.0928	.0783	.0696	.0522	.0696
	F_v	.047	.0048	.0064	.0072	.0048	.0048	.0048
	E	495	66	56	45	56	45	52
10x16 466 lb/beam 38.9 lb/ft	F_b	.584	.0974	.0865	.0730	.0649	.0487	.0649
	F_v	.048	.0051	.0068	.0076	.0051	.0051	.0051
	E	396	53	45	36	45	36	42
8x18 416 lb/beam 34.6 lb/ft	F_b	.588	.0981	.0872	.0735	.0654	.0490	.0654
	F_v	.052	.0057	.0076	.0086	.0057	.0057	.0057
	E	348	46	40	32	40	32	37
12x16 564 lb/beam 47.0 lb/ft	F_b	.483	.0804	.0715	.0603	.0536	.0402	.0536
	F_v	.040	.0042	.0056	.0063	.0042	.0042	.0042
	E	327	44	37	30	37	30	34
8x20 463 lb/beam 38.6 lb/ft	F_b	.480	.0800	.0711	.0600	.0533	.0400	.0533
	F_v	.045	.0051	.0068	.0077	.0051	.0051	.0051
	E	252	34	29	23	29	23	27

13 FOOT SPAN

Nominal Size (Inches)	Property	UNIFORM	Single Load — At Center of Span	Single Load — At Third Point	Single Load — At Quarter Point	Sum of Two Equal Loads — At Third Point	Sum of Two Equal Loads — At Quarter Points From Reactions	Sum of 3 Equal Loads — At Quarter Points and Center of Span
2x6 28 lb/beam 2.2 lb/ft	F_b	33.521	5.1570	4.5840	3.8678	3.4380	2.5785	3.4380
	F_v	1.098	.0909	.1212	.1364	.0909	.0909	.0909
	E	71,308	8.776	7,480	6,034	7,480	6,034	6,948
3x6 47 lb/beam 3.6 lb/ft	F_b	20.112	3.0942	2.7504	2.3207	2.0628	1.5471	2.0628
	F_v	.659	.0545	.0727	.0818	.0545	.0545	.0545
	E	42,785	5,266	4,488	3,620	4,488	3,620	4,169
2x8 37 lb/beam 2.9 lb/ft	F_b	19.291	2.9679	2.6381	2.2259	1.9786	1.4839	1.9786
	F_v	.813	.0690	.0920	.1034	.0690	.0690	.0690
	E	31,132	3,832	3,266	2,634	3,266	2,634	3,033
4x6 66 lb/beam 5.1 lb/ft	F_b	14.366	2.2102	1.9646	1.6576	1.4734	1.1051	1.4734
	F_v	.471	.0390	.0519	.0584	.0390	.0390	.0390
	E	30,560	3,761	3,206	2,586	3,206	2,586	2,978

STRENGTH AND STIFFNESS REQUIREMENTS FOR BEAMS

See instructions for use of tables on page 101. Symbols used in the tables are as follows: Tabulated values are based on net size.

F_b = Extreme fiber stress in bending induced by a uniform load of 1 (one) plf or by a concentrated load of 1 (one) pound, psi.

F_v = Horizontal shear stress induced by a uniform load of 1 (one) plf or a total concentrated load of 1 (one) pound, psi.

E = Modulus of elasticity value needed to limit deflection to 1/360 of the span for a uniform load of 1 (one) plf or a total concentrated load of 1 (one) pound, psi.

13 FOOT SPAN

Nominal Size (Inches)	Property	UNIFORM	Single Load — At Center of Span	Single Load — At Third Point	Single Load — At Quarter Point	Sum of Two Equal Loads — At Third Point	Sum of Two Equal Loads — At Quarter Points From Reactions	Sum of 3 Equal Loads — At Quarter Points and Center of Span
3x14 114 lb/beam 8.7 lb/ft	F_b	3.465	5331	4739	3999	.3554	.2666	.3554
	F_v	.244	.0226	.0302	.0340	.0226	.0226	.0226
	E	3,060	377	321	259	321	259	298
4x12 135 lb/beam 10.4 lb/ft	F_b	3.434	5283	4696	3962	.3522	.2641	.3522
	F_v	.212	.0190	.0254	.0286	.0190	.0190	.0190
	E	3,571	440	375	302	375	302	348
6x10 179 lb/beam 13.8 lb/ft	F_b	3.064	4714	4190	3536	.3143	.2357	.3143
	F_v	.164	.0144	.0191	.0215	.0144	.0144	.0144
	E	3,774	464	396	319	396	319	368
3x16 131 lb/beam 10.1 lb/ft	F_b	2.686	4132	3673	3099	.2755	.2066	.2755
	F_v	.206	.0197	.0262	.0295	.0197	.0197	.0197
	E	2,007	247	211	170	211	170	196
4x14 159 lb/beam 12.2 lb/ft	F_b	2.475	3808	3385	2856	.2539	.1904	.2539
	F_v	.175	.0162	.0216	.0243	.0162	.0162	.0162
	E	2,186	269	229	185	229	185	213
8x10 244 lb/beam 18.8 lb/ft	F_b	2.247	3457	3073	2593	.2305	.1729	.2305
	F_v	.120	.0105	.0140	.0158	.0105	.0105	.0105
	E	2,767	341	290	234	290	234	270
6x12 217 lb/beam 16.7 lb/ft	F_b	2.091	3217	2860	2413	.2145	.1609	.2145
	F_v	.131	.0119	.0158	.0178	.0119	.0119	.0119
	E	2,127	262	223	180	223	180	207
4x16 183 lb/beam 14.1 lb/ft	F_b	1.919	2952	2624	2214	.1968	.1476	.1968
	F_v	.147	.0141	.0187	.0211	.0141	.0141	.0141
	E	1,434	176	150	121	150	121	140
10x10 310 lb/beam 23.8 lb/ft	F_b	1.774	2729	2426	2047	.1820	.1365	.1820
	F_v	.095	.0083	.0111	.0125	.0083	.0083	.0083
	E	2,185	269	229	185	229	185	213
8x12 296 lb/beam 22.8 lb/ft	F_b	1.533	2359	2097	1769	.1573	.1180	.1573
	F_v	.096	.0087	.0116	.0130	.0087	.0087	.0087
	E	1,560	192	164	132	164	132	152

13 FOOT SPAN (Continued)

Nominal Size (Inches)	Property	UNIFORM	Single Load — At Center of Span	Single Load — At Third Point	Single Load — At Quarter Point	Sum of Two Equal Loads — At Third Point	Sum of Two Equal Loads — At Quarter Points From Reactions	Sum of 3 Equal Loads — At Quarter Points and Center of Span
6x14 255 lb/beam 19.6 lb/ft	F_b	1.537	2365	2102	1774	.1577	.1183	.1577
	F_v	.109	.0101	.0135	.0152	.0101	.0101	.0101
	E	1,315	162	138	111	138	111	128
10x12 375 lb/beam 28.8 lb/ft	F_b	1.211	1863	1656	1397	.1242	.0931	.1242
	F_v	.076	.0069	.0092	.0103	.0069	.0069	.0069
	E	1,232	152	129	104	129	104	120
6x16 292 lb/beam 22.5 lb/ft	F_b	1.184	1822	1619	1366	.1215	.0911	.1215
	F_v	.092	.0088	.0117	.0132	.0088	.0088	.0088
	E	869	107	91	74	91	74	85
8x14 347 lb/beam 26.7 lb/ft	F_b	1.127	1734	1542	1301	.1156	.0867	.1156
	F_v	.080	.0074	.0099	.0111	.0074	.0074	.0074
	E	964	119	101	82	101	82	94
12x12 454 lb/beam 34.9 lb/ft	F_b	1.000	1539	1368	1154	.1026	.0769	.1026
	F_v	.063	.0057	.0076	.0085	.0057	.0057	.0057
	E	1,017	125	107	86	107	86	99
6x18 330 lb/beam 25.4 lb/ft	F_b	.942	1449	1288	1086	.0966	.0724	.0966
	F_v	.079	.0078	.0104	.0117	.0078	.0078	.0078
	E	604	74	63	51	63	51	59
10x14 440 lb/beam 33.8 lb/ft	F_b	.890	1369	1217	1027	.0913	.0685	.0913
	F_v	.063	.0058	.0078	.0088	.0058	.0058	.0058
	E	761	94	80	64	80	64	74
8x16 399 lb/beam 30.7 lb/ft	F_b	.868	1336	1188	1002	.0891	.0668	.0891
	F_v	.067	.0065	.0086	.0097	.0065	.0065	.0065
	E	637	78	67	54	67	54	62
6x20 368 lb/beam 28.3 lb/ft	F_b	.768	1181	1050	886	.0788	.0591	.0788
	F_v	.068	.0070	.0093	.0105	.0070	.0070	.0070
	E	436	54	46	37	46	37	43
12x14 533 lb/beam 41.0 lb/ft	F_b	.735	1131	1006	848	.0754	.0566	.0754
	F_v	.052	.0048	.0064	.0072	.0048	.0048	.0048
	E	629	77	66	53	66	53	61
10x16 505 lb/beam 38.9 lb/ft	F_b	.686	1055	938	791	.0703	.0527	.0703
	F_v	.053	.0051	.0068	.0076	.0051	.0051	.0051
	E	503	62	53	43	53	43	49

STRENGTH AND STIFFNESS REQUIREMENTS FOR BEAMS

See instructions for use of tables on page 101. Symbols used in the tables are as follows: Tabulated values are based on net size.

F_b = Extreme fiber stress in bending induced by a uniform load of 1 (one) plf or by a concentrated load of 1 (one) pound, psi

F_v = Horizontal shear stress induced by a uniform load of 1 (one) plf or a total concentrated load of 1 (one) pound, psi.

E = Modulus of elasticity value needed to limit deflection to 1/360 of the span for a uniform load of 1 (one) plf or a total concentrated load of 1 (one) pound, psi.

13 FOOT SPAN (Continued)

Nominal Size (Inches)	Property	UNIFORM	CONCENTRATED — Single Load, At Center of Span	Single Load, At Third Point	Single Load, At Quarter Point	Sum of Two Equal Loads, At Third Point	Sum of Two Equal Loads, At Quarter Points From Reactions	Sum of 3 Equal Loads, At Quarter Points and Center of Span
2x10 — 51 lb/beam, 3.7 lb/ft	F_b	13.744	1.9635	1.7453	1.4726	1.3090	.9817	1.3090
	F_v	.637	.0541	.0721	.0811	.0541	.0541	.0541
	E	18,722	2,140	1,824	1,471	1,824	1,471	1,694
3x8 — 67 lb/beam, 4.8 lb/ft	F_b	13.424	1.9177	1.7046	1.4383	1.2785	.9589	1.2785
	F_v	.529	.0414	.0552	.0621	.0414	.0414	.0414
	E	23,330	2,666	2,272	1,833	2,272	1,833	2,111
6x6 — 112 lb/beam, 8.0 lb/ft	F_b	10.603	1.5147	1.3464	1.1360	1.0098	.7573	1.0098
	F_v	.324	.0248	.0331	.0372	.0248	.0248	.0248
	E	24,289	2,776	2,366	1,908	2,366	1,908	2,198
4x8 — 94 lb/beam, 6.7 lb/ft	F_b	9.589	1.3698	1.2176	1.0273	.9132	.6849	.9132
	F_v	.378	.0296	.0394	.0443	.0296	.0296	.0296
	E	16,664	1,904	1,623	1,309	1,623	1,309	1,508
2x12 — 62 lb/beam, 4.5 lb/ft	F_b	9.292	1.3274	1.1799	.9956	.8849	.6637	.8849
	F_v	.539	.0444	.0593	.0667	.0444	.0444	.0444
	E	10,407	1,189	1,014	818	1,014	818	942
3x10 — 85 lb/beam, 6.1 lb/ft	F_b	8.247	1.1781	1.0432	.8836	.7854	.5890	.7854
	F_v	.404	.0324	.0432	.0486	.0324	.0324	.0324
	E	11,233	1,284	1,094	883	1,094	883	1,016
2x14 — 73 lb/beam, 5.2 lb/ft	F_b	6.698	.9569	.8506	.7177	.6379	.4785	.6379
	F_v	.445	.0377	.0503	.0566	.0377	.0377	.0377
	E	6,370	728	620	500	620	500	576
4x10 — 120 lb/beam, 8.5 lb/ft	F_b	5.890	.8415	.7480	.6311	.5610	.4207	.5610
	F_v	.289	.0232	.0309	.0347	.0232	.0232	.0232
	E	8,024	917	782	630	782	630	726
6x8 — 152 lb/beam, 10.9 lb/ft	F_b	5.702	.8145	.7240	.6109	.5430	.4073	.5430
	F_v	.232	.0182	.0242	.0273	.0182	.0182	.0182
	E	9,579	1,095	933	753	933	753	867
3x12 — 104 lb/beam, 7.4 lb/ft	F_b	5.575	.7964	.7080	.5973	.5310	.3982	.5310
	F_v	.323	.0267	.0356	.0400	.0267	.0267	.0267
	E	6,244	714	608	491	608	491	565
8x8 — 208 lb/beam, 14.8 lb/ft	F_b	4.181	.5973	.5310	.4480	.3982	.2987	.3982
	F_v	.170	.0133	.0178	.0200	.0133	.0133	.0133
	E	7,025	803	684	552	684	552	636

13 FOOT SPAN (Continued)

Nominal Size (Inches)	Property	UNIFORM	Single Load, At Center of Span	Single Load, At Third Point	Single Load, At Quarter Point	Sum of Two Equal Loads, At Third Point	Sum of Two Equal Loads, At Quarter Points From Reactions	Sum of 3 Equal Loads, At Quarter Points and Center of Span
8x18 — 450 lb/beam, 34.6 lb/ft	F_b	.691	.1062	.0944	.0797	.0708	.0531	.0708
	F_v	.058	.0057	.0076	.0086	.0057	.0057	.0057
	E	443	54	46	37	46	37	43
12x16 — 611 lb/beam, 47.0 lb/ft	F_b	.566	.0871	.0775	.0654	.0581	.0436	.0581
	F_v	.044	.0042	.0056	.0063	.0042	.0042	.0042
	E	416	51	44	35	44	35	40
8x20 — 502 lb/beam, 38.6 lb/ft	F_b	.563	.0866	.0770	.0650	.0578	.0433	.0578
	F_v	.050	.0051	.0068	.0077	.0051	.0051	.0051
	E	320	39	34	27	34	27	31
10x18 — 570 lb/beam, 43.9 lb/ft	F_b	.545	.0839	.0745	.0629	.0559	.0419	.0559
	F_v	.045	.0045	.0060	.0068	.0045	.0045	.0045
	E	350	43	37	30	37	30	34
8x22 — 553 lb/beam, 42.6 lb/ft	F_b	.468	.0720	.0640	.0540	.0480	.0360	.0480
	F_v	.044	.0047	.0062	.0070	.0047	.0047	.0047
	E	239	29	25	20	25	20	23

14 FOOT SPAN

Nominal Size (Inches)	Property	UNIFORM	Single Load, At Center of Span	Single Load, At Third Point	Single Load, At Quarter Point	Sum of Two Equal Loads, At Third Point	Sum of Two Equal Loads, At Quarter Points From Reactions	Sum of 3 Equal Loads, At Quarter Points and Center of Span
2x6 — 30 lb/beam, 2.2 lb/ft	F_b	38.876	5.5537	4.9366	4.1653	3.7025	2.7769	3.7025
	F_v	1.189	.0909	.1212	.1364	.0909	.0909	.0909
	E	89,061	10,178	8,675	6,998	8,675	6,998	8,058
3x6 — 51 lb/beam, 3.6 lb/ft	F_b	23.326	3.3322	2.9620	2.4992	2.2215	1.6661	2.2215
	F_v	.714	.0545	.0727	.0818	.0545	.0545	.0545
	E	53,437	6,107	5,205	4,199	5,205	4,199	4,835
2x8 — 40 lb/beam, 2.9 lb/ft	F_b	22.373	3.1962	2.8411	2.3971	2.1308	1.5981	2.1308
	F_v	.882	.0690	.0920	.1034	.0690	.0690	.0690
	E	38,883	4,444	3,787	3,055	3,787	3,055	3,518
4x6 — 71 lb/beam, 5.1 lb/ft	F_b	16.661	2.3802	2.1157	1.7851	1.5868	1.1901	1.5868
	F_v	.510	.0390	.0519	.0584	.0390	.0390	.0390
	E	38,169	4,362	3,718	2,999	3,718	2,999	3,453

STRENGTH AND STIFFNESS REQUIREMENTS FOR BEAMS

See instructions for use of tables on page 101. Symbols used in the tables are as follows: Tabulated values are based on net size.

F_b = Extreme fiber stress in bending induced by a uniform load of 1 (one) plf or by a concentrated load of 1 (one) pound, psi

F_v = Horizontal shear stress induced by a uniform load of 1 (one) plf or a total concentrated load of 1 (one) pound, psi.

E = Modulus of elasticity value needed to limit deflection to 1/360 of the span for a uniform load of 1 (one) plf or a total concentrated load of 1 (one) pound, psi.

Nominal Size (Inches)	Property	UNIFORM	Single Load — At Center of Span	Single Load — At Third Point	Single Load — At Quarter Point	Sum of Two Equal Loads — At Third Point	Sum of Two Equal Loads — At Quarter Points From Reactions	Sum of 3 Equal Loads — At Quarter Points and Center of Span
6x14 274 lb/beam 19.6 lb/ft	F_b F_v E	1.783 .119 1,643	.2547 .0101 188	.2264 .0135 160	.1910 .0152 129	.1698 .0101 160	.1274 .0101 129	.1698 .0101 149
10x12 404 lb/beam 28.8 lb/ft	F_b F_v E	1.404 .083 1,538	.2006 .0069 176	.1783 .0092 150	.1504 .0103 121	.1337 .0069 150	.1003 .0069 121	.1337 .0069 139
6x16 315 lb/beam 22.5 lb/ft	F_b F_v E	1.373 .100 1,085	.1962 .0088 124	.1744 .0117 106	.1472 .0132 85	.1308 .0088 106	.0981 .0088 85	.1308 .0088 98
8x14 374 lb/beam 26.7 lb/ft	F_b F_v E	1.308 .087 1,205	.1868 .0074 138	.1660 .0099 117	.1401 .0111 95	.1245 .0074 117	.0934 .0074 95	.1245 .0074 109
12x12 489 lb/beam 34.9 lb/ft	F_b F_v E	1.160 .069 1,271	.1657 .0057 145	.1473 .0076 124	.1243 .0085 100	.1105 .0057 124	.0828 .0057 100	.1105 .0057 115
6x18 356 lb/beam 25.4 lb/ft	F_b F_v E	1.092 .086 754	.1560 .0078 86	.1387 .0104 73	.1170 .0117 59	.1040 .0078 73	.0780 .0078 59	.1040 .0078 68
10x14 474 lb/beam 33.8 lb/ft	F_b F_v E	1.032 .069 951	.1475 .0058 109	.1311 .0078 93	.1106 .0088 75	.0983 .0058 93	.0737 .0058 75	.0983 .0058 86
8x16 429 lb/beam 30.7 lb/ft	F_b F_v E	1.007 .074 796	.1439 .0065 91	.1279 .0086 78	.1079 .0097 63	.0959 .0065 78	.0719 .0065 63	.0959 .0065 72
6x20 396 lb/beam 28.3 lb/ft	F_b F_v E	.891 .075 545	.1272 .0070 62	.1131 .0093 53	.0954 .0105 43	.0848 .0070 53	.0636 .0070 43	.0848 .0070 49
12x14 574 lb/beam 41.0 lb/ft	F_b F_v E	.853 .057 786	.1218 .0048 90	.1083 .0064 77	.0914 .0072 62	.0812 .0048 77	.0609 .0048 62	.0812 .0048 71
10x16 544 lb/beam 38.9 lb/ft	F_b F_v E	.795 .058 628	.1136 .0051 72	.1010 .0068 61	.0852 .0076 49	.0757 .0051 61	.0568 .0051 49	.0757 .0051 57

14 FOOT SPAN (Continued)

Nominal Size (Inches)	Property	UNIFORM	Single Load — At Center of Span	Single Load — At Third Point	Single Load — At Quarter Point	Sum of Two Equal Loads — At Third Point	Sum of Two Equal Loads — At Quarter Points From Reactions	Sum of 3 Equal Loads — At Quarter Points and Center of Span
3x14 122 lb/beam 8.7 lb/ft	F_b F_v E	4.019 .267 3,822	.5742 .0226 437	.5104 .0302 372	.4306 .0340 300	.3828 .0226 372	.2871 .0226 300	.3828 .0226 346
4x12 145 lb/beam 10.4 lb/ft	F_b F_v E	3.982 .231 4,460	.5689 .0190 510	.5057 .0254 434	.4267 .0286 350	.3793 .0190 434	.2844 .0190 350	.3793 .0190 404
6x10 193 lb/beam 13.8 lb/ft	F_b F_v E	3.554 .178 4,713	.5077 .0144 539	.4513 .0191 459	.3808 .0215 370	.3385 .0144 459	.2538 .0144 370	.3385 .0144 426
3x16 141 lb/beam 10.1 lb/ft	F_b F_v E	3.115 .225 2,507	.4450 .0197 286	.3956 .0262 244	.3338 .0295 197	.2967 .0197 244	.2225 .0197 197	.2967 .0197 227
4x14 171 lb/beam 12.2 lb/ft	F_b F_v E	2.871 .191 2,730	.4101 .0162 312	.3645 .0216 266	.3076 .0243 214	.2734 .0162 266	.2051 .0162 214	.2734 .0162 247
8x10 263 lb/beam 18.8 lb/ft	F_b F_v E	2.606 .131 3,457	.3723 .0105 395	.3309 .0140 337	.2792 .0158 272	.2482 .0105 337	.1861 .0105 272	.2482 .0105 313
6x12 234 lb/beam 16.7 lb/ft	F_b F_v E	2.425 .143 2,657	.3465 .0119 304	.3080 .0158 259	.2598 .0178 209	.2310 .0119 259	.1732 .0119 209	.2310 .0119 240
4x16 197 lb/beam 14.1 lb/ft	F_b F_v E	2.225 .161 1,791	.3179 .0141 205	.2825 .0187 174	.2384 .0211 141	.2119 .0141 174	.1589 .0141 141	.2119 .0141 162
10x10 333 lb/beam 23.8 lb/ft	F_b F_v E	2.057 .103 2,729	.2939 .0083 312	.2613 .0111 266	.2204 .0125 214	.1959 .0083 266	.1470 .0083 214	.1959 .0083 247
8x12 319 lb/beam 22.8 lb/ft	F_b F_v E	1.778 .105 1,949	.2541 .0087 223	.2258 .0116 190	.1905 .0130 153	.1694 .0087 190	.1270 .0087 153	.1694 .0087 176

STRENGTH AND STIFFNESS REQUIREMENTS FOR BEAMS

See instructions for use of tables on page 101. Symbols used in the tables are as follows: Tabulated values are based on net size.

F_b = Extreme fiber stress in bending induced by a uniform load of 1 (one) plf or by a concentrated load of 1 (one) pound, psi

F_v = Horizontal shear stress induced by a uniform load of 1 (one) plf or a total concentrated load of 1 (one) pound, psi.

E = Modulus of elasticity value needed to limit deflection to 1/360 of the span for a uniform load of 1 (one) plf or a total concentrated load of 1 (one) plf or a total concentrated load of 1 (one) pound, psi.

15 FOOT SPAN

Nominal Size (Inches)	Property	UNIFORM	CONCENTRATED — Single Load At Center of Span	Single Load At Third Point	Single Load At Quarter Point	Sum of Two Equal Loads At Third Point	Sum of Two Equal Loads At Quarter Points From Reactions	Sum of 3 Equal Loads At Quarter Points and Center of Span
3x6 54 lb/beam 3.6 lb/ft	F_b / F_v / E	26.777 / .768 / 65,725	3.5702 / .0545 / 7,011	3.1736 / .0727 / 5.975	2.6777 / .0818 / 4,820	2.3802 / .0545 / 5.975	1.7851 / .0545 / 4,820	2.3802 / .0545 / 5,550
2x8 43 lb/beam 2.9 lb/ft	F_b / F_v / E	25.684 / .951 / 47,825	3.4245 / .0690 / 5.101	3.0440 / .0920 / 4,348	2.5684 / .1034 / 3.507	2.2830 / .0690 / 4,348	1.7122 / .0690 / 3,507	2.2830 / .0690 / 4,039
4x6 76 lb/beam 5.1 lb/ft	F_b / F_v / E	19.126 / .549 / 46,946	2.5502 / .0390 / 5,008	2.2668 / .0519 / 4,268	1.9126 / .0584 / 3,443	1.7001 / .0390 / 4,268	1.2751 / .0390 / 3,443	1.7001 / .0390 / 3,964
2x10 55 lb/beam 3.7 lb/ft	F_b / F_v / E	15.778 / .727 / 23,027	2.1037 / .0541 / 2,456	1.8700 / .0721 / 2,093	1.5778 / .0811 / 1,689	1.4025 / .0541 / 2,093	1.0519 / .0541 / 1,689	1.4025 / .0541 / 1,945
3x8 72 lb/beam 4.8 lb/ft	F_b / F_v / E	15.410 / .571 / 28,695	2.0547 / .0414 / 3,061	1.8264 / .0552 / 2,609	1.5410 / .0621 / 2,104	1.3698 / .0414 / 2,609	1.0273 / .0414 / 2,104	1.3698 / .0414 / 2,423
6x6 120 lb/beam 8.0 lb/ft	F_b / F_v / E	12.171 / .349 / 29,875	1.6228 / .0248 / 3,187	1.4425 / .0331 / 2,716	1.2171 / .0372 / 2,191	1.0819 / .0248 / 2,716	.8114 / .0248 / 2,191	1.0819 / .0248 / 2,523
4x8 100 lb/beam 6.7 lb/ft	F_b / F_v / E	11.007 / .408 / 20,496	1.4676 / .0296 / 2,186	1.3046 / .0394 / 1,863	1.1007 / .0443 / 1,503	.9784 / .0296 / 1,863	.7338 / .0296 / 1,503	.9784 / .0296 / 1,731
2x12 67 lb/beam 4.5 lb/ft	F_b / F_v / E	10.667 / .583 / 12,800	1.4222 / .0444 / 1,365	1.2642 / .0593 / 1,164	1.0667 / .0667 / 939	.9481 / .0444 / 1,164	.7111 / .0444 / 939	.9481 / .0444 / 1,081
3x10 92 lb/beam 6.1 lb/ft	F_b / F_v / E	9.467 / .436 / 13,816	1.2622 / .0324 / 1.474	1.1220 / .0432 / 1,256	.9467 / .0486 / 1,013	.8415 / .0324 / 1,256	.6311 / .0324 / 1,013	.8415 / .0324 / 1,167
2x14 79 lb/beam 5.2 lb/ft	F_b / F_v / E	7.690 / .483 / 7,835	1.0253 / .0377 / 836	.9114 / .0503 / 712	.7690 / .0566 / 575	.6835 / .0377 / 712	.5126 / .0377 / 575	.6835 / .0377 / 662
4x10 128 lb/beam 8.5 lb/ft	F_b / F_v / E	6.762 / .312 / 9,869	.9016 / .0232 / 1,053	.8014 / .0309 / 897	.6762 / .0347 / 724	.6011 / .0232 / 897	.4508 / .0232 / 724	.6011 / .0232 / 833

14 FOOT SPAN (Continued)

Nominal Size (Inches)	Property	UNIFORM	CONCENTRATED — Single Load At Center of Span	Single Load At Third Point	Single Load At Quarter Point	Sum of Two Equal Loads At Third Point	Sum of Two Equal Loads At Quarter Points From Reactions	Sum of 3 Equal Loads At Quarter Points and Center of Span
8x18 485 lb/beam 34.6 lb/ft	F_b / F_v / E	.801 / .063 / 553	.1144 / .0057 / 63	.1017 / .0076 / 54	.0858 / .0086 / 43	.0763 / .0057 / 54	.0572 / .0057 / 43	.0763 / .0057 / 50
12x16 659 lb/beam 47.0 lb/ft	F_b / F_v / E	.657 / .048 / 519	.0938 / .0042 / 59	.0834 / .0056 / 51	.0704 / .0063 / 41	.0626 / .0042 / 51	.0469 / .0042 / 41	.0626 / .0042 / 47
8x20 540 lb/beam 38.6 lb/ft	F_b / F_v / E	.653 / .055 / 400	.0933 / .0051 / 46	.0829 / .0068 / 39	.0700 / .0077 / 31	.0622 / .0051 / 39	.0467 / .0051 / 31	.0622 / .0051 / 36
10x18 614 lb/beam 43.9 lb/ft	F_b / F_v / E	.632 / .050 / 437	.0903 / .0045 / 50	.0803 / .0060 / 43	.0677 / .0068 / 34	.0602 / .0045 / 43	.0452 / .0045 / 34	.0602 / .0045 / 39
8x22 596 lb/beam 42.6 lb/ft	F_b / F_v / E	.543 / .048 / 298	.0776 / .0047 / 34	.0690 / .0062 / 29	.0582 / .0070 / 23	.0517 / .0047 / 29	.0388 / .0047 / 23	.0517 / .0047 / 27
12x18 744 lb/beam 53.1 lb/ft	F_b / F_v / E	.522 / .041 / 361	.0746 / .0037 / 41	.0663 / .0050 / 35	.0560 / .0056 / 28	.0497 / .0037 / 35	.0373 / .0037 / 28	.0497 / .0037 / 33
10x20 684 lb/beam 48.9 lb/ft	F_b / F_v / E	.516 / .044 / 316	.0737 / .0040 / 36	.0655 / .0054 / 31	.0552 / .0061 / 25	.0491 / .0040 / 31	.0368 / .0040 / 25	.0491 / .0040 / 29
8x24 651 lb/beam 46.5 lb/ft	F_b / F_v / E	.459 / .043 / 228	.0656 / .0043 / 26	.0583 / .0057 / 22	.0492 / .0064 / 18	.0437 / .0043 / 22	.0328 / .0043 / 18	.0437 / .0043 / 21

15 FOOT SPAN

Nominal Size (Inches)	Property	UNIFORM	CONCENTRATED — Single Load At Center of Span	Single Load At Third Point	Single Load At Quarter Point	Sum of Two Equal Loads At Third Point	Sum of Two Equal Loads At Quarter Points From Reactions	Sum of 3 Equal Loads At Quarter Points and Center of Span
2x6 33 lb/beam 2.2 lb/ft	F_b / F_v / E	44.628 / 1.280 / 109,542	5.9504 / .0909 / 11,684	5.2893 / .1212 / 9.958	4.4628 / .1364 / 8,033	3.9669 / .0909 / 9.958	2.9752 / .0909 / 8,033	3.9669 / .0909 / 9,250

STRENGTH AND STIFFNESS REQUIREMENTS FOR BEAMS

See instructions for use of tables on page 101. Symbols used in the tables are as follows: Tabulated values are based on net size.

F_b = Extreme fiber stress in bending induced by a uniform load of 1 (one) plf or by a concentrated load of 1 (one) pound, psi

F_v = Horizontal shear stress induced by a uniform load of 1 (one) plf or a total concentrated load of 1 (one) pound, psi.

E = Modulus of elasticity value needed to limit deflection to 1/360 of the span for a uniform load of 1 (one) plf or a total concentrated load of 1 (one) pound, psi.

15 FOOT SPAN

Nominal Size (Inches)	Property	UNIFORM	Single Load — At Center of Span	Single Load — At Third Point	Single Load — At Quarter Point	Sum of Two Equal Loads — At Third Point	Sum of Two Equal Loads — At Quarter Points From Reactions	Sum of 3 Equal Loads — At Quarter Points and Center of Span
6x8 163 lb/beam 10.9 lb/ft	F_b F_v E	6.545 .250 11,782	.8727 .0182 1,257	.7758 .0242 1,071	.6545 .0273 864	.5818 .0182 1,071	.4364 .0182 864	.5818 .0182 995
3x12 111 lb/beam 7.4 lb/ft	F_b F_v E	6.400 .350 7,680	.8533 .0267 819	.7585 .0356 698	.6400 .0400 563	.5689 .0267 698	.4267 .0267 563	.5689 .0267 649
8x8 223 lb/beam 14.8 lb/ft	F_b F_v E	4.800 .183 8,640	.6400 .0133 922	.5689 .0178 785	.4800 .0200 634	.4267 .0133 785	.3200 .0133 634	.4267 .0133 730
3x14 131 lb/beam 8.7 lb/ft	F_b F_v E	4.614 .290 4,701	.6152 .0226 501	.5468 .0302 427	.4614 .0340 345	.4101 .0226 427	.3076 .0226 345	.4101 .0226 397
4x12 156 lb/beam 10.4 lb/ft	F_b F_v E	4.571 .250 5,486	.6095 .0190 585	.5418 .0254 499	.4571 .0286 402	.4063 .0190 499	.3048 .0190 402	.4063 .0190 463
6x10 207 lb/beam 13.8 lb/ft	F_b F_v E	4.080 .193 5,797	.5439 .0144 618	.4835 .0191 527	.4080 .0215 425	.3626 .0144 527	.2720 .0144 425	.3626 .0144 490
3x16 151 lb/beam 10.1 lb/ft	F_b F_v E	3.576 .245 3,083	.4768 .0197 329	.4238 .0262 280	.3576 .0295 226	.3179 .0197 280	.2384 .0197 226	.3179 .0197 260
4x14 184 lb/beam 12.2 lb/ft	F_b F_v E	3.296 .207 3,358	.4394 .0162 358	.3906 .0216 305	.3296 .0243 246	.2929 .0162 305	.2197 .0162 246	.2929 .0162 284
8x10 282 lb/beam 18.8 lb/ft	F_b F_v E	2.992 .141 4,251	.3989 .0105 453	.3546 .0140 386	.2992 .0158 312	.2659 .0105 386	.1994 .0105 312	.2659 .0105 359
6x12 250 lb/beam 16.7 lb/ft	F_b F_v E	2.784 .155 3,268	.3712 .0119 349	.3300 .0158 297	.2784 .0178 240	.2475 .0119 297	.1856 .0119 240	.2475 .0119 276

15 FOOT SPAN (Continued)

Nominal Size (Inches)	Property	UNIFORM	Single Load — At Center of Span	Single Load — At Third Point	Single Load — At Quarter Point	Sum of Two Equal Loads — At Third Point	Sum of Two Equal Loads — At Quarter Points From Reactions	Sum of 3 Equal Loads — At Quarter Points and Center of Span
4x16 211 lb/beam 14.1 lb/ft	F_b F_v E	2.554 .175 2,202	.3406 .0141 235	.3027 .0187 200	.2554 .0211 162	.2270 .0141 200	.1703 .0141 162	.2270 .0141 186
10x10 357 lb/beam 23.8 lb/ft	F_b F_v E	2.362 .111 3,356	.3149 .0083 358	.2799 .0111 305	.2362 .0125 246	.2099 .0083 305	.1575 .0083 246	.2099 .0083 283
8x12 341 lb/beam 22.8 lb/ft	F_b F_v E	2.042 .114 2,397	.2722 .0087 256	.2420 .0116 218	.2042 .0130 176	.1815 .0087 218	.1361 .0087 176	.1815 .0087 202
6x14 294 lb/beam 19.6 lb/ft	F_b F_v E	2.047 .129 2,020	.2729 .0101 215	.2426 .0135 184	.2047 .0152 148	.1819 .0101 184	.1365 .0101 148	.1819 .0101 171
10x12 432 lb/beam 28.8 lb/ft	F_b F_v E	1.612 .090 1,892	.2149 .0069 202	.1910 .0092 172	.1612 .0103 139	.1433 .0069 172	.1075 .0069 139	.1433 .0069 160
6x16 337 lb/beam 22.5 lb/ft	F_b F_v E	1.577 .109 1,335	.2102 .0088 142	.1869 .0117 121	.1577 .0132 98	.1401 .0088 121	.1051 .0088 98	.1401 .0088 113
8x14 401 lb/beam 26.7 lb/ft	F_b F_v E	1.501 .094 1,481	.2001 .0074 158	.1779 .0099 135	.1501 .0111 109	.1334 .0074 135	.1001 .0074 109	.1334 .0074 125
12x12 523 lb/beam 34.9 lb/ft	F_b F_v E	1.331 .074 1,563	.1775 .0057 167	.1578 .0076 142	.1331 .0085 115	.1184 .0057 142	.0888 .0057 115	.1184 .0057 132
6x18 381 lb/beam 25.4 lb/ft	F_b F_v E	1.254 .094 927	.1672 .0078 99	.1486 .0104 84	.1254 .0117 68	.1114 .0078 84	.0836 .0078 68	.1114 .0078 78
10x14 508 lb/beam 33.8 lb/ft	F_b F_v E	1.185 .075 1,170	.1580 .0058 125	.1404 .0078 106	.1185 .0088 86	.1053 .0058 106	.0790 .0058 86	.1053 .0058 99
8x16 460 lb/beam 30.7 lb/ft	F_b F_v E	1.156 .080 979	.1542 .0065 104	.1370 .0086 89	.1156 .0097 72	.1028 .0065 89	.0771 .0065 72	.1028 .0065 83

STRENGTH AND STIFFNESS REQUIREMENTS FOR BEAMS

See instructions for use of tables on page 101. Symbols used in the tables are as follows: Tabulated values are based on net size.

F_b = Extreme fiber stress in bending induced by a uniform load of 1 (one) plf or by a concentrated load of 1 (one) pound, psi

F_v = Horizontal shear stress induced by a uniform load of 1 (one) plf or a total concentrated load of 1 (one) pound, psi.

E = Modulus of elasticity value needed to limit deflection to 1/360 of the span for a uniform load of 1 (one) plf or a total concentrated load of 1 (one) pound, psi.

16 FOOT SPAN

Nominal Size (Inches)	Property	UNIFORM	Single Load — At Center of Span	At Third Point	At Quarter Point	Sum of Two — At Third Point	At Quarter Points From Reactions	Sum of 3 — At Quarter Points and Center of Span
8x24 698 lb/beam 46.5 lb/ft	F_b F_v E	.527 .047 281	.0702 .0043 30	.0624 .0057 26	.0527 .0064 21	.0468 .0043 26	.0351 .0043 21	.0468 .0043 24
2x8 46 lb/beam 2.9 lb/ft	F_b F_v E	29.222 1.020 58,042	3.6528 .0690 5,804	3.2469 .0920 4,947	2.7396 .1034 3,990	2.4352 .0690 4,947	1.8264 .0690 3,990	2.4352 .0690 4,595
4x6 81 lb/beam 5.1 lb/ft	F_b F_v E	21.762 .588 56,976	2.7202 .0390 5,698	2.4179 .0519 4,856	2.0401 .0584 3,917	1.8135 .0390 4,856	1.3601 .0390 3,917	1.8135 .0390 4,511
2x10 59 lb/beam 3.7 lb/ft	F_b F_v E	17.952 .782 27,947	2.2440 .0541 2,795	1.9946 .0721 2,382	1.6830 .0811 1,921	1.4960 .0541 2,382	1.1220 .0541 1,921	1.4960 .0541 2,212
3x8 77 lb/beam 4.8 lb/ft	F_b F_v E	17.533 .612 34,825	2.1917 .0414 3,482	1.9482 .0552 2,968	1.6438 .0621 2,394	1.4611 .0414 2,968	1.0958 .0414 2,394	1.4611 .0414 2,757
6x6 128 lb/beam 8.0 lb/ft	F_b F_v E	13.848 .374 36,257	1.7310 .0248 3,626	1.5387 .0331 3,090	1.2983 .0372 2,493	1.1540 .0248 3,090	.8655 .0248 2,493	1.1540 .0248 2,870
4x8 107 lb/beam 6.7 lb/ft	F_b F_v E	12.524 .437 24,875	1.5655 .0296 2,487	1.3915 .0394 2,120	1.1741 .0443 1,710	1.0437 .0296 2,120	.7827 .0296 1,710	1.0437 .0296 1,969
2x12 71 lb/beam 4.5 lb/ft	F_b F_v E	12.136 .628 15,534	1.5170 .0444 1,553	1.3485 .0593 1,324	1.1378 .0667 1,068	1.0114 .0444 1,324	.7585 .0444 1,068	1.0114 .0444 1,230
3x10 98 lb/beam 6.1 lb/ft	F_b F_v E	10.771 .469 16,768	1.3464 .0324 1,677	1.1968 .0432 1,429	1.0098 .0486 1,153	.8976 .0324 1,429	.6732 .0324 1,153	.8976 .0324 1,327
2x14 84 lb/beam 5.2 lb/ft	F_b F_v E	8.749 .520 9,508	1.0936 .0377 951	.9721 .0503 810	.8202 .0566 654	.7291 .0377 810	.5468 .0377 654	.7291 .0377 753

15 FOOT SPAN (Continued)

Nominal Size (Inches)	Property	UNIFORM	Single Load — At Center of Span	At Third Point	At Quarter Point	Sum of Two — At Third Point	At Quarter Points From Reactions	Sum of 3 — At Quarter Points and Center of Span
6x20 425 lb/beam 28.3 lb/ft	F_b F_v E	1.022 .082 670	.1363 .0070 72	.1212 .0093 61	.1022 .0105 49	.0909 .0070 61	.0682 .0070 49	.0909 .0070 57
12x14 615 lb/beam 41.0 lb/ft	F_b F_v E	.979 .062 966	.1305 .0048 103	.1160 .0064 88	.0979 .0072 71	.0870 .0048 88	.0653 .0048 71	.0870 .0048 82
10x16 583 lb/beam 38.9 lb/ft	F_b F_v E	.913 .063 773	.1217 .0051 82	.1082 .0068 70	.0913 .0076 57	.0811 .0051 70	.0609 .0051 57	.0811 .0051 65
8x18 520 lb/beam 34.6 lb/ft	F_b F_v E	.919 .069 680	.1226 .0057 73	.1090 .0076 62	.0919 .0086 50	.0817 .0057 62	.0613 .0057 50	.0817 .0057 57
12x16 706 lb/beam 47.0 lb/ft	F_b F_v E	.754 .052 638	.1005 .0042 68	.0894 .0056 58	.0754 .0063 47	.0670 .0042 58	.0503 .0042 47	.0670 .0042 54
8x20 579 lb/beam 38.6 lb/ft	F_b F_v E	.750 .060 492	.1000 .0051 52	.0889 .0068 45	.0750 .0077 36	.0666 .0051 45	.0500 .0051 36	.0666 .0051 42
10x18 658 lb/beam 43.9 lb/ft	F_b F_v E	.726 .055 537	.0968 .0045 57	.0860 .0060 49	.0726 .0068 39	.0645 .0045 49	.0484 .0045 39	.0645 .0045 45
8x22 638 lb/beam 42.6 lb/ft	F_b F_v E	.623 .053 367	.0831 .0047 39	.0739 .0062 33	.0623 .0070 27	.0554 .0047 33	.0416 .0047 27	.0554 .0047 31
12x18 797 lb/beam 53.1 lb/ft	F_b F_v E	.600 .045 444	.0799 .0037 47	.0711 .0050 40	.0600 .0056 33	.0533 .0037 40	.0400 .0037 33	.0533 .0037 37
10x20 733 lb/beam 48.9 lb/ft	F_b F_v E	.592 .048 388	.0789 .0040 41	.0702 .0054 35	.0592 .0061 28	.0526 .0040 35	.0395 .0040 28	.0526 .0040 33

STRENGTH AND STIFFNESS REQUIREMENTS FOR BEAMS

See instructions for use of tables on page 101. Symbols used in the tables are as follows: Tabulated values are based on net size.

F_b = Extreme fiber stress in bending induced by a uniform load of 1 (one) plf or by a concentrated load of 1 (one) pound, psi.

F_v = Horizontal shear stress induced by a uniform load of 1 (one) plf or a total concentrated load of 1 (one) pound, psi.

E = Modulus of elasticity value needed to limit deflection to 1/360 of the span for a uniform load of 1 (one) plf or a total concentrated load of 1 (one) plf or a total concentrated load of 1 (one) pound, psi.

16 FOOT SPAN (Continued)

Nominal Size (Inches)	Property	UNIFORM	CONCENTRATED — Single Load — At Center of Span	CONCENTRATED — Single Load — At Third Point	CONCENTRATED — Single Load — At Quarter Point	Sum of Two Equal Loads — At Third Point	Sum of Two Equal Loads — At Quarter Points From Reactions	Sum of 3 Equal Loads — At Quarter Points and Center of Span
4x10 — 137 lb/beam — 8.5 lb/ft	F_b	7.694	.9617	.8548	.7213	.6411	.4809	.6411
	F_v	.335	.0232	.0309	.0347	.0232	.0232	.0232
	E	11,977	1,198	1,021	823	1,021	823	948
6x8 — 174 lb/beam — 10.9 lb/ft	F_b	7.447	.9309	.8275	.6982	.6206	.4655	.6206
	F_v	.268	.0182	.0242	.0273	.0182	.0182	.0182
	E	14,299	1,430	1,219	983	1,219	983	1,132
3x12 — 119 lb/beam — 7.4 lb/ft	F_b	7.282	.9102	.8091	.6827	.6068	.4551	.6068
	F_v	.377	.0267	.0356	.0400	.0267	.0267	.0267
	E	9,321	932	794	641	794	641	738
8x8 — 238 lb/beam — 14.8 lb/ft	F_b	5.461	.6827	.6068	.5120	.4551	.3413	.4551
	F_v	.197	.0133	.0178	.0200	.0133	.0133	.0133
	E	10,486	1,049	894	721	894	721	830
3x14 — 140 lb/beam — 8.7 lb/ft	F_b	5.249	.6562	.5833	.4921	.4375	.3281	.4375
	F_v	.312	.0226	.0302	.0340	.0226	.0226	.0226
	E	5,705	571	486	392	486	392	452
4x12 — 166 lb/beam — 10.4 lb/ft	F_b	5.201	.6502	.5779	.4876	.4334	.3251	.4334
	F_v	.269	.0190	.0254	.0286	.0190	.0190	.0190
	E	6,658	666	567	458	567	458	527
6x10 — 221 lb/beam — 13.8 lb/ft	F_b	4.642	.5802	.5157	.4352	.3868	.2901	.3868
	F_v	.207	.0144	.0191	.0215	.0144	.0144	.0144
	E	7,036	704	600	484	600	484	557
3x16 — 161 lb/beam — 10.1 lb/ft	F_b	4.069	.5086	.4521	.3814	.3390	.2543	.3390
	F_v	.265	.0197	.0262	.0295	.0197	.0197	.0197
	E	3,742	374	319	257	319	257	296
4x14 — 196 lb/beam — 12.2 lb/ft	F_b	3.750	.4687	.4166	.3515	.3125	.2343	.3125
	F_v	.223	.0162	.0216	.0243	.0162	.0162	.0162
	E	4,075	408	347	280	347	280	323
8x10 — 301 lb/beam — 18.8 lb/ft	F_b	3.404	.4255	.3782	.3191	.2837	.2127	.2837
	F_v	.152	.0105	.0140	.0158	.0105	.0105	.0105
	E	5,160	516	440	355	440	355	408

Nominal Size (Inches)	Property	UNIFORM	CONCENTRATED — Single Load — At Center of Span	CONCENTRATED — Single Load — At Third Point	CONCENTRATED — Single Load — At Quarter Point	Sum of Two Equal Loads — At Third Point	Sum of Two Equal Loads — At Quarter Points From Reactions	Sum of 3 Equal Loads — At Quarter Points and Center of Span
6x12 — 267 lb/beam — 16.7 lb/ft	F_b	3.168	.3959	.3520	.2970	.2640	.1980	.2640
	F_v	.167	.0119	.0158	.0178	.0119	.0119	.0119
	E	3,966	397	338	273	338	273	314
4x16 — 225 lb/beam — 14.1 lb/ft	F_b	2.906	.3633	.3229	.2725	.2422	.1816	.2422
	F_v	.189	.0141	.0187	.0211	.0141	.0141	.0141
	E	2,673	267	228	184	228	184	212
10x10 — 381 lb/beam — 23.8 lb/ft	F_b	2.687	.3359	.2986	.2519	.2239	.1680	.2239
	F_v	.120	.0083	.0111	.0125	.0083	.0083	.0083
	E	4,073	407	347	280	347	280	322
8x12 — 364 lb/beam — 22.8 lb/ft	F_b	2.323	.2904	.2581	.2178	.1936	.1452	.1936
	F_v	.122	.0087	.0116	.0130	.0087	.0087	.0087
	E	2,909	291	248	200	248	200	230
6x14 — 314 lb/beam — 19.6 lb/ft	F_b	2.329	.2911	.2588	.2183	.1941	.1456	.1941
	F_v	.139	.0101	.0135	.0152	.0101	.0101	.0101
	E	2,452	245	209	169	209	169	194
10x12 — 461 lb/beam — 28.8 lb/ft	F_b	1.834	.2292	.2038	.1719	.1528	.1146	.1528
	F_v	.097	.0069	.0092	.0103	.0069	.0069	.0069
	E	2,296	230	196	158	196	158	182
6x16 — 360 lb/beam — 22.5 lb/ft	F_b	1.794	.2242	.1993	.1682	.1495	.1121	.1495
	F_v	.118	.0088	.0117	.0132	.0088	.0088	.0088
	E	1,620	162	138	111	138	111	128
8x14 — 428 lb/beam — 26.7 lb/ft	F_b	1.708	.2135	.1898	.1601	.1423	.1067	.1423
	F_v	.102	.0074	.0099	.0111	.0074	.0074	.0074
	E	1,798	180	153	124	153	124	142
12x12 — 558 lb/beam — 34.9 lb/ft	F_b	1.515	.1894	.1683	.1420	.1262	.0947	.1262
	F_v	.080	.0057	.0076	.0085	.0057	.0057	.0057
	E	1,897	190	162	130	162	130	150
6x18 — 406 lb/beam — 25.4 lb/ft	F_b	1.426	.1783	.1585	.1337	.1189	.0891	.1189
	F_v	.102	.0078	.0104	.0117	.0078	.0078	.0078
	E	1,126	113	96	77	96	77	89
10x14 — 542 lb/beam — 33.8 lb/ft	F_b	1.348	.1685	.1498	.1264	.1124	.0843	.1124
	F_v	.080	.0058	.0078	.0088	.0058	.0058	.0058
	E	1,419	142	121	98	121	98	112

STRENGTH AND STIFFNESS REQUIREMENTS FOR BEAMS

See instructions for use of tables on page 101. Symbols used in the tables are as follows: Tabulated values are based on net size.

F_b = Extreme fiber stress in bending induced by a uniform load of 1 (one) plf or by a concentrated load of 1 (one) pound, psi

F_v = Horizontal shear stress induced by a uniform load of 1 (one) plf or a total concentrated load of 1 (one) pound, psi

E = Modulus of elasticity value needed to limit deflection to 1/360 of the span for a uniform load of 1 (one) plf or a total concentrated load of 1 (one) pound, psi.

16 FOOT SPAN (Continued)

Nominal Size (Inches)	Property	UNIFORM	Single Load — At Center of Span	Single Load — At Third Point	Single Load — At Quarter Point	Sum of Two Equal Loads — At Third Point	Sum of Two Equal Loads — At Quarter Points From Reactions	Sum of 3 Equal Loads — At Quarter Points and Center of Span
8x16, 491 lb/beam, 30.7 lb/ft	F_b	1.316	.1644	.1462	.1233	.1096	.0822	.1096
	F_v	.087	.0065	.0086	.0097	.0065	.0065	.0065
	E	1,188	119	101	82	101	82	94
6x20, 453 lb/beam, 28.3 lb/ft	F_b	1.163	.1454	.1293	.1091	.0969	.0727	.0969
	F_v	.089	.0070	.0093	.0105	.0070	.0070	.0070
	E	814	81	69	56	69	56	64
12x14, 656 lb/beam, 41.0 lb/ft	F_b	1.114	.1392	.1238	.1044	.0928	.0696	.0928
	F_v	.066	.0048	.0064	.0072	.0048	.0048	.0048
	E	1,173	117	100	81	100	81	93
10x16, 622 lb/beam, 38.9 lb/ft	F_b	1.039	.1298	.1154	.0974	.0865	.0649	.0865
	F_v	.068	.0051	.0068	.0076	.0051	.0051	.0051
	E	938	94	80	64	80	64	74
8x18, 554 lb/beam, 34.6 lb/ft	F_b	1.046	.1307	.1162	.0981	.0872	.0654	.0872
	F_v	.075	.0057	.0076	.0086	.0057	.0057	.0057
	E	825	83	70	57	70	57	65
12x16, 753 lb/beam, 47.0 lb/ft	F_b	.858	.1072	.0953	.0804	.0715	.0536	.0715
	F_v	.056	.0042	.0056	.0063	.0042	.0042	.0042
	E	775	77	66	53	66	53	61
8x20, 618 lb/beam, 38.6 lb/ft	F_b	.853	.1066	.0948	.0800	.0711	.0533	.0711
	F_v	.065	.0051	.0068	.0077	.0051	.0051	.0051
	E	597	60	51	41	51	41	47
10x18, 702 lb/beam, 43.9 lb/ft	F_b	.826	.1032	.0918	.0774	.0688	.0516	.0688
	F_v	.059	.0045	.0060	.0068	.0045	.0045	.0045
	E	652	65	56	45	56	45	52
8x22, 681 lb/beam, 42.6 lb/ft	F_b	.709	.0887	.0788	.0665	.0591	.0443	.0591
	F_v	.058	.0047	.0062	.0070	.0047	.0047	.0047
	E	445	45	38	31	38	31	35
12x18, 850 lb/beam, 53.1 lb/ft	F_b	.682	.0853	.0758	.0640	.0568	.0426	.0568
	F_v	.049	.0037	.0050	.0056	.0037	.0037	.0037
	E	538	54	46	37	46	37	43

(16 FOOT SPAN continued — upper sizes)

Nominal Size (Inches)	Property	UNIFORM	Single Load — At Center of Span	Single Load — At Third Point	Single Load — At Quarter Point	Sum of Two Equal Loads — At Third Point	Sum of Two Equal Loads — At Quarter Points From Reactions	Sum of 3 Equal Loads — At Quarter Points and Center of Span
10x20, 782 lb/beam, 48.9 lb/ft	F_b	.674	.0842	.0748	.0631	.0561	.0421	.0561
	F_v	.052	.0040	.0054	.0061	.0040	.0040	.0040
	E	471	47	40	32	40	32	37
8x24, 744 lb/beam, 46.5 lb/ft	F_b	.599	.0749	.0666	.0562	.0600	.0375	.0500
	F_v	.051	.0043	.0057	.0064	.0043	.0043	.0043
	E	341	34	29	23	29	23	27
12x20, 947 lb/beam, 59.2 lb/ft	F_b	.556	.0695	.0618	.0522	.0464	.0348	.0464
	F_v	.043	.0033	.0045	.0050	.0033	.0033	.0033
	E	389	39	33	27	33	27	31
10x22, 862 lb/beam, 53.9 lb/ft	F_b	.560	.0700	.0622	.0525	.0467	.0350	.0467
	F_v	.046	.0037	.0049	.0055	.0037	.0037	.0037
	E	351	35	30	24	30	24	28
10x24, 943 lb/beam, 58.9 lb/ft	F_b	.473	.0592	.0526	.0444	.0394	.0296	.0394
	F_v	.041	.0034	.0045	.0050	.0034	.0034	.0034
	E	269	27	23	19	23	19	21

17 FOOT SPAN

Nominal Size (Inches)	Property	UNIFORM	Single Load — At Center of Span	Single Load — At Third Point	Single Load — At Quarter Point	Sum of Two Equal Loads — At Third Point	Sum of Two Equal Loads — At Quarter Points From Reactions	Sum of 3 Equal Loads — At Quarter Points and Center of Span
2x8, 49 lb/beam, 2.9 lb/ft	F_b	32.989	3.8811	3.4499	2.9108	2.5874	1.9405	2.5874
	F_v	1.089	.0690	.0920	.1034	.0690	.0690	.0690
	E	69,619	6,552	5,584	4,505	5,584	4,505	5,187
4x6, 86 lb/beam, 5.1 lb/ft	F_b	24.567	2.8902	2.5691	2.1677	1.9268	1.4451	1.9268
	F_v	.627	.0390	.0519	.0584	.0390	.0390	.0390
	E	68,340	6,432	5,482	4,422	5,482	4,422	5,092
2x10, 62 lb/beam, 3.7 lb/ft	F_b	20.266	2.3842	2.1193	1.7882	1.5895	1.1921	1.5895
	F_v	.836	.0541	.0721	.0811	.0541	.0541	.0541
	E	33,521	3,155	2,689	2,169	2,689	2,169	2,498
3x8, 81 lb/beam, 4.8 lb/ft	F_b	19.794	2.3287	2.0699	1.7465	1.5524	1.1643	1.5524
	F_v	.653	.0414	.0552	.0621	.0414	.0414	.0414
	E	41,771	3,931	3,351	2,703	3,351	2,703	3,112
6x6, 136 lb/beam, 8.0 lb/ft	F_b	15.633	1.8392	1.6349	1.3794	1.2261	.9196	1.2261
	F_v	.399	.0248	.0331	.0372	.0248	.0248	.0248
	E	43,489	4,093	3,488	2,814	3,488	2,814	3,240

STRENGTH AND STIFFNESS REQUIREMENTS FOR BEAMS

See instructions for use of tables on page 101. Symbols used in the tables are as follows: Tabulated values are based on net size.

F_b = Extreme fiber stress in bending induced by a uniform load of 1 (one) plf or by a concentrated load of 1 (one) pound, psi

F_v = Horizontal shear stress induced by a uniform load of 1 (one) plf or a total concentrated load of 1 (one) pound, psi.

E = Modulus of elasticity value needed to limit deflection to 1/360 of the span for a uniform load of 1 (one) plf or a total concentrated load of 1 (one) pound, psi.

17 FOOT SPAN (Continued)

Nominal Size (Inches)	Property	UNIFORM	Single Load — At Center of Span	Single Load — At Third Point	Single Load — At Quarter Point	Sum of Two Equal Loads — At Third Point	Sum of Two Equal Loads — At Quarter Points From Reactions	Sum of 3 Equal Loads — At Quarter Points and Center of Span
4x8 114 lb/beam 6.7 lb/ft	F_b	14.138	1.6633	1.4785	1.2475	1.1089	.8317	1.1089
	F_v	.467	.0296	.0394	.0443	.0296	.0296	.0296
	E	29,837	2,808	2,393	1,931	2,393	1,931	2,223
2x12 76 lb/beam 4.5 lb/ft	F_b	13.701	1.6119	1.4328	1.2089	1.0746	.8059	1.0746
	F_v	.672	.0444	.0593	.0667	.0444	.0444	.0444
	E	18,633	1,754	1,495	1,206	1,495	1,206	1,388
3x10 104 lb/beam 6.1 lb/ft	F_b	12.160	1.4305	1.2716	1.0729	.9537	.7153	.9537
	F_v	.501	.0324	.0432	.0486	.0324	.0324	.0324
	E	20,113	1,893	1,613	1,301	1,613	1,301	1,499
2x14 89 lb/beam 5.2 lb/ft	F_b	9.877	1.1620	1.0329	.8715	.7747	.5810	.7747
	F_v	.558	.0377	.0503	.0566	.0377	.0377	.0377
	E	11,405	1,073	915	738	915	738	850
4x10 145 lb/beam 8.5 lb/ft	F_b	8.685	1.0218	.9083	.7664	.6812	.5109	.6812
	F_v	.358	.0232	.0309	.0347	.0232	.0232	.0232
	E	14,366	1,352	1,152	930	1,152	930	1,070
6x8 185 lb/beam 10.9 lb/ft	F_b	8.407	.9891	.8792	.7418	.6594	.4945	.6594
	F_v	.286	.0182	.0242	.0273	.0182	.0182	.0182
	E	17,151	1,614	1,376	1,110	1,376	1,110	1,278
3x12 126 lb/beam 7.4 lb/ft	F_b	8.220	.9671	.8597	.7253	.6447	.4836	.6447
	F_v	.403	.0267	.0356	.0400	.0267	.0267	.0267
	E	11,180	1,052	897	723	897	723	833
8x8 252 lb/beam 14.8 lb/ft	F_b	6.165	.7253	.6447	.5440	.4836	.3627	.4836
	F_v	.210	.0133	.0178	.0200	.0133	.0133	.0133
	E	12,577	1,184	1,009	814	1,009	814	937
3x14 149 lb/beam 8.7 lb/ft	F_b	5.926	.6972	.6197	.5229	.4648	.3486	.4648
	F_v	.335	.0226	.0302	.0340	.0226	.0226	.0226
	E	6,843	644	549	443	549	443	510
4x12 177 lb/beam 10.4 lb/ft	F_b	5.872	.6908	.6140	.5181	.4605	.3454	.4605
	F_v	.288	.0190	.0254	.0286	.0190	.0190	.0190
	E	7,986	752	641	517	641	517	595

Nominal Size (Inches)	Property	UNIFORM	Single Load — At Center of Span	Single Load — At Third Point	Single Load — At Quarter Point	Sum of Two Equal Loads — At Third Point	Sum of Two Equal Loads — At Quarter Points From Reactions	Sum of 3 Equal Loads — At Quarter Points and Center of Span
6x10 234 lb/beam 13.8 lb/ft	F_b	5.240	.6165	.5480	.4624	.4110	.3082	.4110
	F_v	.221	.0144	.0191	.0215	.0144	.0144	.0144
	E	8,439	794	677	546	677	546	629
3x16 171 lb/beam 10.1 lb/ft	F_b	4.593	.5404	.4803	.4053	.3602	.2702	.3602
	F_v	.284	.0197	.0262	.0295	.0197	.0197	.0197
	E	4,488	422	360	290	360	290	334
4x14 208 lb/beam 12.2 lb/ft	F_b	4.233	.4980	.4427	.3735	.3320	.2490	.3320
	F_v	.239	.0162	.0216	.0243	.0162	.0162	.0162
	E	4,888	460	392	316	392	316	364
8x10 320 lb/beam 18.8 lb/ft	F_b	3.843	.4521	.4018	.3391	.3014	.2260	.3014
	F_v	.162	.0105	.0140	.0158	.0105	.0105	.0105
	E	6,189	582	496	400	496	400	461
6x12 284 lb/beam 16.7 lb/ft	F_b	3.576	.4207	.3739	.3155	.2805	.2103	.2805
	F_v	.179	.0119	.0158	.0178	.0119	.0119	.0119
	E	4,757	448	382	308	382	308	354
4x16 239 lb/beam 14.1 lb/ft	F_b	3.281	.3860	.3431	.2895	.2573	.1930	.2573
	F_v	.203	.0141	.0187	.0211	.0141	.0141	.0141
	E	3,206	302	257	207	257	207	239
10x10 405 lb/beam 23.8 lb/ft	F_b	3.034	.3569	.3172	.2677	.2379	.1785	.2379
	F_v	.128	.0083	.0111	.0125	.0083	.0083	.0083
	E	4,886	460	392	316	392	316	364
8x12 387 lb/beam 22.8 lb/ft	F_b	2.622	.3085	.2742	.2314	.2057	.1543	.2057
	F_v	.131	.0087	.0116	.0130	.0087	.0087	.0087
	E	3,489	328	280	226	280	226	260
6x14 333 lb/beam 19.6 lb/ft	F_b	2.629	.3093	.2749	.2320	.2062	.1546	.2062
	F_v	.149	.0101	.0135	.0152	.0101	.0101	.0101
	E	2,941	277	236	190	236	190	219
10x12 490 lb/beam 28.8 lb/ft	F_b	2.070	.2436	.2165	.1827	.1624	.1218	.1624
	F_v	.104	.0069	.0092	.0103	.0069	.0069	.0069
	E	2,754	259	221	178	221	178	205
6x16 382 lb/beam 22.5 lb/ft	F_b	2.025	.2382	.2118	.1787	.1588	.1191	.1588
	F_v	.127	.0088	.0117	.0132	.0088	.0088	.0088
	E	1,943	183	156	126	156	126	145

STRENGTH AND STIFFNESS REQUIREMENTS FOR BEAMS

See instructions for use of tables on page 101. Symbols used in the tables are as follows: Tabulated values are based on net size.

F_b = Extreme fiber stress in bending induced by a uniform load of 1 (one) plf or by a concentrated load of 1 (one) pound, psi

F_v = Horizontal shear stress induced by a uniform load of 1 (one) plf or a total concentrated load of 1 (one) pound, psi.

E = Modulus of elasticity value needed to limit deflection to 1/360 of the span for a uniform load of 1 (one) plf or a total concentrated load of 1 (one) pound, psi.

17 FOOT SPAN (Continued)

Nominal Size (Inches)	Property	UNIFORM	CONCENTRATED — Single Load: At Center of Span	Single Load: At Third Point	Single Load: At Quarter Point	Sum of Two Equal Loads: At Third Point	Sum of Two Equal Loads: At Quarter Points From Reactions	Sum of 3 Equal Loads: At Quarter Points and Center of Span
8x14 — 454 lb/beam — 26.7 lb/ft	F_b F_v E	1.928 .109 2,157	.2268 .0074 203	.2016 .0099 173	.1701 .0111 140	.1512 .0074 173	.1134 .0074 140	.1512 .0074 161
12x12 — 593 lb/beam — 34.9 lb/ft	F_b F_v E	1.710 .086 2,275	.2012 .0057 214	.1788 .0076 183	.1509 .0085 147	.1341 .0057 183	.1006 .0057 147	.1341 .0057 170
6x18 — 432 lb/beam — 25.4 lb/ft	F_b F_v E	1.610 .110 1,350	.1894 .0078 127	.1684 .0104 108	.1421 .0117 87	.1263 .0078 108	.0947 .0078 87	.1263 .0078 101
10x14 — 575 lb/beam — 33.8 lb/ft	F_b F_v E	1.522 .086 1,703	.1791 .0058 160	.1592 .0078 137	.1343 .0088 110	.1194 .0058 137	.0895 .0058 110	.1194 .0058 127
8x16 — 522 lb/beam — 30.7 lb/ft	F_b F_v E	1.485 .093 1,425	.1747 .0065 134	.1553 .0086 114	.1310 .0097 92	.1165 .0065 114	.0874 .0065 92	.1165 .0065 106
6x20 — 481 lb/beam — 28.3 lb/ft	F_b F_v E	1.313 .096 976	.1545 .0070 92	.1373 .0093 78	.1159 .0105 63	.1030 .0070 78	.0773 .0070 63	.1030 .0070 73
12x14 — 696 lb/beam — 41.0 lb/ft	F_b F_v E	1.257 .071 1,406	.1479 .0048 132	.1315 .0064 113	.1109 .0072 91	.0986 .0048 113	.0740 .0048 91	.0986 .0048 105
10x16 — 661 lb/beam — 38.9 lb/ft	F_b F_v E	1.172 .073 1,125	.1379 .0051 106	.1226 .0068 90	.1035 .0076 73	.0920 .0051 90	.0690 .0051 73	.0920 .0051 84
8x18 — 589 lb/beam — 34.6 lb/ft	F_b F_v E	1.181 .080 990	.1389 .0057 93	.1235 .0076 79	.1042 .0086 64	.0926 .0057 79	.0695 .0057 64	.0926 .0057 74
12x16 — 800 lb/beam — 47.0 lb/ft	F_b F_v E	.969 .061 929	.1139 .0042 87	.1013 .0056 75	.0855 .0063 60	.0760 .0042 75	.0570 .0042 60	.0760 .0042 69

17 FOOT SPAN (Continued)

Nominal Size (Inches)	Property	UNIFORM	CONCENTRATED — Single Load: At Center of Span	Single Load: At Third Point	Single Load: At Quarter Point	Sum of Two Equal Loads: At Third Point	Sum of Two Equal Loads: At Quarter Points From Reactions	Sum of 3 Equal Loads: At Quarter Points and Center of Span
8x20 — 656 lb/beam — 38.6 lb/ft	F_b F_v E	.963 .071 716	.1133 .0051 67	.1007 .0068 57	.0850 .0077 46	.0755 .0051 57	.0567 .0051 46	.0755 .0051 53
10x18 — 746 lb/beam — 43.9 lb/ft	F_b F_v E	.932 .064 782	.1097 .0045 74	.0975 .0060 63	.0823 .0068 51	.0731 .0045 63	.0548 .0045 51	.0731 .0045 58
8x22 — 723 lb/beam — 42.6 lb/ft	F_b F_v E	.801 .062 534	.0942 .0047 50	.0837 .0062 43	.0706 .0070 35	.0628 .0047 43	.0471 .0047 35	.0628 .0047 40
12x18 — 903 lb/beam — 53.1 lb/ft	F_b F_v E	.770 .052 646	.0906 .0037 61	.0805 .0050 52	.0680 .0056 42	.0604 .0037 52	.0453 .0037 42	.0604 .0037 48
10x20 — 831 lb/beam — 48.9 lb/ft	F_b F_v E	.760 .056 565	.0894 .0040 53	.0795 .0054 45	.0671 .0061 37	.0596 .0040 45	.0447 .0040 37	.0596 .0040 42
8x24 — 791 lb/beam — 46.5 lb/ft	F_b F_v E	.677 .056 409	.0796 .0043 38	.0708 .0057 33	.0597 .0064 26	.0531 .0043 33	.0398 .0043 26	.0531 .0043 30
12x20 — 1006 lb/beam — 59.2 lb/ft	F_b F_v E	.628 .046 467	.0739 .0033 44	.0657 .0045 37	.0554 .0050 30	.0493 .0033 37	.0369 .0033 30	.0493 .0033 35
10x22 — 916 lb/beam — 53.9 lb/ft	F_b F_v E	.632 .049 422	.0744 .0037 40	.0661 .0049 34	.0558 .0055 27	.0496 .0037 34	.0372 .0037 27	.0496 .0037 31
10x24 — 1002 lb/beam — 58.9 lb/ft	F_b F_v E	.534 .044 323	.0629 .0034 30	.0559 .0045 26	.0471 .0050 21	.0419 .0034 26	.0314 .0034 21	.0419 .0034 24

18 FOOT SPAN

Nominal Size (Inches)	Property	UNIFORM	CONCENTRATED — Single Load: At Center of Span	Single Load: At Third Point	Single Load: At Quarter Point	Sum of Two Equal Loads: At Third Point	Sum of Two Equal Loads: At Quarter Points From Reactions	Sum of 3 Equal Loads: At Quarter Points and Center of Span
2x8 — 52 lb/beam — 2.9 lb/ft	F_b F_v E	36.985 1.158 82,641	4.1094 .0690 7,346	3.6528 .0920 6,261	3.0820 .1034 5,050	2.7396 .0690 6,261	2.0547 .0690 5,050	2.7396 .0690 5,816

STRENGTH AND STIFFNESS REQUIREMENTS FOR BEAMS

See instructions for use of tables on page 101. Symbols used in the tables are as follows: Tabulated values are based on net size.

F_b = Extreme fiber stress in bending induced by a uniform load of 1 (one) plf or by a concentrated load of 1 (one) pound, psi

F_v = Horizontal shear stress induced by a uniform load of 1 (one) plf or a total concentrated load of 1 (one) pound, psi.

E = Modulus of elasticity value needed to limit deflection to 1/360 of the span for a uniform load of 1 (one) plf or a total concentrated load of 1 (one) plf or a total concentrated load of 1 (one) pound, psi.

(Continued)

Nominal Size (Inches)	Property	UNIFORM	CONCENTRATED — Single Load: At Center of Span	Single Load: At Third Point	Single Load: At Quarter Point	Sum of Two Equal Loads: At Third Point	Sum of Two Equal Loads: At Quarter Points From Reactions	Sum of 3 Equal Loads: At Quarter Points and Center of Span
3x12 (134 lb/beam, 7.4 lb/ft)	F_b	9.216	1.0240	.9102	.7680	.6827	.5120	.6827
	F_v	.430	.0267	.0356	.0400	.0267	.0267	.0267
	E	13,271	1,180	1,005	811	1,005	811	934
8x8 (267 lb/beam, 14.8 lb/ft)	F_b	6.912	.7680	.6827	.5760	.5120	.3840	.5120
	F_v	.223	.0133	.0178	.0200	.0133	.0133	.0133
	E	14,930	1,327	1,131	912	1,131	912	1,051
3x14 (157 lb/beam, 8.7 lb/ft)	F_b	6.644	.7382	.6562	.5536	.4921	.3691	.4921
	F_v	.358	.0226	.0302	.0340	.0226	.0226	.0226
	E	8,123	722	615	496	615	496	572
4x12 (187 lb/beam, 10.4 lb/ft)	F_b	6.583	.7314	.6502	.5486	.4876	.3657	.4876
	F_v	.307	.0190	.0254	.0286	.0190	.0190	.0190
	E	9,479	843	718	579	718	579	667
6x10 (248 lb/beam, 13.8 lb/ft)	F_b	5.875	.6527	.5802	.4895	.4352	.3264	.4352
	F_v	.236	.0144	.0191	.0215	.0144	.0144	.0144
	E	10,018	890	759	612	759	612	705
3x16 (181 lb/beam, 10.1 lb/ft)	F_b	5.149	.5721	.5086	.4291	.3814	.2861	.3814
	F_v	.304	.0197	.0262	.0295	.0197	.0197	.0197
	E	5,328	474	404	326	404	326	375
4x14 (220 lb/beam, 12.2 lb/ft)	F_b	4.746	.5273	.4687	.3955	.3515	.2636	.3515
	F_v	.255	.0162	.0216	.0243	.0162	.0162	.0162
	E	5,802	516	440	355	440	355	408
8x10 (338 lb/beam, 18.8 lb/ft)	F_b	4.308	.4787	.4255	.3590	.3191	.2393	.3191
	F_v	.173	.0105	.0140	.0158	.0105	.0105	.0105
	E	7,346	653	557	449	557	449	517
6x12 (300 lb/beam, 16.7 lb/ft)	F_b	4.009	.4454	.3959	.3341	.2970	.2227	.2970
	F_v	.191	.0119	.0158	.0178	.0119	.0119	.0119
	E	5,647	502	428	345	428	345	397
4x16 (254 lb/beam, 14.1 lb/ft)	F_b	3.678	.4087	.3633	.3065	.2725	.2043	.2725
	F_v	.217	.0141	.0187	.0211	.0141	.0141	.0141
	E	3,806	338	288	233	288	233	268
10x10 (429 lb/beam, 23.8 lb/ft)	F_b	3.401	.3779	.3359	.2834	.2519	.1889	.2519
	F_v	.136	.0083	.0111	.0125	.0083	.0083	.0083
	E	5,800	516	439	354	439	354	408

18 FOOT SPAN (Continued)

Nominal Size (Inches)	Property	UNIFORM	CONCENTRATED — Single Load: At Center of Span	Single Load: At Third Point	Single Load: At Quarter Point	Sum of Two Equal Loads: At Third Point	Sum of Two Equal Loads: At Quarter Points From Reactions	Sum of 3 Equal Loads: At Quarter Points and Center of Span
4x6 (91 lb/beam, 5.1 lb/ft)	F_b	27.542	3.0602	2.7202	2.2952	2.0401	1.5301	2.0401
	F_v	.666	.0390	.0519	.0584	.0390	.0390	.0390
	E	81,123	7,211	6,146	4,958	6,146	4,958	5,709
2x10 (66 lb/beam, 3.7 lb/ft)	F_b	22.720	2.5245	2.2440	1.8934	1.6830	1.2622	1.6830
	F_v	.890	.0541	.0721	.0811	.0541	.0541	.0541
	E	39,791	3,537	3,014	2,432	3,014	2,432	2,800
3x8 (86 lb/beam, 4.8 lb/ft)	F_b	22.191	2.4656	2.1917	1.8492	1.6438	1.2328	1.6438
	F_v	.695	.0414	.0552	.0621	.0414	.0414	.0414
	E	49,585	4,408	3,756	3,030	3,756	3,030	3,489
6x6 (144 lb/beam, 8.0 lb/ft)	F_b	17.527	1.9474	1.7310	1.4606	1.2983	.9737	1.2983
	F_v	.424	.0248	.0331	.0372	.0248	.0248	.0248
	E	51,624	4,589	3,911	3,155	3,911	3,155	3,633
4x8 (121 lb/beam, 6.7 lb/ft)	F_b	15.851	1.7612	1.5655	1.3209	1.1741	.8806	1.1741
	F_v	.496	.0296	.0394	.0443	.0296	.0296	.0296
	E	35,418	3,148	2,683	2,164	2,683	2,164	2,492
2x12 (80 lb/beam, 4.5 lb/ft)	F_b	15.360	1.7067	1.5170	1.2800	1.1378	.8533	1.1378
	F_v	.717	.0444	.0593	.0667	.0444	.0444	.0444
	E	22,118	1,966	1,676	1,352	1,676	1,352	1,556
3x10 (110 lb/beam, 6.1 lb/ft)	F_b	13.632	1.5147	1.3464	1.1360	1.0098	.7573	1.0098
	F_v	.534	.0324	.0432	.0486	.0324	.0324	.0324
	E	23,875	2,122	1,809	1,459	1,809	1,459	1,680
2x14 (94 lb/beam, 5.2 lb/ft)	F_b	11.073	1.2303	1.0936	.9227	.8202	.6152	.8202
	F_v	.596	.0362	.0483	.0543	.0362	.0362	.0362
	E	13,538	1,203	1,026	827	1,026	827	953
4x10 (154 lb/beam, 8.5 lb/ft)	F_b	9.737	1.0819	.9617	.8114	.7213	.5410	.7213
	F_v	.381	.0232	.0309	.0347	.0232	.0232	.0232
	E	17,053	1,516	1,292	1,042	1,292	1,042	1,200
6x8 (196 lb/beam, 10.9 lb/ft)	F_b	9.425	1.0473	.9309	.7855	.6982	.5236	.6982
	F_v	.305	.0182	.0242	.0273	.0182	.0182	.0182
	E	20,359	1,810	1,542	1,244	1,542	1,244	1,433

STRENGTH AND STIFFNESS REQUIREMENTS FOR BEAMS

See instructions for use of tables on page 101. Symbols used in the tables are as follows: Tabulated values are based on net size.

F_b = Extreme fiber stress in bending induced by a uniform load of 1 (one) plf or by a concentrated load of 1 (one) plf or a total concentrated load of 1 (one) pound, psi.

F_v = Horizontal shear stress induced by a uniform load of 1 (one) plf or a total concentrated load of 1 (one) pound, psi.

E = Modulus of elasticity value needed to limit deflection to 1/360 of the span for a uniform load of 1 (one) plf or a total concentrated load of 1 (one) pound, psi.

18 FOOT SPAN (Continued)

Nominal Size (Inches)	Property	UNIFORM	Single Load — At Center of Span	Single Load — At Third Point	Single Load — At Quarter Point	Sum of Two Equal Loads — At Third Point	Sum of Two Equal Loads — At Quarter Points From Reactions	Sum of 3 Equal Loads — At Quarter Points and Center of Span
8x12 410 lb/beam 22.8 lb/ft	F_b F_v E	2.940 .140 4,141	.3267 .0087 368	.2904 .0116 314	.2450 .0130 253	.2178 .0087 314	.1633 .0087 253	.2178 .0087 291
6x14 353 lb/beam 19.6 lb/ft	F_b F_v E	2.947 .159 3,491	.3275 .0101 310	.2911 .0135 264	.2456 .0152 213	.2183 .0101 264	.1637 .0101 213	.2183 .0101 246
10x12 519 lb/beam 28.8 lb/ft	F_b F_v E	2.321 .110 3,270	.2579 .0069 291	.2292 .0092 248	.1934 .0103 200	.1719 .0069 248	.1289 .0069 200	.1719 .0069 230
6x16 405 lb/beam 22.5 lb/ft	F_b F_v E	2.270 .136 2,306	.2523 .0088 205	.2242 .0117 175	.1892 .0132 141	.1682 .0088 175	.1261 .0088 141	.1682 .0088 162
8x14 481 lb/beam 26.7 lb/ft	F_b F_v E	2.161 .117 2,560	.2402 .0074 228	.2135 .0099 194	.1801 .0111 156	.1601 .0074 194	.1201 .0074 156	.1601 .0074 180
12x12 628 lb/beam 34.9 lb/ft	F_b F_v E	1.917 .091 2,701	.2130 .0057 240	.1894 .0076 205	.1598 .0085 165	.1420 .0057 205	.1065 .0057 165	.1420 .0057 190
6x18 457 lb/beam 25.4 lb/ft	F_b F_v E	1.805 .118 1,603	.2006 .0078 142	.1783 .0104 121	.1504 .0117 98	.1337 .0078 121	.1003 .0078 98	.1337 .0078 113
10x14 609 lb/beam 33.8 lb/ft	F_b F_v E	1.706 .092 2,021	.1896 .0058 180	.1685 .0078 153	.1422 .0088 124	.1264 .0058 153	.0948 .0058 124	.1264 .0058 142
8x16 552 lb/beam 30.7 lb/ft	F_b F_v E	1.665 .099 1,691	.1850 .0065 150	.1644 .0086 128	.1387 .0097 103	.1233 .0065 128	.0925 .0065 103	.1233 .0065 119
6x20 509 lb/beam 28.3 lb/ft	F_b F_v E	1.472 .103 1,158	.1636 .0070 103	.1454 .0093 88	.1227 .0105 71	.1091 .0070 88	.0818 .0070 71	.1091 .0070 82

Nominal Size (Inches)	Property	UNIFORM	Single Load — At Center of Span	Single Load — At Third Point	Single Load — At Quarter Point	Sum of Two Equal Loads — At Third Point	Sum of Two Equal Loads — At Quarter Points From Reactions	Sum of 3 Equal Loads — At Quarter Points and Center of Span
12x14 737 lb/beam 41.0 lb/ft	F_b F_v E	1.410 .076 1,670	.1566 .0048 148	.1392 .0064 126	.1175 .0072 102	.1044 .0048 126	.0783 .0048 102	.1044 .0048 117
10x16 699 lb/beam 38.9 lb/ft	F_b F_v E	1.314 .079 1,335	.1460 .0051 119	.1298 .0068 101	.1095 .0076 82	.0974 .0051 101	.0730 .0051 82	.0974 .0051 94
8x18 623 lb/beam 34.6 lb/ft	F_b F_v E	1.324 .086 1,175	.1471 .0057 104	.1307 .0076 89	.1103 .0086 72	.0981 .0057 89	.0735 .0057 72	.0981 .0057 83
12x16 847 lb/beam 47.0 lb/ft	F_b F_v E	1.086 .065 1,103	.1206 .0042 98	.1072 .0056 84	.0905 .0063 67	.0804 .0042 84	.0603 .0042 67	.0804 .0042 78
8x20 695 lb/beam 38.6 lb/ft	F_b F_v E	1.080 .076 849	.1200 .0051 76	.1066 .0068 64	.0900 .0077 52	.0800 .0051 64	.0600 .0051 52	.0800 .0051 60
10x18 790 lb/beam 43.9 lb/ft	F_b F_v E	1.045 .068 928	.1161 .0045 82	.1032 .0060 70	.0871 .0068 57	.0774 .0045 70	.0581 .0045 57	.0774 .0045 65
8x22 766 lb/beam 42.6 lb/ft	F_b F_v E	.898 .067 634	.0997 .0047 56	.0887 .0062 48	.0748 .0070 39	.0665 .0047 48	.0499 .0047 39	.0665 .0047 45
12x18 956 lb/beam 53.1 lb/ft	F_b F_v E	.863 .056 766	.0959 .0037 68	.0853 .0050 58	.0719 .0056 47	.0640 .0037 58	.0480 .0037 47	.0640 .0037 54
10x20 880 lb/beam 48.9 lb/ft	F_b F_v E	.852 .060 671	.0947 .0040 60	.0842 .0054 51	.0710 .0061 41	.0631 .0040 51	.0474 .0040 41	.0631 .0040 47
8x24 837 lb/beam 46.5 lb/ft	F_b F_v E	.759 .060 485	.0843 .0043 43	.0749 .0057 37	.0632 .0064 30	.0562 .0043 37	.0421 .0043 30	.0562 .0043 34
12x20 1065 lb/beam 59.2 lb/ft	F_b F_v E	.704 .049 554	.0782 .0033 49	.0695 .0045 42	.0587 .0050 34	.0522 .0033 42	.0391 .0033 34	.0522 .0033 39

STRENGTH AND STIFFNESS REQUIREMENTS FOR BEAMS

See instructions for use of tables on page 101. Symbols used in the tables are as follows: Tabulated values are based on net size.

F_b = Extreme fiber stress in bending induced by a uniform load of 1 (one) plf or by a concentrated load of 1 (one) pound, psi

F_v = Horizontal shear stress induced by a uniform load of 1 (one) plf or a total concentrated load of 1 (one) pound, psi.

E = Modulus of elasticity value needed to limit deflection to 1/360 of the span for a uniform load of 1 (one) plf or a total concentrated load of 1 (one) pound, psi.

18 FOOT SPAN (Continued)

Nominal Size (Inches)	Property	UNIFORM	Single Load — At Center of Span	Single Load — At Third Point	Single Load — At Quarter Point	Sum of Two Equal Loads — At Third Point	Sum of Two Equal Loads — At Quarter Points From Reactions	Sum of 3 Equal Loads — At Quarter Points and Center of Span
3x10 116 lb/beam 6.1 lb/ft	F_b F_v E	15.189 .566 28,079	1.5988 .0324 2,365	1.4212 .0432 2,015	1.1991 .0486 1,626	1.0659 .0324 2,015	.7994 .0324 1,626	1.0659 .0324 1,872
2x14 100 lb/beam 5.2 lb/ft	F_b F_v E	12.337 .634 15,922	1.2987 .0377 1,341	1.1544 .0503 1,143	.9740 .0566 922	.8658 .0377 1,143	.6493 .0377 922	.8658 .0377 1,061
4x10 162 lb/beam 8.5 lb/ft	F_b F_v E	10.849 .404 20,056	1.1420 .0232 1,689	1.0151 .0309 1,439	.8565 .0347 1,161	.7613 .0232 1,439	.5710 .0232 1,161	.7613 .0232 1,337
6x8 207 lb/beam 10.9 lb/ft	F_b F_v E	10.502 .323 23,944	1.1055 .0182 2,016	.9826 .0242 1,718	.8291 .0273 1,386	.7370 .0182 1,718	.5527 .0182 1,386	.7370 .0182 1,596
3x12 141 lb/beam 7.4 lb/ft	F_b F_v E	10.268 .457 15,608	1.0809 .0267 1,314	.9608 .0356 1,120	.8107 .0400 904	.7206 .0267 1,120	.5404 .0267 904	.7206 .0267 1,041
8x8 282 lb/beam 14.8 lb/ft	F_b F_v E	7.701 .237 17,559	.8107 .0133 1,479	.7206 .0178 1,260	.6080 .0200 1,017	.5404 .0133 1,260	.4053 .0133 1,017	.5404 .0133 1,171

19 FOOT SPAN

Nominal Size (Inches)	Property	UNIFORM	Single Load — At Center of Span	Single Load — At Third Point	Single Load — At Quarter Point	Sum of Two Equal Loads — At Third Point	Sum of Two Equal Loads — At Quarter Points From Reactions	Sum of 3 Equal Loads — At Quarter Points and Center of Span
3x14 166 lb/beam 8.7 lb/ft	F_b F_v E	7.402 .380 9,553	.7792 .0226 804	.6926 .0302 686	.5844 .0340 553	.5195 .0226 686	.3896 .0226 553	.5195 .0226 637
4x12 197 lb/beam 10.4 lb/ft	F_b F_v E	7.335 .326 11,149	.7721 .0190 939	.6863 .0254 800	.5790 .0286 645	.5147 .0190 800	.3860 .0190 645	.5147 .0190 743
6x10 262 lb/beam 13.8 lb/ft	F_b F_v E	6.545 .250 11,782	.6890 .0144 992	.6124 .0191 846	.5167 .0215 682	.4593 .0144 846	.3445 .0144 682	.4593 .0144 785
3x16 191 lb/beam 10.1 lb/ft	F_b F_v E	5.737 .324 6,266	.6039 .0197 528	.5368 .0262 450	.4529 .0295 363	.4026 .0197 450	.3020 .0197 363	.4026 .0197 418
4x14 233 lb/beam 12.2 lb/ft	F_b F_v E	5.287 .272 6,824	.5562 .0162 575	.4947 .0216 490	.4174 .0243 395	.3711 .0162 490	.2783 .0162 395	.3711 .0162 455

18 FOOT SPAN (Continued)

Nominal Size (Inches)	Property	UNIFORM	Single Load — At Center of Span	Single Load — At Third Point	Single Load — At Quarter Point	Sum of Two Equal Loads — At Third Point	Sum of Two Equal Loads — At Quarter Points From Reactions	Sum of 3 Equal Loads — At Quarter Points and Center of Span
10x22 970 lb/beam 53.9 lb/ft	F_b F_v E	.709 .053 500	.0787 .0037 44	.0700 .0049 38	.0591 .0055 31	.0525 .0037 38	.0394 .0037 31	.0525 .0037 35
10x24 1060 lb/beam 58.9 lb/ft	F_b F_v E	.599 .047 383	.0665 .0034 34	.0592 .0045 29	.0499 .0050 23	.0444 .0034 29	.0333 .0034 23	.0444 .0034 27
12x22 1174 lb/beam 65.2 lb/ft	F_b F_v E	.585 .044 413	.0650 .0030 37	.0578 .0040 31	.0488 .0046 25	.0434 .0030 31	.0325 .0030 25	.0434 .0030 29
12x24 1284 lb/beam 71.3 lb/ft	F_b F_v E	.495 .039 317	.0550 .0028 28	.0489 .0037 24	.0412 .0042 19	.0366 .0028 24	.0275 .0028 19	.0366 .0028 22

19 FOOT SPAN

Nominal Size (Inches)	Property	UNIFORM	Single Load — At Center of Span	Single Load — At Third Point	Single Load — At Quarter Point	Sum of Two Equal Loads — At Third Point	Sum of Two Equal Loads — At Quarter Points From Reactions	Sum of 3 Equal Loads — At Quarter Points and Center of Span
2x10 70 lb/beam 3.7 lb/ft	F_b F_v E	25.315 .944 46,798	2.6647 .0541 3,941	2.3686 .0721 3,359	1.9985 .0811 2,709	1.7765 .0541 3,359	1.3324 .0541 2,709	1.7765 .0541 3,120
3x8 91 lb/beam 4.8 lb/ft	F_b F_v E	24.725 .736 58,317	2.6026 .0414 4,911	2.3134 .0552 4,185	1.9520 .0621 3,376	1.7351 .0414 4,185	1.3013 .0414 3,376	1.7351 .0414 3,888
6x6 152 lb/beam 8.0 lb/ft	F_b F_v E	19.528 .448 60,715	2.0556 .0248 5,113	1.8272 .0331 4,358	1.5417 .0372 3,515	1.3704 .0248 4,358	1.0278 .0248 3,515	1.3704 .0248 4,048
4x8 127 lb/beam 6.7 lb/ft	F_b F_v E	17.661 .526 41,655	1.8590 .0296 3,508	1.6525 .0394 2,990	1.3943 .0443 2,412	1.2393 .0296 2,990	.9295 .0296 2,412	1.2393 .0296 2,777
2x12 85 lb/beam 4.5 lb/ft	F_b F_v E	17.114 .761 26,013	1.8015 .0444 2,191	1.6013 .0593 1,867	1.3511 .0667 1,506	1.2010 .0444 1,867	.9007 .0444 1,506	1.2010 .0444 1,734

STRENGTH AND STIFFNESS REQUIREMENTS FOR BEAMS

See instructions for use of tables on page 101. Symbols used in the tables are as follows: Tabulated values are based on net size.

F_b = Extreme fiber stress in bending induced by a uniform load of 1 (one) plf or by a concentrated load of 1 (one) pound, psi

F_v = Horizontal shear stress induced by a uniform load of 1 (one) plf or a total concentrated load of 1 (one) pound. psi.

E = Modulus of elasticity value needed to limit deflection to 1/360 of the span for a uniform load of 1 (one) plf or a total concentrated load of 1 (one) pound. psi.

(Continued)

Nominal Size (Inches)	Property	UNIFORM	Single Load — At Center of Span	Single Load — At Third Point	Single Load — At Quarter Point	Sum of Two — At Third Point	Sum of Two — At Quarter Points From Reactions	Sum of 3 — At Quarter Points and Center of Span
6x18 483 lb/beam 25.4 lb/ft	F_b F_v E	2.011 .125 1,885	2117 .0078 159	1882 .0104 135	1588 .0117 109	1411 .0078 135	1059 .0078 109	1411 .0078 126
10x14 643 lb/beam 33.8 lb/ft	F_b F_v E	1.901 .098 2,377	2001 .0058 200	1779 .0078 171	1501 .0088 138	1334 .0058 171	1001 .0058 138	1334 .0058 158
8x16 583 lb/beam 30.7 lb/ft	F_b F_v E	1.855 .106 1,989	1953 .0065 168	1736 .0086 143	1465 .0097 115	1302 .0065 143	976 .0065 115	1302 .0065 133
6x20 538 lb/beam 28.3 lb/ft	F_b F_v E	1.640 .110 1,362	1727 .0070 115	1535 .0093 98	1295 .0105 79	1151 .0070 98	863 .0070 79	1151 .0070 91
12x14 778 lb/beam 41.0 lb/ft	F_b F_v E	1.571 .081 1,964	1653 .0048 165	1470 .0064 141	1240 .0072 114	1102 .0048 141	827 .0048 114	1102 .0048 131
10x16 738 lb/beam 38.9 lb/ft	F_b F_v E	1.465 .084 1,570	1542 .0051 132	1370 .0068 113	1156 .0076 91	1028 .0051 113	771 .0051 91	1028 .0051 105
8x18 658 lb/beam 34.6 lb/ft	F_b F_v E	1.475 .092 1,382	1553 .0057 116	1380 .0076 99	1164 .0086 80	1035 .0057 99	776 .0057 80	1035 .0057 92
12x16 894 lb/beam 47.0 lb/ft	F_b F_v E	1.210 .069 1,297	1274 .0042 109	1132 .0056 93	955 .0063 75	849 .0042 93	637 .0042 75	849 .0042 86
8x20 733 lb/beam 38.6 lb/ft	F_b F_v E	1.203 .081 999	1266 .0051 84	1126 .0068 72	950 .0077 58	844 .0051 72	633 .0051 58	844 .0051 67
10x18 834 lb/beam 43.9 lb/ft	F_b F_v E	1.164 .073 1,091	1226 .0045 92	1090 .0060 78	919 .0068 63	817 .0045 78	613 .0045 63	817 .0045 73
8x22 808 lb/beam 42.6 lb/ft	F_b F_v E	1.000 .072 745	1053 .0047 63	936 .0062 53	790 .0070 43	702 .0047 53	526 .0047 43	702 .0047 50

19 FOOT SPAN (Continued)

Nominal Size (Inches)	Property	UNIFORM	Single Load — At Center of Span	Single Load — At Third Point	Single Load — At Quarter Point	Sum of Two — At Third Point	Sum of Two — At Quarter Points From Reactions	Sum of 3 — At Quarter Points and Center of Span
8x10 357 lb/beam 18.8 lb/ft	F_b F_v E	4.800 .183 8,640	5053 .0105 728	4491 .0140 620	3789 .0158 500	3368 .0105 620	2526 .0105 500	3368 .0105 576
6x12 317 lb/beam 16.7 lb/ft	F_b F_v E	4.467 .203 6,642	4702 .0119 559	4179 .0158 477	3526 .0178 385	3135 .0119 477	2351 .0119 385	3135 .0119 443
4x16 268 lb/beam 14.1 lb/ft	F_b F_v E	4.098 .231 4,476	4314 .0141 377	3834 .0187 321	3235 .0211 259	2876 .0141 321	2157 .0141 259	2876 .0141 298
10x10 453 lb/beam 23.8 lb/ft	F_b F_v E	3.789 .145 6,821	3989 .0083 574	3546 .0111 490	2992 .0125 395	2659 .0083 490	1994 .0083 395	2659 .0083 455
8x12 432 lb/beam 22.8 lb/ft	F_b F_v E	3.276 .149 4,871	3448 .0087 410	3065 .0116 350	2586 .0130 282	2299 .0087 350	1724 .0087 282	2299 .0087 325
6x14 372 lb/beam 19.6 lb/ft	F_b F_v E	3.284 .169 4,106	3457 .0101 346	3073 .0135 295	2593 .0152 238	2305 .0101 295	1728 .0101 238	2305 .0101 274
10x12 548 lb/beam 28.8 lb/ft	F_b F_v E	2.586 .117 3,845	2722 .0069 324	2420 .0092 276	2042 .0103 223	1815 .0069 276	1361 .0069 223	1815 .0069 256
6x16 427 lb/beam 22.5 lb/ft	F_b F_v E	2.530 .144 2,713	2663 .0088 228	2367 .0117 195	1997 .0132 157	1775 .0088 195	1331 .0088 157	1775 .0088 181
8x14 508 lb/beam 26.7 lb/ft	F_b F_v E	2.408 .124 3,011	2535 .0074 254	2253 .0099 216	1901 .0111 174	1690 .0074 216	1268 .0074 174	1690 .0074 201
12x12 663 lb/beam 34.9 lb/ft	F_b F_v E	2.136 .097 3,177	2249 .0057 267	1999 .0076 228	1687 .0085 184	1499 .0057 228	1124 .0057 184	1499 .0057 212

STRENGTH AND STIFFNESS REQUIREMENTS FOR BEAMS

See instructions for use of tables on page 101. Symbols used in the tables are as follows: Tabulated values are based on net size.

F_b = Extreme fiber stress in bending induced by a uniform load of 1 (one) plf or by a concentrated load of 1 (one) pound, psi

F_v = Horizontal shear stress induced by a uniform load of 1 (one) plf or a total concentrated load of 1 (one) pound, psi.

E = Modulus of elasticity value needed to limit deflection to 1/360 of the span for a uniform load of 1 (one) plf or a total concentrated load of 1 (one) pound, psi.

Each cell lists three values in order: F_b / F_v / E.

19 FOOT SPAN (Continued)

Nominal Size (Inches)	UNIFORM	Single Load — At Center of Span	Single Load — At Third Point	Single Load — At Quarter Point	Sum of Two Equal Loads — At Third Point	Sum of Two Equal Loads — At Quarter Points From Reactions	Sum of 3 Equal Loads — At Quarter Points and Center of Span
3x8 — 96 lb/beam — 4.8 lb/ft	27.396 / .778 / 68,018	2.7396 / .0414 / 5,441	2.4352 / .0552 / 4,638	2.0547 / .0621 / 3,741	1.8264 / .0414 / 4,638	1.3698 / .0414 / 3,741	1.8264 / .0414 / 4,308
6x6 — 160 lb/beam — 8.0 lb/ft	21.638 / .473 / 70,815	2.1638 / .0248 / 5,665	1.9234 / .0331 / 4,828	1.6228 / .0372 / 3,895	1.4425 / .0248 / 4,828	1.0819 / .0248 / 3,895	1.4425 / .0248 / 4,485
4x8 — 134 lb/beam — 6.7 lb/ft	19.569 / .555 / 48,584	1.9569 / .0296 / 3,887	1.7394 / .0394 / 3,313	1.4676 / .0443 / 2,672	1.3046 / .0296 / 3,313	.9784 / .0296 / 2,672	1.3046 / .0296 / 3,077
2x12 — 89 lb/beam — 4.5 lb/ft	18.963 / .806 / 30,341	1.8963 / .0444 / 2,427	1.6856 / .0593 / 2,069	1.4222 / .0667 / 1,669	1.2642 / .0444 / 2,069	.9481 / .0444 / 1,669	1.2642 / .0444 / 1,922
3x10 — 122 lb/beam — 6.1 lb/ft	16.830 / .599 / 32,750	1.6830 / .0324 / 2,620	1.4960 / .0432 / 2,233	1.2622 / .0486 / 1,801	1.1220 / .0324 / 2,233	.8415 / .0324 / 1,801	1.1220 / .0324 / 2,074
2x14 — 105 lb/beam — 5.2 lb/ft	13.670 / .671 / 18,571	1.3670 / .0377 / 1,486	1.2151 / .0503 / 1,266	1.0253 / .0566 / 1,021	.9114 / .0377 / 1,266	.6835 / .0377 / 1,021	.9114 / .0377 / 1,176
4x10 — 171 lb/beam — 8.5 lb/ft	12.021 / .428 / 23,393	1.2021 / .0232 / 1,871	1.0686 / .0309 / 1,595	.9016 / .0347 / 1,287	.8014 / .0232 / 1,595	.6011 / .0232 / 1,287	.8014 / .0232 / 1,482
6x8 — 218 lb/beam — 10.9 lb/ft	11.636 / .341 / 27,927	1.1636 / .0182 / 2,234	1.0343 / .0242 / 1,904	.8727 / .0273 / 1,536	.7758 / .0182 / 1,904	.5818 / .0182 / 1,536	.7758 / .0182 / 1,769
3x12 — 148 lb/beam — 7.4 lb/ft	11.378 / .483 / 18,204	1.1378 / .0267 / 1,456	1.0114 / .0356 / 1,241	.8533 / .0400 / 1,001	.7585 / .0267 / 1,241	.5689 / .0267 / 1,001	.7585 / .0267 / 1,153
8x8 — 297 lb/beam — 14.8 lb/ft	8.533 / .250 / 20,480	.8533 / .0133 / 1,638	.7585 / .0178 / 1,396	.6400 / .0200 / 1,126	.5689 / .0133 / 1,396	.4267 / .0133 / 1,126	.5689 / .0133 / 1,297
3x14 — 175 lb/beam — 8.7 lb/ft	8.202 / .403 / 11,143	.8202 / .0226 / 891	.7291 / .0302 / 760	.6152 / .0340 / 613	.5468 / .0226 / 760	.4101 / .0226 / 613	.5468 / .0226 / 706
12x18 — 1009 lb/beam — 53.1 lb/ft	.962 / .060 / 901	.1013 / .0037 / 76	.0900 / .0050 / 65	.0759 / .0056 / 52	.0675 / .0037 / 65	.0506 / .0037 / 52	.0675 / .0037 / 60
10x20 — 929 lb/beam — 48.9 lb/ft	.950 / .064 / 789	.1000 / .0040 / 66	.0889 / .0054 / 57	.0750 / .0061 / 46	.0666 / .0040 / 57	.0500 / .0040 / 46	.0666 / .0040 / 53
8x24 — 884 lb/beam — 46.5 lb/ft	.845 / .064 / 571	.0890 / .0043 / 48	.0791 / .0057 / 41	.0667 / .0064 / 33	.0593 / .0043 / 41	.0445 / .0043 / 33	.0593 / .0043 / 38
12x20 — 1124 lb/beam — 59.2 lb/ft	.785 / .053 / 652	.0826 / .0033 / 55	.0734 / .0045 / 47	.0619 / .0050 / 38	.0551 / .0033 / 47	.0413 / .0033 / 38	.0551 / .0033 / 43
10x22 — 1024 lb/beam — 53.9 lb/ft	.790 / .057 / 588	.0831 / .0037 / 50	.0739 / .0049 / 42	.0623 / .0055 / 34	.0554 / .0037 / 42	.0416 / .0037 / 34	.0554 / .0037 / 39
10x24 — 1119 lb/beam — 58.9 lb/ft	.667 / .051 / 451	.0702 / .0034 / 38	.0624 / .0045 / 32	.0527 / .0050 / 26	.0468 / .0034 / 32	.0351 / .0034 / 26	.0468 / .0034 / 30
12x22 — 1240 lb/beam — 65.2 lb/ft	.652 / .047 / 486	.0687 / .0030 / 41	.0610 / .0040 / 35	.0515 / .0046 / 28	.0458 / .0030 / 35	.0343 / .0030 / 28	.0458 / .0030 / 32
12x24 — 1355 lb/beam — 71.3 lb/ft	.551 / .042 / 372	.0580 / .0028 / 31	.0516 / .0037 / 27	.0435 / .0042 / 22	.0387 / .0028 / 27	.0290 / .0028 / 22	.0387 / .0028 / 25

20 FOOT SPAN

Nominal Size (Inches)	UNIFORM	Single Load — At Center of Span	Single Load — At Third Point	Single Load — At Quarter Point	Sum of Two Equal Loads — At Third Point	Sum of Two Equal Loads — At Quarter Points From Reactions	Sum of 3 Equal Loads — At Quarter Points and Center of Span
2x10 — 73 lb/beam — 3.7 lb/ft	28.050 / .998 / 54,583	2.8050 / .0541 / 4,367	2.4933 / .0721 / 3,722	2.1037 / .0811 / 3,002	1.8700 / .0541 / 3,722	1.4025 / .0541 / 3,002	1.8700 / .0541 / 3,457

STRENGTH AND STIFFNESS REQUIREMENTS FOR BEAMS

See instructions for use of tables on page 101. Symbols used in the tables are as follows: Tabulated values are based on net size.

F_b = Extreme fiber stress in bending induced by a uniform load of 1 (one) plf or by a concentrated load of 1 (one) pound, psi

F_v = Horizontal shear stress induced by a uniform load of 1 (one) plf or a total concentrated load of 1 (one) pound, psi.

E = Modulus of elasticity value needed to limit deflection to 1/360 of the span for a uniform load of 1 (one) plf or a total concentrated load of 1 (one) pound, psi.

20 FOOT SPAN

Nominal Size (Inches)	Property	UNIFORM	CONCENTRATED Single Load — At Center of Span	At Third Point	At Quarter Point	Sum of Two Equal Loads — At Third Point	At Quarter Points From Reactions	Sum of 3 Equal Loads — At Quarter Points and Center of Span
4x12 208 lb/beam 10.4 lb/ft	F_b F_v E	8.127 .345 13,003	.8127 .0190 1,040	.7224 .0254 887	.6095 .0286 715	.5418 .0190 887	.4063 .0190 715	.5418 .0190 824
6x10 276 lb/beam 13.8 lb/ft	F_b F_v E	7.253 .264 13,742	.7253 .0144 1,099	.6447 .0191 937	.5439 .0215 756	.4835 .0144 937	.3626 .0144 756	.4835 .0144 870
3x16 201 lb/beam 10.1 lb/ft	F_b F_v E	6.357 .343 7,308	.6357 .0197 585	.5651 .0262 498	.4768 .0295 402	.4238 .0197 498	.3179 .0197 402	.4238 .0197 463
4x14 245 lb/beam 12.2 lb/ft	F_b F_v E	5.859 .288 7,959	.5859 .0162 637	.5208 .0216 543	.4394 .0243 438	.3906 .0162 543	.2929 .0162 438	.3906 .0162 504
8x10 376 lb/beam 18.8 lb/ft	F_b F_v E	5.319 .194 10,077	.5319 .0105 806	.4728 .0140 687	.3989 .0158 554	.3546 .0105 687	.2659 .0105 554	.3546 .0105 638
6x12 334 lb/beam 16.7 lb/ft	F_b F_v E	4.949 .214 7,747	.4949 .0119 620	.4399 .0158 528	.3712 .0178 426	.3300 .0119 528	.2475 .0119 426	.3300 .0119 491
4x16 282 lb/beam 14.1 lb/ft	F_b F_v E	4.541 .245 5,220	.4541 .0141 418	.4036 .0187 356	.3406 .0211 287	.3027 .0141 356	.2270 .0141 287	.3027 .0141 331
10x10 476 lb/beam 23.8 lb/ft	F_b F_v E	4.199 .153 7,956	.4199 .0083 636	.3732 .0111 542	.3149 .0125 438	.2799 .0083 542	.2099 .0083 438	.2799 .0083 504
8x12 455 lb/beam 22.8 lb/ft	F_b F_v E	3.629 .157 5,681	.3629 .0087 454	.3226 .0116 387	.2722 .0130 312	.2420 .0087 387	.1815 .0087 312	.2420 .0087 360
6x14 392 lb/beam 19.6 lb/ft	F_b F_v E	3.639 .179 4,789	.3639 .0101 383	.3234 .0135 326	.2729 .0152 263	.2426 .0101 326	.1819 .0101 263	.2426 .0101 303

(Continued)

Nominal Size (Inches)	Property	UNIFORM	CONCENTRATED Single Load — At Center of Span	At Third Point	At Quarter Point	Sum of Two Equal Loads — At Third Point	At Quarter Points From Reactions	Sum of 3 Equal Loads — At Quarter Points and Center of Span
10x12 577 lb/beam 28.8 lb/ft	F_b F_v E	2.865 .124 4,485	.2865 .0069 359	.2547 .0092 306	.2149 .0103 247	.1910 .0069 306	.1433 .0069 247	.1910 .0069 284
6x16 450 lb/beam 22.5 lb/ft	F_b F_v E	2.803 .153 3,164	.2803 .0088 253	.2491 .0117 216	.2102 .0132 174	.1869 .0088 216	.1401 .0088 174	.1869 .0088 200
8x14 534 lb/beam 26.7 lb/ft	F_b F_v E	2.668 .131 3,512	.2668 .0074 281	.2372 .0099 239	.2001 .0111 193	.1779 .0074 239	.1334 .0074 193	.1779 .0074 222
12x12 698 lb/beam 34.9 lb/ft	F_b F_v E	2.367 .103 3,705	.2367 .0057 296	.2104 .0076 253	.1775 .0085 204	.1578 .0057 253	.1184 .0057 204	.1578 .0057 235
6x18 508 lb/beam 25.4 lb/ft	F_b F_v E	2.229 .133 2,198	.2229 .0078 176	.1981 .0104 150	.1672 .0117 121	.1486 .0078 150	.1114 .0078 121	.1486 .0078 139
10x14 677 lb/beam 33.8 lb/ft	F_b F_v E	2.107 .104 2,772	.2107 .0058 222	.1873 .0078 189	.1580 .0088 152	.1404 .0058 189	.1053 .0058 152	.1404 .0058 176
8x16 614 lb/beam 30.7 lb/ft	F_b F_v E	2.055 .112 2,320	.2055 .0065 186	.1827 .0086 158	.1542 .0097 128	.1370 .0065 158	.1028 .0065 128	.1370 .0065 147
6x20 566 lb/beam 28.3 lb/ft	F_b F_v E	1.818 .117 1,589	.1818 .0070 127	.1616 .0093 108	.1363 .0105 87	.1212 .0070 108	.0909 .0070 87	.1212 .0070 101
12x14 819 lb/beam 41.0 lb/ft	F_b F_v E	1.740 .086 2,290	.1740 .0048 183	.1547 .0064 156	.1305 .0072 126	.1160 .0048 156	.0870 .0048 126	.1160 .0048 145
10x16 777 lb/beam 38.9 lb/ft	F_b F_v E	1.623 .089 1,832	.1623 .0051 147	.1442 .0068 125	.1217 .0076 101	.1082 .0051 125	.0811 .0051 101	.1082 .0051 116
8x18 693 lb/beam 34.6 lb/ft	F_b F_v E	1.634 .098 1,612	.1634 .0057 129	.1453 .0076 110	.1226 .0086 89	.1090 .0057 110	.0817 .0057 89	.1090 .0057 102

STRENGTH AND STIFFNESS REQUIREMENTS FOR BEAMS

See instructions for use of tables on page 101. Symbols used in the tables are as follows: Tabulated values are based on net size.

F_b = Extreme fiber stress in bending induced by a uniform load of 1 (one) plf or by a concentrated load of 1 (one) pound, psi

F_v = Horizontal shear stress induced by a uniform load of 1 (one) plf or a total concentrated load of 1 (one) pound, psi.

E = Modulus of elasticity value needed to limit deflection to 1/360 of the span for a uniform load of 1 (one) plf or a total concentrated load of 1 (one) pound, psi.

20 FOOT SPAN (Continued)

Nominal Size (Inches)	Property	UNIFORM	CONCENTRATED — Single Load: At Center of Span	Single Load: At Third Point	Single Load: At Quarter Point	Sum of Two Equal Loads: At Third Point	Sum of Two Equal Loads: At Quarter Points From Reactions	Sum of 3 Equal Loads: At Quarter Points and Center of Span
12x16 941 lb/beam 47.0 lb/ft	F_b	1.341	.1341	.1192	.1005	.0894	.0670	.0894
	F_v	.073	.0042	.0056	.0063	.0042	.0042	.0042
	E	1,513	121	103	83	103	83	96
8x20 772 lb/beam 38.6 lb/ft	F_b	1.333	.1333	.1185	.1000	.0889	.0666	.0889
	F_v	.086	.0051	.0068	.0077	.0051	.0051	.0051
	E	1,165	93	79	64	79	64	74
10x18 877 lb/beam 43.9 lb/ft	F_b	1.290	.1290	.1147	.0968	.0860	.0645	.0860
	F_v	.077	.0045	.0060	.0068	.0045	.0045	.0045
	E	1,273	102	87	70	87	70	81
8x22 851 lb/beam 42.6 lb/ft	F_b	1.108	.1108	.0985	.0831	.0739	.0554	.0739
	F_v	.076	.0047	.0062	.0070	.0047	.0047	.0047
	E	869	70	59	48	59	48	55
12x18 1062 lb/beam 53.1 lb/ft	F_b	1.066	.1066	.0947	.0799	.0711	.0533	.0711
	F_v	.064	.0037	.0050	.0056	.0037	.0037	.0037
	E	1,051	84	72	58	72	58	67
10x20 978 lb/beam 48.9 lb/ft	F_b	1.052	.1052	.0935	.0789	.0702	.0526	.0702
	F_v	.068	.0040	.0054	.0061	.0040	.0040	.0040
	E	920	74	63	51	63	51	58
8x24 930 lb/beam 46.5 lb/ft	F_b	.937	.0937	.0833	.0702	.0624	.0468	.0624
	F_v	.068	.0043	.0057	.0064	.0043	.0043	.0043
	E	666	53	45	37	45	37	42
12x20 1184 lb/beam 59.2 lb/ft	F_b	.869	.0869	.0773	.0652	.0580	.0435	.0580
	F_v	.056	.0033	.0045	.0050	.0033	.0033	.0033
	E	760	61	52	42	52	42	48
10x22 1078 lb/beam 53.9 lb/ft	F_b	.875	.0875	.0778	.0656	.0583	.0437	.0583
	F_v	.060	.0037	.0049	.0055	.0037	.0037	.0037
	E	686	55	47	38	47	38	43
10x24 1178 lb/beam 58.9 lb/ft	F_b	.739	.0739	.0657	.0555	.0493	.0370	.0493
	F_v	.054	.0034	.0045	.0050	.0034	.0034	.0034
	E	526	42	36	29	36	29	33

21 FOOT SPAN

Nominal Size (Inches)	Property	UNIFORM	CONCENTRATED — Single Load: At Center of Span	Single Load: At Third Point	Single Load: At Quarter Point	Sum of Two Equal Loads: At Third Point	Sum of Two Equal Loads: At Quarter Points From Reactions	Sum of 3 Equal Loads: At Quarter Points and Center of Span
12x22 1305 lb/beam 65.2 lb/ft	F_b	.723	.0723	.0642	.0542	.0482	.0361	.0482
	F_v	.050	.0030	.0040	.0046	.0030	.0030	.0030
	E	567	45	39	31	39	31	36
12x24 1426 lb/beam 71.3 lb/ft	F_b	.611	.0611	.0543	.0458	.0407	.0305	.0407
	F_v	.045	.0028	.0037	.0042	.0028	.0028	.0028
	E	434	35	30	24	30	24	27
2x10 77 lb/beam 3.7 lb/ft	F_b	30.925	2.9452	2.6180	2.2089	1.9635	1.4726	1.9635
	F_v	1.052	.0541	.0721	.0811	.0541	.0541	.0541
	E	63,187	4,814	4,103	3,310	4,103	3,310	3,811
3x8 100 lb/beam 4.8 lb/ft	F_b	30.204	2.8766	2.5570	2.1574	1.9177	1.4383	1.9177
	F_v	.819	.0414	.0552	.0621	.0414	.0414	.0414
	E	78,739	5,999	5,113	4,124	5,113	4,124	4,749
6x6 168 lb/beam 8.0 lb/ft	F_b	23.856	2.2720	2.0195	1.7040	1.5147	1.1360	1.5147
	F_v	.498	.0248	.0331	.0372	.0248	.0248	.0248
	E	81,977	6,246	5,323	4,294	5,323	4,294	4,945
4x8 141 lb/beam 6.7 lb/ft	F_b	21.574	2.0547	1.8264	1.5410	1.3698	1.0273	1.3698
	F_v	.585	.0296	.0394	.0443	.0296	.0296	.0296
	E	56,242	4,285	3,652	2,946	3,652	2,946	3,392
2x12 94 lb/beam 4.5 lb/ft	F_b	20.907	1.9911	1.7699	1.4933	1.3274	.9956	1.3274
	F_v	.850	.0444	.0593	.0667	.0444	.0444	.0444
	E	35,123	2,676	2,281	1,840	2,281	1,840	2,119
3x10 128 lb/beam 6.1 lb/ft	F_b	18.555	1.7671	1.5708	1.3253	1.1781	.8836	1.1781
	F_v	.631	.0324	.0432	.0486	.0324	.0324	.0324
	E	37,912	2,889	2,462	1,986	2,462	1,986	2,287
2x14 110 lb/beam 5.2 lb/ft	F_b	15.072	1.4354	1.2759	1.0765	.9569	.7177	.9569
	F_v	.709	.0377	.0503	.0566	.0377	.0377	.0377
	E	21,498	1,638	1,396	1,126	1,396	1,126	1,297
4x10 179 lb/beam 8.5 lb/ft	F_b	13.253	1.2622	1.1220	.9467	.8415	.6311	.8415
	F_v	.451	.0232	.0309	.0347	.0232	.0232	.0232
	E	27,080	2,063	1,758	1,418	1,758	1,418	1,633

STRENGTH AND STIFFNESS REQUIREMENTS FOR BEAMS

See instructions for use of tables on page 101. Symbols used in the tables are as follows: Tabulated values are based on net size.

F_b = Extreme fiber stress in bending induced by a uniform load of 1 (one) plf or by a concentrated load of 1 (one) pound, psi.

F_v = Horizontal shear stress induced by a uniform load of 1 (one) plf or a total concentrated load of 1 (one) pound, psi.

E = Modulus of elasticity value needed to limit deflection to 1/360 of the span for a uniform load of 1 (one) plf or a total concentrated load of 1 (one) pound, psi.

21 FOOT SPAN (Continued)

Nominal Size (Inches)	Property	UNIFORM	Single Load — At Center of Span	Single Load — At Third Point	Single Load — At Quarter Point	Sum of Two Equal Loads — At Third Point	Sum of Two Equal Loads — At Quarter Points From Reactions	Sum of 3 Equal Loads — At Quarter Points and Center of Span
6x8 229 lb/beam 10.9 lb/ft	F_b F_v E	12.829 .359 32,329	1.2218 .0182 2,463	1.0861 .0242 2,099	.9164 .0273 1,693	.8145 .0182 2,099	.6109 .0182 1,693	.8145 .0182 1,950
3x12 156 lb/beam 7.4 lb/ft	F_b F_v E	12.544 .510 21,074	1.1947 .0267 1,606	1.0619 .0356 1,368	.8960 .0400 1,104	.7964 .0267 1,368	.5973 .0267 1,104	.7964 .0267 1,271
8x8 312 lb/beam 14.8 lb/ft	F_b F_v E	9.408 .263 23,708	.8960 .0133 1,806	.7964 .0178 1,539	.6720 .0200 1,242	.5973 .0133 1,539	.4480 .0133 1,242	.5973 .0133 1,430
3x14 184 lb/beam 8.7 lb/ft	F_b F_v E	9.043 .425 12,899	.8612 .0226 983	.7655 .0302 838	.6459 .0340 676	.5742 .0226 838	.4306 .0226 676	.5742 .0226 778
4x12 218 lb/beam 10.4 lb/ft	F_b F_v E	8.960 .364 15,053	.8533 .0190 1,147	.7585 .0254 977	.6400 .0286 788	.5689 .0190 977	.4267 .0190 788	.5689 .0190 908
6x10 290 lb/beam 13.8 lb/ft	F_b F_v E	7.996 .279 15,908	.7615 .0144 1,212	.6769 .0191 1,033	.5711 .0215 833	.5077 .0144 1,033	.3808 .0144 833	.5077 .0144 960
3x16 211 lb/beam 10.1 lb/ft	F_b F_v E	7.009 .363 8,460	.6675 .0197 645	.5933 .0262 549	.5006 .0295 443	.4450 .0197 549	.3338 .0197 443	.4450 .0197 510
4x14 257 lb/beam 12.2 lb/ft	F_b F_v E	6.459 .304 9,214	.6152 .0162 702	.5468 .0216 598	.4614 .0243 483	.4101 .0162 598	.3076 .0162 483	.4101 .0162 556
8x10 395 lb/beam 18.8 lb/ft	F_b F_v E	5.864 .204 11,666	.5584 .0105 889	.4964 .0140 758	.4188 .0158 611	.3723 .0105 758	.2792 .0105 611	.3723 .0105 704
6x12 351 lb/beam 16.7 lb/ft	F_b F_v E	5.457 .226 8,968	.5197 .0119 683	.4619 .0158 582	.3898 .0178 470	.3465 .0119 582	.2598 .0119 470	.3465 .0119 541

Nominal Size (Inches)	Property	UNIFORM	Single Load — At Center of Span	Single Load — At Third Point	Single Load — At Quarter Point	Sum of Two Equal Loads — At Third Point	Sum of Two Equal Loads — At Quarter Points From Reactions	Sum of 3 Equal Loads — At Quarter Points and Center of Span
4x16 296 lb/beam 14.1 lb/ft	F_b F_v E	5.006 .259 6,043	.4768 .0141 460	.4238 .0187 392	.3576 .0211 317	.3179 .0141 392	.2384 .0141 317	.3179 .0141 365
10x10 500 lb/beam 23.8 lb/ft	F_b F_v E	4.629 .161 9,210	.4409 .0083 702	.3919 .0111 598	.3307 .0125 482	.2939 .0083 598	.2204 .0083 482	.2939 .0083 556
8x12 478 lb/beam 22.8 lb/ft	F_b F_v E	4.002 .166 6,576	.3811 .0087 501	.3388 .0116 427	.2858 .0130 344	.2541 .0087 427	.1905 .0087 344	.2541 .0087 397
6x14 411 lb/beam 19.6 lb/ft	F_b F_v E	4.012 .189 5,543	.3821 .0101 422	.3396 .0135 360	.2866 .0152 290	.2547 .0101 360	.1910 .0101 290	.2547 .0101 334
10x12 605 lb/beam 28.8 lb/ft	F_b F_v E	3.159 .131 5,192	.3009 .0069 396	.2674 .0092 337	.2256 .0103 272	.2006 .0069 337	.1504 .0069 272	.2006 .0069 313
6x16 472 lb/beam 22.5 lb/ft	F_b F_v E	3.090 .162 3,663	.2943 .0088 279	.2616 .0117 238	.2207 .0132 192	.1962 .0088 238	.1472 .0088 192	.1962 .0088 221
8x14 561 lb/beam 26.7 lb/ft	F_b F_v E	2.942 .139 4,065	.2802 .0074 310	.2491 .0099 264	.2101 .0111 213	.1868 .0074 264	.1401 .0074 213	.1868 .0074 245
12x12 733 lb/beam 34.9 lb/ft	F_b F_v E	2.610 .108 4,289	.2485 .0057 327	.2209 .0076 279	.1864 .0085 225	.1657 .0057 279	.1243 .0057 225	.1657 .0057 259
6x18 533 lb/beam 25.4 lb/ft	F_b F_v E	2.457 .141 2,545	.2340 .0078 194	.2080 .0104 165	.1755 .0117 133	.1560 .0078 165	.1170 .0078 133	.1560 .0078 154
10x14 711 lb/beam 33.8 lb/ft	F_b F_v E	2.323 .110 3,209	.2212 .0058 245	.1966 .0078 208	.1659 .0088 168	.1475 .0058 208	.1106 .0058 168	.1475 .0058 194
8x16 644 lb/beam 30.7 lb/ft	F_b F_v E	2.266 .119 2,686	.2158 .0065 205	.1918 .0086 174	.1619 .0097 141	.1439 .0065 174	.1079 .0065 141	.1439 .0065 162

STRENGTH AND STIFFNESS REQUIREMENTS FOR BEAMS

See instructions for use of tables on page 101. Symbols used in the tables are as follows: Tabulated values are based on net size.

F_b = Extreme fiber stress in bending induced by a uniform load of 1 (one) plf or by a concentrated load of 1 (one) pound, psi

F_v = Horizontal shear stress induced by a uniform load of 1 (one) plf or a total concentrated load of 1 (one) pound. psi.

E = Modulus of elasticity value needed to limit deflection to 1/360 of the span for a uniform load of 1 (one) plf or a total concentrated load of 1 (one) pound, psi.

21 FOOT SPAN (Continued) / 22 FOOT SPAN

Nominal Size (Inches)	Property	UNIFORM	CONCENTRATED — Single Load At Center of Span	At Third Point	At Quarter Point	Sum of Two Equal Loads At Third Point	At Quarter Points From Reactions	Sum of 3 Equal Loads At Quarter Points and Center of Span
8x24 — 977 lb/beam, 46.5 lb/ft	F_b / F_v / E	1.033 / .073 / 771	.0983 / .0043 / 59	.0874 / .0057 / 50	.0738 / .0064 / 40	.0656 / .0043 / 50	.0492 / .0043 / 40	.0656 / .0043 / 46
12x20 — 1243 lb/beam, 59.2 lb/ft	F_b / F_v / E	.958 / .059 / 880	.0913 / .0033 / 67	.0811 / .0045 / 57	.0685 / .0050 / 46	.0609 / .0033 / 57	.0456 / .0033 / 46	.0609 / .0033 / 53
10x22 — 1132 lb/beam, 53.9 lb/ft	F_b / F_v / E	.965 / .064 / 795	.0919 / .0037 / 61	.0817 / .0049 / 52	.0689 / .0055 / 42	.0612 / .0037 / 52	.0459 / .0037 / 42	.0612 / .0037 / 48
10x24 — 1237 lb/beam, 58.9 lb/ft	F_b / F_v / E	.815 / .057 / 608	.0776 / .0034 / 46	.0690 / .0045 / 40	.0582 / .0050 / 32	.0518 / .0034 / 40	.0388 / .0034 / 32	.0518 / .0034 / 37
12x22 — 1370 lb/beam, 65.2 lb/ft	F_b / F_v / E	.797 / .053 / 656	.0759 / .0030 / 50	.0675 / .0040 / 43	.0569 / .0046 / 34	.0506 / .0030 / 43	.0379 / .0030 / 34	.0506 / .0030 / 40
12x24 — 1498 lb/beam, 71.3 lb/ft	F_b / F_v / E	.673 / .047 / 503	.0641 / .0028 / 38	.0570 / .0037 / 33	.0481 / .0042 / 26	.0428 / .0028 / 33	.0321 / .0028 / 26	.0428 / .0028 / 30
22 FOOT SPAN								
2x12 — 98 lb/beam, 4.5 lb/ft	F_b / F_v / E	22.945 / .894 / 40,384	2.0859 / .0444 / 2,937	1.8542 / .0593 / 2,503	1.5644 / .0667 / 2,019	1.3906 / .0444 / 2,503	1.0430 / .0444 / 2,019	1.3906 / .0444 / 2,325
3x10 — 134 lb/beam, 6.1 lb/ft	F_b / F_v / E	20.364 / .664 / 43,590	1.8513 / .0324 / 3,170	1.6456 / .0432 / 2,702	1.3885 / .0486 / 2,180	1.2342 / .0324 / 2,702	.9256 / .0324 / 2,180	1.2342 / .0324 / 2,510
2x14 — 115 lb/beam, 5.2 lb/ft	F_b / F_v / E	16.541 / .747 / 24,718	1.5037 / .0377 / 1,798	1.3367 / .0503 / 1,532	1.1278 / .0566 / 1,236	1.0025 / .0377 / 1,532	.7519 / .0377 / 1,236	1.0025 / .0377 / 1,423
4x10 — 188 lb/beam, 8.5 lb/ft	F_b / F_v / E	14.546 / .474 / 31,136	1.3223 / .0232 / 2,264	1.1754 / .0309 / 1,930	.9918 / .0347 / 1,557	.8816 / .0232 / 1,930	.6612 / .0232 / 1,557	.8816 / .0232 / 1,793

21 FOOT SPAN (Continued)

Nominal Size (Inches)	Property	UNIFORM	CONCENTRATED — Single Load At Center of Span	At Third Point	At Quarter Point	Sum of Two Equal Loads At Third Point	At Quarter Points From Reactions	Sum of 3 Equal Loads At Quarter Points and Center of Span
6x20 — 594 lb/beam, 28.3 lb/ft	F_b / F_v / E	2.004 / .124 / 1,839	.1909 / .0070 / 140	.1697 / .0093 / 119	.1431 / .0105 / 96	.1272 / .0070 / 119	.0954 / .0070 / 96	.1272 / .0070 / 111
12x14 — 860 lb/beam, 41.0 lb/ft	F_b / F_v / E	1.919 / .091 / 2,651	.1827 / .0048 / 202	.1624 / .0064 / 172	.1370 / .0072 / 139	.1218 / .0048 / 172	.0914 / .0048 / 139	.1218 / .0048 / 160
10x16 — 816 lb/beam, 38.9 lb/ft	F_b / F_v / E	1.789 / .094 / 2,120	.1704 / .0051 / 162	.1515 / .0068 / 138	.1278 / .0076 / 111	.1136 / .0051 / 138	.0852 / .0051 / 111	.1136 / .0051 / 128
8x18 — 727 lb/beam, 34.6 lb/ft	F_b / F_v / E	1.802 / .103 / 1,866	.1716 / .0057 / 142	.1525 / .0076 / 121	.1287 / .0086 / 98	.1144 / .0057 / 121	.0858 / .0057 / 98	.1144 / .0057 / 113
12x16 — 988 lb/beam, 47.0 lb/ft	F_b / F_v / E	1.478 / .077 / 1,752	.1408 / .0042 / 133	.1251 / .0056 / 114	.1056 / .0063 / 92	.0938 / .0042 / 114	.0704 / .0042 / 92	.0938 / .0042 / 106
8x20 — 810 lb/beam, 38.6 lb/ft	F_b / F_v / E	1.470 / .091 / 1,349	.1400 / .0051 / 103	.1244 / .0068 / 88	.1050 / .0077 / 71	.0933 / .0051 / 88	.0700 / .0051 / 71	.0933 / .0051 / 81
10x18 — 921 lb/beam, 43.9 lb/ft	F_b / F_v / E	1.423 / .082 / 1,473	.1355 / .0045 / 112	.1204 / .0060 / 96	.1016 / .0068 / 77	.0903 / .0045 / 96	.0677 / .0045 / 77	.0903 / .0045 / 89
8x22 — 894 lb/beam, 42.6 lb/ft	F_b / F_v / E	1.222 / .081 / 1,006	.1164 / .0047 / 77	.1034 / .0062 / 65	.0873 / .0070 / 53	.0776 / .0047 / 65	.0582 / .0047 / 53	.0776 / .0047 / 61
12x18 — 1115 lb/beam, 53.1 lb/ft	F_b / F_v / E	1.175 / .067 / 1,217	.1119 / .0037 / 93	.0995 / .0050 / 79	.0839 / .0056 / 64	.0746 / .0037 / 79	.0560 / .0037 / 64	.0746 / .0037 / 73
10x20 — 1027 lb/beam, 48.9 lb/ft	F_b / F_v / E	1.160 / .072 / 1,065	.1105 / .0040 / 81	.0982 / .0054 / 69	.0829 / .0061 / 56	.0737 / .0040 / 69	.0552 / .0040 / 56	.0737 / .0040 / 64

STRENGTH AND STIFFNESS REQUIREMENTS FOR BEAMS

See instructions for use of tables on page 101. Symbols used in the tables are as follows: Tabulated values are based on net size.

F_b = Extreme fiber stress in bending induced by a uniform load of 1 (one) plf or by a concentrated load of 1 (one) pound, psi

F_v = Horizontal shear stress induced by a uniform load of 1 (one) plf or a total concentrated load of 1 (one) pound, psi.

E = Modulus of elasticity value needed to limit deflection to 1/360 of the span for a uniform load of 1 (one) plf or a total concentrated load of 1 (one) pound, psi.

22 FOOT SPAN (Continued)

Nominal Size (Inches)	Property	UNIFORM	CONCENTRATED Single Load — At Center of Span	Single Load — At Third Point	Single Load — At Quarter Point	Sum of Two Equal Loads — At Third Point	Sum of Two Equal Loads — At Quarter Points From Reactions	Sum of 3 Equal Loads — At Quarter Points and Center of Span
6x8 (239 lb/beam, 10.9 lb/ft)	F_b	14.080	1.2800	1.1378	.9600	.8533	.6400	.8533
	F_v	.377	.0182	.0242	.0273	.0182	.0182	.0182
	E	37.171	2.703	2.304	1,859	2,304	1,859	2,140
3x12 (163 lb/beam, 7.4 lb/ft)	F_b	13.767	1.2516	1.1125	.9387	.8344	.6258	.8344
	F_v	.537	.0267	.0356	.0400	.0267	.0267	.0267
	E	24.230	1.762	1.502	1,212	1,502	1,212	1,395
8x8 (327 lb/beam, 14.8 lb/ft)	F_b	10.325	.9387	.8344	.7040	.6258	.4693	.6258
	F_v	.277	.0133	.0178	.0200	.0133	.0133	.0133
	E	27.259	1.982	1.690	1,363	1,690	1,363	1,569
3x14 (192 lb/beam, 8.7 lb/ft)	F_b	9.925	.9022	.8020	.6767	.6015	.4511	.6015
	F_v	.448	.0226	.0302	.0340	.0226	.0226	.0226
	E	14.831	1.079	919	742	919	742	854
4x12 (229 lb/beam, 10.4 lb/ft)	F_b	9.834	.8940	.7946	.6705	.5960	.4470	.5960
	F_v	.383	.0190	.0254	.0286	.0190	.0190	.0190
	E	17.307	1.259	1,073	865	1,073	865	996
6x10 (303 lb/beam, 13.8 lb/ft)	F_b	8.776	.7978	.7091	.5983	.5319	.3989	.5319
	F_v	.293	.0144	.0191	.0215	.0144	.0144	.0144
	E	18.290	1.330	1,134	915	1,134	915	1,053
3x16 (221 lb/beam, 10.1 lb/ft)	F_b	7.692	.6993	.6216	.5245	.4662	.3496	.4662
	F_v	.383	.0197	.0262	.0295	.0197	.0197	.0197
	E	9.728	707	603	486	603	486	560
4x14 (269 lb/beam, 12.2 lb/ft)	F_b	7.089	.6445	.5729	.4833	.4296	.3222	.4296
	F_v	.320	.0162	.0216	.0243	.0162	.0162	.0162
	E	10.593	770	657	530	657	530	610
8x10 (414 lb/beam, 18.8 lb/ft)	F_b	6.435	.5850	.5200	.4388	.3900	.2925	.3900
	F_v	.215	.0105	.0140	.0158	.0105	.0105	.0105
	E	13.413	975	831	671	831	671	772
6x12 (367 lb/beam, 16.7 lb/ft)	F_b	5.989	.5444	.4839	.4083	.3629	.2722	.3629
	F_v	.238	.0119	.0158	.0178	.0119	.0119	.0119
	E	10.311	750	639	516	639	516	594

Nominal Size (Inches)	Property	UNIFORM	CONCENTRATED Single Load — At Center of Span	Single Load — At Third Point	Single Load — At Quarter Point	Sum of Two Equal Loads — At Third Point	Sum of Two Equal Loads — At Quarter Points From Reactions	Sum of 3 Equal Loads — At Quarter Points and Center of Span
4x16 (310 lb/beam, 14.1 lb/ft)	F_b	5.494	.4995	.4440	.3746	.3330	.2497	.3330
	F_v	.273	.0141	.0187	.0211	.0141	.0141	.0141
	E	6.948	505	431	347	431	347	400
10x10 (524 lb/beam, 23.8 lb/ft)	F_b	5.081	.4619	.4106	.3464	.3079	.2309	.3079
	F_v	.170	.0083	.0111	.0125	.0083	.0083	.0083
	E	10.589	770	656	529	656	529	610
8x12 (501 lb/beam, 22.8 lb/ft)	F_b	4.392	.3992	.3549	.2994	.2662	.1996	.2662
	F_v	.175	.0087	.0116	.0130	.0087	.0087	.0087
	E	7.561	550	469	378	469	378	435
6x14 (431 lb/beam, 19.6 lb/ft)	F_b	4.403	.4003	.3558	.3002	.2668	.2001	.2668
	F_v	.199	.0101	.0135	.0152	.0101	.0101	.0101
	E	6.374	464	395	319	395	319	367
10x12 (634 lb/beam, 28.8 lb/ft)	F_b	3.467	.3152	.2802	.2364	.2101	.1576	.2101
	F_v	.138	.0069	.0092	.0103	.0069	.0069	.0069
	E	5.969	434	370	298	370	298	344
6x16 (495 lb/beam, 22.5 lb/ft)	F_b	3.392	.3083	.2741	.2312	.2055	.1542	.2055
	F_v	.171	.0088	.0117	.0132	.0088	.0088	.0088
	E	4.211	306	261	211	261	211	242
8x14 (588 lb/beam, 26.7 lb/ft)	F_b	3.229	.2935	.2609	.2201	.1957	.1468	.1957
	F_v	.146	.0074	.0099	.0111	.0074	.0074	.0074
	E	4.674	340	290	234	290	234	269
12x12 (768 lb/beam, 34.9 lb/ft)	F_b	2.864	.2604	.2314	.1953	.1736	.1302	.1736
	F_v	.114	.0057	.0076	.0085	.0057	.0057	.0057
	E	4.931	359	306	247	306	247	284
6x18 (559 lb/beam, 25.4 lb/ft)	F_b	2.697	.2452	.2179	.1839	.1634	.1226	.1634
	F_v	.149	.0078	.0104	.0117	.0078	.0078	.0078
	E	2.926	213	181	146	181	146	168
10x14 (745 lb/beam, 33.8 lb/ft)	F_b	2.549	.2317	.2060	.1738	.1545	.1159	.1545
	F_v	.115	.0058	.0078	.0088	.0058	.0058	.0058
	E	3.690	268	229	185	229	185	212
8x16 (675 lb/beam, 30.7 lb/ft)	F_b	2.487	.2261	.2010	.1696	.1507	.1131	.1507
	F_v	.125	.0065	.0086	.0097	.0065	.0065	.0065
	E	3.088	225	191	154	191	154	178

STRENGTH AND STIFFNESS REQUIREMENTS FOR BEAMS

See instructions for use of tables on page 101. Symbols used in the tables are as follows: Tabulated values are based on net size.

F_b = Extreme fiber stress in bending induced by a uniform load of 1 (one) plf or by a concentrated load of 1 (one) pound, psi

F_v = Horizontal shear stress induced by a uniform load of 1 (one) plf or a total concentrated load of 1 (one) pound, psi.

E = Modulus of elasticity value needed to limit deflection to 1/360 of the span for a uniform load of 1 (one) plf or a total concentrated load of 1 (one) pound, psi.

22 FOOT SPAN

Nominal Size (Inches)	Property	UNIFORM	Single Load At Center of Span	At Third Point	At Quarter Point	Sum of Two At Third Point	At Quarter Points From Reactions	Sum of 3 At Quarter Points and Center of Span
6x20 623 lb/beam 28.3 lb/ft	F_b F_v E	2.199 .131 2.115	.1999 .0070 154	.1777 .0093 131	.1500 .0105 106	.1333 .0070 131	.1000 .0070 106	.1333 .0070 122
12x14 901 lb/beam 41.0 lb/ft	F_b F_v E	2.106 .095 3.048	.1914 .0048 222	.1702 .0064 189	.1436 .0072 152	.1276 .0048 189	.0957 .0048 152	.1276 .0048 176
10x16 855 lb/beam 38.9 lb/ft	F_b F_v E	1.964 .099 2.438	.1785 .0051 177	.1587 .0068 151	.1339 .0076 122	.1190 .0051 151	.0893 .0051 122	.1190 .0051 140
8x18 762 lb/beam 34.6 lb/ft	F_b F_v E	1.978 .109 2.146	.1798 .0057 156	.1598 .0076 133	.1348 .0086 107	.1199 .0057 133	.0899 .0057 107	.1199 .0057 124
12x16 1035 lb/beam 47.0 lb/ft	F_b F_v E	1.622 .082 2.014	.1475 .0042 146	.1311 .0056 125	.1106 .0063 101	.0983 .0042 125	.0737 .0042 101	.0983 .0042 116
8x20 849 lb/beam 38.6 lb/ft	F_b F_v E	1.613 .096 1.551	.1466 .0051 113	.1303 .0068 96	.1100 .0077 78	.0978 .0051 96	.0733 .0051 78	.0978 .0051 89
10x18 965 lb/beam 43.9 lb/ft	F_b F_v E	1.561 .086 1.694	.1419 .0045 123	.1262 .0060 105	.1064 .0068 85	.0946 .0045 105	.0710 .0045 85	.0946 .0045 98
8x22 936 lb/beam 42.6 lb/ft	F_b F_v E	1.341 .086 1.157	.1219 .0047 84	.1084 .0062 72	.0914 .0070 58	.0813 .0047 72	.0610 .0047 58	.0813 .0047 67
12x18 1168 lb/beam 53.1 lb/ft	F_b F_v E	1.290 .071 1.399	.1172 .0037 102	.1042 .0050 87	.0879 .0056 70	.0782 .0037 87	.0586 .0037 70	.0782 .0037 81
10x20 1075 lb/beam 48.9 lb/ft	F_b F_v E	1.273 .076 1.224	.1158 .0040 89	.1029 .0054 76	.0868 .0061 61	.0772 .0040 76	.0579 .0040 61	.0772 .0040 70

22 FOOT SPAN (Continued)

Nominal Size (Inches)	Property	UNIFORM	Single Load At Center of Span	At Third Point	At Quarter Point	Sum of Two At Third Point	At Quarter Points From Reactions	Sum of 3 At Quarter Points and Center of Span
8x24 1023 lb/beam 46.5 lb/ft	F_b F_v E	1.133 .077 886	.1030 .0043 64	.0916 .0057 55	.0773 .0064 44	.0687 .0043 55	.0515 .0043 44	.0687 .0043 51
12x20 1302 lb/beam 59.2 lb/ft	F_b F_v E	1.052 .063 1,011	.0956 .0033 74	.0850 .0045 63	.0717 .0050 51	.0638 .0033 63	.0478 .0033 51	.0638 .0033 58
10x22 1186 lb/beam 53.9 lb/ft	F_b F_v E	1.059 .068 914	.0962 .0037 66	.0855 .0049 57	.0722 .0055 46	.0642 .0037 57	.0481 .0037 46	.0642 .0037 53
10x24 1296 lb/beam 58.9 lb/ft	F_b F_v E	.895 .061 700	.0813 .0034 51	.0723 .0045 43	.0610 .0050 35	.0542 .0034 43	.0407 .0034 35	.0542 .0034 40
12x22 1435 lb/beam 65.2 lb/ft	F_b F_v E	.875 .056 755	.0795 .0030 55	.0707 .0040 47	.0596 .0046 38	.0530 .0030 47	.0398 .0030 38	.0530 .0030 43
12x24 1569 lb/beam 71.3 lb/ft	F_b F_v E	.739 .050 578	.0672 .0028 42	.0597 .0037 36	.0504 .0042 29	.0448 .0028 36	.0336 .0028 29	.0448 .0028 33

23 FOOT SPAN

Nominal Size (Inches)	Property	UNIFORM	Single Load At Center of Span	At Third Point	At Quarter Point	Sum of Two At Third Point	At Quarter Points From Reactions	Sum of 3 At Quarter Points and Center of Span
2x12 102 lb/beam 4.5 lb/ft	F_b F_v E	25.079 .939 46.144	2.1807 .0444 3.210	1.9384 .0593 2.736	1.6356 .0667 2.207	1.4538 .0444 2.736	1.0904 .0444 2.207	1.4538 .0444 2.541
3x10 140 lb/beam 6.1 lb/ft	F_b F_v E	22.257 .696 49.808	1.9354 .0324 3.465	1.7204 .0432 2.953	1.4516 .0486 2.382	1.2903 .0324 2.953	.9677 .0324 2.382	1.2903 .0324 2.743
2x14 121 lb/beam 5.2 lb/ft	F_b F_v E	18.079 .785 28.244	1.5721 .0377 1.965	1.3974 .0503 1.675	1.1791 .0566 1.351	1.0481 .0377 1.675	.7860 .0377 1.351	1.0481 .0377 1.555
4x10 196 lb/beam 8.5 lb/ft	F_b F_v E	15.898 .497 35.577	1.3824 .0232 2.475	1.2288 .0309 2.109	1.0368 .0347 1.702	.9216 .0232 2.109	.6912 .0232 1.702	.9216 .0232 1.959

STRENGTH AND STIFFNESS REQUIREMENTS FOR BEAMS

See instructions for use of tables on page 101. Symbols used in the tables are as follows: Tabulated values are based on net size.

F_b = Extreme fiber stress in bending induced by a uniform load of 1 (one) plf or by a concentrated load of 1 (one) pound, psi

F_v = Horizontal shear stress induced by a uniform load of 1 (one) plf or a total concentrated load of 1 (one) pound, psi.

E = Modulus of elasticity value needed to limit deflection to 1/360 of the span for a uniform load of 1 (one) plf or a total concentrated load of 1 (one) pound, psi.

Nominal Size (Inches)	Property	UNIFORM	Single Load At Center of Span	Single Load At Third Point	Single Load At Quarter Point	Sum of Two Equal Loads At Third Point	Sum of Two Equal Loads At Quarter Points From Reactions	Sum of 3 Equal Loads At Quarter Points and Center of Span
4x16 324 lb/beam 14.1 lb/ft	F_b	6.005	.5222	.4642	.3916	.3481	.2611	.3481
	F_v	.287	.0141	.0187	.0211	.0141	.0141	.0141
	E	7,939	552	471	380	471	380	437
10x10 548 lb/beam 23.8 lb/ft	F_b	5.553	.4829	.4292	.3622	.3219	.2414	.3219
	F_v	.178	.0083	.0111	.0125	.0083	.0083	.0083
	E	12,100	842	717	579	717	579	666
8x12 523 lb/beam 22.8 lb/ft	F_b	4.800	.4174	.3710	.3130	.2783	.2087	.2783
	F_v	.183	.0087	.0116	.0130	.0087	.0087	.0087
	E	8,640	601	512	413	512	413	476
6x14 451 lb/beam 19.6 lb/ft	F_b	4.812	.4185	.3720	.3138	.2790	.2092	.2790
	F_v	.210	.0101	.0135	.0152	.0101	.0101	.0101
	E	7,283	507	432	348	432	348	401
10x12 663 lb/beam 28.8 lb/ft	F_b	3.789	.3295	.2929	.2471	.2197	.1648	.2197
	F_v	.145	.0069	.0092	.0103	.0069	.0069	.0069
	E	6,821	475	404	326	404	326	376
6x16 517 lb/beam 22.5 lb/ft	F_b	3.707	.3223	.2865	.2418	.2149	.1612	.2149
	F_v	.180	.0088	.0117	.0132	.0088	.0088	.0088
	E	4,812	335	285	230	285	230	265
8x14 615 lb/beam 26.7 lb/ft	F_b	3.529	.3069	.2728	.2302	.2046	.1534	.2046
	F_v	.154	.0074	.0099	.0111	.0074	.0074	.0074
	E	5,341	372	317	255	317	255	294
12x12 803 lb/beam 34.9 lb/ft	F_b	3.130	.2722	.2420	.2042	.1815	.1361	.1815
	F_v	.120	.0057	.0076	.0085	.0057	.0057	.0057
	E	5,635	392	334	269	334	269	310
6x18 584 lb/beam 25.4 lb/ft	F_b	2.947	.2563	.2278	.1922	.1709	.1281	.1709
	F_v	.156	.0078	.0104	.0117	.0078	.0078	.0078
	E	3,343	233	198	160	198	160	184
10x14 778 lb/beam 33.8 lb/ft	F_b	2.786	.2423	.2153	.1817	.1615	.1211	.1615
	F_v	.121	.0058	.0078	.0088	.0058	.0058	.0058
	E	4,216	293	250	202	250	202	232
8x16 706 lb/beam 30.7 lb/ft	F_b	2.718	.2364	.2101	.1773	.1576	.1182	.1576
	F_v	.132	.0065	.0086	.0097	.0065	.0065	.0065
	E	3,529	245	209	169	209	169	194

23 FOOT SPAN (Continued)

Nominal Size (Inches)	Property	UNIFORM	Single Load At Center of Span	Single Load At Third Point	Single Load At Quarter Point	Sum of Two Equal Loads At Third Point	Sum of Two Equal Loads At Quarter Points From Reactions	Sum of 3 Equal Loads At Quarter Points and Center of Span
6x8 250 lb/beam 10.9 lb/ft	F_b	15.389	1.3382	1.1895	1.0036	.8921	.6691	.8921
	F_v	.395	.0182	.0242	.0273	.0182	.0182	.0182
	E	42,474	2,955	2,518	2,031	2,518	2,031	2,339
3x12 171 lb/beam 7.4 lb/ft	F_b	15.047	1.3084	1.1631	.9813	.8723	.6542	.8723
	F_v	.563	.0267	.0356	.0400	.0267	.0267	.0267
	E	27,687	1,926	1,642	1,324	1,642	1,324	1,525
8x8 341 lb/beam 14.8 lb/ft	F_b	11.285	.9813	.8723	.7360	.6542	.4907	.6542
	F_v	.290	.0133	.0178	.0200	.0133	.0133	.0133
	E	31,148	2,167	1,847	1,490	1,847	1,490	1,715
3x14 201 lb/beam 8.7 lb/ft	F_b	10.847	.9433	.8384	.7074	.6288	.4716	.6288
	F_v	.471	.0226	.0302	.0340	.0226	.0226	.0226
	E	16,947	1,179	1,005	810	1,005	810	933
4x12 239 lb/beam 10.4 lb/ft	F_b	10.748	.9346	.8308	.7010	.6231	.4673	.6231
	F_v	.402	.0190	.0254	.0286	.0190	.0190	.0190
	E	19,776	1,376	1,173	946	1,173	946	1,089
6x10 317 lb/beam 13.8 lb/ft	F_b	9.592	.8340	.7414	.6255	.5560	.4170	.5560
	F_v	.307	.0144	.0191	.0215	.0144	.0144	.0144
	E	20,899	1,454	1,239	1,000	1,239	1,000	1,151
3x16 231 lb/beam 10.1 lb/ft	F_b	8.407	.7311	.6498	.5483	.4874	.3655	.4874
	F_v	.402	.0197	.0262	.0295	.0197	.0197	.0197
	E	11,115	773	659	532	659	532	612
4x14 281 lb/beam 12.2 lb/ft	F_b	7.748	.6738	.5989	.5053	.4492	.3369	.4492
	F_v	.336	.0162	.0216	.0243	.0162	.0162	.0162
	E	12,105	842	718	579	718	579	667
8x10 432 lb/beam 18.8 lb/ft	F_b	7.034	.6116	.5437	.4587	.4078	.3058	.4078
	F_v	.225	.0105	.0140	.0158	.0105	.0105	.0105
	E	15,326	1,066	909	733	909	733	844
6x12 384 lb/beam 16.7 lb/ft	F_b	6.545	.5692	.5059	.4269	.3794	.2846	.3794
	F_v	.250	.0119	.0158	.0178	.0119	.0119	.0119
	E	11,782	820	699	563	699	563	649

STRENGTH AND STIFFNESS REQUIREMENTS FOR BEAMS

See instructions for use of tables on page 101. Symbols used in the tables are as follows: Tabulated values are based on net size.

F_b = Extreme fiber stress in bending induced by a uniform load of 1 (one) plf or by a concentrated load of 1 (one) pound, psi.

F_v = Horizontal shear stress induced by a uniform load of 1 (one) plf or a total concentrated load of 1 (one) pound, psi.

E = Modulus of elasticity value needed to limit deflection to 1/360 of the span for a uniform load of 1 (one) plf or a total concentrated load of 1 (one) pound, psi.

23 FOOT SPAN (Continued)

Nominal Size (Inches)	Property	UNIFORM	Single Load — At Center of Span	Single Load — At Third Point	Single Load — At Quarter Point	Sum of Two Equal Loads — At Third Point	Sum of Two Equal Loads — At Quarter Points From Reactions	Sum of 3 Equal Loads — At Quarter Points and Center of Span
6x20 — 651 lb/beam, 28.3 lb/ft	F_b	2.404	.2090	.1858	.1568	.1394	.1045	.1394
	F_v	.138	.0070	.0093	.0105	.0070	.0070	.0070
	E	2,417	168	143	116	143	116	133
12x14 — 942 lb/beam, 41.0 lb/ft	F_b	2.302	.2001	.1779	.1501	.1334	.1001	.1334
	F_v	.100	.0048	.0064	.0072	.0048	.0048	.0048
	E	3,483	242	207	167	207	167	192
10x16 — 894 lb/beam, 38.9 lb/ft	F_b	2.146	.1866	.1659	.1400	.1244	.0933	.1244
	F_v	.104	.0051	.0068	.0076	.0051	.0051	.0051
	E	2,786	194	165	133	165	133	153
8x18 — 797 lb/beam, 34.6 lb/ft	F_b	2.161	.1880	.1671	.1410	.1253	.0940	.1253
	F_v	.115	.0057	.0076	.0086	.0057	.0057	.0057
	E	2,452	171	145	117	145	117	135
12x16 — 1082 lb/beam, 47.0 lb/ft	F_b	1.773	.1542	.1370	.1156	.1028	.0771	.1028
	F_v	.086	.0042	.0056	.0063	.0042	.0042	.0042
	E	2,301	160	136	110	136	110	127
8x20 — 888 lb/beam, 38.6 lb/ft	F_b	1.763	.1533	.1363	.1150	.1022	.0766	.1022
	F_v	.101	.0051	.0068	.0077	.0051	.0051	.0051
	E	1,772	123	105	85	105	85	98
10x18 — 1009 lb/beam, 43.9 lb/ft	F_b	1.706	.1484	.1319	.1113	.0989	.0742	.0989
	F_v	.091	.0045	.0060	.0068	.0045	.0045	.0045
	E	1,936	135	115	93	115	93	107
8x22 — 979 lb/beam, 42.6 lb/ft	F_b	1.466	.1274	.1133	.0956	.0850	.0637	.0850
	F_v	.090	.0047	.0062	.0070	.0047	.0047	.0047
	E	1,322	92	78	63	78	63	73
12x18 — 1221 lb/beam, 53.1 lb/ft	F_b	1.410	.1226	.1090	.0919	.0817	.0613	.0817
	F_v	.075	.0037	.0050	.0056	.0037	.0037	.0037
	E	1,599	111	95	76	95	76	88
10x20 — 1124 lb/beam, 48.9 lb/ft	F_b	1.392	.1210	.1076	.0908	.0807	.0605	.0807
	F_v	.080	.0040	.0054	.0061	.0040	.0040	.0040
	E	1,399	97	83	67	83	67	77

24 FOOT SPAN

Nominal Size (Inches)	Property	UNIFORM	Single Load — At Center of Span	Single Load — At Third Point	Single Load — At Quarter Point	Sum of Two Equal Loads — At Third Point	Sum of Two Equal Loads — At Quarter Points From Reactions	Sum of 3 Equal Loads — At Quarter Points and Center of Span
8x24 — 1070 lb/beam, 46.5 lb/ft	F_b	1.239	.1077	.0957	.0808	.0718	.0539	.0718
	F_v	.081	.0043	.0057	.0064	.0043	.0043	.0043
	E	1,013	70	60	48	60	48	56
12x20 — 1361 lb/beam, 59.2 lb/ft	F_b	1.150	.1000	.0889	.0750	.0666	.0500	.0666
	F_v	.066	.0033	.0045	.0050	.0033	.0033	.0033
	E	1,156	80	69	55	69	55	64
10x22 — 1240 lb/beam, 53.9 lb/ft	F_b	1.157	.1006	.0894	.0755	.0671	.0503	.0671
	F_v	.071	.0037	.0049	.0055	.0037	.0037	.0037
	E	1,044	73	62	50	62	50	57
10x24 — 1355 lb/beam, 58.9 lb/ft	F_b	.978	.0850	.0756	.0638	.0567	.0425	.0567
	F_v	.064	.0034	.0045	.0050	.0034	.0034	.0034
	E	799	56	47	38	47	38	44
12x22 — 1501 lb/beam, 65.2 lb/ft	F_b	.956	.0831	.0739	.0623	.0554	.0416	.0554
	F_v	.059	.0030	.0040	.0046	.0030	.0030	.0030
	E	862	60	51	41	51	41	47
12x24 — 1640 lb/beam, 71.3 lb/ft	F_b	.808	.0702	.0624	.0527	.0468	.0351	.0468
	F_v	.053	.0028	.0037	.0042	.0028	.0028	.0028
	E	660	46	39	32	39	32	36
2x12 — 107 lb/beam, 4.5 lb/ft	F_b	27.307	2.2756	2.0227	1.7067	1.5170	1.1378	1.5170
	F_v	.983	.0444	.0593	.0667	.0444	.0444	.0444
	E	52,429	3,495	2,979	2,403	2,979	2,403	2,767
3x10 — 146 lb/beam, 6.1 lb/ft	F_b	24.235	2.0196	1.7952	1.5147	1.3464	1.0098	1.3464
	F_v	.728	.0324	.0432	.0486	.0324	.0324	.0324
	E	56,592	3,773	3,215	2,594	3,215	2,594	2,987
2x14 — 126 lb/beam, 5.2 lb/ft	F_b	19.685	1.6404	1.4582	1.2303	1.0936	.8202	1.0936
	F_v	.822	.0377	.0503	.0566	.0377	.0377	.0377
	E	32,091	2,139	1,823	1,471	1,823	1,471	1,694
4x10 — 205 lb/beam, 8.5 lb/ft	F_b	17.311	1.4426	1.2823	1.0819	.9617	.7213	.9617
	F_v	.520	.0232	.0309	.0347	.0232	.0232	.0232
	E	40,423	2,695	2,297	1,853	2,297	1,853	2,133

STRENGTH AND STIFFNESS REQUIREMENTS FOR BEAMS

See instructions for use of tables on page 101. Symbols used in the tables are as follows: Tabulated values are based on net size.

F_b = Extreme fiber stress in bending induced by a uniform load of 1 (one) plf or by a concentrated load of 1 (one) pound, psi

F_v = Horizontal shear stress induced by a uniform load of 1 (one) plf or a total concentrated load of 1 (one) pound, psi.

E = Modulus of elasticity value needed to limit deflection to 1/360 of the span for a uniform load of 1 (one) plf or a total concentrated load of 1 (one) pound, psi.

24 FOOT SPAN

Nominal Size (Inches)	Property	UNIFORM	CONCENTRATED — Single Load — At Center of Span	At Third Point	At Quarter Point	Sum of Two Equal Loads — At Third Point	At Quarter Points From Reactions	Sum of 3 Equal Loads — At Quarter Points and Center of Span
4x16 338 lb/beam 14.1 lb/ft	F_b F_v E	6.539 .302 9,021	5449 .0141 601	4844 .0187 513	4087 .0211 413	3633 .0141 513	2725 .0141 413	3633 .0141 476
10x10 572 lb/beam 23.8 lb/ft	F_b F_v E	6.046 .186 13,748	5039 .0083 917	4479 .0111 781	3779 .0125 630	3359 .0083 781	2519 .0083 630	3359 .0083 726
8x12 546 lb/beam 22.8 lb/ft	F_b F_v E	5.226 .192 9,817	4355 .0087 654	3871 .0116 558	3267 .0130 450	2904 .0087 558	2178 .0087 450	2904 .0087 518
6x14 470 lb/beam 19.6 lb/ft	F_b F_v E	5.240 .220 8,275	4367 .0101 552	3881 .0135 470	3275 .0152 379	2911 .0101 470	2183 .0101 379	2911 .0101 437
10x12 692 lb/beam 28.8 lb/ft	F_b F_v E	4.126 .152 7,750	3438 .0069 517	3056 .0092 440	2579 .0103 355	2292 .0069 440	1719 .0069 355	2292 .0069 409
6x16 540 lb/beam 22.5 lb/ft	F_b F_v E	4.036 .188 5,467	3364 .0088 364	2990 .0117 311	2523 .0132 251	2242 .0088 311	1682 .0088 251	2242 .0088 289
8x14 641 lb/beam 26.7 lb/ft	F_b F_v E	3.843 .161 6,068	3202 .0074 405	2846 .0099 345	2402 .0111 278	2135 .0074 345	1601 .0074 278	2135 .0074 320
12x12 838 lb/beam 34.9 lb/ft	F_b F_v E	3.409 .125 6,402	2840 .0057 427	2525 .0076 364	2130 .0085 293	1894 .0057 364	1420 .0057 293	1894 .0057 338
6x18 610 lb/beam 25.4 lb/ft	F_b F_v E	3.209 .164 3,799	2674 .0078 253	2377 .0104 216	2006 .0117 174	1783 .0078 216	1337 .0078 174	1783 .0078 200
10x14 812 lb/beam 33.8 lb/ft	F_b F_v E	3.034 .127 4,791	2528 .0058 319	2247 .0078 272	1896 .0088 220	1685 .0058 272	1264 .0058 220	1685 .0058 253
8x16 736 lb/beam 30.7 lb/ft	F_b F_v E	2.960 .138 4,009	2467 .0065 267	2193 .0086 228	1850 .0097 184	1644 .0065 228	1233 .0065 184	1644 .0065 212

24 FOOT SPAN (Continued)

Nominal Size (Inches)	Property	UNIFORM	CONCENTRATED — Single Load — At Center of Span	At Third Point	At Quarter Point	Sum of Two Equal Loads — At Third Point	At Quarter Points From Reactions	Sum of 3 Equal Loads — At Quarter Points and Center of Span
6x8 261 lb/beam 10.9 lb/ft	F_b F_v E	16.756 .414 48,258	1.3964 .0182 3,217	1.2412 .0242 2,742	1.0473 .0273 2,212	.9309 .0182 2,742	.6982 .0182 2,212	.9309 .0182 2,547
3x12 178 lb/beam 7.4 lb/ft	F_b F_v E	16.384 .590 31,457	1.3653 .0267 2,097	1.2136 .0356 1,787	1.0240 .0400 1,442	.9102 .0267 1,787	.6827 .0267 1,442	.9102 .0267 1,660
8x8 356 lb/beam 14.8 lb/ft	F_b F_v E	12.288 .303 35,389	1.0240 .0133 2,359	.9102 .0178 2,011	.7680 .0200 1,622	.6827 .0133 2,011	.5120 .0133 1,622	.6827 .0133 1,868
3x14 210 lb/beam 8.7 lb/ft	F_b F_v E	11.811 .493 19,254	.9843 .0226 1,284	.8749 .0302 1,094	.7382 .0340 882	.6562 .0226 1,094	.4921 .0226 882	.6562 .0226 1,016
4x12 249 lb/beam 10.4 lb/ft	F_b F_v E	11.703 .421 22,469	.9752 .0190 1,498	.8669 .0254 1,277	.7314 .0286 1,030	.6502 .0190 1,277	.4876 .0190 1,030	.6502 .0190 1,186
6x10 331 lb/beam 13.8 lb/ft	F_b F_v E	10.444 .322 23,746	.8703 .0144 1,583	.7736 .0191 1,349	.6527 .0215 1,088	.5802 .0144 1,349	.4352 .0144 1,088	.5802 .0144 1,253
3x16 241 lb/beam 10.1 lb/ft	F_b F_v E	9.154 .422 12,629	.7629 .0197 842	.6781 .0262 718	.5721 .0295 579	.5086 .0197 718	.3814 .0197 579	.5086 .0197 667
4x14 294 lb/beam 12.2 lb/ft	F_b F_v E	8.437 .352 13,753	.7030 .0162 917	.6249 .0216 781	.5273 .0243 630	.4687 .0162 781	.3515 .0162 630	.4687 .0162 726
8x10 451 lb/beam 18.8 lb/ft	F_b F_v E	7.659 .236 17,414	.6382 .0105 1,161	.5673 .0140 989	.4787 .0158 798	.4255 .0105 989	.3191 .0105 798	.4255 .0105 919
6x12 401 lb/beam 16.7 lb/ft	F_b F_v E	7.127 .262 13,386	.5939 .0119 892	.5279 .0158 761	.4454 .0178 614	.3959 .0119 761	.2970 .0119 614	.3959 .0119 707

STRENGTH AND STIFFNESS REQUIREMENTS FOR BEAMS

See instructions for use of tables on page 101. Symbols used in the tables are as follows: Tabulated values are based on net size.

F_b = Extreme fiber stress in bending induced by a uniform load of 1 (one) plf or by a concentrated load of 1 (one) pound, psi

F_v = Horizontal shear stress induced by a uniform load of 1 (one) plf or a total concentrated load of 1 (one) pound, psi.

E = Modulus of elasticity value needed to limit deflection to 1/360 of the span for a uniform load of 1 (one) plf or a total concentrated load of 1 (one) pound, psi.

24 FOOT SPAN (Continued)

Nominal Size (Inches)	Property	UNIFORM	Concentrated Single Load — At Center of Span	Single Load — At Third Point	Single Load — At Quarter Point	Sum of Two Equal Loads — At Third Point	Sum of Two Equal Loads — At Quarter Points From Reactions	Sum of 3 Equal Loads — At Quarter Points and Center of Span
6x20 679 lb/beam 28.3 lb/ft	F_b F_v E	2.617 .145 2,746	.2181 .0070 183	.1939 .0093 156	.1636 .0105 126	.1454 .0070 156	.1091 .0070 126	.1454 .0070 145
12x14 983 lb/beam 41.0 lb/ft	F_b F_v E	2.506 .105 3,957	.2088 .0048 264	.1856 .0064 225	.1566 .0072 181	.1392 .0048 225	.1044 .0048 181	.1392 .0048 209
10x16 933 lb/beam 38.9 lb/ft	F_b F_v E	2.337 .109 3,165	.1947 .0051 211	.1731 .0068 180	.1460 .0076 145	.1298 .0051 180	.0974 .0051 145	.1298 .0051 167
8x18 831 lb/beam 34.6 lb/ft	F_b F_v E	2.353 .120 2,786	.1961 .0057 186	.1743 .0076 158	.1471 .0086 128	.1307 .0057 158	.0981 .0057 128	.1307 .0057 147
12x16 1129 lb/beam 47.0 lb/ft	F_b F_v E	1.930 .090 2,615	.1609 .0042 174	.1430 .0056 149	.1206 .0063 120	.1072 .0042 149	.0804 .0042 120	.1072 .0042 138
8x20 926 lb/beam 38.6 lb/ft	F_b F_v E	1.919 .106 2,014	.1600 .0051 134	.1422 .0068 114	.1200 .0077 92	.1066 .0051 114	.0800 .0051 92	.1066 .0051 106
10x18 1053 lb/beam 43.9 lb/ft	F_b F_v E	1.858 .095 2,199	.1548 .0045 147	.1376 .0060 125	.1161 .0068 101	.1032 .0045 125	.0774 .0045 101	.1032 .0045 116
8x22 1021 lb/beam 42.6 lb/ft	F_b F_v E	1.596 .095 1,502	.1330 .0047 100	.1182 .0062 85	.0997 .0070 69	.0887 .0047 85	.0665 .0047 69	.0887 .0047 79
12x18 1275 lb/beam 53.1 lb/ft	F_b F_v E	1.535 .079 1,817	.1279 .0037 121	.1137 .0050 103	.0959 .0056 83	.0853 .0037 103	.0640 .0037 83	.0853 .0037 96
10x20 1173 lb/beam 48.9 lb/ft	F_b F_v E	1.515 .084 1,590	.1263 .0040 106	.1123 .0054 90	.0947 .0061 73	.0842 .0040 90	.0631 .0040 73	.0842 .0040 84
8x24 1116 lb/beam 46.5 lb/ft	F_b F_v E	1.349 .085 1,150	.1124 .0043 77	.0999 .0057 65	.0843 .0064 53	.0749 .0043 65	.0562 .0043 53	.0749 .0043 61
12x20 1420 lb/beam 59.2 lb/ft	F_b F_v E	1.252 .069 1,313	.1043 .0033 88	.0927 .0045 75	.0782 .0050 60	.0695 .0033 75	.0522 .0033 60	.0695 .0033 69
10x22 1294 lb/beam 53.9 lb/ft	F_b F_v E	1.260 .075 1,186	.1050 .0037 79	.0933 .0049 67	.0787 .0055 54	.0700 .0037 67	.0525 .0037 54	.0700 .0037 63
10x24 1414 lb/beam 58.9 lb/ft	F_b F_v E	1.065 .067 908	.0887 .0034 61	.0789 .0045 52	.0665 .0050 42	.0592 .0034 52	.0444 .0034 42	.0592 .0034 48
12x22 1566 lb/beam 65.2 lb/ft	F_b F_v E	1.041 .062 980	.0867 .0030 65	.0771 .0040 56	.0650 .0046 45	.0578 .0030 56	.0434 .0030 45	.0578 .0030 52
12x24 1712 lb/beam 71.3 lb/ft	F_b F_v E	.880 .056 750	.0733 .0028 50	.0652 .0037 43	.0550 .0042 34	.0489 .0028 43	.0367 .0028 34	.0489 .0028 40

25 FOOT SPAN

Nominal Size (Inches)	Property	UNIFORM	Single Load — At Center of Span	Single Load — At Third Point	Single Load — At Quarter Point	Sum of Two Equal Loads — At Third Point	Sum of Two Equal Loads — At Quarter Points From Reactions	Sum of 3 Equal Loads — At Quarter Points and Center of Span
2x12 111 lb/beam 4.5 lb/ft	F_b F_v E	29.630 1.028 59,259	2.3704 .0444 3,793	2.1070 .0593 3,232	1.7778 .0667 2,607	1.5802 .0444 3,232	1.1852 .0444 2,607	1.5802 .0444 3,002
3x10 153 lb/beam 6.1 lb/ft	F_b F_v E	26.297 .761 63,965	2.1037 .0324 4,094	1.8700 .0432 3,489	1.5778 .0486 2,814	1.4025 .0324 3,489	1.0519 .0324 2,814	1.4025 .0324 3,241
2x14 131 lb/beam 5.2 lb/ft	F_b F_v E	21.360 .860 36,272	1.7088 .0377 2,321	1.5189 .0503 1,978	1.2816 .0566 1,596	1.1392 .0377 1,978	.8544 .0377 1,596	1.1392 .0377 1,838
4x10 214 lb/beam 8.5 lb/ft	F_b F_v E	18.783 .543 45,689	1.5027 .0232 2,924	1.3357 .0309 2,492	1.1270 .0347 2,010	1.0018 .0232 2,492	.7513 .0232 2,010	1.0018 .0232 2,315

STRENGTH AND STIFFNESS REQUIREMENTS FOR BEAMS

See instructions for use of tables on page 101. Symbols used in the tables are as follows: Tabulated values are based on net size.

F_b = Extreme fiber stress in bending induced by a uniform load of 1 (one) plf or by a concentrated load of 1 (one) pound, psi

F_v = Horizontal shear stress induced by a uniform load of 1 (one) plf or a total concentrated load of 1 (one) pound, psi.

E' = Modulus of elasticity value needed to limit deflection to 1/360 of the span for a uniform load of 1 (one) plf or a total concentrated load of 1 (one) pound, psi.

25 FOOT SPAN (Continued)

Nominal Size (Inches)	Property	UNIFORM	Single Load — At Center of Span	Single Load — At Third Point	Single Load — At Quarter Point	Sum of Two Equal Loads — At Third Point	Sum of Two Equal Loads — At Quarter Points From Reactions	Sum of 3 Equal Loads — At Quarter Points and Center of Span
6x8 — 272 lb/beam — 10.9 lb/ft	F_b	18.182	1.4545	1.2929	1.0909	.9697	.7273	.9697
	F_v	.432	.0182	.0242	.0273	.0182	.0182	.0182
	E'	54,545	3,491	2,975	2,400	2,975	2,400	2,764
3x12 — 186 lb/beam — 7.4 lb/ft	F_b	17.778	1.4222	1.2642	1.0667	.9481	.7111	.9481
	F_v	.617	.0267	.0356	.0400	.0267	.0267	.0267
	E'	35,556	2,276	1,939	1,564	1,939	1,564	1,801
8x8 — 371 lb/beam — 14.8 lb/ft	F_b	13.333	1.0667	.9481	.8000	.7111	.5333	.7111
	F_v	.317	.0133	.0178	.0200	.0133	.0133	.0133
	E'	40,000	2,560	2,182	1,760	2,182	1,760	2,027
3x14 — 219 lb/beam — 8.7 lb/ft	F_b	12.816	1.0253	.9114	.7690	.6835	.5126	.6835
	F_v	.516	.0226	.0302	.0340	.0226	.0226	.0226
	E'	21,763	1,393	1,187	958	1,187	958	1,103
4x12 — 260 lb/beam — 10.4 lb/ft	F_b	12.698	1.0159	.9030	.7619	.6772	.5079	.6772
	F_v	.440	.0190	.0254	.0286	.0190	.0190	.0190
	E'	25,397	1,625	1,385	1,117	1,385	1,117	1,287
6x10 — 345 lb/beam — 13.8 lb/ft	F_b	11.332	.9066	.8058	.6799	.6044	.4533	.6044
	F_v	.336	.0144	.0191	.0215	.0144	.0144	.0144
	E'	26,839	1,718	1,464	1,181	1,464	1,181	1,360
3x16 — 252 lb/beam — 10.1 lb/ft	F_b	9.933	.7946	.7064	.5960	.5298	.3973	.5298
	F_v	.442	.0197	.0262	.0295	.0197	.0197	.0197
	E'	14,274	914	779	628	779	628	723
4x14 — 306 lb/beam — 12.2 lb/ft	F_b	9.154	.7323	.6510	.5493	.4882	.3662	.4882
	F_v	.369	.0162	.0216	.0243	.0162	.0162	.0162
	E'	15,545	995	848	684	848	684	788
8x10 — 470 lb/beam — 18.8 lb/ft	F_b	8.310	.6648	.5910	.4986	.4432	.3324	.4432
	F_v	.246	.0105	.0140	.0158	.0105	.0105	.0105
	E'	19,682	1,260	1,074	866	1,074	866	997
6x12 — 417 lb/beam — 16.7 lb/ft	F_b	7.733	.6187	.5499	.4640	.4124	.3093	.4124
	F_v	.274	.0119	.0158	.0178	.0119	.0119	.0119
	E'	15,130	968	825	666	825	666	767

Nominal Size (Inches)	Property	UNIFORM	Single Load — At Center of Span	Single Load — At Third Point	Single Load — At Quarter Point	Sum of Two Equal Loads — At Third Point	Sum of Two Equal Loads — At Quarter Points From Reactions	Sum of 3 Equal Loads — At Quarter Points and Center of Span
4x16 — 352 lb/beam — 14.1 lb/ft	F_b	7.095	.5676	.5045	.4257	.3784	.2838	.3784
	F_v	.316	.0141	.0187	.0211	.0141	.0141	.0141
	E'	10,196	653	556	449	556	449	517
10x10 — 595 lb/beam — 23.8 lb/ft	F_b	6.561	.5249	.4665	.3936	.3499	.2624	.3499
	F_v	.195	.0083	.0111	.0125	.0083	.0083	.0083
	E'	15,539	994	848	684	848	684	787
8x12 — 569 lb/beam — 22.8 lb/ft	F_b	5.671	.4537	.4033	.3403	.3025	.2268	.3025
	F_v	.201	.0087	.0116	.0130	.0087	.0087	.0087
	E'	11,096	710	605	488	605	488	562
6x14 — 490 lb/beam — 19.6 lb/ft	F_b	5.686	.4548	.4043	.3411	.3032	.2274	.3032
	F_v	.230	.0101	.0135	.0152	.0101	.0101	.0101
	E'	9,353	599	510	412	510	412	474
10x12 — 721 lb/beam — 28.8 lb/ft	F_b	4.477	.3582	.3184	.2686	.2388	.1791	.2388
	F_v	.158	.0069	.0092	.0103	.0069	.0069	.0069
	E'	8,760	561	478	385	478	385	444
6x16 — 562 lb/beam — 22.5 lb/ft	F_b	4.380	.3504	.3114	.2628	.2336	.1752	.2336
	F_v	.197	.0088	.0117	.0132	.0088	.0088	.0088
	E'	6,179	395	337	272	337	272	313
8x14 — 668 lb/beam — 26.7 lb/ft	F_b	4.169	.3336	.2965	.2502	.2224	.1668	.2224
	F_v	.169	.0074	.0099	.0111	.0074	.0074	.0074
	E'	6,859	439	374	302	374	302	348
12x12 — 872 lb/beam — 34.9 lb/ft	F_b	3.699	.2959	.2630	.2219	.1973	.1479	.1973
	F_v	.131	.0057	.0076	.0085	.0057	.0057	.0057
	E'	7,236	463	395	318	395	318	367
6x18 — 635 lb/beam — 25.4 lb/ft	F_b	3.482	.2786	.2476	.2089	.1857	.1393	.1857
	F_v	.172	.0078	.0104	.0117	.0078	.0078	.0078
	E'	4,294	275	234	189	234	189	218
10x14 — 846 lb/beam — 33.8 lb/ft	F_b	3.292	.2633	.2341	.1975	.1756	.1317	.1756
	F_v	.133	.0058	.0078	.0088	.0058	.0058	.0058
	E'	5,415	347	295	238	295	238	274
8x16 — 767 lb/beam — 30.7 lb/ft	F_b	3.212	.2569	.2284	.1927	.1713	.1285	.1713
	F_v	.145	.0065	.0086	.0097	.0065	.0065	.0065
	E'	4,532	290	247	199	247	199	230

STRENGTH AND STIFFNESS REQUIREMENTS FOR BEAMS

See instructions for use of tables on page 101. Symbols used in the tables are as follows: Tabulated values are based on net size.

F_b = Extreme fiber stress in bending induced by a uniform load of 1 (one) plf or by a concentrated load of 1 (one) plf or a total concentrated load of 1 (one) pound, psi

F_v = Horizontal shear stress induced by a uniform load of 1 (one) plf or a total concentrated load of 1 (one) pound. psi.

E = Modulus of elasticity value needed to limit deflection to 1/360 of the span for a uniform load of 1 (one) plf or a total concentrated load of 1 (one) pound, psi.

25 FOOT SPAN (Continued)

Nominal Size (Inches)	Property	UNIFORM	CONCENTRATED — Single Load — At Center of Span	At Third Point	At Quarter Point	Sum of Two Equal Loads — At Third Point	At Quarter Points From Reactions	Sum of 3 Equal Loads — At Quarter Points and Center of Span
8x24 1163 lb/beam 46.5 lb/ft	F_b F_v E	1.463 .090 1,300	.1171 .0043 83	.1041 .0057 71	.0878 .0064 57	.0781 .0043 71	.0585 .0043 57	.0781 .0043 66
12x20 1479 lb/beam 59.2 lb/ft	F_b F_v E	1.358 .073 1,484	.1087 .0033 95	.0966 .0045 81	.0815 .0050 65	.0724 .0033 81	.0543 .0033 65	.0724 .0033 75
10x22 1347 lb/beam 53.9 lb/ft	F_b F_v E	1.367 .079 1,340	.1094 .0037 86	.0972 .0049 73	.0820 .0055 59	.0729 .0037 73	.0547 .0037 59	.0729 .0037 68
10x24 1473 lb/beam 58.9 lb/ft	F_b F_v E	1.155 .071 1,027	.0924 .0034 66	.0822 .0045 56	.0693 .0050 45	.0616 .0034 56	.0462 .0034 45	.0616 .0034 52
12x22 1631 lb/beam 65.2 lb/ft	F_b F_v E	1.129 .065 1,107	.0903 .0030 71	.0803 .0040 60	.0678 .0046 49	.0602 .0030 60	.0452 .0030 49	.0602 .0030 56
12x24 1783 lb/beam 71.3 lb/ft	F_b F_v E	.954 .059 848	.0764 .0028 54	.0679 .0037 46	.0573 .0042 37	.0509 .0028 46	.0382 .0028 37	.0509 .0028 43

26 FOOT SPAN

Nominal Size (Inches)	Property	UNIFORM	CONCENTRATED — Single Load — At Center of Span	At Third Point	At Quarter Point	Sum of Two Equal Loads — At Third Point	At Quarter Points From Reactions	Sum of 3 Equal Loads — At Quarter Points and Center of Span
2x14 136 lb/beam 5.2 lb/ft	F_b F_v E	23.103 .898 40,801	1.7771 .0377 2,511	1.5797 .0503 2,140	1.3329 .0566 1,726	1.1848 .0377 2,140	.8886 .0377 1,726	1.1848 .0377 1,988
4x10 222 lb/beam 8.5 lb/ft	F_b F_v E	20.316 .567 51,394	1.5628 .0232 3,163	1.3891 .0309 2,695	1.1721 .0347 2,174	1.0418 .0232 2,695	.7814 .0232 2,174	1.0418 .0232 2,504
6x8 283 lb/beam 10.9 lb/ft	F_b F_v E	19.665 .450 61,356	1.5127 .0182 3,776	1.3446 .0242 3,218	1.1345 .0273 2,596	1.0085 .0182 3,218	.7564 .0182 2,596	1.0085 .0182 2,989
3x12 193 lb/beam 7.4 lb/ft	F_b F_v E	19.228 .643 39,995	1.4791 .0267 2,461	1.3148 .0356 2,098	1.1093 .0400 1,692	.9861 .0267 2,098	.7396 .0267 1,692	.9861 .0267 1,948

25 FOOT SPAN

Nominal Size (Inches)	Property	UNIFORM	CONCENTRATED — Single Load — At Center of Span	At Third Point	At Quarter Point	Sum of Two Equal Loads — At Third Point	At Quarter Points From Reactions	Sum of 3 Equal Loads — At Quarter Points and Center of Span
6x20 708 lb/beam 28.3 lb/ft	F_b F_v E	2.840 .152 3,103	.2272 .0070 199	.2020 .0093 169	.1704 .0105 137	.1515 .0070 169	.1136 .0070 137	.1515 .0070 157
12x14 1024 lb/beam 41.0 lb/ft	F_b F_v E	2.719 .110 4,473	.2175 .0048 286	.1934 .0064 244	.1632 .0072 197	.1450 .0048 244	.1088 .0048 197	.1450 .0048 227
10x16 971 lb/beam 38.9 lb/ft	F_b F_v E	2.536 .114 3,578	.2028 .0051 229	.1803 .0068 195	.1521 .0076 157	.1352 .0051 195	.1014 .0051 157	.1352 .0051 181
8x18 866 lb/beam 34.6 lb/ft	F_b F_v E	2.554 .126 3,149	.2043 .0057 202	.1816 .0076 172	.1532 .0086 139	.1362 .0057 172	.1021 .0057 139	.1362 .0057 160
12x16 1176 lb/beam 47.0 lb/ft	F_b F_v E	2.095 .094 2,955	.1676 .0042 189	.1489 .0056 161	.1257 .0063 130	.1117 .0042 161	.0838 .0042 130	.1117 .0042 150
8x20 965 lb/beam 38.6 lb/ft	F_b F_v E	2.083 .112 2,276	.1666 .0051 146	.1481 .0068 124	.1250 .0077 100	.1111 .0051 124	.0833 .0051 100	.1111 .0051 115
10x18 1097 lb/beam 43.9 lb/ft	F_b F_v E	2.016 .100 2,486	.1613 .0045 159	.1434 .0060 136	.1210 .0068 109	.1075 .0045 136	.0806 .0045 109	.1075 .0045 126
8x22 1064 lb/beam 42.6 lb/ft	F_b F_v E	1.732 .100 1,698	.1385 .0047 109	.1231 .0062 93	.1039 .0070 75	.0924 .0047 93	.0693 .0047 75	.0924 .0047 86
12x18 1328 lb/beam 53.1 lb/ft	F_b F_v E	1.665 .082 2,053	.1332 .0037 131	.1184 .0050 112	.0999 .0056 90	.0888 .0037 112	.0666 .0037 90	.0888 .0037 104
10x20 1222 lb/beam 48.9 lb/ft	F_b F_v E	1.644 .088 1,797	.1315 .0040 115	.1169 .0054 98	.0987 .0061 79	.0877 .0040 98	.0658 .0040 79	.0877 .0040 91

STRENGTH AND STIFFNESS REQUIREMENTS FOR BEAMS

See instructions for use of tables on page 101. Symbols used in the tables are as follows: Tabulated values are based on net size.

F_b = Extreme fiber stress in bending induced by a uniform load of 1 (one) plf or by a concentrated load of 1 (one) pound, psi

F_v = Horizontal shear stress induced by a uniform load of 1 (one) plf or a total concentrated load of 1 (one) pound, psi.

E = Modulus of elasticity value needed to limit deflection to 1/360 of the span for a uniform load of 1 (one) plf or a total concentrated load of 1 (one) pound, psi.

26 FOOT SPAN (Continued)

Nominal Size (Inches)	Property	UNIFORM	Single Load — At Center of Span	Single Load — At Third Point	Single Load — At Quarter Point	Sum of Two Equal Loads — At Third Point	Sum of Two Equal Loads — At Quarter Points From Reactions	Sum of 3 Equal Loads — At Quarter Points and Center of Span
8x8 386 lb/beam 14.8 lb/ft	F_b F_v E	14.421 .330 44.995	1.1093 .0133 2.769	.9861 .0178 2.360	.8320 .0200 1.904	.7396 .0133 2.360	.5547 .0133 1.904	.7396 .0133 2.192
3x14 227 lb/beam 8.7 lb/ft	F_b F_v E	13.862 .539 24.480	1.0663 .0226 1.506	.9478 .0302 1.284	.7997 .0340 1.036	.7109 .0226 1.284	.5331 .0226 1.036	.7109 .0226 1.193
4x12 270 lb/beam 10.4 lb/ft	F_b F_v E	13.735 .460 28.568	1.0565 .0190 1.758	.9391 .0254 1.498	.7924 .0286 1.209	.7043 .0190 1.498	.5283 .0190 1.209	.7043 .0190 1.392
6x10 358 lb/beam 13.8 lb/ft	F_b F_v E	12.257 .350 30.191	.9428 .0144 1.858	.8381 .0191 1.583	.7071 .0215 1.277	.6286 .0144 1.583	.4714 .0144 1.277	.6286 .0144 1.471
3x16 262 lb/beam 10.1 lb/ft	F_b F_v E	10.744 .461 16.057	.8264 .0197 988	.7346 .0262 842	.6198 .0295 679	.5510 .0197 842	.4132 .0197 679	.5510 .0197 782
4x14 318 lb/beam 12.2 lb/ft	F_b F_v E	9.901 .385 17.486	.7616 .0162 1,076	.6770 .0216 917	.5712 .0243 740	.5078 .0162 917	.3808 .0162 740	.5078 .0162 852
8x10 489 lb/beam 18.8 lb/ft	F_b F_v E	8.988 .257 22.140	.6914 .0105 1,362	.6146 .0140 1,161	.5186 .0158 937	.4609 .0105 1,161	.3457 .0105 937	.4609 .0105 1,079
6x12 434 lb/beam 16.7 lb/ft	F_b F_v E	8.364 .286 17.020	.6434 .0119 1,047	.5719 .0158 893	.4826 .0178 720	.4289 .0119 893	.3217 .0119 720	.4289 .0119 829
4x16 366 lb/beam 14.1 lb/ft	F_b F_v E	7.674 .330 11.469	.5903 .0141 706	.5247 .0187 602	.4427 .0211 485	.3935 .0141 602	.2952 .0141 485	.3935 .0141 559
10x10 619 lb/beam 23.8 lb/ft	F_b F_v E	7.096 .203 17.479	.5459 .0083 1,076	.4852 .0111 917	.4094 .0125 739	.3639 .0083 917	.2729 .0083 739	.3639 .0083 852

Nominal Size (Inches)	Property	UNIFORM	Single Load — At Center of Span	Single Load — At Third Point	Single Load — At Quarter Point	Sum of Two Equal Loads — At Third Point	Sum of Two Equal Loads — At Quarter Points From Reactions	Sum of 3 Equal Loads — At Quarter Points and Center of Span
8x12 592 lb/beam 22.8 lb/ft	F_b F_v E	6.134 .209 12,481	.4718 .0087 768	.4194 .0116 655	.3539 .0130 528	.3146 .0087 655	.2359 .0087 528	.3146 .0087 608
6x14 509 lb/beam 19.6 lb/ft	F_b F_v E	6.150 .240 10,521	.4730 .0101 647	.4205 .0135 552	.3548 .0152 445	.3154 .0101 552	.2365 .0101 445	.3154 .0101 513
10x12 750 lb/beam 28.8 lb/ft	F_b F_v E	4.843 .165 9,853	.3725 .0069 606	.3311 .0092 517	.2794 .0103 417	.2483 .0069 517	.1863 .0069 417	.2483 .0069 480
6x16 585 lb/beam 22.5 lb/ft	F_b F_v E	4.737 .206 6,951	.3644 .0088 428	.3239 .0117 365	.2733 .0132 294	.2429 .0088 365	.1822 .0088 294	.2429 .0088 339
8x14 695 lb/beam 26.7 lb/ft	F_b F_v E	4.510 .176 7,715	.3469 .0074 475	.3084 .0099 405	.2602 .0111 326	.2313 .0074 405	.1734 .0074 326	.2313 .0074 376
12x12 907 lb/beam 34.9 lb/ft	F_b F_v E	4.000 .137 8,140	.3077 .0057 501	.2735 .0076 427	.2308 .0085 344	.2051 .0057 427	.1539 .0057 344	.2051 .0057 397
6x18 660 lb/beam 25.4 lb/ft	F_b F_v E	3.766 .180 4,830	.2897 .0078 297	.2575 .0104 253	.2173 .0117 204	.1932 .0078 253	.1449 .0078 204	.1932 .0078 235
10x14 880 lb/beam 33.8 lb/ft	F_b F_v E	3.560 .139 6,091	.2739 .0058 375	.2434 .0078 319	.2054 .0088 258	.1826 .0058 319	.1369 .0058 258	.1826 .0058 297
8x16 798 lb/beam 30.7 lb/ft	F_b F_v E	3.474 .151 5,097	.2672 .0065 314	.2375 .0086 267	.2004 .0097 216	.1781 .0065 267	.1336 .0065 216	.1781 .0065 248
6x20 736 lb/beam 28.3 lb/ft	F_b F_v E	3.072 .159 3,491	.2363 .0070 215	.2100 .0093 183	.1772 .0105 148	.1575 .0070 183	.1182 .0070 148	.1575 .0070 170
12x14 1065 lb/beam 41.0 lb/ft	F_b F_v E	2.941 .115 5,032	.2262 .0048 310	.2011 .0064 264	.1697 .0072 213	.1508 .0048 264	.1131 .0048 213	.1508 .0048 245

STRENGTH AND STIFFNESS REQUIREMENTS FOR BEAMS

See instructions for use of tables on page 101. Symbols used in the tables are as follows: Tabulated values are based on net size.

F_b = Extreme fiber stress in bending induced by a uniform load of 1 (one) plf or by a concentrated load of 1 (one) pound, psi

F_v = Horizontal shear stress induced by a uniform load of 1 (one) plf or a total concentrated load of 1 (one) pound. psi.

E = Modulus of elasticity value needed to limit deflection to 1/360 of the span for a uniform load of 1 (one) plf or a total concentrated load of 1 (one) pound. psi.

26 FOOT SPAN

Nominal Size (Inches)	Property	UNIFORM	Single Load At Center of Span	Single Load At Third Point	Single Load At Quarter Point	Sum of Two Equal Loads At Third Point	Sum of Two Equal Loads At Quarter Points From Reactions	Sum of 3 Equal Loads At Quarter Points and Center of Span
10x16 1010 lb/beam 38.9 lb/ft	F_b F_v E	2.742 .119 4.024	.2110 .0051 248	.1875 .0068 211	.1582 .0076 170	.1406 .0051 211	.1055 .0051 170	.1406 .0051 196
8x18 901 lb/beam 34.6 lb/ft	F_b F_v E	2.762 .132 3.542	.2125 .0057 218	.1889 .0076 186	.1593 .0086 150	.1416 .0057 186	.1062 .0057 150	.1416 .0057 173
12x16 1223 lb/beam 47.0 lb/ft	F_b F_v E	2.265 .099 3.324	.1743 .0042 205	.1549 .0056 174	.1307 .0063 141	.1162 .0042 174	.0871 .0042 141	.1162 .0042 162
8x20 1003 lb/beam 38.6 lb/ft	F_b F_v E	2.253 .117 2.560	.1733 .0051 158	.1540 .0068 134	.1300 .0077 108	.1155 .0051 134	.0866 .0051 108	.1155 .0051 125
10x18 1141 lb/beam 43.9 lb/ft	F_b F_v E	2.181 .104 2.796	.1677 .0045 172	.1491 .0060 147	.1258 .0068 118	.1118 .0045 147	.0839 .0045 118	.1118 .0045 136
8x22 1106 lb/beam 42.6 lb/ft	F_b F_v E	1.873 .104 1.910	.1441 .0047 118	.1281 .0062 100	.1081 .0070 81	.0960 .0047 100	.0720 .0047 81	.0960 .0047 93
12x18 1381 lb/beam 53.1 lb/ft	F_b F_v E	1.801 .086 2.310	.1386 .0037 142	.1232 .0050 121	.1039 .0056 98	.0924 .0037 121	.0693 .0037 98	.0924 .0037 113
10x20 1271 lb/beam 48.9 lb/ft	F_b F_v E	1.778 .092 2.021	.1368 .0040 124	.1216 .0054 106	.1026 .0061 86	.0912 .0040 106	.0684 .0040 86	.0912 .0040 98
8x24 1209 lb/beam 46.5 lb/ft	F_b F_v E	1.583 .094 1.463	.1218 .0043 90	.1082 .0057 77	.0913 .0064 62	.0812 .0043 77	.0609 .0043 62	.0812 .0043 71
12x20 1539 lb/beam 59.2 lb/ft	F_b F_v E	1.469 .076 1.670	.1130 .0033 103	.1005 .0045 88	.0848 .0050 71	.0753 .0033 88	.0565 .0033 71	.0753 .0033 81

26 FOOT SPAN (Continued)

Nominal Size (Inches)	Property	UNIFORM	Single Load At Center of Span	Single Load At Third Point	Single Load At Quarter Point	Sum of Two Equal Loads At Third Point	Sum of Two Equal Loads At Quarter Points From Reactions	Sum of 3 Equal Loads At Quarter Points and Center of Span
10x22 1401 lb/beam 53.9 lb/ft	F_b F_v E	1.479 .082 1.508	.1137 .0037 93	.1011 .0049 79	.0853 .0055 64	.0758 .0037 79	.0569 .0037 64	.0758 .0037 73
10x24 1532 lb/beam 58.9 lb/ft	F_b F_v E	1.250 .074 1.155	.0961 .0034 71	.0854 .0045 61	.0721 .0050 49	.0641 .0034 61	.0481 .0034 49	.0641 .0034 56
12x22 1696 lb/beam 65.2 lb/ft	F_b F_v E	1.221 .068 1.246	.0940 .0030 77	.0835 .0040 65	.0705 .0046 53	.0626 .0030 65	.0470 .0030 53	.0626 .0030 61
12x24 1854 lb/beam 71.3 lb/ft	F_b F_v E	1.032 .061 954	.0794 .0028 59	.0706 .0037 50	.0596 .0042 40	.0529 .0028 50	.0397 .0028 40	.0529 .0028 46

27 FOOT SPAN

Nominal Size (Inches)	Property	UNIFORM	Single Load At Center of Span	Single Load At Third Point	Single Load At Quarter Point	Sum of Two Equal Loads At Third Point	Sum of Two Equal Loads At Quarter Points From Reactions	Sum of 3 Equal Loads At Quarter Points and Center of Span
2x14 142 lb/beam 5.2 lb/ft	F_b F_v E	24.914 .936 45.692	1.8455 .0377 2.708	1.6404 .0503 2.308	1.3841 .0566 1.862	1.2303 .0377 2.308	.9227 .0377 1.862	1.2303 .0377 2.144
4x10 231 lb/beam 8.5 lb/ft	F_b F_v E	21.909 .590 57.555	1.6229 .0232 3.411	1.4426 .0309 2.907	1.2172 .0347 2.345	1.0819 .0232 2.907	.8114 .0232 2.345	1.0819 .0232 2.700
6x8 294 lb/beam 10.9 lb/ft	F_b F_v E	21.207 .468 68.712	1.5709 .0182 4.072	1.3964 .0242 3.470	1.1782 .0273 2.799	1.0473 .0182 3.470	.7855 .0182 2.799	1.0473 .0182 3.224
3x12 200 lb/beam 7.4 lb/ft	F_b F_v E	20.736 .670 44.790	1.5360 .0267 2.654	1.3653 .0356 2.262	1.1520 .0400 1.825	1.0240 .0267 2.262	.7680 .0267 1.825	1.0240 .0267 2.101
8x8 401 lb/beam 14.8 lb/ft	F_b F_v E	15.552 .343 50.388	1.1520 .0133 2.986	1.0240 .0178 2.545	.8640 .0200 2.053	.7680 .0133 2.545	.5760 .0133 2.053	.7680 .0133 2.364
3x14 236 lb/beam 8.7 lb/ft	F_b F_v E	14.949 .561 27.415	1.1073 .0226 1.625	.9843 .0302 1.385	.8305 .0340 1.117	.7382 .0226 1.385	.5536 .0226 1.117	.7382 .0226 1.286

STRENGTH AND STIFFNESS REQUIREMENTS FOR BEAMS

See instructions for use of the tables on page 101. Symbols used in the tables are as follows: Tabulated values are based on net size.

F_b = Extreme fiber stress in bending induced by a uniform load of 1 (one) plf or by a concentrated load of 1 (one) pound, psi

F_v = Horizontal shear stress induced by a uniform load of 1 (one) plf or a total concentrated load of 1 (one) pound, psi.

E = Modulus of elasticity value needed to limit deflection to 1/360 of the span for a uniform load of 1 (one) plf or a total concentrated load of 1 (one) pound, psi.

27 FOOT SPAN

Nominal Size (Inches)	Property	UNIFORM	CONCENTRATED — Single Load — At Center of Span	At Third Point	At Quarter Point	Sum of Two Equal Loads — At Third Point	At Quarter Points From Reactions	Sum of 3 Equal Loads — At Quarter Points and Center of Span
4x12 281 lb/beam 10.4 lb/ft	F_b F_v E	14.811 .479 31,993	1.0971 .0190 1,896	.9752 .0254 1,616	.8229 .0286 1,303	.7314 .0190 1,616	.5486 .0190 1,303	.7314 .0190 1,501
6x10 372 lb/beam 13.8 lb/ft	F_b F_v E	13.218 .365 33,810	.9791 .0144 2,004	.8703 .0191 1,708	.7343 .0215 1,377	.6527 .0144 1,708	.4895 .0144 1,377	.6527 .0144 1,586
3x16 272 lb/beam 10.1 lb/ft	F_b F_v E	11.586 .481 17,982	.8582 .0197 1,066	.7629 .0262 908	.6437 .0295 733	.5721 .0197 908	.4291 .0197 733	.5721 .0197 844
4x14 330 lb/beam 12.2 lb/ft	F_b F_v E	10.678 .401 19,582	.7909 .0162 1,160	.7030 .0216 989	.5932 .0243 798	.5273 .0162 989	.3955 .0162 798	.5273 .0162 919
8x10 508 lb/beam 18.8 lb/ft	F_b F_v E	9.693 .268 24,794	.7180 .0105 1,469	.6382 .0140 1,252	.5385 .0158 1,010	.4787 .0105 1,252	.3590 .0105 1,010	.4787 .0105 1,163
6x12 451 lb/beam 16.7 lb/ft	F_b F_v E	9.202 .297 19,060	.6682 .0119 1,129	.5939 .0158 963	.5011 .0178 777	.4454 .0119 963	.3341 .0119 777	.4454 .0119 894
4x16 380 lb/beam 14.1 lb/ft	F_b F_v E	8.276 .344 12,844	.6130 .0141 761	.5449 .0187 649	.4598 .0211 523	.4087 .0141 649	.3065 .0141 523	.4087 .0141 603
10x10 643 lb/beam 23.8 lb/ft	F_b F_v E	7.652 .211 19,574	.5668 .0083 1,160	.5039 .0111 989	.4251 .0125 797	.3779 .0083 989	.2834 .0083 797	.3779 .0083 918
8x12 615 lb/beam 22.8 lb/ft	F_b F_v E	6.615 .218 13,977	.4900 .0087 828	.4355 .0116 706	.3675 .0130 569	.3267 .0087 706	.2450 .0087 569	.3267 .0087 656
6x14 529 lb/beam 19.6 lb/ft	F_b F_v E	6.632 .250 11,782	.4912 .0101 698	.4367 .0135 595	.3684 .0152 480	.3275 .0101 595	.2456 .0101 480	.3275 .0101 553

27 FOOT SPAN (Continued)

Nominal Size (Inches)	Property	UNIFORM	CONCENTRATED — Single Load — At Center of Span	At Third Point	At Quarter Point	Sum of Two Equal Loads — At Third Point	At Quarter Points From Reactions	Sum of 3 Equal Loads — At Quarter Points and Center of Span
10x12 778 lb/beam 28.8 lb/ft	F_b F_v E	5.222 .172 11,035	.3868 .0069 654	.3438 .0092 557	.2901 .0103 450	.2579 .0069 557	.1934 .0069 450	.2579 .0069 518
6x16 607 lb/beam 22.5 lb/ft	F_b F_v E	5.108 .215 7,784	.3784 .0088 461	.3363 .0117 393	.2838 .0132 317	.2523 .0088 393	.1892 .0088 317	.2523 .0088 365
8x14 721 lb/beam 26.7 lb/ft	F_b F_v E	4.863 .183 8,640	.3602 .0074 512	.3202 .0099 436	.2702 .0111 352	.2402 .0074 436	.1801 .0074 352	.2402 .0074 405
12x12 942 lb/beam 34.9 lb/ft	F_b F_v E	4.314 .142 9,116	.3196 .0057 540	.2840 .0076 460	.2397 .0085 371	.2130 .0057 460	.1598 .0057 371	.2130 .0057 428
6x18 686 lb/beam 25.4 lb/ft	F_b F_v E	4.062 .188 5,409	.3009 .0078 321	.2674 .0104 273	.2257 .0117 220	.2006 .0078 273	.1504 .0078 220	.2006 .0078 254
10x14 914 lb/beam 33.8 lb/ft	F_b F_v E	3.839 .145 6,821	.2844 .0058 404	.2528 .0078 344	.2133 .0088 278	.1896 .0058 344	.1422 .0058 278	.1896 .0058 320
8x16 828 lb/beam 30.7 lb/ft	F_b F_v E	3.746 .158 5,708	.2775 .0065 338	.2467 .0086 288	.2081 .0097 233	.1850 .0065 288	.1387 .0065 233	.1850 .0065 268
6x20 764 lb/beam 28.3 lb/ft	F_b F_v E	3.313 .166 3,909	.2454 .0070 232	.2181 .0093 197	.1840 .0105 159	.1636 .0070 197	.1227 .0070 159	.1636 .0070 183
12x14 1106 lb/beam 41.0 lb/ft	F_b F_v E	3.172 .120 5,635	.2349 .0048 334	.2088 .0064 285	.1762 .0072 230	.1566 .0048 285	.1175 .0048 230	.1566 .0048 264
10x16 1049 lb/beam 38.9 lb/ft	F_b F_v E	2.957 .124 4,507	.2191 .0051 267	.1947 .0068 228	.1643 .0076 184	.1460 .0051 228	.1095 .0051 184	.1460 .0051 211
8x18 935 lb/beam 34.6 lb/ft	F_b F_v E	2.979 .138 3,966	.2206 .0057 235	.1961 .0076 200	.1655 .0086 162	.1471 .0057 200	.1103 .0057 162	.1471 .0057 186

STRENGTH AND STIFFNESS REQUIREMENTS FOR BEAMS

See instructions for use of tables on page 101. Symbols used in the tables are as follows: Tabulated values are based on net size.

F_b = Extreme fiber stress in bending induced by a uniform load of 1 (one) plf or by a concentrated load of 1 (one) pound, psi

F_v = Horizontal shear stress induced by a uniform load of 1 (one) plf or a total concentrated load of 1 (one) pound, psi.

E = Modulus of elasticity value needed to limit deflection to 1/360 of the span for a uniform load of 1 (one) plf or a total concentrated load of 1 (one) pound, psi.

27 FOOT SPAN

Nominal Size (Inches)	Property	UNIFORM	Single Load — At Center of Span	Single Load — At Third Point	Single Load — At Quarter Point	Sum of Two Equal Loads — At Third Point	Sum of Two Equal Loads — At Quarter Points From Reactions	Sum of 3 Equal Loads — At Quarter Points and Center of Span
12x16 1270 lb/beam 47.0 lb/ft	F_b / F_v / E	2.443 / .103 / 3,723	.1810 / .0042 / 221	.1609 / .0056 / 188	.1357 / .0063 / 152	.1206 / .0042 / 188	.0905 / .0042 / 152	.1206 / .0042 / 175
8x20 1042 lb/beam 38.6 lb/ft	F_b / F_v / E	2.429 / .122 / 2,867	.1800 / .0051 / 170	.1600 / .0068 / 145	.1350 / .0077 / 117	.1200 / .0051 / 145	.0900 / .0051 / 117	.1200 / .0051 / 134
10x18 1185 lb/beam 43.9 lb/ft	F_b / F_v / E	2.352 / .109 / 3,131	.1742 / .0045 / 186	.1548 / .0060 / 158	.1306 / .0068 / 128	.1161 / .0045 / 158	.0871 / .0045 / 128	.1161 / .0045 / 147
8x22 1149 lb/beam 42.6 lb/ft	F_b / F_v / E	2.020 / .109 / 2,139	.1496 / .0047 / 127	.1330 / .0062 / 108	.1122 / .0070 / 87	.0997 / .0047 / 108	.0748 / .0047 / 87	.0997 / .0047 / 100
12x18 1434 lb/beam 53.1 lb/ft	F_b / F_v / E	1.943 / .090 / 2,587	.1439 / .0037 / 153	.1279 / .0050 / 131	.1079 / .0056 / 105	.0959 / .0037 / 131	.0719 / .0037 / 105	.0959 / .0037 / 121
10x20 1320 lb/beam 48.9 lb/ft	F_b / F_v / E	1.918 / .096 / 2,263	.1421 / .0040 / 134	.1263 / .0054 / 114	.1066 / .0061 / 92	.0947 / .0040 / 114	.0710 / .0040 / 92	.0947 / .0040 / 106
8x24 1256 lb/beam 46.5 lb/ft	F_b / F_v / E	1.707 / .098 / 1,638	.1264 / .0043 / 97	.1124 / .0057 / 83	.0948 / .0064 / 67	.0843 / .0043 / 83	.0632 / .0043 / 67	.0843 / .0043 / 77
12x20 1598 lb/beam 59.2 lb/ft	F_b / F_v / E	1.584 / .079 / 1,870	.1174 / .0033 / 111	.1043 / .0045 / 94	.0880 / .0050 / 76	.0782 / .0033 / 94	.0587 / .0033 / 76	.0782 / .0033 / 88
10x22 1455 lb/beam 53.9 lb/ft	F_b / F_v / E	1.595 / .086 / 1,689	.1181 / .0037 / 100	.1050 / .0049 / 85	.0886 / .0055 / 69	.0787 / .0037 / 85	.0591 / .0037 / 69	.0787 / .0037 / 79
10x24 1591 lb/beam 58.9 lb/ft	F_b / F_v / E	1.348 / .078 / 1,293	.0998 / .0034 / 77	.0887 / .0045 / 65	.0749 / .0050 / 53	.0665 / .0034 / 65	.0499 / .0034 / 53	.0665 / .0034 / 61

27 FOOT SPAN (Continued)

Nominal Size (Inches)	Property	UNIFORM	Single Load — At Center of Span	Single Load — At Third Point	Single Load — At Quarter Point	Sum of Two Equal Loads — At Third Point	Sum of Two Equal Loads — At Quarter Points From Reactions	Sum of 3 Equal Loads — At Quarter Points and Center of Span
12x22 1762 lb/beam 65.2 lb/ft	F_b / F_v / E	1.317 / .071 / 1,395	.0976 / .0030 / 83	.0867 / .0040 / 70	.0732 / .0046 / 57	.0650 / .0030 / 70	.0488 / .0030 / 57	.0650 / .0030 / 65
12x24 1926 lb/beam 71.3 lb/ft	F_b / F_v / E	1.113 / .064 / 1,068	.0825 / .0028 / 63	.0733 / .0037 / 54	.0618 / .0042 / 44	.0550 / .0028 / 54	.0412 / .0028 / 44	.0550 / .0028 / 50

28 FOOT SPAN

Nominal Size (Inches)	Property	UNIFORM	Single Load — At Center of Span	Single Load — At Third Point	Single Load — At Quarter Point	Sum of Two Equal Loads — At Third Point	Sum of Two Equal Loads — At Quarter Points From Reactions	Sum of 3 Equal Loads — At Quarter Points and Center of Span
3x12 208 lb/beam 7.4 lb/ft	F_b / F_v / E	22.300 / .697 / 49.953	1.5929 / .0267 / 2,854	1.4159 / .0356 / 2,433	1.1947 / .0400 / 1,962	1.0619 / .0267 / 2,433	.7964 / .0267 / 1,962	1.0619 / .0267 / 2,260
8x8 416 lb/beam 14.8 lb/ft	F_b / F_v / E	16.725 / .357 / 56.197	1.1947 / .0133 / 3,211	1.0619 / .0178 / 2,737	.8960 / .0200 / 2,208	.7964 / .0133 / 2,737	.5973 / .0133 / 2,208	.7964 / .0133 / 2,542
3x14 245 lb/beam 8.7 lb/ft	F_b / F_v / E	16.076 / .584 / 30.575	1.1483 / .0226 / 1,747	1.0207 / .0302 / 1,489	.8612 / .0340 / 1,201	.7655 / .0226 / 1,489	.5742 / .0226 / 1,201	.7655 / .0226 / 1,383
4x12 291 lb/beam 10.4 lb/ft	F_b / F_v / E	15.929 / .498 / 35.681	1.1378 / .0190 / 2,039	1.0114 / .0254 / 1,738	.8533 / .0286 / 1,402	.7585 / .0190 / 1,738	.5689 / .0190 / 1,402	.7585 / .0190 / 1,614
6x10 386 lb/beam 13.8 lb/ft	F_b / F_v / E	14.215 / .379 / 37.707	1.0154 / .0144 / 2,155	.9025 / .0191 / 1,836	.7615 / .0215 / 1,481	.6769 / .0144 / 1,836	.5077 / .0144 / 1,481	.6769 / .0144 / 1,706
3x16 282 lb/beam 10.1 lb/ft	F_b / F_v / E	12.460 / .501 / 20.054	.8900 / .0197 / 1,146	.7911 / .0262 / 977	.6675 / .0295 / 788	.5933 / .0197 / 977	.4450 / .0197 / 788	.5933 / .0197 / 907
4x14 343 lb/beam 12.2 lb/ft	F_b / F_v / E	11.483 / .417 / 21.840	.8202 / .0162 / 1,248	.7291 / .0216 / 1,064	.6152 / .0243 / 858	.5468 / .0162 / 1,064	.4101 / .0162 / 858	.5468 / .0162 / 988
8x10 526 lb/beam 18.8 lb/ft	F_b / F_v / E	10.424 / .278 / 27.652	.7446 / .0105 / 1,580	.6619 / .0140 / 1,347	.5584 / .0158 / 1,086	.4964 / .0105 / 1,347	.3723 / .0105 / 1,086	.4964 / .0105 / 1,251

STRENGTH AND STIFFNESS REQUIREMENTS FOR BEAMS

See instructions for use of tables on page 101. Symbols used in the tables are as follows: Tabulated values are based on net size.

F_b = Extreme fiber stress in bending induced by a uniform load of 1 (one) plf or by a concentrated load of 1 (one) pound, psi

F_v = Horizontal shear stress induced by a uniform load of 1 (one) plf or a total concentrated load of 1 (one) pound, psi.

E = Modulus of elasticity value needed to limit deflection to 1/360 of the span for a uniform load of 1 (one) plf or a total concentrated load of 1 (one) plf or a total concentrated load of 1 (one) pound, psi.

28 FOOT SPAN (Continued)

Nominal Size (Inches)	Property	UNIFORM	CONCENTRATED — Single Load — At Center of Span	Single Load — At Third Point	Single Load — At Quarter Point	Sum of Two Equal Loads — At Third Point	Sum of Two Equal Loads — At Quarter Points From Reactions	Sum of 3 Equal Loads — At Quarter Points and Center of Span
10x14 948 lb/beam 33.8 lb/ft	F_b F_v E	4.129 .151 7,607	.2949 .0058 435	.2622 .0078 370	.2212 .0088 299	.1966 .0058 370	.1475 .0058 299	.1966 .0058 344
8x16 859 lb/beam 30.7 lb/ft	F_b F_v E	4.029 .164 6,367	.2878 .0065 364	.2558 .0086 310	.2158 .0097 250	.1918 .0065 310	.1439 .0065 250	.1918 .0065 288
6x20 792 lb/beam 28.3 lb/ft	F_b F_v E	3.563 .173 4,360	.2545 .0070 249	.2262 .0093 212	.1909 .0105 171	.1697 .0070 212	.1272 .0070 171	.1697 .0070 197
12x14 1147 lb/beam 41.0 lb/ft	F_b F_v E	3.411 .124 6,284	.2436 .0048 359	.2166 .0064 306	.1827 .0072 247	.1624 .0048 306	.1218 .0048 247	.1624 .0048 284
10x16 1088 lb/beam 38.9 lb/ft	F_b F_v E	3.181 .129 5,026	.2272 .0051 287	.2019 .0068 245	.1704 .0076 197	.1515 .0051 245	.1136 .0051 197	.1515 .0051 227
8x18 970 lb/beam 34.6 lb/ft	F_b F_v E	3.203 .143 4,424	.2288 .0057 253	.2034 .0076 215	.1716 .0086 174	.1525 .0057 215	.1144 .0057 174	.1525 .0057 200
12x16 1317 lb/beam 47.0 lb/ft	F_b F_v E	2.627 .107 4,152	.1877 .0042 237	.1668 .0056 202	.1408 .0063 163	.1251 .0042 202	.0938 .0042 163	.1251 .0042 188
8x20 1081 lb/beam 38.6 lb/ft	F_b F_v E	2.613 .127 3,197	.1866 .0051 183	.1659 .0068 156	.1400 .0077 126	.1244 .0051 156	.0933 .0051 126	.1244 .0051 145
10x18 1228 lb/beam 43.9 lb/ft	F_b F_v E	2.529 .113 3,492	.1806 .0045 200	.1606 .0060 170	.1355 .0068 137	.1204 .0045 170	.0903 .0045 137	.1204 .0045 158
8x22 1191 lb/beam 42.6 lb/ft	F_b F_v E	2.172 .114 2,386	.1552 .0047 136	.1379 .0062 116	.1164 .0070 94	.1034 .0047 116	.0776 .0047 94	.1034 .0047 108
12x18 1487 lb/beam 53.1 lb/ft	F_b F_v E	2.089 .093 2,885	.1492 .0037 165	.1326 .0050 141	.1119 .0056 113	.0995 .0037 141	.0746 .0037 113	.0995 .0037 131

28 FOOT SPAN (Continued)

Nominal Size (Inches)	Property	UNIFORM	CONCENTRATED — Single Load — At Center of Span	Single Load — At Third Point	Single Load — At Quarter Point	Sum of Two Equal Loads — At Third Point	Sum of Two Equal Loads — At Quarter Points From Reactions	Sum of 3 Equal Loads — At Quarter Points and Center of Span
6x12 467 lb/beam 16.7 lb/ft	F_b F_v E	9.701 .309 21,257	.6929 .0119 1,215	.6159 .0158 1,035	.5197 .0178 835	.4619 .0119 1,035	.3465 .0119 835	.4619 .0119 962
4x16 394 lb/beam 14.1 lb/ft	F_b F_v E	8.900 .358 14,325	.6357 .0141 819	.5651 .0187 698	.4768 .0211 563	.4238 .0141 698	.3179 .0141 563	.4238 .0141 648
10x10 667 lb/beam 23.8 lb/ft	F_b F_v E	8.230 .220 21,831	.5878 .0083 1,247	.5225 .0111 1,063	.4409 .0125 858	.3919 .0083 1,063	.2939 .0083 858	.3919 .0083 988
8x12 637 lb/beam 22.8 lb/ft	F_b F_v E	7.114 .227 15,589	.5081 .0087 891	.4517 .0116 759	.3811 .0130 612	.3388 .0087 759	.2541 .0087 612	.3388 .0087 705
6x14 549 lb/beam 19.6 lb/ft	F_b F_v E	7.132 .260 13,140	.5094 .0101 751	.4528 .0135 640	.3821 .0152 516	.3396 .0101 640	.2547 .0101 516	.3396 .0101 594
10x12 807 lb/beam 28.8 lb/ft	F_b F_v E	5.616 .179 12,307	.4012 .0069 703	.3566 .0092 599	.3009 .0103 483	.2674 .0069 599	.2006 .0069 483	.2674 .0069 557
6x16 630 lb/beam 22.5 lb/ft	F_b F_v E	5.494 .224 8,682	.3924 .0088 496	.3488 .0117 423	.2943 .0132 341	.2616 .0088 423	.1962 .0088 341	.2616 .0088 393
8x14 748 lb/beam 26.7 lb/ft	F_b F_v E	5.230 .191 9,636	.3736 .0074 551	.3321 .0099 469	.2802 .0111 379	.2491 .0074 469	.1868 .0074 379	.2491 .0074 436
12x12 977 lb/beam 34.9 lb/ft	F_b F_v E	4.639 .148 10,166	.3314 .0057 581	.2946 .0076 495	.2485 .0085 399	.2209 .0057 495	.1657 .0057 399	.2209 .0057 460
6x18 711 lb/beam 25.4 lb/ft	F_b F_v E	4.368 .195 6,032	.3120 .0078 345	.2773 .0104 294	.2340 .0117 237	.2080 .0078 294	.1560 .0078 237	.2080 .0078 273

STRENGTH AND STIFFNESS REQUIREMENTS FOR BEAMS

See instructions for use of tables on page 101. Symbols used in the tables are as follows: Tabulated values are based on net size.

F_b = Extreme fiber stress in bending induced by a uniform load of 1 (one) plf or by a concentrated load of 1 (one) pound, psi

F_v = Horizontal shear stress induced by a uniform load of 1 (one) plf or a total concentrated load of 1 (one) pound, psi.

E = Modulus of elasticity value needed to limit deflection to 1/360 of the span for a uniform load of 1 (one) plf or a total concentrated load of 1 (one) pound, psi.

28 FOOT SPAN (Continued)

Nominal Size (Inches)	Property	UNIFORM	Single Load — At Center of Span	Single Load — At Third Point	Single Load — At Quarter Point	Sum of Two Equal Loads — At Third Point	Sum of Two Equal Loads — At Quarter Points From Reactions	Sum of 3 Equal Loads — At Quarter Points and Center of Span
3x14 253 lb/beam 8.7 lb/ft	F_b	17.245	1.1893	1.0572	.8920	.7929	.5947	.7929
	F_v	.607	.0226	.0302	.0340	.0226	.0226	.0226
	E	33.970	1,874	1,597	1,289	1,597	1,289	1,484
4x12 301 lb/beam 10.4 lb/ft	F_b	17.087	1.1784	1.0475	.8838	.7856	.5892	.7856
	F_v	.517	.0190	.0254	.0286	.0190	.0190	.0190
	E	39.642	2,187	1,864	1,504	1,864	1,504	1,731
6x10 400 lb/beam 13.8 lb/ft	F_b	15.249	1.0516	.9348	.7887	.7011	.5258	.7011
	F_v	.394	.0144	.0191	.0215	.0144	.0144	.0144
	E	41.893	2,311	1,970	1,589	1,970	1,589	1,830
3x16 292 lb/beam 10.1 lb/ft	F_b	13.366	.9218	.8194	.6913	.6145	.4609	.6145
	F_v	.520	.0197	.0262	.0295	.0197	.0197	.0197
	E	22.281	1,229	1,048	845	1,048	845	973
4x14 355 lb/beam 12.2 lb/ft	F_b	12.318	.8495	.7551	.6371	.5663	.4248	.5663
	F_v	.433	.0162	.0216	.0243	.0162	.0162	.0162
	E	24.264	1,339	1,141	920	1,141	920	1,060
8x10 545 lb/beam 18.8 lb/ft	F_b	11.182	.7712	.6855	.5784	.5141	.3856	.5141
	F_v	.289	.0105	.0140	.0158	.0105	.0105	.0105
	E	30.722	1,695	1,445	1,165	1,445	1,165	1,342
6x12 484 lb/beam 16.7 lb/ft	F_b	10.406	.7176	.6379	.5382	.4784	.3588	.4784
	F_v	.321	.0119	.0158	.0178	.0119	.0119	.0119
	E	23.617	1,303	1,111	896	1,111	896	1,032
4x16 408 lb/beam 14.1 lb/ft	F_b	9.547	.6584	.5853	.4938	.4389	.3292	.4389
	F_v	.372	.0141	.0187	.0211	.0141	.0141	.0141
	E	15.915	878	748	604	748	604	695
10x10 691 lb/beam 23.8 lb/ft	F_b	8.828	.6088	.5412	.4566	.4059	.3044	.4059
	F_v	.228	.0083	.0111	.0125	.0083	.0083	.0083
	E	24.254	1,338	1,140	920	1,140	920	1,059
8x12 660 lb/beam 22.8 lb/ft	F_b	7.631	.5263	.4678	.3947	.3509	.2631	.3509
	F_v	.236	.0087	.0116	.0130	.0087	.0087	.0087
	E	17.319	956	814	657	814	657	756
6x14 568 lb/beam 19.6 lb/ft	F_b	7.651	.5276	.4690	.3957	.3517	.2638	.3517
	F_v	.270	.0101	.0135	.0152	.0101	.0101	.0101
	E	14.599	805	686	554	686	554	638

28 FOOT SPAN (Continued)

Nominal Size (Inches)	Property	UNIFORM	Single Load — At Center of Span	Single Load — At Third Point	Single Load — At Quarter Point	Sum of Two Equal Loads — At Third Point	Sum of Two Equal Loads — At Quarter Points From Reactions	Sum of 3 Equal Loads — At Quarter Points and Center of Span
10x20 1369 lb/beam 48.9 lb/ft	F_b	2.063	.1473	.1310	.1105	.0982	.0737	.0982
	F_v	.100	.0040	.0054	.0061	.0040	.0040	.0040
	E	2.524	144	123	99	123	99	114
8x24 1302 lb/beam 46.5 lb/ft	F_b	1.836	.1311	.1166	.0983	.0874	.0656	.0874
	F_v	.102	.0043	.0057	.0064	.0043	.0043	.0043
	E	1.827	104	89	72	89	72	83
12x20 1657 lb/beam 59.2 lb/ft	F_b	1.704	.1217	.1082	.0913	.0811	.0609	.0811
	F_v	.083	.0033	.0045	.0050	.0033	.0033	.0033
	E	2.085	119	102	82	102	82	94
10x22 1509 lb/beam 53.9 lb/ft	F_b	1.715	.1225	.1089	.0919	.0817	.0612	.0817
	F_v	.090	.0037	.0049	.0055	.0037	.0037	.0037
	E	1.883	108	92	74	92	74	85
10x24 1650 lb/beam 58.9 lb/ft	F_b	1.449	.1035	.0920	.0776	.0690	.0518	.0690
	F_v	.081	.0034	.0045	.0050	.0034	.0034	.0034
	E	1.442	82	70	57	70	57	65
12x22 1827 lb/beam 65.2 lb/ft	F_b	1.417	.1012	.0899	.0759	.0675	.0506	.0675
	F_v	.074	.0030	.0040	.0046	.0030	.0030	.0030
	E	1.556	89	76	61	76	61	70
12x24 1997 lb/beam 71.3 lb/ft	F_b	1.197	.0855	.0760	.0641	.0570	.0428	.0570
	F_v	.067	.0028	.0037	.0042	.0028	.0028	.0028
	E	1.191	68	58	47	58	47	54

29 FOOT SPAN

Nominal Size (Inches)	Property	UNIFORM	Single Load — At Center of Span	Single Load — At Third Point	Single Load — At Quarter Point	Sum of Two Equal Loads — At Third Point	Sum of Two Equal Loads — At Quarter Points From Reactions	Sum of 3 Equal Loads — At Quarter Points and Center of Span
3x12 215 lb/beam 7.4 lb/ft	F_b	23.922	1.6498	1.4665	1.2373	1.0999	.8249	1.0999
	F_v	.723	.0267	.0356	.0400	.0267	.0267	.0267
	E	55.499	3,062	2,610	2,105	2,610	2,105	2,424
8x8 430 lb/beam 14.8 lb/ft	F_b	17.941	1.2373	1.0999	.9280	.8249	.6187	.8249
	F_v	.370	.0133	.0178	.0200	.0133	.0133	.0133
	E	62.436	3,445	2,936	2,368	2,936	2,368	2,727

STRENGTH AND STIFFNESS REQUIREMENTS FOR BEAMS

See instructions for use of tables on page 101. Symbols used in the tables are as follows: Tabulated values are based on net size.

F_b = Extreme fiber stress in bending induced by a uniform load of 1 (one) plf or by a concentrated load of 1 (one) pound, psi

F_v = Horizontal shear stress induced by a uniform load of 1 (one) plf or a total concentrated load of 1 (one) pound, psi.

E = Modulus of elasticity value needed to limit deflection to 1/360 of the span for a uniform load of 1 (one) plf or a total concentrated load of 1 (one) pound, psi.

29 FOOT SPAN

Nominal Size (Inches)	Property	UNIFORM	Single Load – At Center of Span	Single Load – At Third Point	Single Load – At Quarter Point	Sum of Two Equal Loads – At Third Point	Sum of Two Equal Loads – At Quarter Points From Reactions	Sum of 3 Equal Loads – At Quarter Points and Center of Span
8x18 1004 lb/beam 34.6 lb/ft	F_b	3.436	2.370	2.107	1.777	.1580	.1185	.1580
	F_v	.149	.0057	.0076	.0086	.0057	.0057	.0057
	E	4,915	271	231	186	231	186	215
12x16 1364 lb/beam 47.0 lb/ft	F_b	2.818	1.944	1.728	1.458	.1296	.0972	.1296
	F_v	.111	.0042	.0056	.0063	.0042	.0042	.0042
	E	4,613	255	217	175	217	175	201
8x20 1119 lb/beam 38.6 lb/ft	F_b	2.803	1.933	1.718	1.450	.1289	.0966	.1289
	F_v	.132	.0051	.0068	.0077	.0051	.0051	.0051
	E	3,552	196	167	135	167	135	155
10x18 1272 lb/beam 43.9 lb/ft	F_b	2.713	1.871	1.663	1.403	.1247	.0935	.1247
	F_v	.118	.0045	.0060	.0068	.0045	.0045	.0045
	E	3,880	214	182	147	182	147	169
8x22 1234 lb/beam 42.6 lb/ft	F_b	2.330	1.607	1.428	1.205	.1071	.0803	.1071
	F_v	.118	.0047	.0062	.0070	.0047	.0047	.0047
	E	2,650	146	125	101	125	101	116
12x18 1540 lb/beam 53.1 lb/ft	F_b	2.241	1.546	1.374	1.159	.1030	.0773	.1030
	F_v	.097	.0037	.0050	.0056	.0037	.0037	.0037
	E	3,205	177	151	122	151	122	140
10x20 1418 lb/beam 48.9 lb/ft	F_b	2.213	1.526	1.356	1.144	.1017	.0763	.1017
	F_v	.104	.0040	.0054	.0061	.0040	.0040	.0040
	E	2,804	155	132	106	132	106	122
8x24 1349 lb/beam 46.5 lb/ft	F_b	1.969	1.358	1.207	1.019	.0905	.0679	.0905
	F_v	.107	.0043	.0057	.0064	.0043	.0043	.0043
	E	2,030	112	95	77	95	77	89
12x20 1716 lb/beam 59.2 lb/ft	F_b	1.828	1.261	1.120	.0945	.0840	.0630	.0840
	F_v	.086	.0033	.0045	.0050	.0033	.0033	.0033
	E	2,317	128	109	88	109	88	101
10x22 1563 lb/beam 53.9 lb/ft	F_b	1.840	1.269	1.128	.0951	.0846	.0634	.0846
	F_v	.093	.0037	.0049	.0055	.0037	.0037	.0037
	E	2,092	115	98	79	98	79	91
10x24 1708 lb/beam 58.9 lb/ft	F_b	1.555	1.072	.0953	.0804	.0715	.0536	.0715
	F_v	.084	.0034	.0045	.0050	.0034	.0034	.0034
	E	1,602	88	75	61	75	61	70

29 FOOT SPAN (Continued)

Nominal Size (Inches)	Property	UNIFORM	Single Load – At Center of Span	Single Load – At Third Point	Single Load – At Quarter Point	Sum of Two Equal Loads – At Third Point	Sum of Two Equal Loads – At Quarter Points From Reactions	Sum of 3 Equal Loads – At Quarter Points and Center of Span
10x12 836 lb/beam 28.8 lb/ft	F_b	6.024	4.155	3.693	3.116	.2770	.2077	.2770
	F_v	.186	.0069	.0092	.0103	.0069	.0069	.0069
	E	13,673	754	643	519	643	519	597
6x16 652 lb/beam 22.5 lb/ft	F_b	5.893	4.064	3.613	3.048	.2709	.2032	.2709
	F_v	.232	.0088	.0117	.0132	.0088	.0088	.0088
	E	9,645	532	454	366	454	366	421
8x14 775 lb/beam 26.7 lb/ft	F_b	5.610	3.869	3.439	2.902	.2579	.1935	.2579
	F_v	.198	.0074	.0099	.0111	.0074	.0074	.0074
	E	10,706	591	503	406	503	406	468
12x12 1012 lb/beam 34.9 lb/ft	F_b	4.977	3.432	3.051	2.574	.2288	.1716	.2288
	F_v	.154	.0057	.0076	.0085	.0057	.0057	.0057
	E	11,295	623	531	428	531	428	493
6x18 737 lb/beam 25.4 lb/ft	F_b	4.686	3.232	2.873	2.424	.2154	.1616	.2154
	F_v	.203	.0078	.0104	.0117	.0078	.0078	.0078
	E	6,702	370	315	254	315	254	293
10x14 981 lb/beam 33.8 lb/ft	F_b	4.429	3.055	2.715	2.291	.2036	.1527	.2036
	F_v	.156	.0058	.0078	.0088	.0058	.0058	.0058
	E	8,452	466	397	321	397	321	369
8x16 890 lb/beam 30.7 lb/ft	F_b	4.322	2.980	2.649	2.235	.1987	.1490	.1987
	F_v	.170	.0065	.0086	.0097	.0065	.0065	.0065
	E	7,073	390	333	268	333	268	309
6x20 821 lb/beam 28.3 lb/ft	F_b	3.822	2.636	2.343	1.977	.1757	.1318	.1757
	F_v	.180	.0070	.0093	.0105	.0070	.0070	.0070
	E	4,844	267	228	184	228	184	212
12x14 1188 lb/beam 41.0 lb/ft	F_b	3.659	2.523	2.243	1.893	.1682	.1262	.1682
	F_v	.129	.0048	.0064	.0072	.0048	.0048	.0048
	E	6,982	385	328	265	328	265	305
10x16 1127 lb/beam 38.9 lb/ft	F_b	3.412	2.353	2.092	1.765	.1569	.1176	.1569
	F_v	.135	.0051	.0068	.0076	.0051	.0051	.0051
	E	5,584	308	263	212	263	212	244

STRENGTH AND STIFFNESS REQUIREMENTS FOR BEAMS

See instructions for use of tables on page 101. Symbols used in the tables are as follows: Tabulated values are based on net size.

F_b = Extreme fiber stress in bending induced by a uniform load of 1 (one) plf or by a concentrated load of 1 (one) pound, psi

F_v = Horizontal shear stress induced by a uniform load of 1 (one) plf or a total concentrated load of 1 (one) pound, psi

E = Modulus of elasticity value needed to limit deflection to 1/360 of the span for a uniform load of 1 (one) plf or a total concentrated load of 1 (one) pound, psi.

Nominal Size (Inches)	Property	UNIFORM	CONCENTRATED Single Load — At Center of Span	Single Load — At Third Point	Single Load — At Quarter Point	Sum of Two Equal Loads — At Third Point	Sum of Two Equal Loads — At Quarter Points From Reactions	Sum of 3 Equal Loads — At Quarter Points and Center of Span
4x16 423 lb/beam 14.1 lb/ft	F_b	10.217	.6811	.6054	.5108	.4541	.3406	.4541
	F_v	.386	.0141	.0187	.0211	.0141	.0141	.0141
	E	17,619	940	801	646	801	646	744
10x10 714 lb/beam 23.8 lb/ft	F_b	9.447	.6298	.5598	.4724	.4199	.3149	.4199
	F_v	.236	.0083	.0111	.0125	.0083	.0083	.0083
	E	26,851	1,432	1,220	985	1,220	985	1,134
8x12 683 lb/beam 22.8 lb/ft	F_b	8.166	.5444	.4839	.4083	.3629	.2722	.3629
	F_v	.244	.0087	.0116	.0130	.0087	.0087	.0087
	E	19,173	1,023	872	703	872	703	810
6x14 588 lb/beam 19.6 lb/ft	F_b	8.187	.5458	.4852	.4094	.3639	.2729	.3639
	F_v	.280	.0101	.0135	.0152	.0101	.0101	.0101
	E	16,162	862	735	593	735	593	682
10x12 865 lb/beam 28.8 lb/ft	F_b	6.447	.4298	.3821	.3224	.2865	.2149	.2865
	F_v	.193	.0069	.0092	.0103	.0069	.0069	.0069
	E	15,137	807	688	555	688	555	639
6x16 675 lb/beam 22.5 lb/ft	F_b	6.307	.4204	.3737	.3153	.2803	.2102	.2803
	F_v	.241	.0088	.0117	.0132	.0088	.0088	.0088
	E	10,678	569	485	392	485	392	451
8x14 802 lb/beam 26.7 lb/ft	F_b	6.004	.4003	.3558	.3002	.2668	.2001	.2668
	F_v	.206	.0074	.0099	.0111	.0074	.0074	.0074
	E	11,852	632	539	435	539	435	500
12x12 1047 lb/beam 34.9 lb/ft	F_b	5.326	.3551	.3156	.2663	.2367	.1775	.2367
	F_v	.159	.0057	.0076	.0085	.0057	.0057	.0057
	E	12,504	667	568	458	568	458	528
6x18 762 lb/beam 25.4 lb/ft	F_b	5.015	.3343	.2972	.2507	.2229	.1672	.2229
	F_v	.211	.0078	.0104	.0117	.0078	.0078	.0078
	E	7,419	396	337	272	337	272	313
10x14 1015 lb/beam 33.8 lb/ft	F_b	4.740	.3160	.2809	.2370	.2107	.1580	.2107
	F_v	.162	.0058	.0078	.0088	.0058	.0058	.0058
	E	9,357	499	425	343	425	343	395
8x16 920 lb/beam 30.7 lb/ft	F_b	4.625	.3083	.2741	.2312	.2055	.1542	.2055
	F_v	.177	.0065	.0086	.0097	.0065	.0065	.0065
	E	7,831	418	356	287	356	287	331

29 FOOT SPAN (Continued)

Nominal Size (Inches)	Property	UNIFORM	CONCENTRATED Single Load — At Center of Span	Single Load — At Third Point	Single Load — At Quarter Point	Sum of Two Equal Loads — At Third Point	Sum of Two Equal Loads — At Quarter Points From Reactions	Sum of 3 Equal Loads — At Quarter Points and Center of Span
12x22 1892 lb/beam 65.2 lb/ft	F_b	1.520	.1048	.0932	.0786	.0699	.0524	.0699
	F_v	.077	.0030	.0040	.0046	.0030	.0030	.0030
	E	1,728	95	81	66	81	66	75
12x24 2068 lb/beam 71.3 lb/ft	F_b	1.284	.0886	.0787	.0664	.0590	.0443	.0590
	F_v	.070	.0028	.0037	.0042	.0028	.0028	.0028
	E	1,324	73	62	50	62	50	58

30 FOOT SPAN

Nominal Size (Inches)	Property	UNIFORM	CONCENTRATED Single Load — At Center of Span	Single Load — At Third Point	Single Load — At Quarter Point	Sum of Two Equal Loads — At Third Point	Sum of Two Equal Loads — At Quarter Points From Reactions	Sum of 3 Equal Loads — At Quarter Points and Center of Span
3x14 262 lb/beam 8.7 lb/ft	F_b	18.455	1.2303	1.0936	.9227	.8202	.6152	.8202
	F_v	.629	.0226	.0302	.0340	.0226	.0226	.0226
	E	37,606	2,006	1,709	1,379	1,709	1,379	1,588
4x12 312 lb/beam 10.4 lb/ft	F_b	18.286	1.2190	1.0836	.9143	.8127	.6095	.8127
	F_v	.536	.0190	.0254	.0286	.0190	.0190	.0190
	E	43,886	2,341	1,995	1,609	1,995	1,609	1,853
6x10 414 lb/beam 13.8 lb/ft	F_b	16.318	1.0879	.9670	.8159	.7253	.5439	.7253
	F_v	.408	.0144	.0191	.0215	.0144	.0144	.0144
	E	46,378	2,474	2,108	1,701	2,108	1,701	1,958
3x16 302 lb/beam 10.1 lb/ft	F_b	14.304	.9536	.8476	.7152	.6357	.4768	.6357
	F_v	.540	.0197	.0262	.0295	.0197	.0197	.0197
	E	24,666	1,316	1,121	904	1,121	904	1,041
4x14 367 lb/beam 12.2 lb/ft	F_b	13.182	.8788	.7812	.6591	.5859	.4394	.5859
	F_v	.449	.0162	.0216	.0243	.0162	.0162	.0162
	E	26,862	1,433	1,221	985	1,221	985	1,134
8x10 564 lb/beam 18.8 lb/ft	F_b	11.967	.7978	.7091	.5983	.5319	.3989	.5319
	F_v	.299	.0105	.0140	.0158	.0105	.0105	.0105
	E	34,011	1,814	1,546	1,247	1,546	1,247	1,436
6x12 501 lb/beam 16.7 lb/ft	F_b	11.136	.7424	.6599	.5568	.4949	.3712	.4949
	F_v	.333	.0119	.0158	.0178	.0119	.0119	.0119
	E	26,145	1,394	1,188	959	1,188	959	1,104

STRENGTH AND STIFFNESS REQUIREMENTS FOR BEAMS

See instructions for use of tables on page 101. Symbols used in the tables are as follows: Tabulated values are based on net size.

F_b = Extreme fiber stress in bending induced by a uniform load of 1 (one) plf or by a concentrated load of 1 (one) pound, psi

F_v = Horizontal shear stress induced by a uniform load of 1 (one) plf or a total concentrated load of 1 (one) pound, psi.

E = Modulus of elasticity value needed to limit deflection to 1/360 of the span for a uniform load of 1 (one) plf or a total concentrated load of 1 (one) pound, psi.

30 FOOT SPAN (Continued)

Nominal Size (Inches)	Property	Uniform	Single Load — At Center of Span	Single Load — At Third Point	Single Load — At Quarter Point	Sum of Two Equal Loads — At Third Point	Sum of Two Equal Loads — At Quarter Points From Reactions	Sum of 3 Equal Loads — At Quarter Points and Center of Span
6x20 849 lb/beam 28.3 lb/ft	F_b	4.090	2.727	2.424	2.045	1.818	1.363	1.818
	F_v	.187	.0070	.0093	.0105	.0070	.0070	.0070
	E	5,363	286	244	197	244	197	226
12x14 1229 lb/beam 41.0 lb/ft	F_b	3.916	2.610	2.320	1.958	1.740	1.305	1.740
	F_v	.134	.0048	.0064	.0072	.0048	.0048	.0048
	E	7,729	412	351	283	351	283	326
10x16 1166 lb/beam 38.9 lb/ft	F_b	3.651	2.434	2.164	1.826	1.623	1.217	1.623
	F_v	.140	.0051	.0068	.0076	.0051	.0051	.0051
	E	6,182	330	281	227	281	227	261
8x18 1039 lb/beam 34.6 lb/ft	F_b	3.677	2.452	2.179	1.839	1.634	1.226	1.634
	F_v	.155	.0057	.0076	.0086	.0057	.0057	.0057
	E	5,441	290	247	200	247	200	230
12x16 1411 lb/beam 47.0 lb/ft	F_b	3.016	2.011	1.787	1.508	1.341	1.005	1.341
	F_v	.115	.0042	.0056	.0063	.0042	.0042	.0042
	E	5,107	272	232	187	232	187	216
8x20 1158 lb/beam 38.6 lb/ft	F_b	2.999	1.999	1.777	1.500	1.333	1.000	1.333
	F_v	.137	.0051	.0068	.0077	.0051	.0051	.0051
	E	3,933	210	179	144	179	144	166
10x18 1316 lb/beam 43.9 lb/ft	F_b	2.903	1.935	1.720	1.452	1.290	.0968	1.290
	F_v	.122	.0045	.0060	.0068	.0045	.0045	.0045
	E	4,295	229	195	158	195	158	181
8x22 1277 lb/beam 42.6 lb/ft	F_b	2.493	1.662	1.478	1.247	1.108	.0831	1.108
	F_v	.123	.0047	.0062	.0070	.0047	.0047	.0047
	E	2,934	156	133	108	133	108	124
12x18 1593 lb/beam 53.1 lb/ft	F_b	2.398	1.599	1.421	1.199	1.066	.0799	1.066
	F_v	.101	.0037	.0050	.0056	.0037	.0037	.0037
	E	3,548	189	161	130	161	130	150
10x20 1467 lb/beam 48.9 lb/ft	F_b	2.368	1.579	1.403	1.184	1.052	.0789	1.052
	F_v	.108	.0040	.0054	.0061	.0040	.0040	.0040
	E	3,105	166	141	114	141	114	131
8x24 1395 lb/beam 46.5 lb/ft	F_b	2.107	1.405	1.249	1.054	.0937	.0702	.0937
	F_v	.111	.0043	.0057	.0064	.0043	.0043	.0043
	E	2,247	120	102	82	102	82	95
12x20 1775 lb/beam 59.2 lb/ft	F_b	1.956	1.304	1.159	.0978	.0869	.0652	.0869
	F_v	.089	.0033	.0045	.0050	.0033	.0033	.0033
	E	2,565	137	117	94	117	94	108
10x22 1617 lb/beam 53.9 lb/ft	F_b	1.969	1.312	1.167	.0984	.0875	.0656	.0875
	F_v	.097	.0037	.0049	.0055	.0037	.0037	.0037
	E	2,316	124	105	85	105	85	98
10x24 1767 lb/beam 58.9 lb/ft	F_b	1.664	1.109	.0986	.0832	.0739	.0555	.0739
	F_v	.088	.0034	.0045	.0050	.0034	.0034	.0034
	E	1,774	95	81	65	81	65	75
12x22 1957 lb/beam 65.2 lb/ft	F_b	1.626	1.084	.0964	.0813	.0723	.0542	.0723
	F_v	.080	.0030	.0040	.0046	.0030	.0030	.0030
	E	1,914	102	87	70	87	70	81
12x24 2139 lb/beam 71.3 lb/ft	F_b	1.374	.0916	.0814	.0687	.0611	.0458	.0611
	F_v	.072	.0028	.0037	.0042	.0028	.0028	.0028
	E	1,465	78	67	54	67	54	62

31 FOOT SPAN

Nominal Size (Inches)	Property	Uniform	Single Load — At Center of Span	Single Load — At Third Point	Single Load — At Quarter Point	Sum of Two Equal Loads — At Third Point	Sum of Two Equal Loads — At Quarter Points From Reactions	Sum of 3 Equal Loads — At Quarter Points and Center of Span
3x14 271 lb/beam 8.7 lb/ft	F_b	19.706	1.2713	1.1301	.9535	.8476	.6357	.8476
	F_v	.652	.0226	.0302	.0340	.0226	.0226	.0226
	E	41,494	2,142	1,825	1,472	1,825	1,472	1,695
4x12 322 lb/beam 10.4 lb/ft	F_b	19.525	1.2597	1.1197	.9448	.8398	.6298	.8398
	F_v	.555	.0190	.0254	.0286	.0190	.0190	.0190
	E	48,422	2,499	2,130	1,718	2,130	1,718	1,979
6x10 427 lb/beam 13.8 lb/ft	F_b	17.424	1.1242	.9992	.8431	.7494	.5621	.7494
	F_v	.422	.0144	.0191	.0215	.0144	.0144	.0144
	E	51,173	2,641	2,251	1,816	2,251	1,816	2,091
3x16 312 lb/beam 10.1 lb/ft	F_b	15.273	.9854	.8759	.7390	.6569	.4927	.6569
	F_v	.560	.0197	.0262	.0295	.0197	.0197	.0197
	E	27,216	1,405	1,197	966	1,197	966	1,112

STRENGTH AND STIFFNESS REQUIREMENTS FOR BEAMS

See instructions for use of tables on page 101. Symbols used in the tables are as follows: Tabulated values are based on net size.

F_b = Extreme fiber stress in bending induced by a uniform load of 1 (one) plf or by a concentrated load of 1 (one) pound, psi

F_v = Horizontal shear stress induced by a uniform load of 1 (one) plf or a total concentrated load of 1 (one) pound, psi.

E = Modulus of elasticity value needed to limit deflection to 1/360 of the span for a uniform load of 1 (one) plf or a total concentrated load of 1 (one) pound, psi.

31 FOOT SPAN

Nominal Size (Inches)	Property	UNIFORM	Single Load — At Center of Span	Single Load — At Third Point	Single Load — At Quarter Point	Sum of Two Equal Loads — At Third Point	Sum of Two Equal Loads — At Quarter Points From Reactions	Sum of 3 Equal Loads — At Quarter Points and Center of Span
12x12 1082 lb/beam 34.9 lb/ft	F_b	5.687	3669	3261	2752	2446	1834	2446
	F_v	.165	.0057	.0076	.0085	.0057	.0057	.0057
	E	13,797	712	607	490	607	490	564
6x18 787 lb/beam 25.4 lb/ft	F_b	5.354	3454	3071	2591	2303	1727	2303
	F_v	.219	.0078	.0104	.0117	.0078	.0078	.0078
	E	8,186	423	360	290	360	290	334
10x14 1049 lb/beam 33.8 lb/ft	F_b	5.061	3265	2903	2449	2177	1633	2177
	F_v	.168	.0058	.0078	.0088	.0058	.0058	.0058
	E	10,324	533	454	366	454	366	422
8x16 951 lb/beam 30.7 lb/ft	F_b	4.938	3186	2832	2389	2124	1593	2124
	F_v	.183	.0065	.0086	.0097	.0065	.0065	.0065
	E	8,640	446	380	307	380	307	353
6x20 877 lb/beam 28.3 lb/ft	F_b	4.367	2817	2504	2113	1878	1409	1878
	F_v	.194	.0070	.0093	.0105	.0070	.0070	.0070
	E	5,917	305	260	210	260	210	242
12x14 1270 lb/beam 41.0 lb/ft	F_b	4.181	2697	2398	2023	1798	1349	1798
	F_v	.139	.0048	.0064	.0072	.0048	.0048	.0048
	E	8,528	440	375	303	375	303	348
10x16 1205 lb/beam 38.9 lb/ft	F_b	3.899	2515	2236	1886	1677	1258	1677
	F_v	.145	.0051	.0068	.0076	.0051	.0051	.0051
	E	6,821	352	300	242	300	242	279
8x18 1074 lb/beam 34.6 lb/ft	F_b	3.927	2533	2252	1900	1689	1267	1689
	F_v	.160	.0057	.0076	.0086	.0057	.0057	.0057
	E	6,003	310	264	213	264	213	245
12x16 1458 lb/beam 47.0 lb/ft	F_b	3.221	2078	1847	1558	1385	1039	1385
	F_v	.120	.0042	.0056	.0063	.0042	.0042	.0042
	E	5,635	291	248	200	248	200	230
8x20 1196 lb/beam 38.6 lb/ft	F_b	3.202	2066	1837	1550	1377	1033	1377
	F_v	.142	.0051	.0068	.0077	.0051	.0051	.0051
	E	4,339	224	191	154	191	154	177
10x18 1360 lb/beam 43.9 lb/ft	F_b	3.100	2000	1778	1500	1333	1000	1333
	F_v	.127	.0045	.0060	.0068	.0045	.0045	.0045
	E	4,739	245	208	168	208	168	194

31 FOOT SPAN (Continued)

Nominal Size (Inches)	Property	UNIFORM	Single Load — At Center of Span	Single Load — At Third Point	Single Load — At Quarter Point	Sum of Two Equal Loads — At Third Point	Sum of Two Equal Loads — At Quarter Points From Reactions	Sum of 3 Equal Loads — At Quarter Points and Center of Span
4x14 379 lb/beam 12.2 lb/ft	F_b	14.076	9081	8072	6811	6054	4541	6054
	F_v	.466	.0162	.0216	.0243	.0162	.0162	.0162
	E	29,638	1,530	1,304	1,052	1,304	1,052	1,211
8x10 583 lb/beam 18.8 lb/ft	F_b	12.778	8244	7328	6183	5496	4122	5496
	F_v	.310	.0105	.0140	.0158	.0105	.0105	.0105
	E	37,527	1,937	1,651	1,332	1,651	1,332	1,533
6x12 517 lb/beam 16.7 lb/ft	F_b	11.891	7671	6819	5754	5114	3836	5114
	F_v	.345	.0119	.0158	.0178	.0119	.0119	.0119
	E	28,848	1,489	1,269	1,024	1,269	1,024	1,179
4x16 437 lb/beam 14.1 lb/ft	F_b	10.909	7038	6256	5279	4692	3519	4692
	F_v	.400	.0141	.0187	.0211	.0141	.0141	.0141
	E	19,440	1,003	855	690	855	690	794
10x10 738 lb/beam 23.8 lb/ft	F_b	10.088	6508	5785	4881	4339	3254	4339
	F_v	.244	.0083	.0111	.0125	.0083	.0083	.0083
	E	29,626	1,529	1,303	1,051	1,303	1,051	1,211
8x12 706 lb/beam 22.8 lb/ft	F_b	8.720	5626	5001	4219	3750	2813	3750
	F_v	.253	.0087	.0116	.0130	.0087	.0087	.0087
	E	21,155	1,092	931	751	931	751	864
6x14 607 lb/beam 19.6 lb/ft	F_b	8.742	5640	5013	4230	3760	2820	3760
	F_v	.290	.0101	.0135	.0152	.0101	.0101	.0101
	E	17,832	920	784	633	784	633	729
10x12 894 lb/beam 28.8 lb/ft	F_b	6.884	4441	3948	3331	2961	2221	2961
	F_v	.200	.0069	.0092	.0103	.0069	.0069	.0069
	E	16,701	862	735	593	735	593	682
6x16 697 lb/beam 22.5 lb/ft	F_b	6.734	4345	3862	3258	2896	2172	2896
	F_v	.250	.0088	.0117	.0132	.0088	.0088	.0088
	E	11,782	608	518	418	518	418	481
8x14 828 lb/beam 26.7 lb/ft	F_b	6.411	4136	3677	3102	2757	2068	2757
	F_v	.213	.0074	.0099	.0111	.0074	.0074	.0074
	E	13,077	675	575	464	575	464	534

STRENGTH AND STIFFNESS REQUIREMENTS FOR BEAMS

See instructions for use of tables on page 101. Symbols used in the tables are as follows: Tabulated values are based on net size.

F_b = Extreme fiber stress in bending induced by a uniform load of 1 (one) plf or by a concentrated load of 1 (one) pound, psi

F_v = Horizontal shear stress induced by a uniform load of 1 (one) plf or a total concentrated load of 1 (one) pound, psi.

E = Modulus of elasticity value needed to limit deflection to 1/360 of the span for a uniform load of 1 (one) plf or a total concentrated load of 1 (one) pound, psi.

32 FOOT SPAN

Nominal Size (Inches)	Property	UNIFORM	Single Load — At Center of Span	Single Load — At Third Point	Single Load — At Quarter Point	Sum of Two Equal Loads — At Third Point	Sum of Two Equal Loads — At Quarter Points From Reactions	Sum of 3 Equal Loads — At Quarter Points and Center of Span
3x14 280 lb/beam 8.7 lb/ft	F_b F_v E	20.998 .675 45,640	1.3124 .0226 2,282	1.1665 .0302 1,945	.9843 .0340 1,569	.8749 .0226 1,945	.6562 .0226 1,569	.8749 .0226 1,807
4x12 333 lb/beam 10.4 lb/ft	F_b F_v E	20.805 .574 53,261	1.3003 .0190 2,663	1.1558 .0254 2,270	.9752 .0286 1,831	.8669 .0190 2,270	.6502 .0190 1,831	.8669 .0190 2,108
6x10 441 lb/beam 13.8 lb/ft	F_b F_v E	18.567 .437 56,286	1.1604 .0144 2,814	1.0315 .0191 2,399	.8703 .0215 1,935	.7736 .0144 2,399	.5802 .0144 1,935	.7736 .0144 2,228
3x16 322 lb/beam 10.1 lb/ft	F_b F_v E	16.274 .580 29,935	1.0171 .0197 1,497	.9041 .0262 1,276	.7629 .0295 1,029	.6781 .0197 1,276	.5086 .0197 1,029	.6781 .0197 1,185
4x14 392 lb/beam 12.2 lb/ft	F_b F_v E	14.998 .482 32,600	.9374 .0162 1,630	.8332 .0216 1,389	.7030 .0243 1,121	.6249 .0162 1,389	.4687 .0162 1,121	.6249 .0162 1,290
8x10 602 lb/beam 18.8 lb/ft	F_b F_v E	13.616 .320 41,277	.8510 .0105 2,064	.7564 .0140 1,759	.6382 .0158 1,419	.5673 .0105 1,759	.4255 .0105 1,419	.5673 .0105 1,634
6x12 534 lb/beam 16.7 lb/ft	F_b F_v E	12.670 .357 31,731	.7919 .0119 1,587	.7039 .0158 1,352	.5939 .0178 1,091	.5279 .0119 1,352	.3959 .0119 1,091	.5279 .0119 1,256
4x16 451 lb/beam 14.1 lb/ft	F_b F_v E	11.625 .414 21,382	.7265 .0141 1,069	.6458 .0187 911	.5449 .0211 735	.4844 .0141 911	.3633 .0141 735	.4844 .0141 846
10x10 762 lb/beam 23.8 lb/ft	F_b F_v E	10.749 .253 32,587	.6718 .0083 1,629	.5972 .0111 1,389	.5039 .0125 1,120	.4479 .0083 1,389	.3359 .0083 1,120	.4479 .0083 1,290

31 FOOT SPAN (Continued)

Nominal Size (Inches)	Property	UNIFORM	Single Load — At Center of Span	Single Load — At Third Point	Single Load — At Quarter Point	Sum of Two Equal Loads — At Third Point	Sum of Two Equal Loads — At Quarter Points From Reactions	Sum of 3 Equal Loads — At Quarter Points and Center of Span
8x22 1319 lb/beam 42.6 lb/ft	F_b F_v E	2.662 .128 3,237	.1718 .0047 167	.1527 .0062 142	.1288 .0070 115	.1145 .0047 142	.0859 .0047 115	.1145 .0047 132
12x18 1646 lb/beam 53.1 lb/ft	F_b F_v E	2.561 .105 3,915	.1652 .0037 202	.1469 .0050 172	.1239 .0056 139	.1101 .0037 172	.0826 .0037 139	.1101 .0037 160
10x20 1515 lb/beam 48.9 lb/ft	F_b F_v E	2.528 .112 3,426	.1631 .0040 177	.1450 .0054 151	.1223 .0061 122	.1087 .0040 151	.0816 .0040 122	.1087 .0040 140
8x24 1442 lb/beam 46.5 lb/ft	F_b F_v E	2.250 .115 2,479	.1452 .0043 128	.1290 .0057 109	.1089 .0064 88	.0968 .0043 109	.0726 .0043 88	.0968 .0043 101
12x20 1834 lb/beam 59.2 lb/ft	F_b F_v E	2.089 .093 2,830	.1347 .0033 146	.1198 .0045 124	.1011 .0050 100	.0898 .0033 124	.0674 .0033 100	.0898 .0033 116
10x22 1671 lb/beam 53.9 lb/ft	F_b F_v E	2.102 .101 2,556	.1356 .0037 132	.1205 .0049 112	.1017 .0055 91	.0904 .0037 112	.0678 .0037 91	.0904 .0037 104
10x24 1826 lb/beam 58.9 lb/ft	F_b F_v E	1.776 .091 1,957	.1146 .0034 101	.1019 .0045 86	.0860 .0050 69	.0764 .0034 86	.0573 .0034 69	.0764 .0034 80
12x22 2023 lb/beam 65.2 lb/ft	F_b F_v E	1.736 .083 2,111	.1120 .0030 109	.0996 .0040 93	.0840 .0046 75	.0747 .0030 93	.0560 .0030 75	.0747 .0030 86
12x24 2211 lb/beam 71.3 lb/ft	F_b F_v E	1.468 .075 1,617	.0947 .0028 83	.0842 .0037 71	.0710 .0042 57	.0631 .0028 71	.0473 .0028 57	.0631 .0028 66

STRENGTH AND STIFFNESS REQUIREMENTS FOR BEAMS

See instructions for use of tables on page 101. Symbols used in the tables are as follows: Tabulated values are based on net size.

F_b = Extreme fiber stress in bending induced by a uniform load of 1 (one) plf or by a concentrated load of 1 (one) pound, psi

F_v = Horizontal shear stress induced by a uniform load of 1 (one) plf or a total concentrated load of 1 (one) pound, psi.

E = Modulus of elasticity value needed to limit deflection to 1/360 of the span for a uniform load of 1 (one) plf or a total concentrated load of 1 (one) pound, psi.

32 FOOT SPAN (Continued)

Nominal Size (Inches)	Property	UNIFORM	Single Load At Center of Span	Single Load At Third Point	Single Load At Quarter Point	Sum of Two Equal Loads At Third Point	Sum of Two Equal Loads At Quarter Points From Reactions	Sum of 3 Equal Loads At Quarter Points and Center of Span
8x12 728 lb/beam 22.8 lb/ft	F_b F_v E	9.291 .262 23,269	.5807 .0087 1,163	.5162 .0116 992	.4355 .0130 800	.3871 .0087 992	.2904 .0087 800	.3871 .0087 921
6x14 627 lb/beam 19.6 lb/ft	F_b F_v E	9.315 .301 19,614	.5822 .0101 981	.5175 .0135 836	.4367 .0152 674	.3881 .0101 836	.2911 .0101 674	.3881 .0101 776
10x12 923 lb/beam 28.8 lb/ft	F_b F_v E	7.335 .207 18,370	.4585 .0069 919	.4075 .0092 783	.3438 .0103 631	.3056 .0069 783	.2292 .0069 631	.3056 .0069 727
6x16 720 lb/beam 22.5 lb/ft	F_b F_v E	7.175 .259 12,959	.4485 .0088 648	.3986 .0117 552	.3363 .0132 445	.2990 .0088 552	.2242 .0088 445	.2990 .0088 513
8x14 855 lb/beam 26.7 lb/ft	F_b F_v E	6.831 .220 14,384	.4270 .0074 719	.3795 .0099 613	.3202 .0111 494	.2846 .0074 613	.2135 .0074 494	.2846 .0074 569
12x12 1117 lb/beam 34.9 lb/ft	F_b F_v E	6.060 .171 15,176	.3787 .0057 759	.3366 .0076 647	.2840 .0085 522	.2525 .0057 647	.1894 .0057 522	.2525 .0057 601
6x18 813 lb/beam 25.4 lb/ft	F_b F_v E	5.705 .227 9,004	.3566 .0078 450	.3170 .0104 384	.2674 .0117 310	.2377 .0078 384	.1783 .0078 310	.2377 .0078 356
10x14 1083 lb/beam 33.8 lb/ft	F_b F_v E	5.393 .174 11,356	.3371 .0058 568	.2996 .0078 484	.2528 .0088 390	.2247 .0058 484	.1685 .0058 390	.2247 .0058 449
8x16 982 lb/beam 30.7 lb/ft	F_b F_v E	5.262 .190 9,503	.3289 .0065 475	.2923 .0086 405	.2467 .0097 327	.2193 .0065 405	.1644 .0065 327	.2193 .0065 376
6x20 906 lb/beam 28.3 lb/ft	F_b F_v E	4.653 .201 6,508	.2908 .0070 325	.2585 .0093 277	.2181 .0105 224	.1939 .0070 277	.1454 .0070 224	.1939 .0070 258

Nominal Size (Inches)	Property	UNIFORM	Single Load At Center of Span	Single Load At Third Point	Single Load At Quarter Point	Sum of Two Equal Loads At Third Point	Sum of Two Equal Loads At Quarter Points From Reactions	Sum of 3 Equal Loads At Quarter Points and Center of Span
12x14 1311 lb/beam 41.0 lb/ft	F_b F_v E	4.455 .144 9,381	.2784 .0048 469	.2475 .0064 400	.2088 .0072 322	.1856 .0048 400	.1392 .0048 322	.1856 .0048 371
10x16 1243 lb/beam 38.9 lb/ft	F_b F_v E	4.154 .150 7,503	.2596 .0051 375	.2308 .0068 320	.1947 .0076 258	.1731 .0051 320	.1298 .0051 258	.1731 .0051 297
8x18 1108 lb/beam 34.6 lb/ft	F_b F_v E	4.184 .166 6,603	.2615 .0057 330	.2324 .0076 281	.1961 .0086 227	.1743 .0057 281	.1307 .0057 227	.1743 .0057 261
12x16 1505 lb/beam 47.0 lb/ft	F_b F_v E	3.432 .124 6,198	.2145 .0042 310	.1907 .0056 264	.1609 .0063 213	.1430 .0042 264	.1072 .0042 213	.1430 .0042 245
8x20 1235 lb/beam 38.6 lb/ft	F_b F_v E	3.412 .147 4,773	.2133 .0051 239	.1896 .0068 203	.1600 .0077 164	.1422 .0051 203	.1066 .0051 164	.1422 .0051 189
10x18 1404 lb/beam 43.9 lb/ft	F_b F_v E	3.303 .131 5,213	.2064 .0045 261	.1835 .0060 222	.1548 .0068 179	.1376 .0045 222	.1032 .0045 179	.1376 .0045 206
8x22 1362 lb/beam 42.6 lb/ft	F_b F_v E	2.837 .132 3,561	.1773 .0047 178	.1576 .0062 152	.1330 .0070 122	.1182 .0047 152	.0887 .0047 122	.1182 .0047 141
12x18 1699 lb/beam 53.1 lb/ft	F_b F_v E	2.729 .108 4,306	.1705 .0037 215	.1516 .0050 184	.1279 .0056 148	.1137 .0037 184	.0853 .0037 148	.1137 .0037 170
10x20 1564 lb/beam 48.9 lb/ft	F_b F_v E	2.694 .116 3,768	.1684 .0040 188	.1497 .0054 161	.1263 .0061 130	.1123 .0040 161	.0842 .0040 130	.1123 .0040 149
8x24 1488 lb/beam 46.5 lb/ft	F_b F_v E	2.398 .120 2,727	.1499 .0043 136	.1332 .0057 116	.1124 .0064 94	.0999 .0043 116	.0749 .0043 94	.0999 .0043 108
12x20 1894 lb/beam 59.2 lb/ft	F_b F_v E	2.225 .096 3,113	.1391 .0033 156	.1236 .0045 133	.1043 .0050 107	.0927 .0033 133	.0695 .0033 107	.0927 .0033 123

STRENGTH AND STIFFNESS REQUIREMENTS FOR BEAMS

See instructions for use of tables on page 101. Symbols used in the tables are as follows: Tabulated values are based on net size.

F_b = Extreme fiber stress in bending induced by a uniform load of 1 (one) plf or by a concentrated load of 1 (one) pound, psi

F_v = Horizontal shear stress induced by a uniform load of 1 (one) plf or a total concentrated load of 1 (one) pound, psi.

E = Modulus of elasticity value needed to limit deflection to 1/360 of the span for a uniform load of 1 (one) plf or a total concentrated load of 1 (one) pound, psi.

32 FOOT SPAN (Continued)

Nominal Size (Inches)	Property	UNIFORM	Single Load — At Center of Span	Single Load — At Third Point	Single Load — At Quarter Point	Sum of Two Equal Loads — At Third Point	Sum of Two Equal Loads — At Quarter Points From Reactions	Sum of 3 Equal Loads — At Quarter Points and Center of Span
10x22 1725 lb/beam 53.9 lb/ft	F_b	2.240	.1400	.1244	.1050	.0933	.0700	.0933
	F_v	.104	.0037	.0049	.0055	.0037	.0037	.0037
	E	2,811	141	120	97	120	97	111
10x24 1885 lb/beam 58.9 lb/ft	F_b	1.893	.1183	.1052	.0887	.0789	.0592	.0789
	F_v	.094	.0034	.0045	.0050	.0034	.0034	.0034
	E	2,153	108	92	74	92	74	85
12x22 2088 lb/beam 65.2 lb/ft	F_b	1.850	.1156	.1028	.0867	.0771	.0578	.0771
	F_v	.086	.0030	.0040	.0046	.0030	.0030	.0030
	E	2,322	116	99	80	99	80	92
12x24 2282 lb/beam 71.3 lb/ft	F_b	1.564	.0977	.0869	.0733	.0652	.0489	.0652
	F_v	.078	.0028	.0037	.0042	.0028	.0028	.0028
	E	1,778	89	76	61	76	61	70

DESIGN — PLANK AND LAMINATED FLOORS AND ROOFS

Plank or laminated decks may be adapted to floor and roof construction for residential, industrial, and other structures. Plank or laminated decks may be supported on joists or stringers, or they may be the principal supporting deck element spanning from beam to beam.

The design of plank decks used in residential construction differs somewhat from those used in industrial construction in that it is generally the stiffness of the decking rather than the fiber strength which determines the deck requirements. In industrial construction, deflection generally is not a limiting factor and it is the fiber strength which controls design.

Lumber Grades

Two factors determine the lumber grade requirements for plank and laminated floors and decks. Of these, one is the appearance desired when the deck is exposed to view. The larger growth characteristics inherent in the lower cost grades are sometimes desired for special rustic effect. The higher priced grades, with growth characteristics severely limited, are best adapted to more critical appearance requirements in exposed construction.

Strength is the remaining factor in grade selection, and high strength, which is associated with the higher priced stress-grades, is not usually required in the design of decks.

Lumber Sizes

Lumber, in the construction grades, is most readily available in multiples of two feet in length. It follows that plank and laminated deck spans of lengths that will utilize lumber to the even feet of length, with a minimum of trimming, will be the most economical.

Extra long lengths and a very large number of any one length are less economical to purchase than pieces 20 feet and less in length and a number of pieces of mixed lengths. This basic economic factor makes plank and laminated decks of random length pieces economically preferred. Details and span data, for the construction of plank and laminated spans using random lengths, are included in this chapter.

Plank Decks

Plank decks consist of pieces of dimension lumber laid with the wide faces bearing on supports and securely nailed to the supporting members. They may be square edged, shiplapped, center matched (T. & G.), or splined.

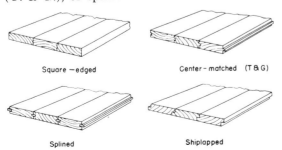

Square–edged   Center-matched (T & G)

Splined   Shiplapped

Figure 7.8—Plank Decks

Nailing Plank Decks

Where a deck consists of planking, each plank should be nailed to each supporting member. Where joints are over supports, both ends of the pieces must be nailed to the support. There are two ways of nailing planks to supporting members. When pieces employ a tongue and groove edge, they are customarily "blind-nailed"; that is, the nails are toe-nailed through the tongue. However, if the nominal width of the pieces is more than three times the nominal thickness, additional face nails should be added. When pieces are square edged or splined, face nailing is customarily used. Face nails may be vertical or slant driven. Nails that are driven at a slant may be expected to stay in place somewhat better than those driven vertically. Toe-nailing of square edged pieces to supporting members along the edges may also be used, but such nailing is not of general practice. Not less than two face nails should be used at each nailing point. Where extra withdrawal strength is desired, or where decks are subject to wetting and drying cycles, special deformed shank nails are recommended. The nails used for any type of plank nailing should be long enough to penetrate two-thirds of the length of the shank into the holding piece.

Laminated Decks

Laminated decks consist of square edged dimension lumber set on edge, side by side, with the laminations side-nailed to each other.

Nailing Laminated Decks

For laminated decks, strips are both side nailed and frequently toe-nailed. Side nails should be

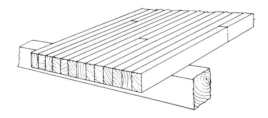

Figure 7.9—Laminated Deck.

long enough to penetrate two laminations and approximately half the thickness of the third. When the deck is supported on closely spaced stringers, 4'0" center to center or less, side nails should be spaced not more than 30 inches on centers and staggered one-third of the spacing in each adjacent lamination. When supported on widely spaced girders or beams, more than 4'0" center to center, side nails should be spaced approximately 18 inches on centers alternately near the upper and lower edges and also staggered one-third of the spacing in the adjacent lamination. Two side nails should be used at each end of butt-jointed pieces whenever supporting stringers or beams are more than 18 inches on

DESIGN — PLANK AND LAMINATED FLOORS AND ROOFS

centers. Laminations, with one exception, are toe-nailed to supporting members. When used, they should not be smaller than 20d common nails. With closely spaced stringers, every other lamination should be toe-nailed to every other stringer and with widely spaced girders or beams, every other lamination should be toe-nailed to each supporting member.

More data on nails may be found on pages 201 to 209.

Partition Loads

When partitions occur parallel to supporting beams but not over a beam, it is necessary to include the partition load in addition to other loads on the deck. Since partitions may produce concentrated loads, and may be anywhere on a span, it is impractical to provide tabular data for such loadings. Usually, supplementary supporting beams are provided under partitions.

Moving Loads

When moving loads are present, such as in warehouses and on docks, the maximum uniform live load is not likely to occur simultaneously with the moving load, since the moving load is generally along aisles. The moving load should be placed in a position to produce maximum stress and the required deck thickness determined. The maximum thickness as determined by moving loads or by other loads should then be used.

Span Types

Uniformly distributed loads are the loading most often associated with plank and laminated spans and the design considerations are primarily either bending stress in extreme fiber or a limiting deflection. For this reason, the basic formulas for determining bending moment, deflection and the tabular span data that are included in this chapter do not cover concentrated or moving loads.

Plank and laminated spans are customarily of four types. Though the arrangement of decking pieces in spanning between supports would vary the determination of maximum moment in a span, the formula:

$$M = \frac{wl^2}{8}$$

in which w = the total uniform load in pounds per square foot,

l = span between supports in feet,

is conservatively used for all of the span types listed herein.

The total deflection from a uniformly distributed load will vary proportionately more than will the moment because of the different arrangement of decking pieces.

The four types are illustrated, along with their distinguishing features and deflection formulas as follows:

Type 1—Simple Spans

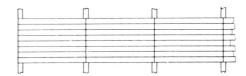

The arrangement of a simple span has planks or laminations bearing on two supports. The end joints between the decking pieces, when of two or more spans, are in line over each intermediate support making the decking pieces uniform in length.

With the simple span arrangement, larger deflections may be expected as compared to the other types. Deflection under uniform loads is determined by the formula:

$$\Delta = \frac{5wl^4}{384EI}$$

Type II—Two-Span Continuous

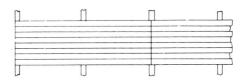

The limiting length of manufactured lumber limits span continuity to two spans or multiples of two spans unless the spans are quite short. Each continuous unit is made up of planks or laminations bearing on three equally spaced supports. The end joints between pieces, when of more than a single two span unit, are in line over every other support. This type requires pieces of uniform and long lengths.

Continuity reduces deflection so that this arrangement of decking pieces provides the stiffest deck of all and the formula for deflection under uniform loads is:

$$\Delta = \frac{wl^4}{185EI}$$

Type III—Combination Simple and Two-Span Continuous

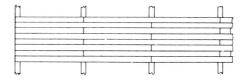

With the exception that every other piece in the end span is of single span length, all other decking pieces are two spans in length. End joints are over intermediate supports and are staggered in adjacent lines of deck pieces. This arrangement is best suited to three spans or any greater odd number of spans.

DESIGN — PLANK AND LAMINATED FLOORS AND ROOFS

The deflection for this type of arrangement is much less than that of a simple span under uniform loading. The deflection formula is:

$$\Delta = \frac{\mathrm{w}l^4}{110EI}$$

Type IV—Controlled Random

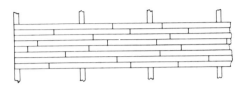

Economical, random lengths of plank or laminations having well scattered joints, and each plank or lamination bearing on at least one support, is the basic arrangement for this type. When random length pieces are used for plank floors or roofs, the edges of the planks should be joined by splines or matched (T. & G.) and for planks 2 inches in nominal thickness under uniform loads and for other thicknesses where concentrated loads may be applied, end joints should be similarly made or metal splines inserted at the ends so that loads may be distributed from end to end as well as across the planks. Metal splines used for end joints should be hot rolled steel of about 10 gauge, inserted with a driving fit into slots pre-cut across the ends of the piece. Special splines are sometimes used which may be driven without pre-cutting a slot. Splines should penetrate each piece not less than ¾ inch. Plank decks constructed of pieces 3 and 4 inches in nominal thickness are customarily side nailed at intervals in addition to side matching and when this procedure is used, end joining or metal splines may be omitted. Laminated decks are not side or end matched, as nailing in accordance with previous recommendations is sufficient. This type is mostly used on multiple spans and is perhaps the most economical.

For plank decks 2″ in thickness, the deflection formula for uniform loading is:

$$\Delta = \frac{\mathrm{w}l^4}{100EI}$$

For plank and laminated decks 3″ and thicker, the allowable tabulated loads for controlled random layup of decking, continuous over three or more spans, were obtained by multiplying the factor of 80% for bending and deflection by the allowable loads obtained from standard engineering formulas for a three-equal-span, continuous, uniformly loaded member. This percentage adjustment takes into account the differences between continuous decking without joints and the controlled random layup of decking as specified herein. This factor of 80% was selected after careful evaluation of tests and previous experience. When controlled random layup as specified herein is used for unequal spans, non-uniform loading, cantilever action, or conditions other than covered herein by the tabulated values, the same

adjustment factor for deflection should be applied to the allowable loads obtained from standard engineering formulas representing the actual conditions of load and span.

For plank and laminated decks 3″ and thicker, the deflection formula for uniform loading is:

$$\Delta = \frac{\mathrm{w}l^4}{116EI}$$

USE OF TABLES

The tables which conclude this chapter show uniform loads in pounds per square foot as limited by fiber stress in bending for normal conditions of loading, and loads as limited by a deflection of 1/180th, 1/240th and 1/360th of the span. The load will vary when allowable stresses are adjusted for other than normal durations of loading. See page 21. As the modulus of elasticity is a constant for all durations of loading, the allowable loading for deflection for a given deck thickness and span does not change, and may become the limiting value when deflection controls. Loads are tabulated for spans from 3 feet to 24 feet and depth of planks or laminations from 2 inches to 10 inches. All thicknesses are not represented for all spans because of impracticality. Computations are based on dimensions of lumber surfaced 4 sides (S4S).

The weight of a square foot of Douglas Fir and Larch decking with a maximum moisture content of 19 percent is shown beneath each tabulated thickness. Since Douglas Fir and Larch is the heaviest species group, its weight was tabulated to provide conservative results. For conversion of tabulated weights to other moisture contents and for other species, see page 3.

The tabulated values of load in pounds per square foot, as limited by fiber stress in bending, are the same for Types I, II, III and IV. The load as limited by a deflection of 1/180th, 1/240th and 1/360th of the span, differs for each type, and is based on initial deflection caused by the total load. Loads for other deflection ratios are proportionate. When deflection due to long time uniform loads needs to be limited, the load for the span must be adjusted for the effect of those loads. See page 73.

Deflection limitations for decking used for floors and roofs are normally based upon live load only, rather than total load as required for decking strength.

Determination of Load for Known Deck Thickness and Span

1. Locate the data for the span length desired and the species and grade to be used.

2. Locate the deck thickness in the column headed "Size (Nominal Depth)".

3. Across from the deck thickness and under the column "Limited by Bending", find the allowable uniform load for Fb = 1000 psi. Allowable bending loads for bending stress (Fb) values other than those tabulated may be determined

DESIGN — PLANK AND LAMINATED FLOORS AND ROOFS

by multiplying the tabulated load values by the grade and species F_b / 1000.

4. The loads causing a deflection of 1/180th, 1/240th and 1/360th of the span for a modulus of elasticity (E) of 1,000,000 psi are found under the column for the span type used and across from the nominal thickness of the deck. Allowable deflection loads for modulus of elasticity (E) values other than those tabulated may be determined by multiplying the tabulated values for E = 1,000,000 psi by the grade and species E/1,000,000. If one of these loads is to be used, it must not exceed the load as determined for bending, as such load will result in the deck being over stressed.

5. Subtract the weight of the deck from the allowable uniform total load to obtain the load which may be added to the deck.

EXAMPLE (1)

Given:
    Type IV deck Controlled random layup
    Thickness: 4 inches (nominal)
    Span: 12 feet
    Decking: DRY Commercial Douglas Fir and Larch
    Deflection: 1/240th of the span
Find capacity load:
    Turn to page 26 for proper grade and find:
        F_b = 1650 psi
        E = 1,700,000 psi
    Turn to page 168 for 4-inch, Type IV deck, 12-foot span and find:

    Bending load   = 113 psf
    Deflection load   = 83 psf
    Weight of deck   = 10.6 psf

Allowable bending load is:

$$113 \times \frac{1650}{1000} = 186.5 \text{ psf}$$

Bending load which may be carried in addition to the decking is:

$$186.5 \text{ psf} - 10.6 \text{ psf} = 175.9 \text{ psf}$$

Allowable total deflection load is:

$$83 \times \frac{1,700,000}{1,000,000} = 141.1 \text{ psf}$$

Deflection load which may be carried in addition to the decking is:

$$141.1 \text{ psf} - 10.6 \text{ psf} = 130.5 \text{ psf}$$

Since deflection controls load capacity, the load is limited to 130.5 psf.

Determination of Deck Thickness for Known Span and Load:

1. Locate the data for the span length desired and the species and grade to be used.

2. If the deflection is not a limitation, select a value for load Limited by Bending which, when multiplied by the species and grade Fb/1000

is slightly greater than the required capacity load.

3. Subtract the weight of the decking from the calculated load to obtain the capacity load. If the resultant capacity load is less than that required, repeat the procedure using the next higher calculated load value. The thickness shown in the column opposite the load value used is the thickness of deck required.

4. If deflection is a limiting factor, under the column for the span type used and for the deflection limitation imposed, select a value which, when multiplied by species and grade E / 1,000,000 is slightly greater than the known load and repeat the procedure of step 3.

The calculated load for deflection must not exceed the calculated load for bending as such load will result in the deck being over stressed in bending.

EXAMPLE (2)

Given:
    Type IV deck (Controlled random layup)
    Load: 125 lb. per sq. ft. (psf)
    Span: 10 feet
    Decking: DRY Commercial Hem-Fir
    Deflection: 1/240th of the span
Find thickness required:
    Turn to page 26 for proper grade and find:
        F_b = 1300 psi
        E = 1,400,000 psi
    Turn to page 168 for 3-inch, Type IV deck, 10-foot span and find:
        Bending load   = 83 psf
        Deflection Load   = 52 psf

Allowable Bending load is:

$$83 \times \frac{1300}{1000} = 107.9 \text{ psf}$$

Since this is less than the required 125 psf,
    Turn to page 168 for 4-inch, Type IV deck, 10-foot span and find:
        Bending load   = 163 psf
        Deflection load   = 144 psf
        Weight of deck   = 10.6 psf

Allowable bending load is:

$$163 \times \frac{1300}{1000} = 211.9 \text{ psf}$$

Bending load which may be carried in addition to the decking is:

211.9 psf − 10.6 psf = 201.3 psf (adequate for bending)

Allowable total deflection load is:

$$144 \times \frac{1,400,000}{1,000,000} = 201.6 \text{ psf}$$

Deflection load which may be carried in addition to the decking is:

201.6 psf − 10.6 psf = 191 psf (adequate for deflection)

Therefore: 4-inch thickness is required.

DESIGN — PLANK AND LAMINATED FLOORS AND ROOFS
PLANK AND LAMINATED SPANS — MAXIMUM LOADS
ALLOWABLE UNIFORMLY DISTRIBUTED TOTAL ROOF LOAD

SIZE (NOMINAL DEPTH)	LIMITED BY BENDING F_b = 1000 PSI LOAD, PSF ANY LAYUP (TYPES I, II, III, IV)	DEFLECTION RATIO	LIMITED BY DEFLECTION E = 1,000,000 PSI LOAD, PSF			
			SIMPLE SPAN TYPE I	TWO SPAN TYPE II	COMBINATION SIMPLE AND TWO SPAN TYPE III	CONTROLLED RANDOM TYPE IV
3'—0 SPAN						
2		1/180	370	892	530	482
	333	1/240	278	669	398	362
4.5 PSF		1/360	185	446	265	241
3		1/180	1,715	4,130	2,456	2,590
	926	1/240	1,286	3,098	1,842	1,942
7.6 PSF		1/360	857	2,065	1,228	1,295
4		1/180	4,705	11,334	6,739	7,107
	1,815	1/240	3,529	8,500	5,054	5,330
10.6 PSF		1/360	2,353	5,667	3,370	3,553
4'—0 SPAN						
2		1/180	156	376	224	203
	188	1/240	117	282	168	153
4.5 PSF		1/360	78	188	112	102
3		1/180	723	1,743	1,036	1,093
	521	1/240	543	1,307	777	819
7.6 PSF		1/360	362	871	518	546
4		1/180	1,985	4,781	2,843	2,998
	1,021	1/240	1,489	3,586	2,132	2,249
10.6 PSF		1/360	992	2,391	1,422	1,499
5'—0 SPAN						
2		1/180	80	193	115	104
	120	1/240	60	145	86	78
4.5 PSF		1/360	40	96	57	52
3		1/180	370	892	530	559
	333	1/240	278	669	398	420
7.6 PSF		1/360	185	446	265	280
4		1/180	1,016	2,448	1,456	1,535
	653	1/240	762	1,836	1,092	1,151
10.6		1/360	508	1,224	728	768
6'—0 SPAN						
2		1/180	46	112	66	60
	83	1/240	35	84	50	45
4.5 PSF		1/360	23	56	33	30
3		1/180	214	516	307	324
	231	1/240	161	387	230	243
7.6 PSF		1/360	107	258	153	162
4		1/180	588	1,417	842	888
	454	1/240	441	1,063	632	666
10.6 PSF		1/360	294	708	421	444
6		1/180	2,282	5,498	3,269	3,447
	1,120	1/240	1,712	4,123	2,452	2,585
16.6 PSF		1/360	1,141	2,749	1,634	1,724
7'—0 SPAN						
2		1/180	29	70	42	38
	61	1/240	22	53	31	28
4.5 PSF		1/360	15	35	21	19
3		1/180	135	325	193	204
	170	1/240	101	244	145	153
7.6 PSF		1/360	67	163	97	102
4		1/180	370	892	530	559
	333	1/240	278	669	398	420
10.6 PSF		1/360	185	446	265	280
6		1/180	1,437	3,462	2,059	2,171
	823	1/240	1,078	2,597	1,544	1,628
16.6 PSF		1/360	719	1,731	1,029	1,085
8'—0 SPAN						
2		1/180	20	47	28	25
	47	1/240	15	35	21	19
4.5 PSF		1/360	10	24	14	13
3		1/180	90	218	130	137
	130	1/240	68	163	97	102
7.6 PSF		1/360	45	109	65	68

DESIGN — PLANK AND LAMINATED FLOORS AND ROOFS
PLANK AND LAMINATED SPANS — MAXIMUM LOADS
ALLOWABLE UNIFORMLY DISTRIBUTED TOTAL ROOF LOAD

SIZE (NOMINAL DEPTH)	LIMITED BY BENDING F_b = 1000 PSI LOAD, PSF ANY LAYUP (TYPES I, II, III, IV)	DEFLECTION RATIO	LIMITED BY DEFLECTION E = 1,000,000 PSI LOAD, PSF SIMPLE SPAN TYPE I	TWO SPAN TYPE II	COMBINATION SIMPLE AND TWO SPAN TYPE III	CONTROLLED RANDOM TYPE IV
			**8'—0 SPAN (CONTINUED)**			
4		1/180	248	598	355	375
	255	1/240	186	448	267	281
10.6 PSF		1/360	124	299	178	187
6		1/180	963	2,319	1,379	1,454
	630	1/240	722	1,739	1,034	1,091
16.6 PSF		1/360	481	1,160	690	727
			9'—0 SPAN			
2		1/180	14	33	20	18
	37	1/240	10	25	15	13
4.5 PSF		1/360	7	17	10	9
3		1/180	64	153	91	96
	103	1/240	48	115	68	72
7.6 PSF		1/360	32	76	45	48
4		1/180	174	420	250	263
	202	1/240	131	315	187	197
10.6 PSF		1/360	87	210	125	132
6		1/180	676	1,629	969	1,021
	498	1/240	507	1,222	726	766
16.6 PSF		1/360	338	814	484	511
8		1/180	1,549	3,731	2,218	2,339
	865	1/240	1,162	2,798	1,664	1,755
22.7 PSF		1/360	774	1,865	1,109	1,170
			10'—0 SPAN			
2		1/180	10	24	14	13
	30	1/240	8	18	11	10
4.5 PSF		1/360	5	12	7	7
3		1/180	46	112	66	70
	83	1/240	35	84	50	52
7.6 PSF		1/360	23	56	33	35
4		1/180	127	306	182	192
	163	1/240	95	230	136	144
10.6 PSF		1/360	64	153	91	96
6		1/180	493	1,187	706	745
	403	1/240	370	891	530	558
16.6 PSF		1/360	246	594	353	372
8		1/180	1,129	2,720	1,617	1,705
	701	1/240	847	2,040	1,213	1,279
22.7 PSF		1/360	565	1,360	809	853
			11'—0 SPAN			
3		1/180	35	84	50	53
	69	1/240	26	63	37	39
7.6 PSF		1/360	17	42	25	26
4		1/180	95	230	137	144
	135	1/240	72	172	103	108
10.6 PSF		1/360	48	115	68	72
6		1/180	370	892	530	559
	333	1/240	278	669	398	420
16.6 PSF		1/360	185	446	265	280
8		1/180	848	2,043	1,215	1,281
	579	1/240	636	1,533	911	961
22.7 PSF		1/360	424	1,022	608	641
10		1/180	1,762	4,244	2,524	2,661
	943	1/240	1,321	3,183	1,893	1,996
28.7 PSF		1/360	881	2,122	1,262	1,331
			12'—0 SPAN			
3		1/180	27	65	38	40
	58	1/240	20	48	29	30
7.6 PSF		1/360	13	32	19	20
4		1/180	74	177	105	111
	113	1/240	55	133	79	83
10.6 PSF		1/360	37	89	53	56

DESIGN — PLANK AND LAMINATED FLOORS AND ROOFS
PLANK AND LAMINATED SPANS — MAXIMUM LOADS
ALLOWABLE UNIFORMLY DISTRIBUTED TOTAL ROOF LOAD

SIZE (NOMINAL DEPTH)	LIMITED BY BENDING F_b = 1000 PSI LOAD, PSF ANY LAYUP (TYPES I, II, III, IV)	DEFLECTION RATIO	LIMITED BY DEFLECTION E = 1,000,000 PSI LOAD, PSF SIMPLE SPAN TYPE I	TWO SPAN TYPE II	COMBINATION SIMPLE AND TWO SPAN TYPE III	CONTROLLED RANDOM TYPE IV
			**12'—0 SPAN (CONTINUED)**			
6		1/180	285	687	409	431
	280	1/240	214	515	306	323
16.6 PSF		1/360	143	344	204	215
8		1/180	653	1,574	936	987
	487	1/240	490	1,181	702	740
22.7 PSF		1/360	327	787	468	493
10		1/180	1,357	3,269	1,944	2,050
	792	1/240	1,018	2,452	1,458	1,537
28.7 PSF		1/360	679	1,635	972	1,025
			13'—0 SPAN			
3		1/180	21	51	30	32
	49	1/240	16	38	23	24
7.6 PSF		1/360	11	25	15	16
4		1/180	58	139	83	87
	97	1/240	43	104	62	66
10.6 PSF		1/360	29	70	41	44
6		1/180	224	540	321	339
	239	1/240	168	405	241	254
16.6 PSF		1/360	112	270	161	169
8		1/180	514	1,238	736	776
	415	1/240	385	929	552	582
22.7 PSF		1/360	257	619	368	388
10		1/180	1,067	2,571	1,529	1,612
	675	1/240	801	1,928	1,147	1,209
28.7 PSF		1/360	534	1,286	764	806
			14'—0 SPAN			
3		1/180	17	41	24	25
	43	1/240	13	30	18	19
7.6 PSF		1/360	8	20	12	13
4		1/180	46	112	66	70
	83	1/240	35	84	50	52
10.6 PSF		1/360	23	56	33	35
6		1/180	180	433	257	271
	206	1/240	135	325	193	204
16.6 PSF		1/360	90	216	129	136
8		1/180	411	991	589	622
	358	1/240	309	743	442	466
22.7 PSF		1/360	206	496	295	311
10		1/180	855	2,059	1,224	1,291
	582	1/240	641	1,544	918	968
28.7 PSF		1/360	427	1,029	612	645
			15'—0 SPAN			
3		1/180	14	33	20	21
	37	1/240	10	25	15	16
7.6 PSF		1/360	7	17	10	10
4		1/180	38	91	54	57
	73	1/240	28	68	40	43
10.6 PSF		1/360	19	45	27	28
6		1/180	146	352	209	221
	179	1/240	110	264	157	165
16.6 PSF		1/360	73	176	105	110
8		1/180	335	806	479	505
	311	1/240	251	604	359	379
22.7 PSF		1/360	167	403	240	253
10		1/180	695	1,674	995	1,049
	507	1/240	521	1,255	746	787
28.7 PSF		1/360	347	837	498	525
			16'—0 SPAN			
3		1/180	11	27	16	17
	33	1/240	8	20	12	13
7.6 PSF		1/360	6	14	8	9

DESIGN — PLANK AND LAMINATED FLOORS AND ROOFS
PLANK AND LAMINATED SPANS — MAXIMUM LOADS
ALLOWABLE UNIFORMLY DISTRIBUTED TOTAL ROOF LOAD

SIZE (NOMINAL DEPTH)	LIMITED BY BENDING F_b = 1000 PSI LOAD, PSF ANY LAYUP (TYPES I, II, III, IV)	DEFLECTION RATIO	LIMITED BY DEFLECTION E = 1,000,000 PSI LOAD, PSF			
			SIMPLE SPAN TYPE I	TWO SPAN TYPE II	COMBINATION SIMPLE AND TWO SPAN TYPE III	CONTROLLED RANDOM TYPE IV
16'—0 SPAN (CONTINUED)						
4	64	1/180	31	75	44	47
		1/240	23	56	33	35
10.6 PSF		1/360	16	37	22	23
6	158	1/180	120	290	172	182
		1/240	90	217	129	136
16.6 PSF		1/360	60	145	86	91
8	274	1/180	276	664	395	416
		1/240	207	498	296	312
22.7 PSF		1/360	138	332	197	208
10	446	1/180	573	1,379	820	865
		1/240	429	1,034	615	649
28.7 PSF		1/360	286	690	410	432
17'—0 SPAN						
3	29	1/180	9	23	13	14
		1/240	7	17	10	11
7.6 PSF		1/360	5	11	7	7
4	57	1/180	26	62	37	39
		1/240	19	47	28	29
10.6 PSF		1/360	13	31	19	20
6	140	1/180	100	242	144	152
		1/240	75	181	108	114
16.6 PSF		1/360	50	121	72	76
8	243	1/180	230	554	329	347
		1/240	172	415	247	260
22.7 PSF		1/360	115	277	165	174
10	395	1/180	477	1,150	684	721
		1/240	358	862	513	541
28.7 PSF		1/360	239	575	342	360
18'—0 SPAN						
4	50	1/180	22	52	31	33
		1/240	16	39	23	25
10.6 PSF		1/360	11	26	16	16
6	124	1/180	85	204	121	128
		1/240	63	153	91	96
16.6 PSF		1/360	42	102	61	64
8	216	1/180	194	466	277	292
		1/240	145	350	208	219
22.7 PSF		1/360	97	233	139	146
10	352	1/180	402	969	576	607
		1/240	302	726	432	456
28.7 PSF		1/360	201	484	288	304
19'—0 SPAN						
4	45	1/180	19	45	27	28
		1/240	14	33	20	21
10.6 PSF		1/360	9	22	13	14
6	112	1/180	72	173	103	109
		1/240	54	130	77	81
16.6 PSF		1/360	36	87	51	54
8	194	1/180	165	397	236	249
		1/240	123	297	177	186
22.7 PSF		1/360	82	198	118	124
10	316	1/180	342	824	490	516
		1/240	256	618	367	387
28.7 PSF		1/360	171	412	245	258
20'—0 SPAN						
4	41	1/180	16	38	23	24
		1/240	12	29	17	18
10.6 PSF		1/360	8	19	11	12
6	101	1/180	62	148	88	93
		1/240	46	111	66	70
16.6 PSF		1/360	31	74	44	47

DESIGN — PLANK AND LAMINATED FLOORS AND ROOFS
PLANK AND LAMINATED SPANS — MAXIMUM LOADS
ALLOWABLE UNIFORMLY DISTRIBUTED TOTAL ROOF LOAD

SIZE (NOMINAL DEPTH)	LIMITED BY BENDING F_b = 1000 PSI LOAD, PSF ANY LAYUP (TYPES I, II, III, IV)	DEFLECTION RATIO	LIMITED BY DEFLECTION E = 1,000,000 PSI LOAD, PSF			
			SIMPLE SPAN TYPE I	TWO SPAN TYPE II	COMBINATION SIMPLE AND TWO SPAN TYPE III	CONTROLLED RANDOM TYPE IV
20'—0 SPAN (CONTINUED)						
8		1/180	141	340	202	213
	175	1/240	106	255	152	160
22.7 PSF		1/360	71	170	101	107
10		1/180	293	706	420	443
	285	1/240	220	530	315	332
28.7 PSF		1/360	147	353	210	221
21'—0 SPAN						
4		1/180	14	33	20	21
	37	1/240	10	25	15	16
10.6 PSF		1/360	7	17	10	10
6		1/180	53	128	76	80
	91	1/240	40	96	57	60
16.6 PSF		1/360	27	64	38	40
8		1/180	122	294	175	184
	159	1/240	91	220	131	138
22.7 PSF		1/360	61	147	87	92
10		1/180	253	610	363	382
	259	1/240	190	457	272	287
28.7 PSF		1/360	127	305	181	191
22'—0 SPAN						
4		1/180	12	29	17	18
	34	1/240	9	22	13	14
10.6 PSF		1/360	6	14	9	9
6		1/180	46	112	66	70
	83	1/240	35	84	50	52
16.6 PSF		1/360	23	56	33	35
8		1/180	106	255	152	160
	145	1/240	80	192	114	120
22.7 PSF		1/360	53	128	76	80
10		1/180	220	531	315	333
	236	1/240	165	398	237	249
28.7 PSF		1/360	110	265	158	166
23'—0 SPAN						
6		1/180	41	98	58	61
	76	1/240	30	73	44	46
16.6 PSF		1/360	20	49	29	31
8		1/180	93	224	133	140
	132	1/240	70	168	100	105
22.7 PSF		1/360	46	112	66	70
10		1/180	193	464	276	291
	216	1/240	145	348	207	218
28.7 PSF		1/360	96	232	138	146
24'—0 SPAN						
6		1/180	36	86	51	54
	70	1/240	27	64	38	40
16.6 PSF		1/360	18	43	26	27
8		1/180	82	197	117	123
	122	1/240	61	148	88	93
22.7 PSF		1/360	41	98	58	62
10		1/180	170	409	243	256
	198	1/240	127	306	182	192
28.7 PSF		1/360	85	204	121	128

DESIGN — LATERAL FORCES

By — HENRY J. DEGENKOLB and LORING A. WYLLIE, JR.

Henry J. Degenkolb is President of H. J. Degenkolb & Associates, Consulting Engineers, San Francisco, California. Mr. Degenkolb is a recognized authority in the field of structural engineering and is the author of many papers in the general area of earthquake resistant design of structures. Mr. Degenkolb has received numerous awards from engineering and construction organizations and serves as a consultant to many Boards and governmental agencies on structural and earthquake engineering matters.

Loring A. Wyllie, Jr., is an Associate in the San Francisco firm of H. J. Degenkolb & Associates and is a licensed civil and structural engineer in California. Mr. Wyllie is active on the Building Codes Committees of the Structural Engineers Association of Northern California and the American Concrete Institute and is an Instructor in the University of California's engineering extension program.

Winds and earthquakes are the two phenomena commonly associated with lateral forces, but there are other ways by which a lateral force can be imposed on buildings, structures, or their structural elements. Blast, for example, is a force that might combine in one action the types of forces caused by winds and earthquakes. Horizontal loads caused by moving cranes are another. In this chapter on lateral force design, only wind and earthquake forces will be discussed, and the design requirements to resist these forces will be related to buildings. However, the principles and data can be applied to the resistance requirements for any other similar loading and for any other structure. The probable magnitude of both wind and earthquake forces is covered in some detail on pages 38 to 45.

For wind or earthquake type of loading, structural design assumes these lateral forces as loads acting horizontally. The true orientation of such uncontrolled forces is from any direction, but for convenience of the designer, forces are usually considered to act along both major axes of the structure.

Wind pressures load the surfaces of structures, but earthquake forces are generated by the inertia of the masses of structures so that each plane of lateral force resistance accumulates its own generated load and the planes of lateral resistance support other planes. In addition to providing adequately for stresses, planes of lateral resistance must have sufficient rigidity so that deflections and their effects on walls are limited to prevent failure of friable or other materials attached or supported.

Methods of Resisting Lateral Forces

There are two basic methods of providing for the horizontal forces created by the earthquake ground motion or wind. In specific structures, the designer may choose one method or the other depending upon conditions, but, because of specific utilitarian requirements it is probable that combinations of both methods will be required in many structures. In both methods, the designer must consider the manner in which lateral loads are to be transferred to the foundation of the structure. Since each structural member must have the strength to resist the applied load, as well as being able to transfer those loads to adjoining elements, the connections between adjoining elements are particularly important. Con-

sequently, care must be taken when designing structural connections so the overall structure will perform as designed. For simplicity here, we will consider only each specific method and not the combination. The first method resists these forces through moment connections or knee braces as illustrated in Figure 7.10. This is typical of many types of mill structures, light sheds and other places where shear walls cannot be used for architectural or utilitarian reasons. The forces are carried to the ground through bending of the columns and girders. This bending resistance must be developed at the joints.

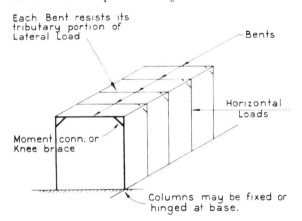

Fig. No. 7.10

This method has the advantage that large open spaces can be created without interference from permanent bracing walls. It is often forced upon the engineer in order to achieve the open effect of large glass areas prevalent in modern architecture. The framing can absorb large amounts of energy and can probably withstand a larger earthquake with less chance of total collapse than any other type of framing. It has two major disadvantages. In general, it is a more expensive method of framing since the member sizes are often larger than those required by vertical loads alone and the connections are more complicated and hence more expensive. However, its major disadvantage lies in the fact that it is usually somewhat flexible. This flexibility denies the proper support of the more expensive finishes common to many of our buildings. Plaster, tile,

DESIGN — LATERAL FORCES

masonry, and veneers of all types are usually quite rigid and brittle and must be supported with a minimum of deflection. Examples of this type of framing are illustrated in Figure 7.11. In the three systems of bent framing shown, the columns are restrained from rotation either at the bottom by fixing to the foundation or at the top by knee braces, or rigid connections to trusses, or a combination of fixity at both top and bottom. The columns of bents must be designed for combined compression and bending stresses and trusses or girders must be designed for the stresses induced by the lateral loads as well as the vertical loads.

The second basic method of providing for lateral forces is through shear walls and diaphragms. The action in this method, illustrated in Figure 7.12, resembles the action of a box. In most cases, this is the most economical method of providing for lateral forces. It is by far the stiffest method and therefore gives the best protection against property damage especially to brittle finishes such as plaster. Its economy lies in the fact that it utilizes building components such as walls, roofs and floors already provided in the building. This method of bracing, used in the vast majority of small buildings and frequently in buildings of large area, will comprise the primary discussion of this chapter.

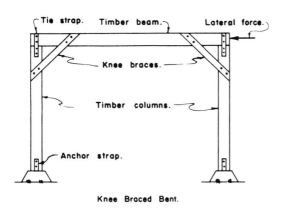

Knee Braced Bent.

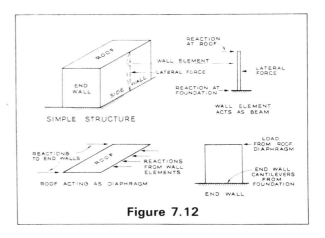

Figure 7.12

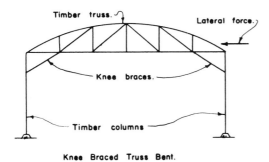

Knee Braced Truss Bent.

Consider the idealized simple structure shown in Figure 7.12, where we have a simple, box-like, one-story structure. The inertia loads of the side walls (or wind pressure and suction in the case of wind) act on the walls. The wall framing spans from the foundation to the roof as a beam and must be designed as such in addition to the column action due to the vertical loads in the roof. The top of the wall thereby produces horizontal loads against the roof framing. The wall must be attached to the roof framing strongly enough to resist the forces involved. The roof framing now acts as a large girder taking the horizontal reactions of the walls and the roof's own inertia horizontal loads. This "girder" spans to the end walls which must resist these reactions, through shear and overturning and carry the reactions to the foundation structure.

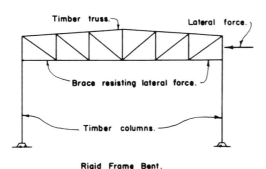

Rigid Frame Bent.

Figure 7.11— Bents resisting lateral forces by column bending.

The roof system that carries these loads is called the diaphragm. In some cases, it is actually framed with diagonal rods or struts to form a bracing truss as shown in Figure 7.13, which is the only case generally considered in engineering literature. From observation, tests, and considerable engineering intuition, the custom has developed of using the actual roof framing, that is, the wood or plywood sheathing, to serve as the structural element to resist these lateral loads. Considering this roof diaphragm as a girder with the external loads shown, we see that there are the usual shear and moment forces to resist.

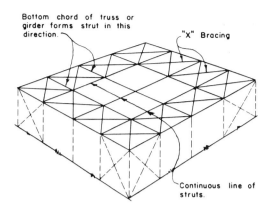

Figure 7.13—Multiple Horizontal "X" Bracing.

Generally, chords are provided to resist the moment stresses. The roof material itself resists the shear stresses.

The following pages will deal with a detailed discussion of various types of floor and roof diaphragms. Walls acting as vertical diaphragms or bracing elements, more commonly referred to as shear walls, will also be discussed. This chapter will first discuss straight, diagonally and double diagonally sheathed lumber diaphragms as they were the original standard methods of engineered wood structures. Plywood diaphragms, which are more commonly used today, will then be discussed. The extension of the concepts developed for horizontal diaphragms will then be applied to shear walls along with the unique features of these bracing elements.

Lumber Built Diaphragms

While trusses, bents and "X" bracing are subject to conventional methods of analysis, and the design of the individual members is covered elsewhere in this book, wood diaphragms are not subject to conventional design procedures. As existing literature on this subject is limited in availability, the remainder of this chapter is devoted to the design of wood diaphragms.

A diaphragm is essentially a cantilever or a beam, depending on its function in the structure. Diaphragms differ from conventional cantilevers or beams in that they have a great deal of depth as compared to their length and they are very thin in cross-section.

The parts of lumber built diaphrams that are of design importance include:
    Sheathing or decking,
    Studs, joists or beams,
    Perimeter members for some types,
    Splices of perimeter members,
    Corner details.

Sheathing or Decking

The sheathing or decking for roof, floor and all wall diaphragms may be of several types depending on the size of the building, the magnitude of the lateral forces, or other functions to be performed.

One inch nominal boards, 6 inches to 8 inches

DESIGN — LATERAL FORCES

wide, either square edged, ship-lapped or tongue and grooved, are most used for lumber sheathing. These boards are supported on studding or joists spaced 12", 16", 18" or 24" on centers. Planks of 2 inch and greater nominal thickness are used the same as boards for roof or floor decking, but are usually supported on beams spaced much wider apart than conventional joist spacing. Laminated walls, floors and decks, usually consisting of 2 inch dimension lumber nailed together with wide face to wide face are often used, not only for their excellent strength and rigidity, but also for the fire resistive characteristics of heavy timber construction plus the thermal insulation provided.

Straight Sheathing

One inch nominal boards may be placed in a single layer, as transverse sheathing, laid at right angles to the direction of the studs or joists. Sheathing placed in this fashion is also called "horizontal sheathing" or "transverse sheathing."

Straight sheathed diaphragms are limited in effectiveness because the strength and stiffness depends on the resistance furnished by the nail couples. This type of diaphragm is suitable for light loads and where lateral deflections are not important. The perimeter members serve only as boundary pieces, but are sometimes doubled for ease of connection to other planes. As the diaphragm strength depends on the resistance of the nail couples, it is necessary that each board be nailed at each stud or joist crossing with two nails. Using three nails does not increase the resistance because the board tends to rotate about the center nail. Generally, 8_d common nails are used with one inch lumber. The use of 10_d common nails will increase the stiffness by about 30 per cent and the strength by about 20 per cent. If four nails per board are used, the strength and stiffness are increased by about 30 per cent. However, a greater gain in strength and stiffness can be achieved, and probably more economically, by applying the sheathing diagonally in lieu of the extra nailing. The span-width and height-width ratios of straight sheathed horizontal and vertical diaphragms will depend on the amount of deflection that can be permitted. The tables concluding this chapter give suggested allowable lineal shear loads for transversely sheathed diaphragms, and are based on the following design procedure which may be used where conditions warrant and codes do not otherwise limit the construction.

For horizontal diaphragms, the moment capacity, formed by the nail couple where each board crosses a joist, is obtained by multiplying the lateral strength for the size of nail used, by the distance between nails in the same board. See Figure 7.14. Dividing this moment by the joist spacing gives the end reaction or shear load per board width. This in turn is multiplied by the ratio of the net-width of the board to one foot, which gives the allowable end reaction or shear load in pounds per lineal foot.

For vertical diaphragms, the nail couple is computed the same as for horizontal diaphragms. The

DESIGN — LATERAL FORCES

resisting moment furnished by the nail couple is the moment per board per stud spacing. Multiplying the moment due to the nail couple by the

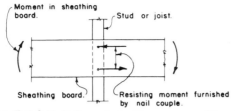

Figure 7.14 Nail Couple in Transverse Sheathing

number of boards in the height of the diaphragm gives the total moment capacity per stud spacing. Since the lateral load is applied to the top of a vertical diaphragm, this load and the resisting force at the foundation form a couple having a lever arm equal to the height of the diaphragm. Dividing the moment capacity from the nail couples by the wall height gives the lateral load capacity in pounds per stud spacing. This can be converted to pounds per lineal foot by dividing by the stud spacing in feet. As the load capacity and stiffness of a vertical diaphragm with transverse sheathing is quite low compared to other types of sheathing, it is suggested that let-in braces be used to increase the strength and stiffness of this type of diaphragm.

Diagonal Sheathing

When diaphragms are sheathed diagonally at an angle of about 45°, great strength and stiffness results because of the triangulated structural system. The sheathing boards are primarily either in direct tension or compression and the tension or compression forces are transmitted from the boards to the studs or joists by the lateral strength of the nails at each crossing. Hence, the strength and stiffness imparted by the diagonal sheathing is determined by the number of nails at each crossing. Although diagonally sheathed diaphragms are stiffer when the sheathing boards are in tension, they must be designed to resist forces from either direction.

Tests have shown that stress concentrations are greater at the corners of conventional, diagonally sheathed diaphragms when the perimeter members are limber. This is because there is a redistribution of the stresses in the diaphragm that concentrates the forces at the more rigid corner assembly. To compensate for this concentration when perimeter members are of small cross-section as related to the size of the diaphragm, and lacking more specific data, it is suggested that the nailing of the sheathing boards at the corners be doubled over that which would seem to be adequate by analysis. However, it is likely that this condition will only occur when the tabulated ratio of diaphragm proportions herein are exceeded.

Where the lateral force produces compression in the diagonal sheathing, an outward thrust is exerted by the sheathing on the perimeter. For this reason, corner connections of perimeter members must be reinforced to prevent separation, and the ends of cross members, such as studs, joists, etc., must be secured to the perimeter members to prevent separation of the boundary pieces from the cross members. In the case of walls, the imposed dead load of upper floors or a roof may be greater than the vertical component of the thrust from the diagonal sheathing, making a special connection between the ends of the studs and the plates unnecessary. The outward or inward thrust from sheathing boards in compression or in tension, introduces bending stresses in the perimeter members in addition to the axial stresses accruing from their position as flange members or end posts under beam action. When the tabulated diaphragm proportions of the load exceed the recommendations, or where deflections must be restricted to less than provided by conventional, diagonally sheathed diaphragms, the perimeter members should be designed for these axial and bending stresses as outlined on page 180.

A conventional, diagonally sheathed cantilever diaphragm, such as a wall, will have a stiffness that is related to the length of the cantilever l and the breadth of the base "b." Comparing other panel proportions to one that is square, $l/b = 1$, it has been found that a panel having a base that is twice the length of the cantilever, $l/b = \frac{1}{2}$, will be at least three times stiffer, and if the length of the cantilever is twice that of the base, $l/b = 2$, the stiffness will be about ¼ of that of the square panel. See Figure 7.15.

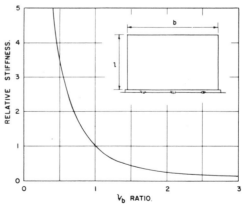

Figure 7.15 Effect of Height-Width Ratio on Stiffness

The direct tension and compression stresses in diagonal sheathing are greatest at the perimeters of diaphragms and the fastenings must be sufficient to transfer these stresses. To ascertain the requirements for nailing sheathing boards to the perimeter, the direct stress per board is derived from the end reaction of horizontal diaphragms, or the lateral load on vertical diaphragms, by converting the shear load per board to the component of this shear acting parallel to the length of the board. This is illustrated in Figure 7.16. For example; with diagonal 1" x 8" shiplap

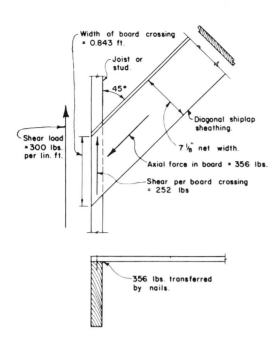

Figure 7.16—Forces in Diagonal Sheathing.

sheathing, which has a net face width of 7⅛ inches, and with an end reaction or lateral load of 300 lbs. per lineal foot, the shear per board crossing at 45° along the perimeter is

$$300 \times \frac{7⅛}{12 \times \sin 45°} = 252 \text{ lbs.}$$

The direct stress per sheathing board is, therefore,

$$\frac{252}{\sin 45°} = 356 \text{ lbs.}$$

DESIGN — LATERAL FORCES

The perimeter nailing must be sufficient to resist this stress, and for 8d nails adjusted for duration of load and multiple nailing, (the multiple nailing factor is explained on page 181), to 135 pounds per nail in lateral strength, the number of nails per board would be

$$\frac{356}{135} = 2.64 \text{ or 3 nails.}$$

Placing the sheathing in a herring-bone pattern, see Figure 7.17, will provide symmetry in panel action and deflection, but is designed the same as for sheathing placed diagonally in one direction only.

Figure 7.17 illustrates the type of diaphragm which uses ordinary board sheathing placed diagonally to the rafters or joists. Here the roof is spanned in the short direction by roof rafters, while sheathing boards span the space between rafters at a 45° angle. Again, the continuous chords on the long sides resist the moment forces, while the diagonal sheathing resists the shear forces. As shown in Figure 7.17, the sheathing boards are in tension, but since lateral loads may come from any direction, the loading can be reversed and the boards would be in compression. Although there may be considerable bending in the sheathing boards, tests verify that the primary load resistance in an efficient diaphragm is due to the axial stress in the sheathing boards and the nailing is calculated from this axial stress. As may be seen from Figure 7.17, there is a component of stress perpendicular to the end posts that creates a bending stress. The end posts must be connected to the longitudinal chords adequately to resist this stress component. There

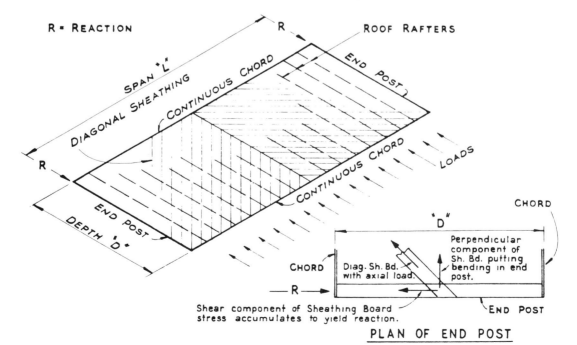

Figure 7.17—Diagonal Sheathing with Rafters Parallel to Lateral Loads

DESIGN — LATERAL FORCES

are similar bending components perpendicular to the long continuous chords, but as in this example, the effect is usually minor because of the comparatively small spacing between rafters, which resist these perpendicular components.

Figure 7.18 shows a most common method of framing a roof which, to date, has not been tested except for one full size test in Los Angeles in 1952. However, by comparison with tests on the diaphragm shown in Figure 7.17, the following inferences may be drawn: The loads from the side walls are delivered to the longitudinal girts which span to the trusses. The end reactions of the girts are delivered through the trusses to the diaphragm, usually through blocking over the truss chords. The girts are spliced for axial load to provide chords to resist the moments on the diaphragm as a whole. The shears on the diaphragm are resisted by the sheathing boards, again primarily by their axial loads, similar to those illustrated in Figure 7.17.

In this case, the force components causing major bending stresses in boundary members occur at the girts. It can be seen in the figure that as the sheathing boards take their axial tensions as shown here, the girts are pulled inward, similar to the end posts of Figure 7.17 and must be designed for this bending force. The axial forces from the sheathing at the end walls also tends to pull these walls in, but here the span is only between purlins. The purlins should be spliced throughout the length of the diaphragm to balance the similar forces at the opposite end of the building.

Dougle Diagonal Sheathing

A substantial increase in strength and stiffness will result when two layers of diagonal sheathing are applied with the boards of one layer at an angle of 90° to the boards in the other as shown in Figure 7.18. When double diagonal sheathing is used, the outward forces on the perimeter members from that portion of the sheathing in compression, are counteracted by the inward forces from that portion of the sheathing in tension. This counter relieves the perimeter members of bending stresses, leaving only the axial stresses from their position as flanges.

The capacity and stiffness of double diagonally sheathed diaphragms depends on the lateral strength of the nails and on the capacity of the perimeter members to resist axial stresses.

The shear load along the perimeter members is divided equally between the two layers of double diagonally sheathed diaphragms and the shear per board crossing, per layer, is computed in the same manner as for single diagonally sheathed diaphragms. The distribution of the shear loads from layer to layer of the sheathing affects the nailing requirements of each layer to the perimeter members. The nailing of the bottom layer of boards to the perimeter must be sufficient to transfer the sum of the shears per board crossing from the two layers to the perimeter member. The nailing of the top layer of boards to the bottom layer along the perimeter need only be sufficient to fulfill the requirements of the axial stress component of the shear per board crossing

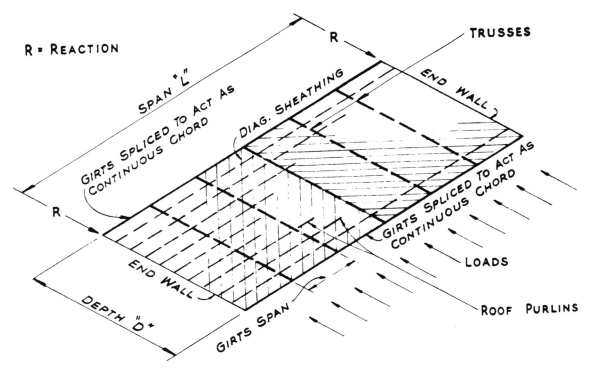

Figure 7.18—Diagonal Sheathing with Purlins Perpendicular to Lateral Loads

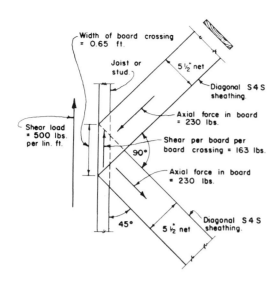

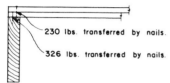

Figure 7.19 — Forces in Double Diagonal Sheathing.

DESIGN — LATERAL FORCES

The end nailing of each board of the bottom layer to the perimeter members, using 8d common nails at 135 lbs. per nail in lateral resistance, and with the nailing sufficient for the shear of the top layer also, is

$$2 \times \frac{163}{135} = 2.4 \text{ or } 3 \text{ nails.}$$

The axial force in the top layer is

$$\frac{163}{\sin 45°} = 230 \text{ lbs.}$$

and the end nailing of each board using 8d nails is

$$\frac{230}{135} = 1.7 \text{ or } 2 \text{ nails.}$$

The nailing area in the perimeter members should be sufficient to accommodate the required number of nails. If the area is too limited for a large number of small nails, a lesser number of larger nails could be used.

Laminated Diaphragms

Diaphragms of 2 inch dimension lumber, spiked together face-to-face, will provide strength, stiffness, thermal insulation, sound insulation and fire resistivity. Because of the large cross-sectional area, unit stresses from all loadings are small, and inexpensive, low-grade lumber can usually be used.

For walls, the laminations are laid horizontally, with pieces laid flat on top of each other. The shear resistance to lateral forces is through the spikes that fasten laminations together. The lateral load at the top of the wall will determine the number of nails required in lateral strength and the desired deflection limitation, for any lamination layer from the top to the bottom. If loading is also accumulated from the top to the

in the top layer. In the example, Figure 7.19, the shear per board crossing for each layer of 1" x 6" S4S boards, at a shear load of 500 lbs. per lineal ft. along the perimeter, is

$$\frac{500}{2} \times \frac{5\frac{1}{2}}{12 \times \sin 45°} = 163 \text{ lbs.}$$

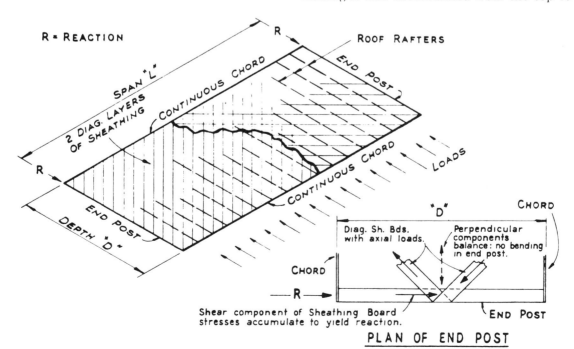

Figure 7.20 — Double Diagonal Sheathing

DESIGN — LATERAL FORCES

bottom, additional nails will need to be added progressively from the top to the bottom of the wall.

At some ratio of height of wall to length of base, the overturning moment can produce an upward force at the end of a wall that exceeds the withdrawal strength of a spike at this point. When this is the case a tie-down from the top of the wall, anchored to the foundation, must be provided at each end.

For a tall wall on a short base, a laminated wall can be designed and built with the laminations stacked vertically. Separation of laminations by overturning moment is avoided and the lumber is used more efficiently to resist lateral forces. This sort of wall is designed as a cantilever beam with the properties of the beam section derived from the fact that the shear is constant throughout the section. The efficiency of beam action will depend on the transmittal of horizontal shear between adjacent laminations with spikes.

Laminated floors or flat roofs, doubling as horizontal diaphragms, will be supported on beams as required by the vertical load. The beams supporting the deck will not increase the strength nor the stiffness of the laminated deck, but perimeter members, parallel to the laminations in each edge of the deck, act as flanges in beam action and increase strength and stiffness.

Horizontal diaphragms that are laminated act as horizontal beams with the face-to-face nailing of adjacent laminations stressed in horizontal shear.

Perimeter Members

Perimeter members increase the strength and stiffness of diagonally sheathed diaphragms, and as the shear loads increase, the transfer of forces from the web to the perimeter members produces axial and bending stresses which are resisted by these members. The bending stresses are caused by the component of the force in the sheathing acting normal to the perimeter member. Because the joists or studs form an integral part of the diaphragm, enabling it to resist forces in a direction at right angles to the direction of the sheathing by interaction between the boards through nailing to joists or studs, the actual component of force normal to the perimeter members is less than its theoretical maximum value. At small shear loads, the sheathing and joists or studs act almost as a homogeneous web and the force normal to the perimeter members is negligible. In this range, conventional, diagonally sheathed diaphragms are limited by the proportions of their overall dimensions. As the shear load increases, the ability of the joist or stud to transfer forces becomes less, and the force normal to the perimeter members increases, until at large shears, it approaches the full theoretical value. Diagonally sheathed diaphragms in this range require perimeter members to be specially designed for these forces.

Tests and experience have indicated that an arbitrary but satisfactory design procedure is to ne-glect the forces acting normal to the perimeter members for shears up to 300 lbs. per lineal foot and when within the suggested diaphragm proportions. For shears greater than 300 lbs. per lineal foot, the perimeter members should be proportioned to resist a transverse force varying uniformly from 50 per cent of the shear load for shears of 300 lbs. per lineal foot to 100 per cent of the shear load for shears of 800 lbs. per lineal foot or more in addition to the axial stresses normally provided for. The graph, Figure 7.21, shows this relationship.

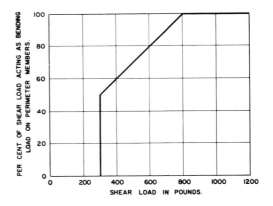

Figure 7.21 — Variation of Transverse Force in Perimeter Members.

Perimeter members, in horizontal diaphragms, are the flange members and the end struts. The axial compression or tension stress in the flanges are computed by dividing the maximum bending moment in the diaphragm by the width of the diaphragm. The bending moment is the same as for a simply supported beam with a uniformly distributed load. The axial stress in the end struts is equal to the shear load per foot multiplied by the maximum spacing in feet of the strut connections to the resisting element.

The perimeter members of vertical diaphragms are the top and bottom plates and the end studs or posts. The axial stress in the top plate is equal to the stress in the end strut of the horizontal diaphragm as transmitted through the connections. The stress in the bottom plate is equal to the stress in the top plate plus an additive cumulative load distributed between the bottom plate connections. The force in the vertical end posts or studs is equal to the moment resulting from the couple formed by the lateral force and the reaction, divided by the width of the diaphragm. Where perimeter members are subject to axial stresses only, as in double diagonally sheathed diaphragms, the cross sectional area required for the perimeter member is equal to the total axial stress divided by the allowable unit stress for the grade of lumber used.

When perimeter members, in addition to the axial loads, are proportioned to resist tranverse loads, they should be designed for combined stresses as described on pages 55 and 72. For the end struts or end posts, the beam span is equal to the width or height of the diaphragm. The flanges or plates resist the transverse force as a beam spanning between joists or studs.

Depending on the magnitude of the lateral force to be resisted, the perimeter member can be reinforced in several ways. Additional strength and stiffness can be imparted to the end struts by doubling or by using a larger size member, or by using one or more end stiffeners, such as 2″ plank with its edge butted to the wide face of the end strut or stud. Flange or plate members should be continuous or spliced for continuity. Where a continuous header is impractical and solid blocking is used, the required strength and stiffness may be furnished by the wall plates, or reinforcing can be accomplished by using 2″ plank let into the joists. Theoretically, stiffening pieces should be placed as close to the plane of the sheathing as possible to avoid eccentricity. Figure 7.22 illustrates several methods of stiffening perimeter members.

Splices
Splices required for continuity should be located, if possible, where bending stresses in the perimeter members are small. Splices may be made with nails, bolts or timber connectors. The choice will depend on the magnitude of the stress in the joint and is further influenced by any limitation on the length available for the splice pad.

Corner Details
Corners of conventional diagonally sheathed diaphragms require no special reinforcing. However, when the magnitude of the shear loads on diagonally sheathed diaphragms requires specially designed perimeter members, high stress concentrations will develop at the corners which must be reinforced to prevent separation. Reinforcing can be accomplished by bolting a steel angle or heavy let-in blocking in the corners. Some typical details of corner reinforcing are illustrated in Figure 7.23.

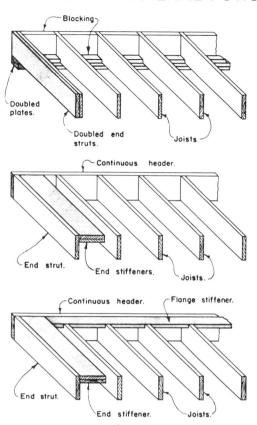

Figure 7.22 — Stiffeners for Perimeter Members.

Multiple Nailing Factor
In the nailing of both lumber built diaphragms and plywood diaphragms there are many repetitions of the pieces and of the nailing pattern. Because of this, further consideration can be given to the relationship of the test value of a nail and the reduced value customarily used in design for individual nails as compared to the conditions existing in diaphragms. Of the several items evaluated as reduction factors applied to test values,

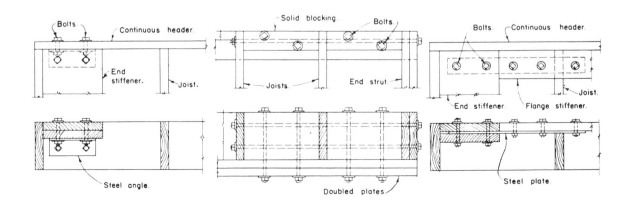

Figure 7.23 — Typical Corner Details

DESIGN — LATERAL FORCES

a large factor for variability is included in deriving design values. With many pieces and many nails in a diaphragm, the variability factor can be reduced to an average rather than using the near maximum. Also, the strength of the diaphragm is not dependent on the strength of the individual nail and some could fail without influencing the strength and stiffness of the diaphragm. For these reasons, an increase of 30 per cent in the allowable lateral resistance of nails, as given on page 207 is recommended in addition to an adjustment for duration of load.

The validity of these increases is borne out by the behavior of many diaphragms that have been designed with similar nail values, and which have been exposed to severe earthquake forces without damage.

Allowable Lateral Loads for Lumber Built Diaphragms

The tabulation of lateral loads in Table 7.4 for lumber built diaphragms is based on the lateral strength of nails, adjusted for duration of load and multiple nailing, used to fasten the sheathing to the framing.

TABLE 7.4

Transversely Sheathed Diaphragms:

Maximum Span-Width or Height Width Ratio			Nominal Width of Sheathing Boards Inches	Number of 8d Common Nails per Board per Crossing of Stud, Joist or Perimeter Member and at Butted Ends.	Allowable Lateral Shear Load lbs. per lineal ft. for Stud or Joist Spacing in inches of		
Horizontal Diaphragms Restraining:		Vertical Diaphragms			12	16	24
Masonry or Concrete Walls	Wood or Similar Walls						
Not recommended	Limited by acceptable deflection of wall	Limited by acceptable deflection	6 8 10	2 2 2	85 100 105	65 75 80	45 50 55

Diagonally Sheathed Diaphragms:

Maximum Span-Width or Height-Width Ratio			Nominal Width of Sheathing Boards Inches	Number of 8d Common Nails per Board per Crossing at:		Allowable Lateral Shear Load lbs. per lineal ft.
Horizontal Diaphragms Restraining:		Vertical Diaphragms		Perimeter Members and Butted Ends of Boards	Stud or Joist	
Masonry or Concrete Walls	Wood or Similar Walls					
3:1	4:1	2:1	6 8	2 2 3	2 2 2	290 220 320

Diagonal Sheathing —— Special Perimeter Framing: *

Maximum Span-Width or Height-Width Ratio			Nominal Width of Sheathing Boards Inches	Number of 8d Common Nails Per Board at Perimeter Members **	Allowable Lateral Shear Load lbs. per lineal ft.
Horizontal Diaphragms Restraining:		Vertical Diaphragms			
Masonry or Concrete Walls	Wood or Similar Walls				
Limited by acceptable deflection of walls	Limited by acceptable deflection of wall	Limited by acceptable deflection	6	3 4 5 6 7 8	440 590 740 880 1030 1180
			8	4 5 6 7 8	430 540 650 760 870

* Perimeter members designed to resist axial and bending stresses as described on page 180.

** Nailing at butted ends of boards to be 75% of perimeter nailing with a minimum of 3 nails. Use minimum of 3 nails per board at stud or joist crossings.

DESIGN — LATERAL FORCES
TABLE 7.4 (continued)

Double Diagonal Sheathing: *

Maximum Span-Width or Height-Width Ratio			Nominal Width of Sheathing Boards	Number of 8d Common Nails per Board at Perimeter Members **		Allowable Lateral Shear Load lbs. per lineal ft.
Horizontal Diaphragms Restraining:		Vertical Diaphragms	Inches	Bottom Layer of Boards	Top Layer of Boards	
Masonry or Concrete Walls	Wood or Similar Walls					
Limited by acceptable deflection of wall	Limited by acceptable deflection of wall	Limited by acceptable deflection	6	2	2	420
				3	3	620
				4	3	830
				5	4	1040
				6	5	1250
				7	5	1460
				8	6	1670
				9	7	1880
			8	3	3	460
				4	3	610
				5	4	760
				6	5	920
				7	5	1070
				8	6	1220
				9	7	1380

* Perimeter members designed to resist axial stresses as described on page 180.

** Nailing at butted ends of boards to be 75% of perimeter nailing with a minimum of 3 nails. Use minimum of 3 nails per board at stud or joist crossings.

Plywood Diaphragms

While the diaphragm concept was developed for lumber diaphragms, timber construction for the past 20 years or more in earthquake country has almost universally employed plywood sheathing as the diaphragm material. The action is much simpler than with horizontal or diagonal sheathing and much higher shears can be developed with much simpler details. There is no "lost compo-nent," and a proper design can account for all stresses. *The Uniform Building Code* permits a rational analysis based on the principles of mechanics without limitation, and also permits some higher tabulated shear loads for commonly used construction based on rather extensive large scale tests.

The basic construction of a roof diaphragm is illustrated in Figure 7.24. The manner of calcula-

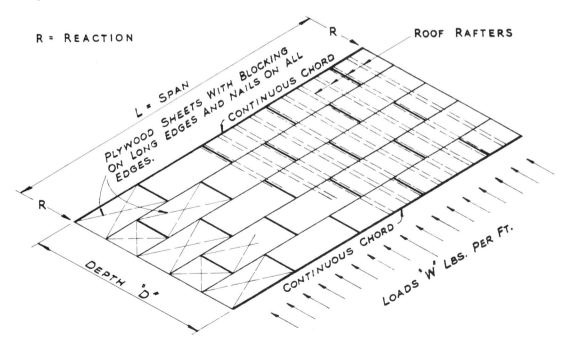

Fig. 7.24 — Plywood Sheathing

DESIGN — LATERAL FORCES

tion is similar to that of a plate girder with many splices in the web, when it is assumed that the web takes no portion of the moment, i.e., it carries shears only. Figure 7.25 indicates the method of calculation and typical construction requirements. This concept is based on the consideration of the free body of a single sheet of plywood shown in Figure 7.26. If shear forces "A", expressed in pounds per linear foot, is to be transferred across the plywood sheet, sufficient nails to provide this transfer are provided at those edges, "A." The moment, tending to twist the sheet are resisted by forces "B" on the other two edges and nails must be provided to resist that restraining force. Simple statics shows that unit force "B", equals

unit force "A" if both are expressed as force per unit length.

The nail values to be used in diaphragms are increased 30% as previously explained. When forces to resist are wind and earthquake forces, the time effect of loading permits a 33% increase over code tabulated values. Using these basic values, we find that the following nail values and shears can be permitted for plywood edge nailing as indicated in Table 7.5. The other limitation on shears is the shear strength of the plywood itself. This depends on the grade of the plywood and the thickness. Values that are usable in most situations are given in Table 7.6.

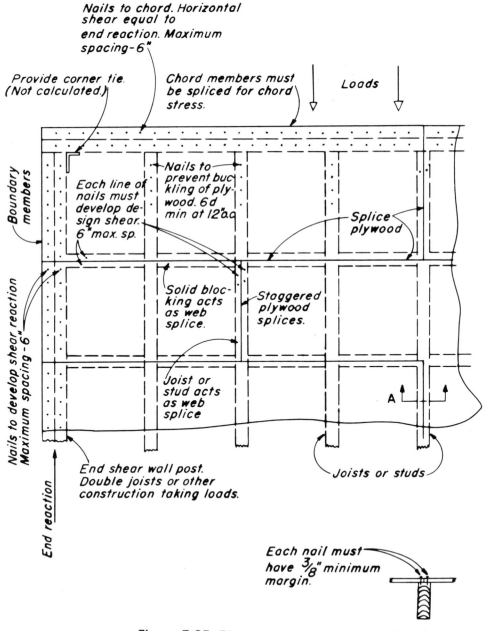

Figure 7.25. Plywood Diaphragm   *Section* **A**

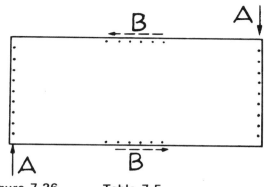

Figure 7.26   Table 7.5

Table 7.5

Nails	Shear Value for Earthquake or Wind	Allowable Shear Per Foot For Certain Nail Spacings			
		6" o.c.	4" o.c.	3" o.c.	2" o.c.
6$_d$	109	218	327	436	654
8$_d$	135	270	405	540	810
10$_d$	163	326	489	652	978
12$_d$	163	326	489	652	978
16$_d$	185	370	555	740	1110

Note: These values are based on allowable nail loads only. See Tables 7.7 and 7.8 for design of diaphragms and shear walls.

It has been found in the tests after the Golden Gate International Exposition that when studs or joists are spaced at either 16" o.c. or 24" o.c., plywood of the sizes permitted for walls, roofs or floors will not buckle at the shear loads usually used for diaphragms and shear walls. Diaphragm tests have also shown that greater spacing can also be used in diaphragm construction. Three-quarter inch plywood on supports spaced 48 inches on center have been tested with ultimate shear loads in excess of 2500 lb. per foot without buckling.

In the basic development and testing of plywood diaphragms, it became clear that in a multiply redundant system such as this that many stress paths could be utilized that are not usually calculated. For example, in Figure 7.25 there are mechanisms that can transfer shear from one sheet of plywood to the next, even when the blocking is omitted. Conversely, by increasing certain nailing, greater strengths can be achieved than would be indicated by the simple analysis. Consequently, based on those tests certain empirical values of shear can be permitted for design purposes when certain construction rules are followed.

In addition to carrying shear, diaphragms must also have sufficient strength and stiffness to carry loads normal to their own plane. In the usual design procedure, the framing members and plywood are first designed for gravity loads. After the plywood thickness has been selected, the allowable shears can be determined using Table 7.7 for roofs and floors, and Table 7.8 for shear

DESIGN — LATERAL FORCES

walls. The diaphragm's boundary nailing will be as tabulated in the table with the thickness of joist or studs adequate in width for splicing. The proper chord strength must also be provided.

TABLE 7.6
Allowable shears on plywood diaphragms for lateral loads of earthquake and wind as limited by shear in the plywood in pounds per linear foot.

Thickness	Grades Using Exterior Glue	Grades Using Interior Glue
5/16"	890	770
⅜"	1050	960
½" (3 ply)	1300	1280
½" (5 ply)	1610	1280
⅝"	1850	1600
¾"	2100	1920
⅞"	2660	2240
1"	2900	2560
1⅛"	3150	2880

This table is for structural grades of plywood and is based on the lesser shear capacity of sanded and unsanded plywood, assuming all Group-4 species. Other species or plywood with face plys of a different species group than the inner plys will have other values. Allowable shears have been increased one-third as allowed for earthquake and wind. Allowable diaphragm shears will rarely be controlled by shear-through-the-thickness of the plywood.

Diaphragm of Plywood Overlaying Decking

Another variation which provides an exceptionally stiff and strong diaphragm is the use of relatively thin plywood (say ⅜ inch thick) overlaying random laid heavy wood decking. Tests performed at Oregon State University have demonstrated the exceptional performance of this type of diaphragm. The plywood can be laid at a diagonal of 45° to the decking. It has been suggested that a diagonal herringbone pattern, as shown in Figure 7.27, will result in even higher test values than the diagonal pattern. It should be noted that the test of this type of diaphragm

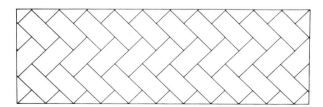

Figure 7.27. A herringbone pattern of plywood sheathing overlaid on decking that probably would improve the strength and stiffness of a diaphragm even more than plywood panels oriented in one diagonal direction (From *Report* T-29, Oregon Forest Research Laboratory, Oregon State University, Corvallis, Ore.)

DESIGN — LATERAL FORCES

Table 7.7 — Recommended Shear in Pounds Per Foot for Horizontal Plywood Diaphragms
for Wind or Seismic Loading
(Plywood and framing assumed already designed for perpendicular loads)

Plywood grade (c)	Common nail size	Minimum nail penetration in framing (in.)	Minimum nominal plywood thickness (in.)	Minimum nominal width of framing member (in.)	Blocked diaphragms				Unblocked diaphragms	
					Nail spacing at diaphragm boundaries (all Cases) and continuous panel edges parallel to load (in.) (Cases 3 and 4) (a)				Nails spaced 6" max. at supported edges (a)	
					6	4	2-1/2	2	Load perpendicular to unblocked edges and continuous panel joints (Case 1)	All other configurations (Cases 2, 3 & 4)
					Nail spacing at other plywood panel edges (in.)					
					6	6	4	3		
STRUCTURAL I INT-DFPA or EXT-DFPA	6d	1-1/4	5/16	2 / 3	185 / 210	250 / 280	375 / 420	420 / 475	165 / 185	125 / 140
	8d	1-1/2	3/8	2 / 3	270 / 300	360 / 400	530 / 600	600 / 675	240 / 265	180 / 200
	10d	1-5/8	1/2	2 / 3	320 / 360	425 / 480	640(b) / 720	730(b) / 820	285 / 320	215 / 240
C-C EXT-DFPA STRUCTURAL II INT-DFPA, STANDARD C-D INT-DFPA, sheathing and other DFPA grades except Species Group 5	6d	1-1/4	5/16	2 / 3	170 / 190	225 / 250	335 / 380	380 / 430	150 / 170	110 / 125
			3/8	2 / 3	185 / 210	250 / 280	375 / 420	420 / 475	165 / 185	125 / 140
	8d	1-1/2	3/8	2 / 3	240 / 270	320 / 360	480 / 540	545 / 610	215 / 240	160 / 180
			1/2	2 / 3	270 / 300	360 / 400	530 / 600	600 / 675	240 / 265	180 / 200
	10d	1-5/8	1/2	2 / 3	290 / 325	385 / 430	575(b) / 650	655(b) / 735	255 / 290	190 / 215
			5/8	2 / 3	320 / 360	425 / 480	640(b) / 720	730(b) / 820	285 / 320	215 / 240

(a) Space nails 12 in. on center along intermediate framing members.
(b) Reduce tabulated allowable shears 10 per cent when boundary members provide less than 3-inch nominal nailing surface.
(c) All recommendations based on the use of DFPA grade-trademarked plywood.
Notes: Design for diaphragm stresses depends on direction of continuous panel joints with reference to load, not on direction of long dimensions of plywood sheet. Continuous framing may be in either direction for blocked diaphragms.

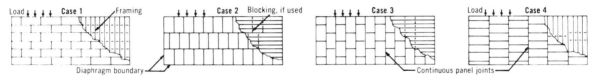

Table 7.8 — Recommended Shear in Pounds Per Foot for Plywood Shear Walls for Wind or Seismic Loading (a)

Plywood grade	Minimum nominal plywood thickness (in.)	Minimum nail penetration in framing (in.)	Plywood applied direct to framing						Plywood applied over 1/2" gypsum sheathing					
			Nail size (common or galvanized box)	Nail spacing at plywood panel edges (in.)					Nail size (common or galvanized box)	Nail spacing at plywood panel edges			
				6	4	2½	2			6	4	2½	2
STRUCTURAL I INT-DFPA or EXT-DFPA	5/16 or 1/4 / 3/8 / 1/2	1-1/4 / 1-1/2 / 1-5/8	6d / 8d / 10d	200 / 280 / 340	300 / 430 / 510	450 / 640 / 770(d)	510 / 730 / 870(d)		8d / 10d / —	200 / 280	300 / 430	450 / 640(d)	510 / 730(d)
C-C EXT-DFPA STRUCTURAL II INT-DFPA STANDARD C-D INT-DFPA DFPA Panel siding and other DFPA grades (c)	5/16 or 1/4 (b) / 3/8 / 1/2	1-1/4 / 1-1/2 / 1-5/8	6d / 8d / 10d	180 / 260 / 310	270 / 380 / 460	400 / 570 / 690(d)	450 / 640 / 770(d)		8d / 10d / —	180 / 260	270 / 380	400 / 570(d)	450 / 640(d)
			Nail size (galvanized casing)						Nail size (galvanized casing)				
DFPA Plywood Panel Siding (c)	5/16 (b) / 3/8	1-1/4 / 1-1/2	6d / 8d	140 / 160	210 / 240	320 / 360	360 / 410		8d / 10d	140 / 160	210 / 240	320 / 360	360 / 410

(a) All panel edges backed with 2-inch nominal or wider framing. Plywood installed either horizontally or vertically. Space nails at 12 in. on center along intermediate framing members.
(b) 3/8" minimum recommended when applied direct to framing as exterior siding.
(c) Except Group 5 species.
(d) Reduce tabulated allowable shears 10% when boundary members provide less than 3-inch nominal nailing surface.

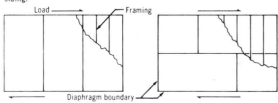
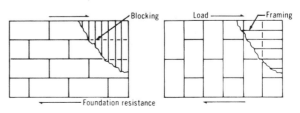

DESIGN — LATERAL FORCES

revealed that at the high load levels which it will resist (in excess of 1600 lb. per ft. at ultimate loads), there is more of a tendency for the plywood to buckle upward than exists in single-layer plywood diaphragms. When using this type of diaphragm for unusually high shears, therefore, the designer should be conservative in specifying the interior nailing. Naturally, the performance of such a diaphragm can be improved by using heavier nailing or lumber species which has a higher fastener holding strength. Diaphragms of this type have also been designed with the plywood at right angles to the decking, but care must be exercised to prevent the plywood joint from aligning with a decking joint which results in a weakened plane in the diaphragm. This type of diaphragm construction is also often used in remodeling older buildings to improve their lateral force resistance, as well as to secure a Heavy Timber fire rating in new construction.

The requirements for Heavy Timber Construction are met by 1⅛ inch thick 2-4-1 plywood over heavy timber beams which has the advantage of being easily constructed in addition to carrying high diaphragm shears as detailed in ICBO Research Report No. 1007. One-half inch plywood over three-inch planks has also received code acceptance for Heavy Timber floors. When determining the allowable shear for the plywood, consider it to be a blocked diaphragm.

Diaphragm Deflections

Deflections of diagonally sheathed diaphragms cannot be computed by rational methods of analysis because of the complexity of the distribution of stresses within the diaphragm. Where it is necessary to determine the probable deflection of a diagonally sheathed diaphragm, a reasonable estimate can be obtained by comparing the diaphragm with one for which test results are available, providing the details of the two diaphragms are similar. Figure 7.28 shows the range of deflections for diagonally sheathed diaphragms at various shear loads as determined by tests. The greatest load for a given deflection is provided

when the perimeter members are specially designed to maximum capacity. The least load for the same deflection is provided by a conventional, diagonally sheathed diaphragm. For the height-width and span depth ratios and allowable lateral loads tabulated at the end of this chapter, experience and tests have shown that deflections will be well within the limits required to maintain the integrity of the structure and determination of deflections is not essential.

The deflection of plywood diaphragms can be calculated accounting for the usual bending and shear components as well as other factors, such as nail deformation, and joint slip in the chords which contribute to the deflection.

The deflection(Δ) of a blocked plywood diaphragm uniformly nailed throughout may be calculated by use of the following formula. If not uniformly nailed, the constant .094 in the third term must be modified accordingly.

$$\Delta = \frac{5vL^3}{8EAb} + \frac{vL}{4Gt} + 0.094\,Le_n + \sum\frac{(\Delta_c X)}{2b}$$

Where:

Δ = the calculated deflection, in inches.

v = maximum shear due to design loads in the direction under consideration, in pounds per lineal foot.

L = diaphragm length in feet.

b = diaphragm width in feet.

E = elastic modulus of chords in pounds per square inch. (Equal to 1.1 times the listed value, since shear will be calculated separately)

A = area of chord cross section in square inches.

G = modulus of rigidity of plywood in pounds per square inch (see Table No. 7.9)

t = effective thickness of plywood for shear in inches (see Table No. 7.10)

e_n = nail deformation in inches (see Figure 7.29)

$\sum(\Delta_c X)$ = sum of individual chord-splice slip values on both sides of the diaphragm, each multiplied by its distance to nearest support.

It is often important to calculate the deflection of diaphragms so that the engineer can properly evaluate the effect of this deflection or movement on other elements of the structure. For example, as shown in Figure 7.30, the deflection of the diaphragm allows the walls to deflect. If the wall is stiff, is short, is brittle, or is fixed at its base and the diaphragm deflects too much, the wall can be cracked or overstressed. If it is assumed that the wall is fixed at its base and that its stiffness does not affect the diaphragm deflection, then it can be shown that

$$f = \frac{\Delta\,ED}{96H^2}$$

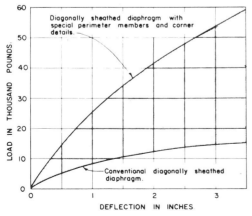

Figure 7.28 — Range of Deflections of Diagonally Sheathed Diaphragms.

DESIGN — LATERAL FORCES

TABLE NO. 7.9 — VALUES OF "G" FOR USE IN CALCULATING DEFLECTION OF PLYWOOD DIAPHRAGMS

PLYWOOD GRADES OR SPECIES GROUP NOS.	G—(MODULUS OF RIGIDITY—P.S.I.)[1]
Group 1	90,000
Group 2	75,000
Group 3	60,000
Group 4	45,000
STRUCTURAL I	90,000
STRUCTURAL II	60,000
Exterior C-C and Standard with Exterior glue	
The combination of Identification Index designation and panel thickness determine the minimum species group and, therefore, the modulus of rigidity to be used: 5/16 — 20/0; 3/8 — 24/0; 1/2 — 32/16; 5/8 — 42/20; 3/4 — 48/24	75,000
All other combinations of C-C and Standard with Exterior glue	45,000

[1]Values of "G" shown apply to plywood bonded with Exterior glue. For plywood bonded with Interior glue, multiply by 0.91.

TABLE NO. 7.10 — EFFECTIVE THICKNESS FOR SHEAR FOR PLYWOOD (12 INCH WIDTHS)

	All plies from same species group, (Includes Structural I and II, Marine Exterior, and all grades using Group 4 plywood stresses.		Face plies of different species group from inner plies.	
Thickness (in.)	All Grades Using Exterior Glue	All Grades Using Interior Glue	All Grades Using Exterior Glue	All Grades Using Interior Glue
Unsanded Panels				
5/16 U	0.318	0.300	0.286	0.270
3/8 U	0.375	0.375	0.323	0.323
1/2 U	0.574	0.500	0.471	0.410
5/8 U	0.662	0.625	0.527	0.498
3/4 U	0.750	0.750	0.585	0.585
13/16 U	0.794	0.813	0.615	0.629
7/8 U	0.949	0.875	0.730	0.673
1 U	1.037	1.000	0.788	0.760
1-1/8 U	1.125	1.125	0.848	0.848
Sanded Panels**				
1/4 S	0.276	0.240	0.241	0.210
3/8 S	0.375	0.375	0.305	0.305
1/2 S	0.574	0.500	0.450	0.392
5/8 S	0.662	0.625	0.508	0.480
3/4 S	0.750	0.750	0.567	0.567
7/8 S	0.949	0.875	0.711	0.655
1 S	1.037	1.000	0.769	0.742
1-1/8 S***	1.125	1.125	0.825	0.825
*For 1/2" 3-ply use the following	0.463	0.500	0.393	0.424
***For 2-4-1 use the following: 1-1/8 2-4-1	238		0.832	0.832

**Includes Touch-Sanded 5/8" 3-ply

Note: All properties adjusted to account for reduced effectiveness of plies with grain perpendicular to applied stress.

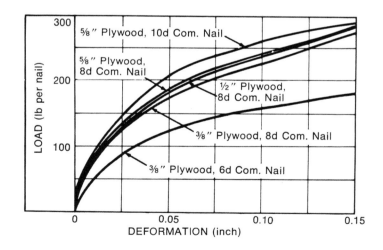

Figure 7.29 — NAIL DEFORMATION FOR DIAPHRAGM DEFLECTION
Douglas fir or southern pine lumber; green when nailed; tested after seasoning to 13% moisture content; average sp. gr. = 0.48

where f = the fiber stress of the rectangular wall stud or post in psi.

Δ = the diaphragm deflection in inches

E = the bending modulus of elasticity of the stud or post in psi.

D = the depth of the stud or post in inches, and

H = the height of the wall in feet.

In a condition where the wall is fixed as by a loading dock in Figure 7.31, or by construction in a story below, this or a similar formula may be very useful in determining wall stresses and the resulting limiting deflections. However, no stretch of the imagination could indicate any validity in the other cases shown such as in a wood stud wall where rotation takes place in the plates and not bending of the studs, or in a masonry wall where the foundation construction does not fix the base. As a result, larger deflections might safely be allowed than indicated by the above formula. In some cases, the end-wall deflection, in addition to the diaphragm deflection, will become a design consideration.

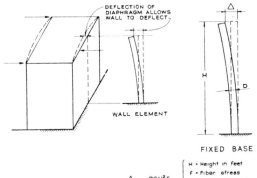

Figure 7.30 Deflections of Wall Elements with Fixed Base

$$\Delta_{(INCHES)} = \frac{.96H^2f}{ED}$$

H · Height in feet
f · Fiber stress
E · Bending Modulus of elasticity
D · In inches

The above conditions are the normal deflections that one usually thinks of when considering diaphragm deflections. However, the diaphragm must have some reserve strength so that it can properly act after the normal vertical load deflections have taken place. Furthermore, as shown in Figure 7.32, when reasonable foundation settlement takes place, the strength of the diaphragm should be relatively unimpared.

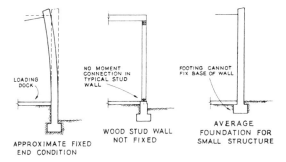

Figure 7.31 — Conditions of fixity for wall bases

DESIGN — LATERAL FORCES

Resistance to Rotation

Where horizontal diaphragms are not supported on all four edges, or where buildings are unsymmetrical, a torsional moment will be induced which must be resisted by the vertical diaphragms supporting the horizontal diaphragms. Where horizontal diaphragms are used in buildings with masonry walls, the masonry walls should be arranged where possible so that torsional moments are minimized.

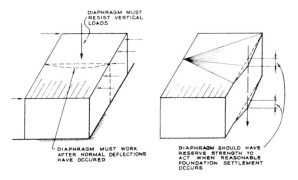

Figure 7.32 Diaphragm deflections which will occur but are usually not calculated.

Openings in Diaphragms

Many openings are constructed in diagonally sheathed diaphragms for doors, windows, stair wells and skylights. The loss in the web area due to the opening increases the shear stress in the remainder of the web. There are also stresses in the perimeter members of the opening, the same as any other perimeter member, and the opening must be reinforced for these stresses. Nailing of the sheathing around the opening is determined by the shear load the same way as for perimeter members.

The perimeter members around openings are the studs, joists and the headers. The studs or joists may be doubled if necessary to accommodate stresses. Headers, to act as perimeter members, need to be anchored beyond the width of the opening. The anchor can be provided by long 1 inch or 2 inch boards, nailed to the header and to solid blocking between studs or joists on each side of the opening, as shown in Figure 7.33.

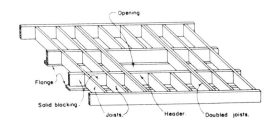

Figure 7.33 — Details of Diaphragm Openings.

DESIGN — LATERAL FORCES

Shear Walls

Vertical diaphragms or shear walls are the most common way of bracing wood framed buildings. A shear wall is basically a diaphragm cantilevered upward from the foundation. The shear wall must have vertical chords at its end which are analogous to the perimeter members of the horizontal diaphragm. Lateral forces on a shear wall will cause an uplift tendency on one of the vertical end chords. If the end chord or the wall as a whole does not contain sufficient dead load to counteract this uplift, then tie down anchors, generally consisting of a steel plate bolted to the vertical chord and well anchored into the concrete foundation, must be provided. Obviously, such tie-down anchors must be provided at both ends of

TABLE 7.11
Properties of Wood Framed and Sheathed Walls:

Wall Type	Relative Rigidity	Relative Strength	Wall Type	Relative Rigidity	Relative Strength
1 x 8 Transverse Sheathing			**1 x 8 Diagonal Sheathing**		
2 8d Nails per stud crossing.	1.0	1.0			
3 8d Nails per stud crossing.	1.0	0.9	2 8d Nails per stud crossing.	1.4	4.0
4 8d Nails per stud crossing.	1.4	1.4			
2 10d Nails per stud crossing.	1.5	1.4			
2 12d Nails per stud crossing.	1.3	1.1			
1 x 8 Transverse Sheathing			**Siding Only**		
2 8d Nails per stud crossing.	0.7	0.8	½ by 6-inch siding, 7d siding nails.	0.7	0.5
			¾ by 8-inch siding, 8d siding nails.	1.0	0.8
1 x 8 Transverse Sheathing			**Siding Only**		
2 8d Nails per stud crossing. 2 by 4-inch cut-in braces.	1.6	1.4	½ by 6-inch siding, 7d siding nails.	3.2	3.3
2 8d Nails per stud crossing. 1 by 4-inch let-in braces.	2.6	3.6	¾ by 8-inch siding, 8d siding nails.	3.1	3.7
1 x 8 Transverse Sheathing			**Siding and Diagonal Sheathing**		
1 by 4-inch let-in bracing.	3.7	3.7			
Same, except sheathing nailed to bracing with 6 8d nails per space.	5.6	5.8	½ by 6-inch bevel siding.	2.0	3.3
2 8d Nails per stud crossing. 1 by 4-inch let-in braces.	4.2	3.5			
1 x 8 Transverse Sheathing			**Siding and Diagonal Sheathing**		
2 8d Nails per stud crossing. 1 by 4-inch let-in braces. Window and door openings.	1.5	2.2	½ by 6-inch bevel siding.	3.3	5.4
1 x 8 Diagonal Sheathing			**Siding and Transverse Sheathing**		
2 8d Nails per stud crossing.	4.3	8+			
3 8d Nails per stud crossing.	5.2	8+	1 by 4-inch let-in braces and ½ by 6-inch bevel siding.	2.7	3.4
4 8d Nails per stud crossing.	7.5	8+			
2 10d Nails per stud crossing.	5.1	8+			

DESIGN — LATERAL FORCES

the wall since the lateral forces can be applied in either direction. In rare cases uplift occurs and the normal footing is still insufficient to resist the uplift. In such cases the foundation size must be increased, grade beams must be added to engage additional footings, or tension or uplift piles must be provided. Sufficient bolting from the concrete foundation to the bottom sill of the shear wall must also be provided to transfer the shears into the footing.

If the building is small with small tributary areas, the necessary rigidity of the wall may be provided by braces, 1″ x 4″ or wider, dapped into and securely nailed to studs at an angle of about 45° and combined with horizontal board sheathing as shown in Figure 7.34. Though not subject to rational design, the strength of let-in bracing is dependent on the number of nails fastening the brace to the stud and the number of nails at each end of the brace. In order to develop compression strength as well as a natural tension value, the slenderness ratio of a brace in compression is kept small by nailing to each stud. Building code provisions generally dictate the proportions, placement and nailing of let-in bracing for small buildings, but such bracing can be proportioned for more severe requirements by comparing rigidities with other wall framing systems. Table 7.11 shows some properties of different wall framings with and without let-in braces. It must be emphasized that the let-in bracing has little strength unless covered by horizontal sheathing with nail-

ing at all contacts, including the horizontal boards contacting the diagonal brace. Without horizontal sheathing, the strength of the let-in brace is essentially the nail values at its ends.

Bracing elements instead of walls can also consist of post, beam and diagonal rods as shown in Figure 7.35. It is most important that all stress transfers be designed and constructed to provide a continuous stress path and that all eccentricities be carefully considered in this type of construction.

Curved or Pitched Diaphragms

The discussion so far has assumed that the diaphragm lies essentially in a single plane so that forces normal to the sheathing may be neglected in analyzing the diaphragm action. However, it is common practice to use either bowstring trusses or pitched trusses of one type or another and, consequently, the diaphragm is either pitched or curved as shown in Figure 7.36. Some studies have been made indicating the secondary forces that may be caused by pitching or curving the diaphragm. The engineer must consider these effects in designing and detailing the structure. The most obvious of these effects is the discontinuity of the diaphragm chord or perimeter member at the peak of a pitched roof. The change in direction of the chord results in a vertical component which must be properly resisted.

Wood Diaphragms Bracing Concrete or Masonry Walls

A common usage of wood roof diaphragms is in conjunction with concrete or masonry walls. This type of construction is particularly widely used in tilt-up concrete buildings. The perimeter members or chords of the diaphragm are usually a portion of the concrete or masonry construction. The plywood sheathing is nailed into a ledger which in turn is bolted to the concrete wall. This connection is generally adequate to transfer shears from the roof diaphragm into the concrete or masonry wall. The other component of force which must be transferred through such a connection is the transmission of the wind or earthquake forces of the wall into the wood diaphragm. In order to insure proper transfer of these forces, a detail similar to Figure 7.37 should be used. Note that the steel strap provides a positive tie between the roof diaphragm and the concrete wall.

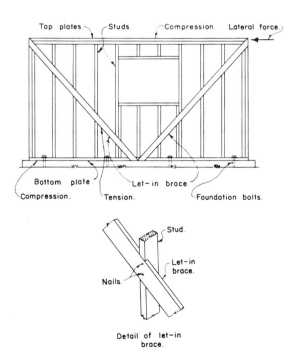

Figure 7.34 — Wall with Let-in Bracing.

This assembly *must* be covered with horizontal sheathing or siding nailed at all contacts to be effective.

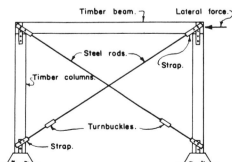

Figure 7.35 — Rod Bracing to resist lateral forces.

DESIGN — LATERAL FORCES

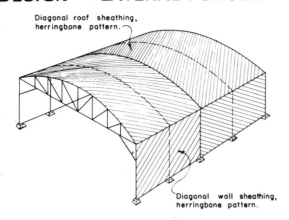

Figure 7.36 — Diagonally Sheathed Curved Roof.

If such a strap is not provided, the ledger is placed in cross grain bending which is not an efficient use of lumber and the edge distance of the plywood nailing may become critical. Not only are such straps often used in structures designed for seismic forces, but it is also common practice to provide a tension capacity at the joist splices by lapping the joists or using scab plates to insure that the diaphragm provides a tie across the building and will not pull apart at an interior girder or truss in a strong earthquake. Proper attention to detail in this type of structure can eliminate failures in diaphragms and in connections between wood diaphragm and concrete and masonry walls.

Diaphragm and Shear Wall Design Example
Wind Load = 30 psf (applied to side of building). Preliminary design for snow load indicates roof framing will be 24" on center.

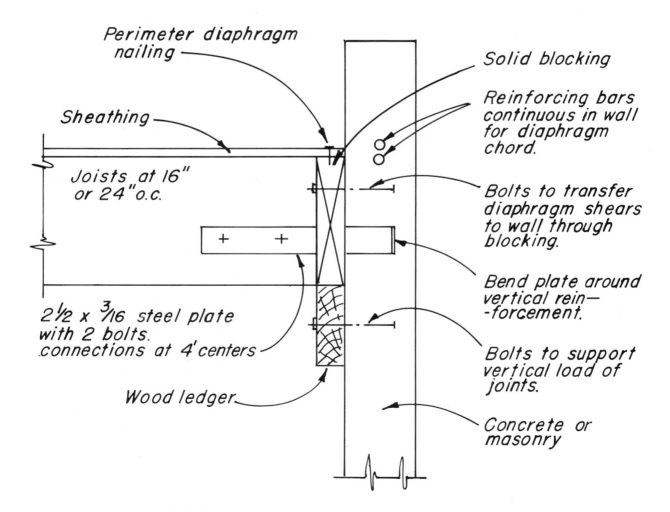

Figure 7.37 — Typical connection of joist to concrete or masonry wall. Steel plates between joist and wall ties them together for forces parallel to joist.

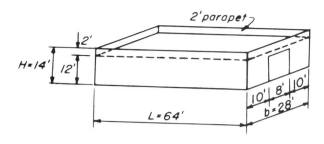

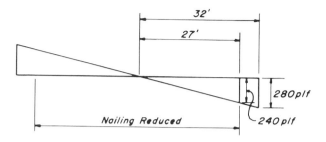

Roof Diaphragm

1. Calculate loads applied to diaphragm. (The following formula is determined by taking moments about the base of the wall.)

$$w = \frac{FH^2}{2h} = \frac{30(14)^2}{2(14-2)} = 245 \text{ lb/ft}$$

2. Calculate diaphragm shears.

$$V = \frac{wL}{2} = \frac{245 \times 64}{2} = 7840 \text{ lb}$$

$$v = \frac{V}{b} = \frac{7840}{28} = 280 \text{ lb/ft}$$

3. Determining Panel Layout. Table 7.7 indicates that this load can be fulfilled by several combinations of plywood grade and thickness, framing, nail size and spacing, and either blocked or unblocked diaphragms. When determining the panel layout the economics and advantages of all the possibilities should be considered. For this example, assume that the best alternate is a blocked diaphragm using ⅜" STANDARD attached to 2" nominal frames with 8d nails (Case 1).

4. Determine Plywood Nailing Schedule. For the selected plywood, framing, and nail size, Table 7.7 shows an allowable shear of 240 lb/ft for a 6" nail spacing at diaphragm boundaries and 6" at other plywood panel edges, and 320 lb/ft for nailing at 4" on diaphragm boundaries and at 6" on other panel edges.

Interpolating between these values for the actual shear of 280 lb/ft, the required nail spacing is found to be 5" on center at diaphragm boundaries and 6" at other panel edges.

Nailing can be reduced to 6" at diaphragm boundaries and all panel edges when shear does not exceed 240 lb/ft.

$$\frac{240}{280} \times \frac{64}{2} = 27 \text{ ft (measured from center of diaphragm).}$$

The following diagram shows the areas where nailing may be reduced and where blocking may be omitted.

5. Determine Required Chord Size. Chords resist axial forces only, due to lateral force effects, since the action of plywood panels in resisting shear does not apply significant bending stresses to the chords. They may resist other forces from vertical loads.

The chord force caused by bending moment in the roof diaphragm is:

$$\frac{wL^2}{8b} = \frac{280 \times (64)^2}{8 \times 28} = 5120 \text{ lb}$$

This force must be resisted by a chord member of adequate strength at the net section (through the bolt holes of the chord splice). A double 2x6 plate supported laterally with butt joints staggered and properly bolted will produce an adequate chord member for both tension and compression. The chord splice for the maximum load will require three ¾ inch round bolts

$$\frac{3150}{2} \times 1.33 \times 3 = 6200 \text{ lb} > 5120 \text{ lb}.$$

Provision must be made for all eccentricities at all splices.

6. Check Deflection. The first part of the following equation comes from the simple beam deflection; the second part represents shear deflection; the third part gives deflection due to nail slip; and the fourth part yields deflection due to slip in the chord splices. (In some cases end-wall deflection should be added.) In this example, assume the chord to be in 16-ft segments, and that 1/16" slip might occur in each of 6 splices (3 on each chord).

$$d = \frac{5vL^3}{8EAb} + \frac{vL}{4Gt} + 0.094 \, Le_n + \frac{\sum (\Delta_c X)}{2b}$$

$$= \frac{5 \times 280 \times (64)^3}{8 \times (1.1 \times 1,700,000) \times (2 \times 8.25) \times 28}$$

$$+ \frac{280 \times 64}{4 \times 68,000 \times 0.323} + 0.094 \times 64 \times 0.02$$

$$+ \frac{2 (2 \times 1/16 \times 16 + 1/16 \times 32)}{2 \times 28}$$

$$= 0.053 + 0.204 + 0.120 + 0.143$$

$$d = 0.520 \text{ in.}$$

DESIGN — LATERAL FORCES

A wood framed wall can tolerate this much deflection, but for other materials, the total deflection may have to be reduced. A reduction in deflection can be achieved by increasing the plywood thickness or by using larger chords. The performance of finish materials or veneer must be considered.

7. Anchorages require that shear stresses from the plywood be transferred to the chord members.

End Walls

1. and 2. Forces and Shears:
Shear walls within any given building will resist shears porportional to their relative rigidity and the building's geometry. If the walls are of the same height and of comparable length, they will carry load in direct proportion to their width.

$$\text{End wall shear} = \frac{280 \times 28}{10 + 10} = 392 \text{ lb/ft}$$

3. Panel Layout. The detailing on the end wall must be such that it will act as two 10-ft-wide shear walls, separated by an 8-ft filler panel. Doubled vertical framing must be carried full height at the opening, with the filler panel less heavily nailed than the shear wall panels, although the filler panel may be more heavily damaged in an earthquake.

4. Plywood Nailing. Table 7.8 shows 410 lb/ft for ⅜" Plywood Panel Siding and 8d nails at 2" on center. For 392 lb/ft the nail spacing could be slightly greater than 2". Since the shear wall acts similar to a cantilever loaded at its top end, shears and nailing are constant throughout.

5. Chord Size. Each 10-ft section of this end wall must be designed separately. Ordinarily, building corners will use three members. Framing around the wall opening will require only a double member and will therefore control the design.

$$\text{Maximum chord forces in 10-ft wall} = \frac{Ph}{b}$$

$$\frac{Ph}{b_1} = \frac{392 \times 10 \times 12}{10} = 4700 \text{ lb}$$

A single 2x6 is adequate for the vertical chord in the shear wall, if a concentric anchor to the foundation is used.

6. Deflection. Since both wall sections act together in resisting deflection, and heavy nailing is required, deflection is within limits, by inspection. If the ratio of height to total width of end shear panels is greater than one, deflection should be calculated. The following formula for deflection at the top of the wall is similar to that for diaphragm deflection:

$$d = \frac{8vh^3}{EAb} + \frac{vh}{Gt} + 0.376 \, he_n + d_a$$

when v = shear load at top of wall, lb/ft
      h = wall height, ft
      b = width of shear wall, ft
      d_a = deflection due to anchorage details (rotation and slip of tie-down bolts)

Using double 2x6 chord members

$$d = \frac{8 \times 392 \times 12^3}{(1.1 \times 1,700,000) \times (2 \times 8.25) 10}$$
$$+ \frac{392 \times 12}{68,000 \times .323}$$
$$+ 0.376 \times 12 \times .01 + (1/16) \, 12/10$$
$$= 0.018 + 0.214 + 0.045 + 0.075 = 0.352"$$

Note that this is a significant deflection which must be added to the roof diaphragm to obtain the total displacement for design wind pressures.

7. Anchorages. An uplift force of 4700 lb. must be resisted at each edge of each 10 foot shear wall. This force can be transferred to the foundation, for example, by 3x¼ inch steel plates each side of the double chord with adequate through bolts. The steel plates must be embedded adequately in the concrete foundation and preferably hooked around reinforcing steel to prevent pullout. The foundation must be of adequate weight to resist the uplift force with appropriate factor of safety. A total shear force of 7840 lbs must be transferred from the shear walls to the foundation. This can be accomplished by bolting the bottom plate to the foundation with a minimum of 6-⅝"φ bolts

$$\frac{2340}{2} \times 1.33 = 1550 \text{ lb/bolt,}$$
$$7840/1550 = 5.1 \text{ bolts,}$$

use min. of 6-⅝" φ bolts
or 10-1/2"φ bolts.

8. Shear Wall Details. The roof diaphragm was designed with an average shear at the end of the diaphragm of 280 plf. The end shear walls, due to the 8 foot opening, have an average shear of 392 plf. Therefore, a collector member must be provided to collect 4 feet of the roof diaphragm shear (4 x 280 = 1120 lb) and transmit it in tension or compression to the shear wall. In this case typical double plate chord members are adequate to resist this force. In some cases, especially with numerous wall openings, the collector members will become quite sizable with substantial connections required.

An alternate framing system possible for the end shear wall, if the spandrel over the door is stiff enough, is to use the spandrel to make the two walls act as one wall. This would result in the overturning force being resisted only at the two ends of the 28 foot long wall. This overturning force must then be transmitted as vertical shear through the spandrel panel which must be adequate, both in shear and resulting moments, to resist these stresses. The chord stresses of the spandrel panel must be adequately anchored into the pier segments of the wall.

The preframed panels shown in the following photographs are often used in diaphragm construction. The panels are usually 4-ft x 8-ft or 8-ft x 20-ft, and can be assembled at either the job site or in a shop. A typical construction is

DESIGN — LATERAL FORCES

½" Strucutral plywood nailed to 2 x 4 sub-purlins spaced 24" o.c., and spanning between 4 x 12 purlins spaced 8-ft o.c. Sub purlins are set flush with the framing, using special metal framing hangers. Such panels can be rapidly erected and fastened in place. Tables 7.7 and 7.8 also apply to design of diaphragms and shear walls constructed of preframed panels. It is important in the detailing of preframed panels that adequate straps and anchorage are provided at exterior walls and at splices between panels. Such details which both anchor the exterior walls and resist tension forces in the "field" of the diaphragm have a tremendous effect on the earthquake performance of such roof diaphragms.

Diaphragm Construction Utilizing 8-ft x 20-ft Pre-framed Panels

Diaphragm Construction Utilizing 4-ft x 8-ft Pre-framed Panels

Conventional Plywood Diaphragm Construction over Wood Roof Joists

CHAPTER VIII

Timber Fasteners

TIMBER FASTENERS

MULTIPLE FASTENERS

For many years it has been known that the distribution of load among fasteners in long metal joints was unequal, with the end fasteners transmitting a greater proportion of the load than the intermediate fasteners. It was not until 1967-1969 that theoretical analyses and experimental data were developed to show that a significant non-uniform distribution of load also occurs in mechanically fastened timber joints.

As a result of these new findings, the Canadian Standards Association incorporated load reduction factors for multiple fasteners in the 1970 edition of CSA 086, *Code of Recommended Practice For Engineering Design in Timber.* In the CSA standard, allowable loads for connector, bolt and lag screw joints are reduced depending upon the number of fasteners in a row, the relative cross sectional areas of the main and side members, and the material used for the side plates.

The recommendations of CSA 086 for multiple fasteners, as modified by the method of presentation developed by the Laminated Timber Institute of Canada in their 1972 edition of the *Timber Design Manual,* are included herein and are recommended for the design of joints consisting of multiple timber connectors, bolts or lag screws.

Row of Fasteners

A row of fasteners is defined as either two or more bolts in single or multiple shear or two or more timber connector units or lag screws loaded in single shear, aligned with the direction of the load. When fasteners in adjacent rows are staggered and the distance "b" between fasteners in adjacent rows (measured parallel to the row) is greater than four times the distance "a" between rows, the two rows shall be considered as one row for the purpose of assigning allowable loads. See Figures 8.1 and 8.2 for the application of this principle to even and odd numbers of rows.

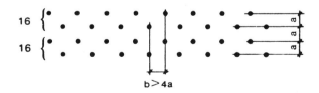

Consider as 2 rows of 16 fasteners

Fig. 8.1

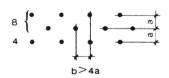

Consider as 1 row of 8 fasteners and 1 row of 4 fasteners

Fig. 8.2

Cross-Sectional Areas

Gross cross-sectional areas shall be used, with no deductions for net section, in calculating cross-sectional area ratios from Table 8.1 or 8.2.

When a member is loaded perpendicular to grain direction, its equivalent cross-sectional area shall be the product of the thickness of the member and the overall width of the fastener group for calculating cross-sectional area ratios. When only one row of fasteners is used, the width of the fastener group shall be considered as the minimum spacing of the fastener for the maximum allowable load. Long rows of fasteners perpendicular to grain should be avoided.

Allowable Load Per Row of Fasteners

To determine the allowable load per row of fasteners as defined above, calculate:

A_1 = Gross cross-sectional area of main member, inches^2
When a member is loaded perpendicular to grain, the value of A_1 is the product of the thickness of the member and the overall width of the fastener group.

A_2 = Sum of gross cross-sectional areas of timber or steel side plates, inches^2

N = Allowable load per fastener, using methods outlined in subsequent sections on timber connectors, bolts and lag screws, pounds

N_A = Actual load to be carried by the fastener row, pounds

and find ratios A_1/A_2 and N_A/N.

Enter Table 8.1 on page 201 if side plates are of wood, or Table 8.2 on page 202 if side plates are of metal, and:

1. Locate the value of A_1/A_2 in first column

2. Locate the value of A_1 in second column and thus define the applicable horizontal row of N_A/N ratios

3. Proceed to the right in that row until the first value higher than the calculated N_A/N ratio is reached

4. Proceed vertically down to read the number of fasteners actually required for each row.

Example

The total tensile force at the bottom chord splice of a timber bowstring truss is 135 kips. The size of the member is 6¾ x 13½ and two ⅜″ x 11″ steel side plates are to be used in conjunction with two rows of 4" shear plates and ⅞″ machine bolts. The allowable load per shear plate in single shear has been found to be 5430 pounds for 100 percent spacing, end distance and edge distance. Find the number of fasteners required.

Now, $A_1 = 6.75 \times 13.5 = 91.13 \text{ in}^2$

$A_2 = 2 \times 0.375 \times 11 = 8.25 \text{ in}^2$

$A_1/A_2 = 11.05$

$N_A = \dfrac{135,000}{2 \times 2} = 33,750$

$N = 5,430$

$N_A/N = 6.22$

TIMBER FASTENERS

From Table 8.2 on page 202, $A_1/A_2 = 11.05$ falls into the first group of values and $A_1 = 91.13$ pinpoints the third line from the top of the chart as the applicable one. Proceeding to the right in that line, the value 6.24 in the 7th column of N_A/N ratios is the first one exceeding 6.22. Proceed to the bottom of that column to find that 8 fasteners are required for each row.

Hence 2 rows of 8-4" shear plates with ⅞" machine bolts are required for each face of the timber member.

Multiple Fastener Table 8.1 — Wood Side Plates
Timber Connectors, Bolts and Lag Screws

A_1/A_2	A_1(inches²)	$\dfrac{N_A}{N} = \dfrac{\text{Actual load per row of fasteners (pounds)}}{\text{Allowable load per fastener (pounds)}}$										
	< 12	2.00	2.76	3.36	3.80	4.08	4.27	4.40	4.41	—	—	—
	12 – 19	2.00	2.85	3.52	4.10	4.50	4.76	4.96	5.13	5.20	5.28	—
	> 19 – 28	2.00	2.91	3.72	4.40	4.92	5.39	5.68	6.03	6.30	6.49	6.60
0.5	> 28 – 40	2.00	2.94	3.84	4.60	5.22	5.81	6.32	6.75	7.10	7.59	7.92
	> 40 – 64	2.00	3.00	3.88	4.70	5.40	6.02	6.64	7.11	7.60	8.14	8.64
	> 64	2.00	3.00	3.92	4.75	5.46	6.16	6.80	7.38	8.00	8.58	9.12
	< 12	2.00	2.91	3.68	4.25	4.68	4.97	5.20	5.31	5.40	—	—
	12 – 19	2.00	2.94	3.76	4.45	5.04	5.46	5.76	5.94	6.10	6.16	—
	> 19 – 28	2.00	3.00	3.88	4.65	5.34	5.95	6.40	6.84	7.20	7.48	7.68
1.0	> 28 – 40	2.00	3.00	3.96	4.80	5.52	6.23	6.88	7.47	8.00	8.58	9.00
	> 40 – 64	2.00	3.00	4.00	4.85	5.64	6.37	7.04	7.65	8.40	9.02	9.60
	> 64	2.00	3.00	4.00	4.95	5.76	6.51	7.28	7.92	8.70	9.46	10.20
Number of fasteners required per row		2	3	4	5	6	7	8	9	10	11	12

A_1 = Cross-sectional area of main member (s) before boring or grooving.
A_2 = Sum of the cross-sectional areas of side members before boring or grooving.

Note: For A_1/A_2 between 0 and 1.0, interpolate or extrapolate from the tabulated values. When A_1/A_2 exceeds 1.0, use A_2 instead of A_1, and A_2/A_1 instead of A_1/A_2.

NAILS AND SPIKES

Nails and spikes are one of the oldest types of metal fastening devices for wood joints. They are economical, easily installed and are well suited for use in many types of construction. Nails and spikes are readily available in a wide assortment of lengths, wire diameter (gauge), kind of head, and kind of point. Shanks may be smooth bright, cement coated, blued, galvanized, etched, or barbed, or they may have special shanks with annular grooves or special grooves. Some of these combinations are available of alloy steel, aluminum, and copper, as well as of common wire steel. All of these several variables have been developed to satisfy many use requirements.

Wire nails and the shorter spikes, regardless of wire gauge, type of head or other variable, have become standardized in "penny", (d) lengths through usage, while the lengths of the longer spikes are measured in inches. By custom, the nominal length, except cement coated or those with countersink heads, is measured from under the head to the tip of the point. The cement coated and countersink nails are measured over their entire length. Dimensional data on some of the more commonly used nails is tabulated in this chapter.

Holding Power

The diameter, penetration, surface condition, and

TIMBER FASTENERS

Multiple Fastener Table 8.2 — Metal Side Plates
Timber Connectors, Bolts and Lag Screws

A_1/A_2	A_1 (inches²)	$\dfrac{N_A}{N} = \dfrac{\text{Actual load per row of fasteners (pounds)}}{\text{Allowable load per fastener (pounds)}}$										
2-12	25 − 39	2.00	2.82	3.48	4.00	4.38	4.69	4.88	5.04	5.10	—	—
	40 − 64	2.00	2.88	3.68	4.35	4.86	5.25	5.60	5.94	6.20	6.38	6.60
	65 − 119	2.00	2.94	3.80	4.55	5.22	5.74	6.24	6.75	7.20	7.59	7.92
	120 − 199	2.00	2.97	3.88	4.75	5.52	6.23	6.88	7.56	8.10	8.69	9.36
12-18	40 − 64	2.00	2.94	3.76	4.50	5.10	5.60	6.00	6.30	6.70	6.82	6.96
	65 − 119	2.00	2.97	3.84	4.65	5.40	6.02	6.56	7.11	7.50	7.92	8.28
	120 − 199	2.00	3.00	3.92	4.80	5.64	6.44	7.12	7.74	8.30	8.80	9.36
	200 or Greater	2.00	3.00	4.00	4.90	5.82	6.65	7.44	8.19	9.00	9.68	10.44
18-24	40 − 64	2.00	3.00	3.84	4.65	5.34	5.88	6.32	6.66	6.90	7.04	7.08
	65 − 119	2.00	3.00	3.88	4.70	5.52	6.23	6.88	7.47	8.00	8.36	8.76
	120 − 199	2.00	3.00	3.96	4.90	5.76	6.58	7.36	8.10	8.80	9.46	10.20
	200 or Greater	2.00	3.00	4.00	5.00	5.88	6.72	7.60	8.37	9.20	10.12	10.92
24-30	40 − 64	2.00	2.94	3.76	4.50	5.10	5.60	5.92	6.21	6.50	6.71	6.96
	65 − 119	2.00	2.97	3.88	4.65	5.40	6.02	6.56	7.11	7.60	8.03	8.52
	120 − 199	2.00	3.00	3.92	4.80	5.64	6.44	7.12	7.83	8.50	9.13	9.72
	200 or Greater	2.00	3.00	3.96	4.90	5.82	6.65	7.44	8.28	9.00	9.79	10.68
30-35	40 − 64	2.00	2.88	3.68	4.30	4.80	5.18	5.44	5.76	6.00	6.27	6.60
	65 − 119	2.00	2.94	3.80	4.50	5.16	5.67	6.08	6.48	6.80	7.15	7.44
	120 − 199	2.00	2.97	3.88	4.75	5.52	6.16	6.80	7.38	8.00	8.58	9.24
	200 or Greater	2.00	3.00	3.92	4.85	5.70	6.51	7.20	8.01	8.70	9.46	10.20
35-42	40 − 64	2.00	2.85	3.56	4.10	4.50	4.83	5.04	5.22	5.30	5.39	5.52
	65 − 119	2.00	2.91	3.72	4.40	4.92	5.39	5.68	6.03	6.30	6.49	6.72
	120 − 199	2.00	2.94	3.84	4.65	5.34	5.95	6.48	7.02	7.60	8.03	8.52
	200 or Greater	2.00	2.97	3.92	4.80	5.58	6.30	6.96	7.56	8.20	8.80	9.36
Number of fasteners required per row		2	3	4	5	6	7	8	9	10	11	12

A_1 = **Cross-sectional area of main member (s) before boring or grooving.**
A_2 = **Sum of cross-sectional areas of metal side plates before drilling.**

metal strength are considerations in determining both the lateral and withdrawal strength of nails and spikes. A further variable is the specific gravity of the species of wood into which the nail or spike is driven. The data presented herein has been narrowed down to those variables most common to structural uses of nails and spikes. These are: smooth bright, "common", steel wire nails and spikes in seasoned wood. See Table 8.4 for species included in various group classifications.

Lateral Strength

Nails and spikes are more efficient, strengthwise, when driven into the side grain of wood and loaded laterally. The lateral strength of a nail or spike so placed is the same whether loaded in a direction parallel to the grain of the pieces joined or at right angles. Under normal conditions of loading, the formula for allowable lateral load on nails or spikes is:

$$P_L = KD^{3/2}$$

in which P_L = the allowable lateral load in pounds when driven into the side grain of seasoned wood,

K = a constant related to specific gravity, (See Table 8.4)

D = the diameter of the nail or spike in inches.

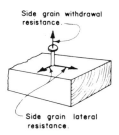

Figure 8.3 — Forces Resisted by Nails

TIMBER FASTENERS

Data on D and D^{3/2} are tabulated herein along with the other dimensional data on nails and spikes.

Deformation of nailed joints, loaded laterally, is the primary consideration in establishing an allowable load; hence, the ultimate load of the joint in softwood lumber will be about five times the load expressed by the preceding formula. Figure 8.4 shows the load deformation characteristics of an 8d common nail. This curve is typical of the performance of common nails.

If the type of construction, method of loading, hazard involved and visibility of joint for inspection are such that it appears safe to the designer to do so, he may increase the calculated lateral holding power of the nailed joint accordingly.

When different species are nailed together, the species of the lowest specific gravity will determine the strength of the joint.

Metal Side Plates
When two wood members are nailed together, the nail deforms in both pieces under load. When a metal plate is nailed to a wood member, the deformation of the nail occurs principally in the wood member and total deformation is less for comparable loads than for a wood-to-wood joint. For this reason, the lateral holding power of nails through metal plates, as determined by the preceding formula, may be increased 25 per cent. Metal side plates must be of adequate thickness and net cross-section to carry the load. A suggested thickness for metal side plates of sheet steel is 18 gauge, when used with nails of 20d or less.

Condition of Lumber and Service
Lateral load values are based on wood seasoned to a maximum moisture content of 19 percent that will remain dry in service. When nails or spikes are driven into lumber that is at or above the fiber saturation point, more lateral joint deformation may be expected than for the same loads with seasoned lumber though the ultimate load values are similar. For this reason, lateral load values for nails and spikes are reduced to 75 per cent of the values determined by the preceding formula when they are driven into unseasoned lumber that will be loaded before seasoning takes place. Similarly, the nail and spike values are reduced when the lumber will be continuously wet in service.

Where the wood fibers surrounding the shank of a nail or spike are subject to alternate wetting and drying, the pressure and friction of the wood fibers that grip the shank will be permanently affected and the adequacy of the strength of the joint becomes questionable. Resetting of the nail will not alter this condition and if inspection of a joint indicates nail loosening, additional nails should be added. If alternate wetting and drying conditions are anticipated when the structure is designed, small bolts may be used in preference to nails or spikes.

The lateral resistance of nails installed in lumber pressure-impregnated with fire-retardant chemicals and kiln-dried after treatment shall be reduced to 90 percent of the tabulated loads. For lumber so treated and not kiln-dried after treatment, the 90 percent value shall be further re-

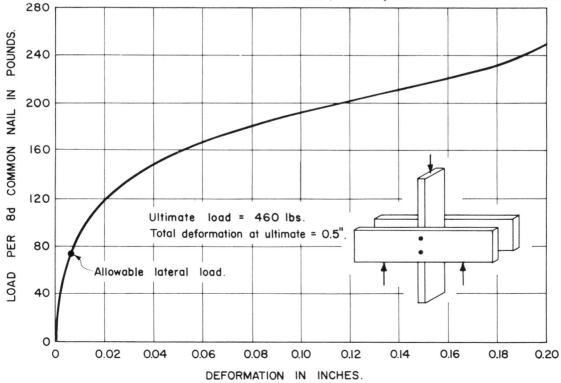

Figure 8.4 — Load Deformation Curve for 8d Common Nail in Douglas Fir.

TIMBER FASTENERS

duced in accordance with the above paragraph relating to unseasoned lumber.

Penetration

The eccentricity of lapped members in nailed joints causes a secondary withdrawal stress on nails or spikes. To prevent separation of the joint, adequate penetration of the shank of the nail or spike into the holding piece is necessary. For maximum holding power, a penetration of the pointed end of the shank equal to 14 times the shank diameter is required in softwood lumber. A minimum penetration of 8½ shank diameters is allowed and the holding power at this penetration is 60 per cent of the maximum value. The value of the holding power is considered as proportionate between zero at no penetration and maximum at a penetration of 14 times the shank diameter. For practical carpentry, the optimum and minimum penetration requirements of nails and spikes in wood-to-wood joints are measured of two-thirds and two-fifths of the nail length respectively. However, these general requirements produce an inconsistency when two pieces of equal thickness are nailed together. This is because penetration requirements would rule out nails whose length would exceed the total thickness of the two pieces. Obviously, a larger nail, even if excessively long, should be permitted as its greater diameter would make a stronger joint in all respects. This suggests that when pieces of equal thickness are nailed together and the nail wholly penetrates both pieces, but the point does not protrude from the wood more than about 20 per cent of the length of the nail, the lateral holding strength of the nail should be calculated as follows:

$$P_{L_1} = P_L \frac{x}{2/3l}$$

in which P_{L_1} = the limited lateral load in pounds,

P_L = the allowable lateral load in pounds for optimum penetration,

x = that portion of the length of the shank within the holding piece in inches,

L = the full length of the nail in inches.

Double Shear

Limited tests in this country and abroad show a considerable increase in the strength of nails in three member, (double shear), over two member, (single shear), joints. These data indicate that at the design level of holding power, the nail capacity in double shear is at least twice that for single shear, but at ultimate loads, the shear efficiency is less and varies according to the ratio of the thickness of the side members to the center member. On the basis of present data, it is suggested that when a nail fully penetrates all

members in a three member joint, the allowable lateral load for nails or spikes can be increased one-third when each side member is not less than about one-third the thickness of the center member and the allowable lateral load may be increased two-thirds when each side member is equal in thickness to the center member.

Nailed joints are considered to be more reliable when members are alternately nailed from each side. However, it is not always practical or economical to nail this way.

Withdrawal Strength

Nails or spikes loaded in direct withdrawal from side grain are not so efficient strengthwise as when loaded laterally. For this reason, it is preferred to arrange nailed structural joints in a manner which loads the nail laterally rather than in withdrawal.

Withdrawal resistance of nails or spikes is materially affected by the specific gravity of wood. The formula for calculating withdrawal resistance for various species, at normal loading condition is:

$$P_W = 1380 \, G^{5/2} D$$

in which P_W = allowable withdrawal resistance in pounds per linear inch of shank from the side grain of the holding piece,

G = specific gravity of the species or species group,

D = diameter of nail or spike in inches.

There are numerous uncertainties in joints with nails loaded in withdrawal, making this type of joint less preferred for most structural purposes. Such uncertainties also influence the choice of a large reduction factor of 6 in adjusting ultimate values to allowable values.

Condition of Lumber and Service

The withdrawal resistance determined by the preceding formula applies to nailing in wood seasoned to a maximum moisture content of 19 percent that will remain dry in service and likewise to unseasoned wood that will remain wet in service.

Nails driven into seasoned or unseasoned wood will have about the same withdrawal resistance, but after the unseasoned wood becomes seasoned, or if there are cycles of wetting and drying of the fibers surrounding the nail shank, the withdrawal resistance may depreciate as much as 75 per cent. Time may also have an effect on withdrawal resistance as the grip of the fibers on the nail shank tends to relax, even under unloaded conditions.

The withdrawal resistance of nails installed in lumber pressure-impregnated with fire-retardant chemicals and kiln-dried after treatment shall be reduced to 90 percent of the tabulated loads. For lumber so treated and not kiln-dried after treatment, the 90 percent value shall be further reduced in accordance with the above paragraph relating to unseasoned lumber.

Clinching

Clinched nails will remove some of the uncertainties associated with nailing that must withstand direct withdrawal. The holding power of a clinched nail is dependent upon the load required to straighten out the bent shank. To be effective, the nail must have a large, full-bodied, flat head of the kind formed on "common" nails.

Limited tests indicate that the withdrawal load of a clinched nail is at least 50 per cent higher than that of an unclinched nail in material of any condition of moisture content or alternate wetting and drying. In the latter case, no reduction of withdrawal resistance is necessary.

The minimum length of the end of the nail or spike required for clinching is estimated to range from ¼ inch for a 6d nail to about ½ inch for a 20d or larger nail. However, the force required to clinch the larger diameter nails may cause splitting of the wood.

The direction in which the clinch is made has been found to affect the maximum withdrawal load. When the clinch is made at right angles to the direction of the grain, the bend must be straightened out more before withdrawal can be accomplished than when the clinch is parallel with the fibers. This is because the withdrawal of nails that have been clinched parallel to the grain is accompanied by some separation of the fibers. The additional force required to withdraw nails that have been clinched at right angles to the grain will permit an additional 20 per cent increase in withdrawal resistance.

When nails are to be clinched, care should be exercised so that the flat heads are not over-driven. In other words, the heads should not be driven below the surface of the wood to a point where the fibers are severely crushed and bearing strength under the head weakened.

Toenailing

Nailing into the end grain of wood does not provide a strong and dependable joint. On the other hand, toenailing, which can usually be used in lieu of end nailing, provides a joint that is equivalent to two-thirds of allowable withdrawal resistance and five-sixths of the lateral load capacity of nails and spikes driven perpendicular and entirely through the side grain of wood. Best results are obtained when toenails are started at one-third of the length of the nail from the end of the piece with the nail driven at an angle of approximately 30° to the face of the piece in which it is started.

Number of Nails or Spikes

When more than one nail or spike of the same or miscellaneous sizes is used in a joint, the total allowable load in withdrawal or lateral resistance is the sum of the allowable loads for the individual nails or spikes. This applies provided spacings, end distances, and edge distances are sufficient to develop the full strength of the nails or spikes without splitting of the member.

Lead Holes

To further reduce splitting, nails and spikes may be driven into lead holes drilled approximately three-fourths the diameter of the nail or spike. Nails and spikes used in this manner actually develop greater withdrawal resistance than if no lead holes had been drilled, but are nevertheless computed on the same basis.

End Grain

Withdrawal resistance of nails and spikes driven into end grain is quite low and connections of this type should be avoided where possible. The allowable lateral load per nail or spike, when driven into end grain is two-thirds of that for nails or spikes driven into side grain.

Deformed-Shank Nails

Special nails are manufactured that have deformations along their shanks in the form of barbs, spiral and annular grooves or other irregular workings. Under conditions involving changes in the moisture content of the wood, some of the special nail forms provide considerably greater withdrawal resistance than the common wire nail. This is especially true of nails driven into unseasoned wood that seasons under load.

Deformed shank nails carry somewhat higher maximum lateral loads than common wire nails, but both types of nails perform similarly at small distortions of the joint. In joints subject to vibration or reversal of stresses, the deformed shank nails with reduced sections, such as the spiral and annular grooved nails, tend to break more easily than the smooth shank nails. In theory, the barbs or surface irregularities will engage the wood fibers and thus increase the resistance to withdrawal. It may be reasoned, however, that the opposite condition occurs because of the rupturing of wood fibers as the nail penetrates the piece. The net result is that these special nails show about the same resistance to withdrawal as a plain nail immediately after driving, but usually have higher holding power than plain nails after large moisture changes take place in the wood.

Surface-Coated Nails

In engineered structures that are expected to give service for many years, cement-coated nails offer no more strength than uncoated nails. Tests show that newly driven cement-coated nails develop considerably greater resistance to direct withdrawal than uncoated nails. However, if there is a time interval of several months or more between driving and pulling, or if appreciable moisture changes occur in the wood, cement-coated nails may lose much of their advantage. Cement-coated nails are intended primarily for use in such things as shipping containers or similar installations where their life expectancy is relatively short.

Nail Points

A nail with a long, sharp point will usually have a higher withdrawal resistance when driven into softwood than the common wire nail, provided its wedging effect does not induce splitting. A blunt or flat point without taper reduces splitting,

TIMBER FASTENERS

but its destruction of the wood fibers during driving reduce withdrawal resistance to less than that of the common wire nail.

Tables of Allowable Nail Loads

For convenience, the allowable lateral and withdrawal loads for "common" nails and spikes driven into seasoned wood which will remain dry are given in the following tables. The tabulated loads for withdrawal are also applicable to wood that will remain wet above the fiber saturation point while in service.

The allowable loads are for normal conditions of loading. Nailed joints may be adjusted for other durations of load as outlined on page 21.

COMMON NAILS AND SPIKES
TABLE 8.3 — Dimensional Data

		Common Nails			Spikes			Box Nails			Finishing Nails		
Size	Length Inches	Gauge Number	D	Diameter Inches $D^{3/2}$	Gauge Number or Diameter	Diameter Inches D	$D^{3/2}$	Gauge Number	Diameter Inches D	$D^{3/2}$	Gauge Number	Diameter Inches D	$D^{3/2}$
2d	1	15	0.072	0.019				15½	0.067	0.018	16½	0.058	0.014
3d	1¼	14	0.080	0.023				14½	0.076	0.021	15½	0.067	0.018
4d	1½	12½	0.099	0.031				14	0.080	0.023	15	0.072	0.019
5d	1¾	12½	0.099	0.031				14	0.080	0.023	15	0.072	0.019
6d	2	11½	0.113	0.038				12½	0.099	0.031	13	0.090	0.027
7d	2¼	11½	0.113	0.038				12½	0.099	0.031	13	0.090	0.027
8d	2½	10¼	0.131	0.048				11½	0.113	0.038	12½	0.099	0.031
9d	2¾	10¼	0.131	0.048				11½	0.113	0.038	12½	0.099	0.031
10d	3	9	0.148	0.057				10½	0.128	0.046	11½	0.113	0.038
12d	3¼	9	0.148	0.057				10½	0.128	0.046	11½	0.113	0.038
16d	3½	8	0.162	0.065				10	0.135	0.050	11	0.121	0.042
20d	4	6	0.192	0.084	4	0.225	0.107	9	0.148	0.057	10	0.135	0.050
30d	4½	5	0.207	0.094	3	0.244	0.120	9	0.148	0.057			
40d	5	4	0.225	0.107	2	0.263	0.135	8	0.162	0.065			
50d	5½	3	0.244	0.120	1	0.283	0.150						
60d	6	2	0.263	0.135	1	0.283	0.150						
	7				5/16"	0.312	0.175						
	8				3/8"	0.375	0.230						
	9				3/8"	0.375	0.230						
	10				3/8"	0.375	0.230						
	12				3/8"	0.375	0.230						

TABLE 8.4 — Grouping of Species for Determining Allowable Lateral Loads for Lag Screws, Nails, Spikes, Wood Screws, and Spiral Dowels.

Group	Species of Wood	Specific Gravity (1)	Lateral Load Constants, K			
			Nails (2)	Screws (2)	Lag Screws (3)	Spiral Dowels (4)
I	Ash, Commercial White	.62	2040	4800	2640	2055
	Beech	.68				
	Birch, Sweet & Yellow	.66				
	Hickory & Pecan	.75				
	Maple, Black & Sugar	.66				
	Oak, Red & White	.67				
II	Douglas Fir - Larch	.51	1650	3960	2280	1775
	Southern Pine	.55				
	Sweetgum & Tupelo	.54				
III	California Redwood (Close grain)	.42	1350	3240	2040	1535
	Douglas Fir, South	.48				
	Eastern Hemlock - Tamarack	.45				
	Eastern Spruce	.43				
	Hem-Fir	.44				
	Idaho White Pine	.42				
	Lodgepole Pine	.44				
	Mountain Hemlock	.47				
	Northern Pine	.46				
	Ponderosa Pine-Sugar Pine	.42				
	Red Pine	.42				
	Sitka Spruce	.43				
	Southern Cypress	.48				
	Spruce-Pine-Fir	.42				
	Yellow Poplar	.46				

Continued on page 207

TIMBER FASTENERS

TABLE 8.4 — (Continued)

Group	Species of Wood	Specific Gravity (1)	Lateral Load Constants, K			
			Nails (2)	Screws (2)	Lag Screws (3)	Spiral Dowels (4)
	Balsam Fir	.38				
	California Redwood (Open grain)	.37				
	Coast Sitka Spruce	.39				
	Cottonwood, Eastern	.41				
IV	Eastern White Pine	.38	1080	2520	1800	1220
	Engelmann Spruce	.37				
	Northern White Cedar	.31				
	Subalpine Fir	.34				
	Western Cedars	.36				
	Western White Pine	.40				

(1) Specific gravity based on oven-dry weight and volume.
(2) For nails or screws inserted perpendicular to grain and loaded either parallel or perpendicular to grain.
(3) For lag screws inserted perpendicular to grain and loaded parallel to grain.

COMMON NAILS AND SPIKES
TABLE 8.5 Allowable Lateral Loads in Single Shear (Pounds)

Size penny weight d	Length (Inches)	Lateral Loads for wood and metal side members							
		Group I		Group II		Group III		Group IV	
		Wood	Metal	Wood	Metal	Wood	Metal	Wood	Metal
NAILS									
2	1	39	49	32	40	26	33	21	26
3	1¼	46	58	37	47	31	38	24	31
4	1½	64	79	51	64	42	53	34	42
5	1¾	64	79	51	64	42	53	34	42
6	2	77	97	63	78	51	64	41	51
7	2¼	77	97	63	78	51	64	41	51
8	2½	97	121	78	98	64	80	51	64
9	2¾	97	121	78	98	64	80	51	64
10	3	116	145	94	117	77	96	61	77
12	3¼	116	145	94	117	77	96	61	77
16	3½	133	166	108	134	88	110	70	88
20	4	172	215	139	174	114	142	91	114
30	4½	192	240	155	194	127	159	102	127
40	5	218	272	176	220	144	180	115	144
50	5½	246	307	199	249	163	203	130	163
60	6	275	344	223	278	182	228	146	182
SPIKES									
20	4	218	272	176	220	144	180	115	144
30	4½	246	307	199	249	163	204	130	163
40	5	275	344	223	278	182	228	146	182
50	5½	307	384	248	311	203	254	163	203
60	6	307	384	248	311	203	254	163	203
5/16″	7	357	447	289	361	236	296	189	236
3/8″	8-12	468	586	379	474	310	388	248	310

(1) When driven into side grain
(2) These loads apply only where the depth of penetration, into the member holding the point, is not less than 10 diameters for Group I species; 11 diameters for Group II species; 13 diameters for Group III species; 14 diameters for Group IV species. When penetration is less than that specified, the allowable load may be determined by straight-line interpolation between zero and the tabulated load, except that penetration shall not be less than one-third of that specified.

TIMBER FASTENERS

TABLE 8.6 — Allowable Loads for Nails and Spikes in Withdrawal.

(Pounds per inch of penetration)

Nail Type and Size				Allowable Loads in Direct Withdrawal lb/in					
Com-mon	Spike	Box	Finish-ing	DF-L	DF S MH	Hem-Fir LP	IWP PP-SP SS	WC ES	SF
			2d	15	13	10	9	6	5
		2d	3d	17	15	12	11	7	6
2d			4&5d	18	16	13	11	8	7
		3d		19	17	13	12	8	7
3d		4&5d		21	18	14	13	9	7
			6&7d	23	20	16	14	10	8
4&5d		6&7d	8&9d	25	22	18	16	11	9
6&7d		8&9d	10&12d	29	25	20	18	12	11
			16d	31	27	21	19	13	11
		10&12d		33	28	23	20	14	12
8&9d				34	29	23	21	14	12
		16d	20d	35	30	24	21	14	13
10&12d		20&30d		38	33	26	23	16	14
16d		40d		42	36	29	26	17	15
20d				49	42	34	30	21	18
30d				53	46	37	33	22	19
40d	20d			58	50	40	35	24	21
50d	30d			63	54	43	38	26	23
60d	40d			67	58	47	41	28	24
	50&60d			73	62	50	45	30	26
	7″			80	69	55	49	34	29
	8-12″			96	83	66	59	40	35

LEGEND:

DF-L = Douglas Fir-Larch
DF S = Douglas Fir South
MH = Mountain Hemlock
Hem-Fir = Hem-Fir
LP = Lodgepole Pine

PP-SP = Ponderosa Pine-Sugar Pine
SS = Sitka Spruce
IWP = Idaho White Pine
WC = Western Cedars
ES = Engelmann Spruce
SF = Subalpine Fir

TIMBER FASTENERS

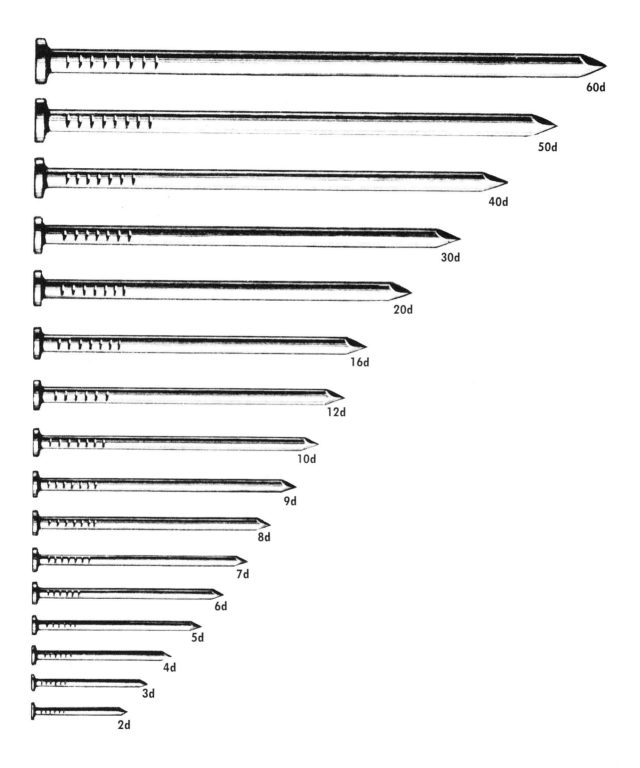

Figure 8.5 — Common Nails — Actual Size

TIMBER FASTENERS

BOLTS

Bolts provide strong, efficient, and economical connections. As bolted joints are easily fabricated they are widely used to connect all types of timber framing.

In determining the strength of a bolted joint there are a number of conditions involved. These are:

> Allowable load for one bolt.
> Wood side members.
> Metal side members.
> Angle of load to grain.
> Duration of load.
> Condition of lumber at the time of fabrication.
> Condition of service.
> Number of bolts.
> Center to center spacing.
> Spacing between rows of bolts.
> End distance.
> Edge distance.
> Net section.

These and other special conditions are explained in detail in this chapter.

Allowable Load for One Bolt

The allowable loads for bolted joints are based on the results of tests, but because of the somewhat limited test data the values are purposely conservative. Allowable bolt loads which vary with the relationship of the bolt length to its diameter, are derived from the average proportional limit joint stress modified to provide working stresses well below the proportional limit stresses.

Basal conditions for the allowable load for one bolt are lumber seasoned to a maximum moisture content of 19 percent that will be dry in use and normal condition of loading on a three piece joint, (double shear), with the wood side members one-half of the thickness of the main member. Specific adjustments are then made for other conditions.

Beginning with test derived constants for species with different specific gravities and for parallel and perpendicular to grain loading, consideration is then given to the projected bearing area of different size bolts and to the slenderness ratio of the bolt length to its diameter which influences strength by virtue of the related stiffness of the bolt under load.

For the basal conditions stated, the allowable load on a bolt loaded parallel to the grain is computed from the following formula:

$$P = SrLD$$

in which
P = allowable bolt load in pounds
S = basic stress based on compression parallel to grain
r = factor depending on the ratio of the length to the diameter (L/D) of the bolt.
L = length of bolt in main member in inches
D = diameter of bolt in inches

For perpendicular to grain loading an adjustment is made for different bolt diameters as the supporting action of wood fibers gives higher values for narrow bearing widths than for wider widths. Hence, for the basal conditions previously stated and with an adjusting factor for bolt diameter, the allowable load for a bolt loaded perpendicular to the grain is computed from the following formula:

$$P = S_1, r_1, LDc$$

in which
P = allowable bolt load in pounds
S_1 = basic stress based on compression perpendicular to grain
r_1 = factor depending on the ratio of the length to the diameter (L/D) of the bolt
L = length of bolt in main member in inches
D = diameter of bolt in inches
c = adjustment factor for bolt diameter

Table 8.7 gives the basic stresses for both parallel and perpendicular to grain loading for the various species and species groups covered in the tables of allowable loads for bolts at the end of this section. Also shown in this table are the Group Numbers for the "r" and "r_1" values in Tables 8.8 and 8.9.

TABLE 8.7: Basic Bolt Values for Parallel and Perpendicular to Grain Loading

Species or Species Group	Basic Stresses		Group Numbers for "r" and "r₁"
	Parallel to Grain "S"	Perpendicular to Grain "S₁"	
Dense Douglas Fir-Larch	1892	399	3
Douglas Fir-Larch	1617	340	3
Douglas Fir South	1458	297	2
Hem-Fir	1344	218	2
Mountain Hemlock	1281	326	2
Western Cedars	1258	262	2
Idaho White Pine	1178	209	1
Lodgepole Pine	1160	222	1
Sitka Spruce	1187	245	1
Ponderosa Pine-Sugar Pine	1090	248	1
Engelmann Spruce	933	173	1
Subalpine Fir	916	219	1

Wood Side Members

Allowable bolt loads are based on the assumption that the bearing thrust on the side members is parallel to the fibers of the side members and that they are one-half the thickness of the main member to develop the full capacity of the joint, as shown in Figure 8.6.

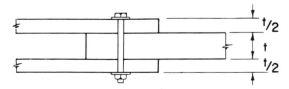

Figure 8.6 — Three Member Joint.

TIMBER FASTENERS

Table 8.8 — Percentage of basic stress parallel to the grain for calculating safe bearing stresses under bolts

Length of bolt in main member divided by its diameter (L/D)	"r" Values for Common Bolts		
	Group 1 woods	Group 2 woods	Group 3 woods
1.0	100.0	100.0	100.0
1.5	100.0	100.0	100.0
2.0	100.0	100.0	100.0
2.5	100.0	100.0	99.7
3.0	100.0	100.0	99.0
3.5	100.0	99.3	96.7
4.0	99.5	97.4	92.5
4.5	97.9	93.8	86.8
5.0	95.4	88.3	80.0
5.5	91.4	82.2	73.0
6.0	85.6	75.8	67.2
6.5	79.0	70.0	62.0
7.0	73.4	65.0	57.6
7.5	68.5	60.6	53.7
8.0	64.2	56.9	50.4
8.5	60.4	53.5	47.4
9.0	57.1	50.6	44.8
9.5	54.1	47.9	42.4
10.0	51.4	45.5	40.3
10.5	48.9	43.3	38.4
11.0	46.7	41.4	36.6
11.5	44.7	39.6	35.0
12.0	42.8	37.9	33.6
12.5	41.1	36.4	32.2
13.0	39.5	35.0	31.0

Table 8.9 — Percentages of basic stress perpendicular to the grain used in calculating safe bearing stresses under bolts

Length of bolt in main member divided by its diameter (L/D)	"r₁" Values for common bolts		
	Group 1	Group 2	Group 3
1.0 to 5.0, inclusive	100.0	100.0	100.0
5.5	100.0	100.0	100.0
6.0	100.0	100.0	100.0
6.5	100.0	100.0	99.5
7.0	100.0	100.0	97.3
7.5	100.0	99.1	93.3
8.0	100.0	96.1	88.1
8.5	98.1	91.7	82.1
9.0	94.6	86.3	76.7
9.5	90.0	80.9	71.9
10.0	85.0	76.2	67.2
10.5	80.1	71.6	62.9
11.0	76.1	67.6	59.3
11.5	72.1	64.1	55.6
12.0	68.6	61.0	52.0
12.5	65.3	58.0	49.0
13.0	62.2	55.3	45.9

The bolt diameter factor "c", used in computing perpendicular to grain values can be determined from the curve of Figure 8.7.

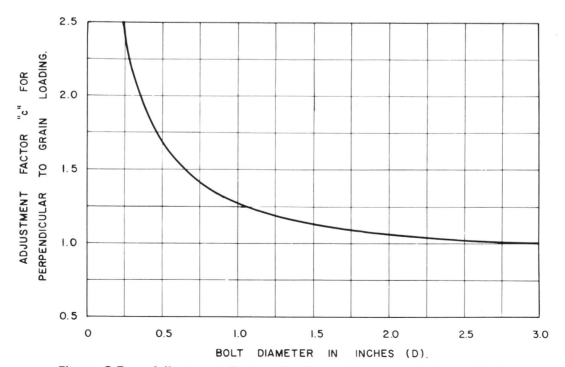

Figure 8.7 — Adjustment Factors for Perpendicular to Grain Loading.

TIMBER FASTENERS

When the side members are less than one-half the thickness of the main member the allowable bolt load is determined on the basis of a main member that is twice the thickness of the thinnest side member since the thickness of the side member limits the load capacity.

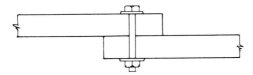

Figure 8.8 — Two Member Joint, Members of Equal Thickness.

When a bolted joint consists of only two members of equal thickness so that the joint is in single shear, as shown in Figure 8.8 the capacity load is one-half of the allowable load for a main member twice the thickness of one of the members. For members of unequal thickness, as shown in Figure 8.9 use one-half the allowable load value for a member twice the thickness of the thinner member.

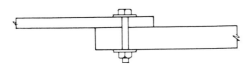

Figure 8.9 — Two Member Joint, Members of Unequal Thickness.

Multiple Member Joints

For multiple-member joints, composed of more than three members all of equal thickness, as illustrated in Figure 8.10, the allowable load varies in accordance with the number of shear planes involved. The allowable load for each shear plane is considered to be one-half the tabulated load for a piece the thickness of one member. Thus, for a joint of four members of equal thickness, which has three shear planes, the allowable joint load is equal to one and one-half times the tabulated load for a piece the thickness of one of the members.

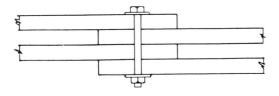

Figure 8.10 — Multiple Member Joint.

Angular Joint

If the load in a joint acts at an angle with the axis of the bolt, as shown in Figure 8.11, the load component acting at 90° with the bolt axis is considered as being equal to one-half of the allowable load for a bolt length of twice the thickness of the thinner piece. Ample bearing area under washers and plates should be provided to resist the load component acting parallel to the axis of the bolt.

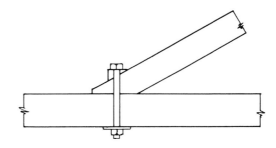

Figure 8.11 — Angular Joint.

Eccentric Joints and Beams Supported by Bolts

As shear stresses may be critical in eccentric bolted joints and in beams supported by bolts, horizontal shear under these conditions should be computed as described on page 77 and checked against the allowable unit horizontal shear.

Steel Side Members

Allowable bolt loads are based on proportional limit loads and tests have shown that for parallel to grain loading with steel side members, the proportional limit load is about 25 per cent greater than for wood side members. Hence, for loads acting parallel to grain, the allowable bolt loads may be increased 25 per cent for steel side members.

For loads acting perpendicular to the grain, the allowable bolt loads are the same as for wood side members as the bearing strength of the wood is the limiting factor.

Steel side members must always be of sufficient thickness to prevent over-stress in the steel.

For the design of steel side members, allowable unit stresses as shown in the *Manual of Steel Construction* by the American Institute of Steel Construction Inc. should be used.

For wind or earthquake loads these stresses may be increased one-third.

Angle of Load to Grain

For joints loaded at an angle to the grain, see Figure 8.12, the allowable load is determined through the Hankinson formula, see page 79. By using the parallel to grain value and the perpendicular to grain value as F_c and $F_{c\perp}$ respectively in the formula, the allowable load for a bolt at

TIMBER FASTENERS

an angle to grain is obtained. This value may be quickly and accurately found by using the nomograph, Figure 7.7 on page 79.

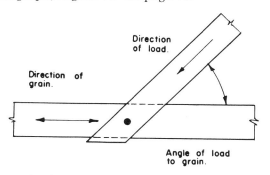

Figure 8.12 — Joint Loaded at an Angle to Grain.

Duration of Load

Allowable loads for bolted joints are subject to adjustment for duration of loading other than the normal condition of loading on which they have been based herein. However, where steel side members are used the allowable value of the steel without duration of load increases, except from wind or earthquake loads, must not be exceeded.

Condition of Lumber

The moisture content, both before and after fabrication, of the lumber used to fabricate bolted joints will affect the load capacity of the joint. Allowable bolt loads are computed on the basis of lumber seasoned to a maximum moisture content of 19 percent prior to fabrication and used under continuously dry conditions as in most covered structures.

Where bolted connections are fabricated of unseasoned lumber having a moisture content at or above the fiber saturation point, and which is permitted to season in place to a maximum moisture content of 19 percent before full load is applied, the bolt values should be reduced to 40 percent of the basal values. For lumber only partially seasoned at the time of fabrication intermediate values may be used.

Where bolted connections are fabricated of lumber pressure-impregnated with fire-retardant chemicals and kiln-dried after treatment, 90 percent of the tabulated bolt loads shall apply. For lumber so treated and not kiln-dried after treatment, the basic values shall be considered as 90 percent of the tabulated bolt loads and further reduced as described for unseasoned lumber.

The large reduction factor for bolted joints fabricated of unseasoned lumber that is permitted to season in place is based on limited test data which indicated that unequal shrinkage in the test specimens caused splitting of the joint with a subsequent reduction in strength. These tests were made with the bolts fitting tightly in the bolt holes, which increased the tendency to split due to shrinkage of the bolt hole. The recommended practice for bolt holes to be 1/32" to 1/16" oversize depending on the bolt size, will relieve splitting tendency to some extent.

When joints are fabricated so that there are no secondary stresses induced by shrinkage, the maximum allowable bolt loads may be used without adjustment for the condition of lumber prior to fabrication. Joints fastened with one bolt and joints consisting of parallel members having one row of bolts loaded parallel to grain as shown in Figure 8.13 are not affected by shrinkage. Joints with steel gusset plates having a single row of bolts parallel to grain in each member and loaded parallel or perpendicular to grain are not affected by shrinkage. If more than one row of bolts is used, as in a splice, there should be a separate splice plate for each row of bolts, as shown in Figure 8.13, to minimize the effect of shrinkage. A saw kerf, terminating in a bored hole, between the rows of bolts will also minimize splitting.

Conditions of Service

The conditions of service to which bolted joints may be subjected also have an effect on the allowable bolt loads. Tests have shown that when joints are subjected to alternate cycles of wetting and drying, the allowable bolt loads should be reduced about 25 per cent. If the lumber remains continuously wet, above the fiber saturation point, the allowable bolt loads should be reduced about one-third.

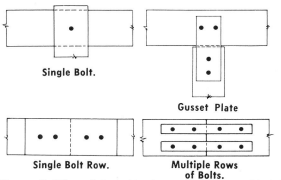

Single Bolt.

Gusset Plate

Single Bolt Row.

Multiple Rows of Bolts.

Figure 8.13 — Joints Having a Minimum Shrinkage Effect.

Number of Bolts

In recent years, research and testing has indicated that the strength of a row of "n" connectors, bolts or lag screws is not necessarily "n" times the strength of one of the fasteners in that row. It thus recognizes the fact that the total load on a row of fasteners is not shared equally between all fasteners. The reader is referred to Page 200 for the design of Multiple Fasteners.

Center-to-Center Spacing

With parallel to grain loading, to develop the full strength of each bolt in a joint having more than one bolt, with either wood or steel side members, the center-to-center spacing along the grain between bolts should be at least four times the bolt diameter. See Figure 8.14.

For perpendicular to grain loading, when wood side members are used and the load approaches the bolt bearing capacity of the side members,

TIMBER FASTENERS

the spacing should be the same as parallel to grain spacing. Spacings may be reduced if the design load is less than bolt bearing capacity of side members or bolts may be staggered to obtain closer spacings. See Figure 8.15.

The minimum center-to-center spacing of bolts for loads acting perpendicular to grain when metal side members are used need only be sufficient to permit the tightening of the nuts and is generally about 2½ times the bolt diameter.

It is suggested that the minimum spacing be also considered as a maximum to avoid secondary joint stresses caused by differential shrinkage of wood members at angles to each other and by dimensional changes in metal side members due to thermal variations.

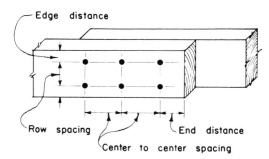

Figure 8.14 — Bolt Spacing Parallel to Grain Loading.

Spacing Between Rows of Bolts

For parallel to grain loading, the spacing across the grain between rows of bolts is determined by the number of rows, the required edge distance, and by the net section requirement. See Figure 8.14.

For perpendicular to grain loading, the spacing between rows of bolts is related to the slenderness ratio of the length to the diameter of the bolt, (L/D), and the bolt diameter. For an L/D ratio of 2, the recommended spacing is 2½ times the bolt diameter and 5 times the bolt diameter for an L/D ratio of 6 or more. For ratios between 2 and 6, the spacing can be obtained by straight line interpolation. See Figure 8.15.

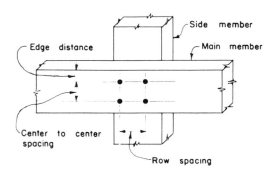

Figure 8.15 — Bolt Spacing — Perpendicular to Grain Loading.

If these spacings are reduced, the allowable joint load should be reduced in the same proportion as lesser spacings will not develop the full bearing strength of the wood. The minimum spacing between rows of bolts should also be considered the maximum to avoid secondary stresses in the joints as for center-to-center spacing.

End Distance

When a member is in tension, the bolt nearest the end of the member should be at a distance of at least seven times the bolt diameter from the end to prevent the possibility of a plug shearing out at the end of the piece. When a member is in compression, the end distance may be a minimum of four times the bolt diameter. Lesser end distances will tend to cause splitting and any decrease in these end distances will decrease the load capacity of the joint by about the same ratio.

Edge Distance

For bolts bearing parallel to the grain, the distance from the edge of a member to the center of a bolt should be at least 1.5 times the bolt diameter to permit the washer to fully bear on the wood. This distance will usually be controlled by the common practice of having an edge distance equal to one half the distance between rows of bolts or by the area requirements at the net section.

For bolts bearing perpendicular to the grain, the distance from the edge toward which the bolt pressure acts to the center of the bolt nearest this edge should be at least four times the bolt diameter to develop the full strength of the bolt. The distance at the opposite edge is relatively unimportant if there is no stress reversal except that sufficient distance should be maintained to permit the washer to fully bear on the wood.

Net Section

The net section of a member, taken at right angles to the direction of load, is the section which gives the maximum stress in the member, and is the maximum cross-sectional area remaining after reductions are made for bolt holes at that section.

Where bolts are staggered, there is a tendency for failure to occur in the wood along planes between adjacent bolt holes, and it is suggested that adjacent staggered bolts be considered as being placed at the net section unless bolts in a row are spaced at a minimum of 8 diameters.

For parallel to grain loading in softwood species, the net area remaining at the net section should be at least 80 per cent of the total area in bearing under all the bolts in the particular joint under consideration so that the bearing stress under the bolts and the tensile stress in the member will both be fully developed.

Bolt Holes

Bolt holes should be correctly spaced and aligned so that the bolts fit neatly with only light tapping required to insert. Bolt holes that are too large cause non-uniform bearing of the bolt and excessive inelastic joint deformation under load. Holes that are too tight require an excessive amount of driving and induce splitting of the wood, either during driving or as a result of further seasoning.

Recommended bolt hole diameters are 1/32 inch to 1/16 inch larger than the bolt, depending on the size of the bolt.

The manner in which the holes are bored has an effect on the amount of joint slippage, and as the allowable load in bolted joints is related to the joint deformation under load, it is important that good workmanship and good tools be used in boring bolt holes.

A bolt hole having a smooth surface will sustain a greater bolt load with less deformation than will one which has a roughened surface. To assure maximum joint strength bits should be kept sharp and proper drill speed used when machine boring is being done.

The effect of different drill feed rates on the surface roughness of a bolt hole is shown in Figure 8.16. The load deformation curve shown illustrates graphically the effect of surface roughness on joint deformation. As ultimate loads, not shown on the curve, are the same, there is no encroachment on the ultimate safety of a joint having rough surfaced bolt holes.

High Rate of Feed Low Speed.

Low Rate of Feed High Speed.

Quality of Bolts

Allowable bolt loads are based on common bolts made of hot rolled steel. Where high strength bolts are used, the extra strength of the bolt results in higher proportional limit loads due to a more uniform distribution of the load along the length of the bolt. This eliminates local crushing of the wood fibers at the shear plane between members as the load is applied, and somewhat larger loads can be developed in the joint. Joint deformation will also be proportionately greater at the higher loads.

Washers

A standard cut washer, or a metal plate or strap, should be between the wood and the bolt head and between the wood and the nut to distribute the bearing stress under the bolt head and nut and to avoid crushing the fibers.

While it is desirable that all nuts remain tightened, it is assumed that some loosening of the

TIMBER FASTENERS

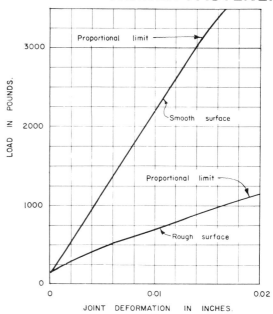

Figure 8.16 — Effect of Rate of Drill Feed on Bolt Hole Surface and on Joint Deformation.

nuts may occur as a result of shrinkage of the lumber. This condition has been provided for in determining the allowable bolt loads.

Joint Deformations

The allowable bolt loads, both parallel and perpendicular to the grain, are accompanied by a limited deformation of such magnitude as to prevent permanent distortion of the joint beyond that generally acceptable in joints under normal conditions of loading or repeated application of the load. While no definite deformation has been established for this limit, joint deformation in excess of the amount caused by the allowable load can occur without danger in certain types of structures. As some movement must take place within the joint before the load is transmitted through the bolt, it is apparent that a large inelastic deformation may take place well below the ultimate load value. This is illustrated in Figure 8.17, which shows a typical load deformation curve for a bolted joint in which 1/2 the proportional limit load was assumed as the allowable load. The joint deformation at a load of 1050 lbs. is 0.018 inches for a 1/2" bolt. At this load and deformation, a reserve of usuable strength remains in the joint and additional load accompanied by larger deformations could be imposed before the ultimate load of 9700 lbs. is reached.

Tables of Allowable Bolt Loads

The tables which conclude this chapter give allowable bolt loads for common bolts in a three member joint acting in double shear, under normal conditions of loading, for lengths of bolt in main members from 1 inch to 14¼ inches and for bolt diameters from ¼ inch to 1¼ inches. Loads are tabulated for wood and for steel side members for loads acting parallel or perpendicu-

TIMBER FASTENERS

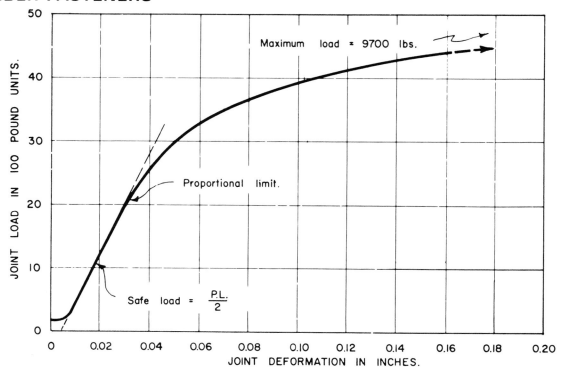

Figure 8.17 — Typical Load Deformation Curve for a Bolted Joint.

lar to grain and are applicable to lumber which has been seasoned prior to fabrication and which will remain dry in service. When referring to the table for a particular value, the dimension to use for "Length of Bolt in Main Member" is the actual thickness of the main member as shown by dimension "t" in Figure 8.6.

The tables of allowable bolt loads may be used to determine:

1. The load capacity of a joint with a given number and size of bolts.

2. The size and number of bolts required when the load is known.

Determining Load Capacity from Tables

1. Determine whether the joint is in single shear, double shear, or multiple shear, and which is the controlling member if wood side members are used,

2. If the main member controls, determine the actual thickness and locate this thickness under the column headed "Length of Bolt in Main Member." If a side member controls, multiply the actual thickness by 2 and locate this value under the column headed "Length of Bolt in Main Member."

3. Across from the bolt diameter for the length of bolt in main member selected, and under the appropriate column for parallel or perpendicular to grain loading is the capacity load for one bolt. If the joint is in single shear, divide this load by 2 to obtain the actual capacity load.

4. Follow the methods shown on Page 200 for Multiple Fasteners to obtain the allowable joint capacity for a joint with multiple bolts.

Example:

Determine the capacity of a three member joint (double shear) for Douglas Fir-Larch with loads acting parallel to the grain and fastened with four bolts of ⅝" diameter.

Main member: 4 x 12 (3-9/16" x 11-½")
Side members: 2 x 12 (1-½" x 11-¼")

The two side members are less than ½ the thickness of the main member and control the allowable bolt load.

For a length of bolt in the main member of 1-½" + 1-½" = 3", the tabulated allowable load for a ⅝" bolt is 2010 pounds.

Following the methods for Multiple Fasteners on Page 200:

$$A_1 = 3.5625 \times 11.5 = 40.97 \text{ in}^2$$
$$A_2 = 2 \times 1\text{-}\tfrac{1}{2} \times 11.25 = 33.75 \text{ in}^2$$
$$A_1/A_2 = 1.21 > 1.0,$$

therefore use $A_2/A_1 = 0.82$

From the table for wood side plates

$$A_2 = 33.75$$
$$N_A/N = 3.84 \text{ for } A_1/A_2 = 0.5$$

and $N_A/N = 3.96$ for $A_1/A_2 = 1.0$

By Interpolation:

$$N_A/N = 3.92 \text{ for } A_2/A_1 = 0.82$$

For ⅝" bolts the allowable load is:
2010 x 3.92 = 7879 lbs.

TIMBER FASTENERS

Determining Size and Number of Bolts for Known Load

1. Determine which is the controlling member in the joint and its actual thickness.

2. Locate this thickness under the column headed "Length of Bolt in Main Member."

3. For this length of bolt in main member select a bolt load from the appropriate column, for the loading under consideration (parallel or perpendicular to grain), that is equal to or greater than the required load per bolt.

4. Follow the methods shown on Page 200 for Multiple Fasteners to obtain the number of bolts of the size selected that are needed to satisfy the actual load on the joint.

Example:

Determine the size and number of bolts for a three member joint under a tensile force of 48,000 pounds consisting of a 6 x 12 main member and two 3 x 12 side plates, all of Douglas Fir — Larch.

Assume two rows of 1" bolts and determine the number required per row.

Following the methods for Multiple Fastenings on Page 200:

$$A_1 = 5.5 \times 11.5 = 62.25 \text{ in}^2$$
$$A_2 = 2 \times 2.5 \times 11.25 = 56.25 \text{ in}^2$$
$$A_1/A_2 = 1.10 \; > \; 1.0,$$

therefore use $A_2/A_1 = 0.9$

For two rows of bolts:

$$N_A = \frac{48000}{2} = 24000 \text{ pounds/row}$$

From the bolt tables, the tabulated load for a 1" bolt is 5200 pounds, therefore $N = 5200$ pounds/bolt.

$$N_A/N = \frac{24000}{5200} = 4.62$$

By inspection of Table 8.1, the N_A/N ratio for A_1/A_2 ratios of 0.5 and 1.0 both exceed the required N_A/N ratio of 4.62, therefore no interpolation is necessary and 5 bolts per row is adequate.

Douglas Fir Highway Truss Bridge and Typical Joint Detail Showing Truss Members Bolted to Steel Gusset Plates.

TIMBER FASTENERS

TABLE 8.10 — BOLTED JOINTS
ALLOWABLE LOADS IN POUNDS ON ONE BOLT IN DOUBLE SHEAR
THREE MEMBER JOINT

Length Of Bolt In Main Member	Diameter Of Bolt	Length / Diameter L/D	Area Of Bolt A = LXD	Dense Douglas Fir-Larch Load Parallel To Grain — Steel Side Members	Dense Douglas Fir-Larch — Wood Side Members	Dense Douglas Fir-Larch — Load Perpendicular To Grain	Douglas Fir-Larch Load Parallel To Grain — Steel Side Members	Douglas Fir-Larch — Wood Side Members	Douglas Fir-Larch — Load Perpendicular To Grain	Douglas Fir South Load Parallel To Grain — Steel Side Members	Douglas Fir South — Wood Side Members	Douglas Fir South — Load Perpendicular To Grain	Hem-Fir Load Parallel To Grain — Steel Side Members	Hem-Fir — Wood Side Members	Hem-Fir — Load Perpendicular To Grain
1	1/4	4.00	.250	440	350	250	370	300	210	340	270	190	330	260	140
	5/16	3.20	.313	580	470	260	500	400	230	430	340	200	420	340	140
	3/8	2.67	.375	710	570	290	600	480	250	520	410	220	500	400	160
	7/16	2.29	.438	830	660	310	710	570	260	600	480	230	590	470	170
	1/2	2.00	.500	950	760	340	810	650	290	690	550	250	670	540	180
	9/16	1.78	.563	1060	850	360	910	730	300	770	620	270	760	610	190
	5/8	1.60	.625	1180	950	380	1010	810	320	860	690	280	840	670	210
	3/4	1.33	.750	1420	1140	420	1210	970	360	1030	830	310	1010	810	230
	7/8	1.14	.875	1660	1320	460	1420	1130	400	1200	960	350	1180	940	250
	1	1.00	1.000	1890	1510	510	1620	1290	430	1380	1100	380	1340	1080	280
1-1/2	1/4	6.00	.375	480	380	370	410	330	320	390	310	280	380	310	200
	5/16	4.80	.469	730	590	400	630	500	340	580	470	300	570	460	220
	3/8	4.00	.563	980	790	440	840	670	370	750	600	330	740	590	240
	7/16	3.43	.656	1210	970	460	1030	830	400	900	720	340	880	700	250
	1/2	3.00	.750	1410	1120	500	1200	960	430	1030	830	370	1010	810	280
	9/16	2.67	.844	1590	1270	530	1360	1090	460	1160	930	400	1130	910	290
	5/8	2.40	.938	1770	1420	570	1510	1210	490	1290	1030	420	1260	1010	310
	3/4	2.00	1.125	2130	1700	630	1820	1460	540	1550	1240	470	1510	1210	350
	7/8	1.71	1.313	2480	1990	700	2120	1700	600	1810	1440	520	1760	1410	380
	1	1.50	1.500	2840	2270	760	2430	1940	650	2060	1650	570	2020	1610	420
2	1/4	8.00	.500	480	380	380	410	330	330	390	310	310	380	310	260
	5/16	6.40	.625	750	600	530	640	510	450	610	490	390	600	480	290
	3/8	5.33	.750	1070	860	580	910	730	500	870	690	430	850	680	320
	7/16	4.57	.875	1420	1140	620	1220	970	530	1120	900	460	1100	880	340
	1/2	4.00	1.000	1750	1400	670	1500	1200	570	1340	1070	500	1310	1050	370
	9/16	3.56	1.125	2050	1640	710	1760	1400	610	1540	1230	530	1500	1200	390
	5/8	3.20	1.250	2330	1860	760	1990	1590	650	1720	1370	560	1680	1340	410
	3/4	2.67	1.500	2830	2260	840	2420	1930	720	2060	1650	630	2020	1610	460
	7/8	2.29	1.750	3300	2640	930	2830	2260	790	2410	1930	690	2350	1880	510
	1	2.00	2.000	3780	3030	1010	3240	2590	870	2750	2200	750	2690	2150	550
2-1/4	1/4	9.00	.563	480	380	380	410	330	330	390	310	310	380	310	270
	5/16	7.20	.703	750	600	570	640	510	490	610	490	440	600	480	320
	3/8	6.00	.844	1070	860	660	920	730	560	880	700	490	860	690	360
	7/16	5.14	.984	1450	1160	690	1240	990	590	1170	940	520	1140	910	380
	1/2	4.50	1.125	1850	1480	750	1580	1260	640	1450	1160	560	1420	1140	410
	9/16	4.00	1.266	2220	1770	800	1890	1520	680	1700	1360	600	1660	1330	440
	5/8	3.60	1.406	2550	2040	850	2180	1750	730	1910	1530	640	1870	1500	470
	3/4	3.00	1.688	3160	2530	950	2700	2160	810	2320	1860	710	2270	1810	520
	7/8	2.57	1.969	3710	2970	1050	3170	2540	890	2710	2170	780	2650	2120	570
	1	2.25	2.250	4250	3400	1140	3630	2910	970	3090	2480	850	3020	2420	620
2-1/2	1/4	10.00	.625	480	380	380	410	330	330	390	310	310	380	310	260
	5/16	8.00	.781	750	600	580	640	510	500	610	490	470	600	480	350
	3/8	6.67	.938	1070	860	720	920	730	620	880	700	540	860	690	400
	7/16	5.71	1.094	1460	1170	770	1250	1000	660	1200	960	570	1170	940	420
	1/2	5.00	1.250	1890	1510	840	1620	1290	720	1520	1210	620	1480	1190	460
	9/16	4.44	1.406	2330	1860	890	1990	1590	760	1820	1460	660	1780	1420	490
	5/8	4.00	1.563	2740	2190	950	2340	1870	810	2090	1670	710	2050	1640	520
	3/4	3.33	1.875	3470	2780	1060	2970	2370	900	2570	2060	790	2510	2010	580
	7/8	2.86	2.188	4110	3290	1160	3520	2810	990	3010	2410	860	2940	2350	630
	1	2.50	2.500	4720	3770	1270	4030	3230	1080	3440	2750	940	3360	2690	690
	1-1/8	2.22	2.813	5320	4250	1380	4550	3640	1180	3870	3090	1030	3780	3020	750
	1-1/4	2.00	3.125	5910	4730	1480	5060	4050	1270	4300	3440	1100	4200	3360	810
	1-1/2	1.67	3.750	7100	5680	1710	6070	4850	1460	5160	4130	1270	5040	4030	930
3	1/4	12.00	.750	480	380	380	410	330	330	390	310	310	380	310	250
	5/16	9.60	.938	750	600	560	640	510	480	610	490	470	600	480	350
	3/8	8.00	1.125	1070	860	770	920	730	660	880	700	630	860	690	460
	7/16	6.86	1.313	1460	1170	910	1250	1000	780	1200	960	690	1170	940	510
	1/2	6.00	1.500	1910	1530	1010	1630	1310	860	1560	1250	750	1530	1220	550
	9/16	5.33	1.688	2400	1920	1070	2060	1650	910	1950	1560	790	1910	1520	580
	5/8	4.80	1.875	2940	2350	1140	2510	2010	970	2340	1870	850	2280	1830	620
	3/4	4.00	2.250	3940	3150	1270	3370	2690	1080	3010	2410	940	2950	2360	690
	7/8	3.43	2.625	4830	3860	1390	4130	3300	1190	3590	2870	1040	3510	2810	760
	1	3.00	3.000	5620	4500	1520	4810	3840	1300	4130	3300	1130	4030	3230	830
	1-1/8	2.67	3.375	6360	5090	1660	5540	4350	1420	4640	3710	1230	4540	3630	910
	1-1/4	2.40	3.750	7080	5670	1780	6060	4840	1520	5160	4130	1330	5040	4030	970
	1-1/2	2.00	4.500	8510	6810	2050	7280	5830	1750	6190	4950	1520	6050	4840	1120

TIMBER FASTENERS

TABLE 8.10 — BOLTED JOINTS
ALLOWABLE LOADS IN POUNDS ON ONE BOLT IN DOUBLE SHEAR
THREE MEMBER JOINT

Length Of Bolt In Main Member	Dia-meter Of Bolt	Length / Dia-meter L/D	Area Of Bolt A = LXD	Load Parallel To Grain		Load Perpen-dicular To Grain	Load Parallel To Grain		Load Perpen-dicular To Grain	Load Parallel To Grain		Load Perpen-dicular To Grain	Load Parallel To Grain		Load Perpen-dicular To Grain
				Steel Side Members	Wood Side Members		Steel Side Members	Wood Side Members		Steel Side Members	Wood Side Members		Steel Side Members	Wood Side Members	
				Mt. Hemlock W. Cedars			Ida. W.-Lpole Pine-S. Spr			Ponderosa-Sugar Pine			Alpine Fir Engel. Spruce		
1	1/4	4.00	.250	310	240	150	290	230	130	270	210	90	220	180	110
	5/16	3.20	.313	390	310	160	360	290	140	330	270	100	280	220	120
	3/8	2.67	.375	470	380	180	440	350	150	400	320	110	330	270	130
	7/16	2.29	.438	550	440	190	510	410	160	470	370	120	390	310	130
	1/2	2.00	.500	630	500	210	580	460	180	530	430	130	440	350	150
	9/16	1.78	.563	710	560	220	650	520	190	600	480	130	500	400	150
	5/8	1.60	.625	780	630	230	730	580	200	670	530	140	550	440	160
	3/4	1.33	.750	940	750	260	870	700	220	800	640	160	660	530	180
	7/8	1.14	.875	1100	880	280	1020	810	240	930	750	170	770	620	200
	1	1.00	1.000	1250	1000	310	1160	930	270	1070	850	190	880	710	220
1-1/2	1/4	6.00	.375	360	290	230	370	300	200	340	270	140	280	230	160
	5/16	4.80	.469	530	430	240	530	420	210	480	390	150	400	320	170
	3/8	4.00	.563	690	550	270	650	520	230	600	480	160	500	400	190
	7/16	3.43	.656	820	660	280	760	610	240	700	560	170	580	460	200
	1/2	3.00	.750	940	750	310	870	700	270	800	640	190	750	600	220
	9/16	2.67	.844	1060	850	330	980	780	280	900	720	200	750	600	230
	5/8	2.40	.938	1180	940	350	1090	870	300	1000	800	210	830	660	250
	3/4	2.00	1.125	1410	1130	390	1310	1040	330	1200	960	240	1000	800	270
	7/8	1.71	1.313	1650	1320	430	1520	1220	370	1400	1120	260	1160	930	300
	1	1.50	1.500	1880	1500	470	1740	1390	400	1600	1280	280	1330	1060	330
2	1/4	8.00	.500	360	290	290	370	300	260	340	270	190	280	230	220
	5/16	6.40	.625	560	450	320	580	470	280	540	430	200	440	360	230
	3/8	5.33	.750	790	630	360	810	650	310	740	590	220	620	490	250
	7/16	4.57	.875	1020	820	380	990	790	320	910	730	230	760	610	270
	1/2	4.00	1.000	1220	980	410	1150	920	350	1060	850	250	880	700	290
	9/16	3.56	1.125	1400	1120	440	1310	1040	370	1200	960	270	1000	800	310
	5/8	3.20	1.250	1570	1250	460	1450	1160	400	1330	1070	280	1110	880	330
	3/4	2.67	1.500	1880	1500	520	1740	1390	440	1600	1280	320	1330	1060	370
	7/8	2.29	1.750	2190	1750	570	2030	1620	490	1870	1490	350	1550	1240	400
	1	2.00	2.000	2510	2010	620	2320	1860	530	2130	1710	380	1770	1410	440
2-1/4	1/4	9.00	.563	360	290	290	370	300	280	340	270	200	280	230	230
	5/16	7.20	.703	560	450	360	580	470	310	540	430	220	440	360	260
	3/8	6.00	.844	800	640	400	840	670	350	770	620	250	640	510	290
	7/16	5.14	.984	1070	850	420	1080	860	370	990	790	260	820	660	300
	1/2	4.50	1.125	1320	1060	460	1280	1020	400	1180	940	280	970	780	330
	9/16	4.00	1.266	1550	1240	490	1460	1170	420	1340	1080	300	1110	890	350
	5/8	3.60	1.406	1740	1400	520	1630	1300	450	1500	1200	320	1240	990	370
	3/4	3.00	1.688	2110	1690	580	1960	1570	500	1800	1440	360	1490	1190	410
	7/8	2.57	1.969	2470	1970	640	2280	1830	550	2100	1680	390	1740	1390	450
	1	2.25	2.250	2820	2260	700	2610	2090	600	2400	1920	430	1990	1590	490
2-1/2	1/4	10.00	.625	360	290	290	370	300	280	340	270	200	280	230	230
	5/16	8.00	.781	560	450	390	580	470	350	540	430	250	440	360	290
	3/8	6.67	.938	800	640	450	840	670	380	770	620	270	640	510	320
	7/16	5.71	1.094	1090	870	470	1130	910	410	1040	830	290	860	690	330
	1/2	5.00	1.250	1380	1110	510	1380	1110	440	1270	1020	310	1050	840	360
	9/16	4.44	1.406	1660	1330	540	1600	1280	470	1470	1180	330	1220	980	390
	5/8	4.00	1.563	1910	1530	580	1800	1440	500	1660	1330	350	1370	1100	410
	3/4	3.33	1.875	2340	1870	650	2180	1740	560	2000	1600	390	1660	1330	460
	7/8	2.86	2.188	2740	2190	710	2540	2030	610	2330	1870	430	1930	1550	500
	1	2.50	2.500	3130	2510	780	2900	2320	670	2670	2130	470	2210	1770	550
	1-1/8	2.22	2.813	3520	2820	840	3260	2610	730	3000	2400	520	2490	1990	600
	1-1/4	2.00	3.125	3920	3130	910	3630	2900	780	3330	2670	550	2760	2210	640
	1-1/2	1.67	3.750	4700	3760	1040	4350	3480	900	4000	3200	640	3320	2650	740
3	1/4	12.00	.750	360	290	280	370	300	270	340	270	190	280	230	220
	5/16	9.60	.938	560	450	390	580	470	370	540	430	260	440	360	310
	3/8	8.00	1.125	800	640	510	840	670	460	770	620	330	640	510	380
	7/16	6.86	1.313	1090	870	570	1140	910	490	1050	840	350	870	690	400
	1/2	6.00	1.500	1430	1140	620	1490	1190	530	1370	1100	380	1140	910	440
	9/16	5.33	1.688	1780	1420	650	1820	1450	560	1670	1340	400	1380	1110	460
	5/8	4.80	1.875	2130	1700	700	2100	1680	600	1930	1540	430	1600	1280	490
	3/4	4.00	2.250	2750	2200	770	2600	2080	670	2390	1910	470	1980	1580	550
	7/8	3.43	2.625	3270	2620	850	3050	2440	730	2800	2240	520	2320	1860	600
	1	3.00	3.000	3760	3010	930	3480	2780	800	3200	2560	570	2650	2120	660
	1-1/8	2.67	3.375	4230	3380	1010	3920	3130	870	3600	2880	620	2980	2390	720
	1-1/4	2.40	3.750	4700	3760	1090	4350	3480	940	4000	3200	670	3320	2650	770
	1-1/2	2.00	4.500	5640	4510	1250	5220	4180	1080	4800	3840	760	3980	3180	890

TIMBER FASTENERS

TABLE 8.10 — BOLTED JOINTS
ALLOWABLE LOADS IN POUNDS ON ONE BOLT IN DOUBLE SHEAR
THREE MEMBER JOINT

Length Of Bolt In Main Member	Diameter Of Bolt	Length / Diameter L/D	Area Of Bolt A = LXD	Load Parallel To Grain — Steel Side Members (Dense Douglas Fir-Larch)	Load Parallel To Grain — Wood Side Members (Dense Douglas Fir-Larch)	Load Perpendicular To Grain	Load Parallel To Grain — Steel Side Members (Douglas Fir-Larch)	Load Parallel To Grain — Wood Side Members (Douglas Fir-Larch)	Load Perpendicular To Grain	Load Parallel To Grain — Steel Side Members (Douglas Fir South)	Load Parallel To Grain — Wood Side Members (Douglas Fir South)	Load Perpendicular To Grain	Load Parallel To Grain — Steel Side Members (Hem-Fir)	Load Parallel To Grain — Wood Side Members (Hem-Fir)	Load Perpendicular To Grain
3-1/8	1/4	12.50	.781	480	380	380	410	330	330	390	310	310	380	310	250
	5/16	10.00	.977	750	600	560	640	510	470	610	490	470	600	480	340
	3/8	8.33	1.172	1070	860	770	920	730	660	880	700	630	860	690	460
	7/16	7.14	1.367	1460	1170	930	1250	1000	790	1190	960	720	1170	930	530
	1/2	6.25	1.563	1910	1530	1050	1630	1310	900	1560	1250	780	1530	1220	570
	9/16	5.56	1.758	2410	1920	1110	2060	1650	950	1970	1570	830	1920	1540	610
	5/8	5.00	1.953	2960	2370	1190	2530	2020	1010	2370	1900	880	2320	1850	650
	3/4	4.17	2.344	4020	3220	1320	3440	2750	1130	3100	2480	980	3030	2430	720
	7/8	3.57	2.734	4980	3980	1450	4260	3410	1240	3730	2980	1080	3650	2920	790
	1	3.13	3.125	5840	4670	1580	4990	3990	1350	4290	3430	1180	4200	3360	870
	1-1/8	2.78	3.516	6610	5290	1730	5650	4520	1480	4830	3870	1280	4730	3780	940
	1-1/4	2.50	3.906	7370	5900	1860	6300	5040	1590	5370	4300	1380	5250	4200	1010
	1-1/2	2.08	4.688	8870	7100	2130	7580	6070	1820	6450	5160	1590	6300	5040	1170
3-1/2	5/16	11.20	1.094	750	600	540	640	510	460	610	490	460	600	480	340
	3/8	9.33	1.313	1070	860	750	920	730	640	880	700	630	860	690	460
	7/16	8.00	1.531	1460	1170	950	1250	1000	810	1200	960	770	1170	940	570
	1/2	7.00	1.750	1910	1530	1140	1630	1310	980	1560	1250	870	1530	1220	640
	9/16	6.22	1.969	2410	1930	1250	2060	1650	1060	1980	1590	930	1940	1550	680
	5/8	5.60	2.188	2970	2380	1330	2540	2030	1130	2430	1950	990	2380	1900	730
	3/4	4.67	2.625	4200	3360	1480	3590	2870	1260	3320	2660	1100	3250	2600	810
	7/8	4.00	3.063	5360	4290	1630	4580	3670	1390	4100	3280	1210	4010	3210	890
	1	3.50	3.500	6400	5120	1770	5480	4380	1520	4780	3820	1320	4670	3740	970
	1-1/8	3.11	3.938	7360	5890	1930	6290	5040	1650	5410	4330	1440	5290	4230	1060
	1-1/4	2.80	4.375	8220	6580	2080	7030	5620	1780	6020	4810	1550	5880	4700	1140
	1-1/2	2.33	5.250	9910	7930	2390	8480	6780	2040	7220	5780	1780	7060	5650	1310
4	5/16	12.80	1.250	750	600	500	640	510	430	610	490	440	600	480	330
	3/8	10.67	1.500	1070	860	720	920	730	610	880	710	610	860	690	450
	7/16	9.14	1.750	1460	1170	930	1250	1000	790	1200	960	780	1170	940	570
	1/2	8.00	2.000	1910	1530	1180	1630	1310	1010	1570	1250	960	1530	1220	700
	9/16	7.11	2.250	2410	1930	1380	2060	1650	1180	1980	1580	1060	1930	1550	780
	5/8	6.40	2.500	2980	2380	1510	2550	2040	1290	2440	1960	1130	2390	1910	830
	3/4	5.33	3.000	4270	3420	1690	3660	2920	1440	3470	2770	1260	3390	2710	920
	7/8	4.57	3.500	5700	4560	1860	4870	3900	1590	4490	3590	1380	4390	3510	1020
	1	4.00	4.000	7000	5600	2030	5990	4790	1730	5360	4290	1510	5240	4190	1110
	1-1/8	3.56	4.500	8210	6570	2210	7020	5620	1890	6140	4910	1640	6000	4800	1210
	1-1/4	3.20	5.000	9320	7450	2370	7970	6380	2030	6870	5500	1770	6710	5370	1300
	1-1/2	2.67	6.000	11310	9050	2730	9670	7740	2330	8250	6600	2030	8060	6450	1490
	1-3/4	2.29	7.000	13220	10570	3070	11300	9040	2630	9630	7700	2290	9410	7530	1680
	2	2.00	8.000	15140	12110	3420	12940	10360	2920	11000	8800	2540	10750	8600	1870
4-1/2	3/8	12.00	1.688	1070	860	680	920	730	580	880	700	600	860	690	440
	7/16	10.29	1.969	1460	1170	900	1250	1000	770	1200	960	760	1170	940	560
	1/2	9.00	2.250	1910	1530	1160	1630	1310	990	1570	1250	970	1530	1220	710
	9/16	8.00	2.531	2410	1930	1410	2060	1650	1210	1980	1580	1150	1940	1550	840
	5/8	7.20	2.813	2980	2380	1640	2550	2040	1400	2440	1950	1270	2390	1910	930
	3/4	6.00	3.375	4290	3430	1900	3670	2940	1620	3520	2810	1410	3440	2750	1040
	7/8	5.14	3.938	5800	4640	2090	4960	3970	1790	4680	3740	1560	4570	3660	1140
	1	4.50	4.500	7390	5910	2280	6320	5060	1950	5800	4640	1700	5670	4540	1250
	1-1/8	4.00	5.063	8860	7090	2490	7580	6060	2120	6780	5420	1850	6630	5300	1360
	1-1/4	3.60	5.625	10220	8170	2670	8740	6990	2280	7660	6130	1990	7480	5990	1460
	1-1/2	3.00	6.750	12640	10120	3070	10810	8650	2620	9280	7430	2290	9070	7260	1680
	1-3/4	2.57	7.875	14840	11870	3460	12690	10150	2950	10830	8660	2570	10580	8470	1890
	2	2.25	9.000	16990	13600	3840	14530	11630	3280	12380	9900	2860	12100	9680	2100
5	7/16	11.43	2.188	1460	1170	860	1250	1000	740	1200	960	740	1170	940	540
	1/2	10.00	2.500	1910	1530	1130	1630	1300	960	1560	1250	950	1530	1220	700
	9/16	8.89	2.813	2410	1930	1390	2060	1650	1190	1980	1580	1160	1940	1550	850
	5/8	8.00	3.125	2980	2380	1670	2550	2040	1430	2450	1960	1360	2390	1910	1000
	3/4	6.67	3.750	4290	3430	2090	3670	2940	1780	3520	2810	1570	3440	2750	1150
	7/8	5.71	4.375	5830	4660	2320	4980	3990	1980	4780	3830	1730	4680	3740	1270
	1	5.00	5.000	7570	6050	2530	6470	5180	2170	6070	4860	1890	5930	4750	1380
	1-1/8	4.44	5.625	9310	7450	2760	7960	6370	2360	7290	5830	2060	7120	5700	1510
	1-1/4	4.00	6.250	10940	8750	2970	9350	7480	2540	8370	6700	2210	8180	6550	1620
	1-1/2	3.33	7.500	13880	11100	3410	11870	9490	2920	10280	8230	2540	10050	8040	1860
	1-3/4	2.86	8.750	16440	13150	3840	14060	11250	3280	12030	9630	2860	11760	9410	2100
	2	2.50	10.000	18860	15090	4270	16130	12910	3650	13750	11000	3180	13440	10750	2330
5-1/8	7/16	11.71	2.242	1460	1160	850	1240	1000	730	1200	960	740	1170	940	540
	1/2	10.25	2.563	1910	1520	1120	1630	1300	950	1560	1250	950	1530	1220	690
	9/16	9.11	2.883	2420	1930	1380	2070	1650	1180	1980	1580	1150	1930	1550	850
	5/8	8.20	3.203	2980	2390	1660	2550	2040	1420	2440	1960	1370	2390	1910	1000

TIMBER FASTENERS

TABLE 8.10 — BOLTED JOINTS
ALLOWABLE LOADS IN POUNDS ON ONE BOLT IN DOUBLE SHEAR
THREE MEMBER JOINT

Length Of Bolt In Main Member	Diameter Of Bolt	Length / Diameter L/D	Area Of Bolt A = LXD	Load Parallel To Grain		Load Perpendicular To Grain	Load Parallel To Grain		Load Perpendicular To Grain	Load Parallel To Grain		Load Perpendicular To Grain	Load Parallel To Grain		Load Perpendicular To Grain
				Steel Side Members	Wood Side Members		Steel Side Members	Wood Side Members		Steel Side Members	Wood Side Members		Steel Side Members	Wood Side Members	
				Mt. Hemlock W. Cedars			Ida. W.-Lpole Pine-S. Spr			Ponderosa-Sugar Pine			Alpine Fir Engel. Spruce		
3-1/8	1/4	12.50	.781	360	290	280	370	300	270	340	270	190	280	230	220
	5/16	10.00	.977	560	450	390	580	470	370	540	430	260	440	360	300
	3/8	8.33	1.172	800	640	520	840	670	480	770	620	340	640	510	390
	7/16	7.14	1.367	1090	870	590	1140	910	510	1050	840	360	870	690	420
	1/2	6.25	1.563	1430	1140	640	1490	1190	550	1370	1100	390	1130	910	450
	9/16	5.56	1.758	1790	1430	680	1850	1480	590	1700	1360	420	1410	1130	480
	5/8	5.00	1.953	2160	1730	720	2160	1730	620	1990	1590	440	1650	1320	510
	3/4	4.17	2.344	2830	2260	810	2690	2160	690	2480	1980	490	2050	1640	570
	7/8	3.57	2.734	3400	2720	890	3170	2540	760	2920	2330	540	2420	1930	630
	1	3.13	3.125	3910	3130	970	3630	2900	830	3330	2670	590	2760	2210	690
	1-1/8	2.78	3.516	4410	3520	1060	4080	3260	910	3750	3000	640	3110	2490	750
	1-1/4	2.50	3.906	4900	3920	1130	4530	3630	980	4170	3330	690	3450	2760	800
	1-1/2	2.08	4.688	5870	4700	1300	5440	4350	1120	5000	4000	800	4140	3320	920
3-1/2	5/16	11.20	1.094	560	450	380	580	470	360	540	430	260	440	350	300
	3/8	9.33	1.313	800	640	520	840	670	490	770	620	350	640	510	410
	7/16	8.00	1.531	1090	870	630	1140	910	570	1050	840	400	870	700	470
	1/2	7.00	1.750	1430	1140	720	1490	1190	620	1370	1100	440	1140	910	510
	9/16	6.22	1.969	1810	1450	760	1890	1510	660	1740	1390	470	1440	1150	540
	5/8	5.60	2.188	2220	1770	810	2290	1840	700	2110	1690	500	1750	1400	580
	3/4	4.67	2.625	3030	2420	900	2960	2370	780	2720	2180	550	2250	1800	640
	7/8	4.00	3.063	3740	2990	990	3540	2830	860	3250	2600	610	2690	2160	710
	1	3.50	3.500	4360	3480	1090	4060	3250	930	3740	2990	660	3090	2480	770
	1-1/8	3.11	3.938	4930	3940	1180	4570	3650	1020	4200	3360	720	3480	2790	840
	1-1/4	2.80	4.375	5480	4390	1270	5080	4060	1090	4670	3740	780	3870	3090	900
	1-1/2	2.33	5.250	6580	5260	1460	6090	4870	1260	5600	4480	890	4640	3710	1040
4	5/16	12.80	1.250	560	450	360	580	470	350	540	430	250	440	350	290
	3/8	10.67	1.500	800	640	500	840	670	480	770	620	340	640	510	400
	7/16	9.14	1.750	1090	870	640	1140	910	610	1050	840	43υ	870	690	500
	1/2	8.00	2.000	1430	1140	790	1490	1190	710	1370	1100	500	1140	910	580
	9/16	7.11	2.250	1800	1440	870	1880	1510	750	1730	1390	530	1440	1150	620
	5/8	6.40	2.500	2230	1780	930	2330	1860	800	2140	1710	570	1780	1420	660
	3/4	5.33	3.000	3160	2530	1030	3230	2580	890	2970	2370	630	2460	1970	730
	7/8	4.57	3.500	4090	3270	1140	3970	3170	980	3650	2920	690	3020	2420	810
	1	4.00	4.000	4880	3910	1240	4620	3690	1070	4250	3400	760	3520	2820	880
	1-1/8	3.56	4.500	5590	4480	1350	5220	4180	1160	4800	3840	830	3980	3180	960
	1-1/4	3.20	5.000	6260	5010	1450	5800	4640	1250	5340	4270	890	4420	3540	1030
	1-1/2	2.67	6.000	7520	6010	1670	6960	5570	1440	6400	5120	1020	5300	4240	1180
	1-3/4	2.29	7.000	8770	7020	1880	8120	6500	1620	7470	5980	1150	6190	4950	1330
	2	2.00	8.000	10020	8020	2090	9280	7420	1800	8540	6830	1280	7070	5660	1480
4-1/2	3/8	12.00	1.688	800	640	490	840	670	470	770	620	340	640	510	390
	7/16	10.29	1.969	1090	870	620	1140	910	600	1050	840	430	870	700	490
	1/2	9.00	2.250	1430	1140	800	1490	1190	750	1370	1100	530	1140	910	620
	9/16	8.00	2.531	1810	1440	940	1890	1510	840	1730	1390	600	1440	1150	690
	5/8	7.20	2.813	2220	1780	1040	2330	1860	900	2140	1710	640	1770	1420	740
	3/4	6.00	3.375	3210	2560	1160	3350	2680	1000	3080	2470	710	2550	2040	820
	7/8	5.14	3.938	4260	3410	1280	4310	3450	1100	3960	3170	780	3280	2630	910
	1	4.50	4.500	5290	4230	1390	5110	4090	1200	4700	3760	850	3890	3120	990
	1-1/8	4.00	5.063	6180	4940	1520	5840	4680	1310	5380	4300	930	4450	3560	1080
	1-1/4	3.60	5.625	6980	5580	1630	6520	5220	1410	6000	4800	1000	4970	3970	1160
	1-1/2	3.00	6.750	8460	6770	1880	7830	6260	1620	7200	5760	1150	5970	4770	1330
	1-3/4	2.57	7.875	9870	7890	2110	9140	7310	1820	8400	6720	1290	6960	5570	1500
	2	2.25	9.000	11280	9020	2350	10440	8350	2020	9600	7680	1440	7960	6370	1670
5	7/16	11.43	2.188	1090	870	610	1140	910	590	1050	840	420	870	700	490
	1/2	10.00	2.500	1430	1140	780	1490	1190	750	1370	1100	530	1140	910	620
	9/16	8.89	2.813	1800	1440	950	1880	1510	890	1730	1390	630	1440	1150	740
	5/8	8.00	3.125	2230	1780	1110	2330	1860	1000	2140	1710	710	1770	1420	820
	3/4	6.67	3.750	3210	2560	1290	3350	2680	1110	3080	2470	790	2550	2040	920
	7/8	5.71	4.375	4360	3490	1420	4530	3620	1220	4160	3330	870	3450	2760	1010
	1	5.00	5.000	5530	4430	1550	5530	4430	1330	5090	4070	950	4220	3370	1100
	1-1/8	4.44	5.625	6640	5310	1690	6410	5130	1450	5890	4720	1030	4880	3910	1200
	1-1/4	4.00	6.250	7630	6100	1820	7210	5770	1560	6640	5310	1110	5500	4400	1290
	1-1/2	3.33	7.500	9370	7500	2090	8700	6960	1800	8000	6400	1270	6630	5300	1480
	1-3/4	2.86	8.750	10960	8750	2350	10150	8120	2020	9340	7470	1430	7740	6190	1670
	2	2.50	10.000	12530	10020	2610	11600	9280	2250	10670	8540	1590	8840	7070	1850
5-1/8	7/16	11.71	2.242	1090	870	610	1140	910	590	1050	840	420	870	700	480
	1/2	10.25	2.563	1430	1140	780	1490	1190	750	1370	1100	530	1140	910	610
	9/16	9.11	2.883	1800	1440	950	1880	1510	900	1730	1390	640	1440	1150	740
	5/8	8.20	3.203	2230	1780	1120	2330	1860	1020	2140	1710	720	1780	1420	840

TIMBER FASTENERS

TABLE 8.10 — BOLTED JOINTS
ALLOWABLE LOADS IN POUNDS ON ONE BOLT IN DOUBLE SHEAR
THREE MEMBER JOINT

Length Of Bolt In Main Member	Dia-meter Of Bolt	Length / Dia-meter L/D	Area Of Bolt A = LXD	Dense Douglas Fir-Larch			Douglas Fir-Larch			Douglas Fir South			Hem-Fir		
				Steel Side Members	Wood Side Members	Load Perpendicular To Grain	Steel Side Members	Wood Side Members	Load Perpendicular To Grain	Steel Side Members	Wood Side Members	Load Perpendicular To Grain	Steel Side Members	Wood Side Members	Load Perpendicular To Grain
5-1/8 continued	3/4	6.83	3.844	4300	3440	2130	3680	2940	1820	3520	2810	1610	3440	2750	1180
	7/8	5.86	4.484	5830	4660	2380	4990	3990	2030	4790	3830	1770	4680	3740	1300
	1	5.13	5.125	7600	6080	2600	6500	5200	2220	6100	4880	1930	5970	4770	1420
	1-1/8	4.56	5.766	9390	7510	2830	8030	6430	2420	7400	5920	2110	7230	5780	1550
	1-1/4	4.10	6.406	11090	8870	3040	9480	7590	2600	8530	6820	2260	8330	6670	1660
	1-1/2	3.42	7.688	14150	11320	3500	12100	9680	2990	10520	8410	2600	10280	8220	1910
	1-3/4	2.93	8.969	16830	13470	3940	14400	11520	3360	12330	9870	2930	12050	9640	2150
	2	2.56	10.250	19320	15450	4380	16520	13220	3740	14090	11280	3260	13780	11020	2390
5-1/2	7/16	12.57	2.406	1460	1170	820	1250	1000	700	1190	960	730	1170	930	530
	1/2	11.00	2.750	1900	1520	1090	1630	1300	930	1570	1250	930	1530	1220	680
	9/16	9.78	3.094	2410	1930	1350	2060	1650	1160	1980	1580	1140	1930	1550	840
	5/8	8.80	3.438	2980	2380	1650	2550	2040	1410	2440	1960	1380	2390	1910	1010
	3/4	7.33	4.125	4290	3430	2200	3660	2930	1880	3520	2810	1720	3440	2750	1270
	7/8	6.29	4.813	5850	4680	2550	5000	4000	2180	4790	3830	1900	4680	3750	1400
	1	5.50	5.500	7600	6080	2790	6500	5200	2380	6220	4970	2080	6080	4860	1520
	1-1/8	4.89	6.188	9550	7640	3040	8170	6540	2600	7620	6100	2260	7450	5960	1660
	1-1/4	4.40	6.875	11450	9160	3260	9790	7830	2790	8950	7160	2430	8750	7000	1780
	1-1/2	3.67	8.250	14910	11930	3750	12750	10200	3210	11210	8970	2790	10960	8760	2050
	1-3/4	3.14	9.625	17970	14380	4220	15370	12300	3610	13220	10580	3140	12920	10340	2310
	2	2.75	11.000	20690	16550	4700	17690	14150	4010	15130	12100	3500	14780	11830	2570
6	1/2	12.00	3.000	1910	1530	1050	1630	1310	890	1560	1250	910	1530	1220	670
	9/16	10.67	3.375	2410	1930	1320	2060	1650	1120	1980	1590	1120	1940	1550	820
	5/8	9.60	3.750	2980	2380	1610	2550	2040	1380	2440	1950	1350	2380	1910	990
	3/4	8.00	4.500	4290	3430	2230	3670	2940	1910	3520	2820	1810	3440	2750	1330
	7/8	6.86	5.250	5840	4670	2740	5000	4000	2340	4790	3830	2070	4680	3740	1520
	1	6.00	6.000	7630	6100	3040	6520	5220	2600	6250	5000	2260	6110	4890	1660
	1-1/8	5.33	6.750	9620	7690	3310	8220	6580	2830	7800	6240	2470	7620	6100	1810
	1-1/4	4.80	7.500	11750	9400	3560	10050	8040	3040	9340	7480	2650	9130	7310	1950
	1-1/2	4.00	9.000	15750	12600	4090	13470	10780	3500	12050	9640	3050	11780	9430	2240
	1-3/4	3.43	10.500	19310	15450	4610	16510	13210	3940	14370	11490	3430	14040	11230	2520
	2	3.00	12.000	22480	17980	5120	19220	15380	4380	16500	13200	3810	16130	12900	2800
6-1/4	1/2	12.50	3.125	1900	1520	1030	1630	1300	880	1560	1250	900	1530	1220	660
	9/16	11.11	3.516	2420	1930	1300	2070	1650	1110	1980	1590	1110	1940	1550	810
	5/8	10.00	3.906	2980	2380	1590	2550	2040	1360	2440	1960	1340	2390	1910	990
	3/4	8.33	4.688	4280	3430	2220	3660	2930	1890	3520	2820	1830	3440	2750	1340
	7/8	7.14	5.469	5840	4670	2800	4990	3990	2390	4780	3820	2160	4670	3730	1580
	1	6.25	6.250	7630	6100	3170	6520	5220	2710	6260	5010	2360	6120	4890	1730
	1-1/8	5.56	7.031	9620	7700	3450	8230	6580	2950	7860	6290	2570	7680	6150	1890
	1-1/4	5.00	7.813	11830	9460	3710	10110	8090	3170	9490	7590	2760	9270	7420	2030
	1-1/2	4.17	9.375	16090	12870	4260	13760	11010	3640	12410	9930	3170	12130	9710	2330
	1-3/4	3.57	10.938	19910	15930	4800	17020	13620	4100	14920	11940	3570	14580	11670	2620
	2	3.13	12.500	23340	18670	5340	19960	15970	4560	17170	13740	3970	16780	13430	2920
6-3/4	9/16	12.00	3.797	2410	1930	1250	2060	1650	1070	1980	1580	1090	1930	1550	800
	5/8	10.80	4.219	2980	2380	1550	2550	2040	1330	2450	1960	1320	2390	1910	970
	3/4	9.00	5.063	4290	3430	2190	3670	2940	1870	3520	2820	1830	3440	2750	1340
	7/8	7.71	5.906	5830	4670	2860	4990	3990	2440	4780	3820	2290	4670	3730	1680
	1	6.75	6.750	7640	6110	3370	6530	5230	2880	6250	5000	2550	6110	4880	1870
	1-1/8	6.00	7.594	9660	7720	3730	8260	6610	3190	7920	6330	2770	7740	6190	2040
	1-1/4	5.40	8.438	11890	9510	4010	10170	8140	3420	9660	7730	2980	9450	7560	2190
	1-1/2	4.50	10.125	16630	13300	4610	14220	11380	3940	13060	10450	3430	12760	10210	2520
	1-3/4	3.86	11.813	20960	16770	5190	17930	14340	4430	15920	12730	3860	15560	12450	2830
	2	3.38	13.500	24930	19940	5760	21320	17060	4930	18490	14790	4290	18070	14460	3150
7	9/16	12.44	3.938	2410	1930	1230	2060	1650	1050	1980	1580	1080	1930	1550	790
	5/8	11.20	4.375	2980	2380	1530	2550	2040	1310	2450	1960	1310	2390	1920	960
	3/4	9.33	5.250	4290	3430	2170	3670	2940	1860	3520	2810	1820	3440	2750	1330
	7/8	8.00	6.125	5840	4670	2860	5000	4000	2450	4790	3830	2330	4680	3750	1710
	1	7.00	7.000	7630	6100	3450	6520	5220	2950	6260	5010	2640	6120	4890	1940
	1-1/8	6.22	7.875	9660	7720	3870	8260	6610	3300	7930	6340	2880	7750	6200	2110
	1-1/4	5.60	8.750	11890	9510	4160	10170	8130	3550	9730	7790	3090	9510	7610	2270
	1-1/2	4.67	10.500	16790	13430	4780	14360	11490	4080	13280	10630	3560	12980	10390	2610
	1-3/4	4.00	12.250	21440	17150	5380	18330	14670	4600	16410	13130	4000	16040	12830	2940
	2	3.50	14.000	25610	20490	5980	21900	17520	5110	19120	15290	4450	18680	14950	3270

TIMBER FASTENERS

TABLE 8.10 — BOLTED JOINTS
ALLOWABLE LOADS IN POUNDS ON ONE BOLT IN DOUBLE SHEAR
THREE MEMBER JOINT

Length Of Bolt In Main Member	Diameter Of Bolt	Length / Diameter L/D	Area Of Bolt A = LXD	Load Parallel To Grain Steel Side Members (Mt. Hemlock)	Load Parallel To Grain Wood Side Members (W. Cedars)	Load Perpendicular To Grain	Load Parallel To Grain Steel Side Members (Ida.)	Load Parallel To Grain Wood Side Members (W.-Lpole Pine-S. Spr)	Load Perpendicular To Grain	Load Parallel To Grain Steel Side Members (Ponderosa)	Load Parallel To Grain Wood Side Members (Sugar Pine)	Load Perpendicular To Grain	Load Parallel To Grain Steel Side Members (Alpine Fir)	Load Parallel To Grain Wood Side Members (Engel. Spruce)	Load Perpendicular To Grain
5-1/8 continued	3/4	6.83	3.844	3200	2560	1320	3340	2680	1140	3080	2460	810	2550	2040	940
	7/8	5.86	4.484	4360	3490	1460	4550	3640	1250	4180	3350	890	3470	2770	1030
	1	5.13	5.125	5560	4450	1590	5620	4490	1370	5170	4130	970	4280	3430	1130
	1-1/8	4.56	5.766	6740	5390	1730	6530	5230	1490	6010	4810	1060	4980	3980	1230
	1-1/4	4.10	6.406	7770	6220	1860	7370	5900	1600	6780	5430	1140	5620	4490	1320
	1-1/2	3.42	7.688	9580	7670	2140	8920	7130	1840	8200	6560	1310	6800	5440	1520
	1-3/4	2.93	8.969	11240	8990	2410	10400	8320	2070	9570	7660	1470	7930	6340	1710
	2	2.56	10.250	12840	10280	2680	11890	9510	2300	10940	8750	1630	9060	7250	1900
5-1/2	7/16	12.57	2.406	1090	870	600	1140	910	580	1050	840	410	870	690	480
	1/2	11.00	2.750	1430	1140	760	1490	1190	740	1370	1100	520	1140	910	610
	9/16	9.78	3.094	1800	1440	940	1880	1510	900	1730	1390	640	1440	1150	740
	5/8	8.80	3.438	2230	1780	1130	2330	1860	1050	2140	1710	750	1770	1420	870
	3/4	7.33	4.125	3210	2560	1420	3350	2680	1220	3080	2470	870	2550	2040	1010
	7/8	6.29	4.813	4370	3490	1560	4570	3650	1340	4200	3360	950	3480	2780	1110
	1	5.50	5.500	5670	4530	1700	5830	4670	1470	5360	4290	1040	4440	3560	1210
	1-1/8	4.89	6.188	6950	5560	1860	6900	5520	1600	6350	5080	1130	5260	4210	1320
	1-1/4	4.40	6.875	8160	6530	2000	7840	6270	1720	7210	5770	1220	5970	4780	1420
	1-1/2	3.67	8.250	10210	8170	2300	9560	7650	1980	8790	7040	1400	7290	5830	1630
	1-3/4	3.14	9.625	12050	9640	2580	11170	8930	2220	10270	8220	1580	8510	6810	1830
	2	2.75	11.000	13780	11030	2870	12760	10210	2470	11740	9390	1750	9720	7780	2040
6	1/2	12.00	3.000	1430	1140	750	1490	1190	730	1370	1100	520	1140	910	600
	9/16	10.67	3.375	1810	1450	920	1880	1510	880	1730	1390	630	1440	1150	730
	5/8	9.60	3.750	2220	1780	1110	2330	1860	1070	2140	1710	760	1770	1420	880
	3/4	8.00	4.500	3210	2570	1490	3350	2680	1330	3080	2470	950	2550	2040	1100
	7/8	6.86	5.250	4360	3490	1700	4560	3640	1470	4190	3350	1040	3470	2780	1210
	1	6.00	6.000	5700	4560	1860	5960	4770	1600	5480	4380	1140	4540	3630	1320
	1-1/8	5.33	6.750	7110	5680	2030	7260	5810	1740	6680	5340	1240	5530	4430	1440
	1-1/4	4.80	7.500	8510	6810	2180	8400	6720	1870	7720	6180	1330	6400	5120	1540
	1-1/2	4.00	9.000	10980	8790	2500	10390	8310	2160	9560	7640	1530	7920	6330	1780
	1-3/4	3.43	10.500	13090	10470	2820	12180	9740	2430	11200	8960	1720	9280	7430	2000
	2	3.00	12.000	15040	12030	3130	13920	11140	2700	12800	10240	1910	10610	8490	2220
6-1/4	1/2	12.50	3.125	1430	1140	740	1490	1190	720	1370	1100	510	1140	910	590
	9/16	11.11	3.516	1810	1450	910	1880	1510	880	1730	1390	620	1440	1150	730
	5/8	10.00	3.906	2230	1780	1100	2330	1860	1060	2140	1710	750	1780	1420	870
	3/4	8.33	4.688	3210	2570	1500	3350	2680	1380	3080	2470	980	2550	2040	1130
	7/8	7.14	5.469	4350	3480	1770	4560	3640	1530	4190	3350	1080	3470	2780	1260
	1	6.25	6.250	5700	4560	1940	5950	4760	1670	5480	4380	1180	4540	3630	1370
	1-1/8	5.56	7.031	7160	5730	2110	7410	5930	1820	6810	5450	1290	5640	4520	1500
	1-1/4	5.00	7.813	8640	6920	2270	8650	6920	1950	7950	6360	1390	6590	5270	1610
	1-1/2	4.17	9.375	11310	9050	2610	10780	8620	2240	9910	7930	1590	8210	6570	1850
	1-3/4	3.57	10.938	13600	10880	2940	12690	10150	2530	11670	9340	1790	9670	7740	2080
	2	3.13	12.500	15650	12520	3260	14500	11600	2810	13340	10670	1990	11050	8840	2310
6-3/4	9/16	12.00	3.797	1800	1440	900	1890	1510	870	1730	1390	620	1440	1150	710
	5/8	10.80	4.219	2230	1790	1080	2330	1860	1050	2140	1710	740	1780	1420	860
	3/4	9.00	5.063	3210	2570	1500	3350	2680	1420	3080	2470	1010	2560	2040	1170
	7/8	7.71	5.906	4350	3480	1880	4560	3650	1650	4190	3350	1170	3470	2780	1360
	1	6.75	6.750	5690	4550	2090	5950	4760	1800	5470	4380	1280	4540	3630	1480
	1-1/8	6.00	7.594	7210	5770	2280	7540	6030	1960	6940	5550	1390	5750	4600	1620
	1-1/4	5.40	8.438	8810	7050	2450	9020	7220	2110	8300	6640	1500	6880	5500	1740
	1-1/2	4.50	10.125	11900	9520	2820	11500	9200	2420	10580	8460	1720	8760	7010	2000
	1-3/4	3.86	11.813	14510	11600	3170	13660	10930	2730	12570	10050	1940	10410	8330	2250
	2	3.38	13.500	16850	13480	3530	15660	12530	3030	14410	11520	2150	11930	9550	2500
7	9/16	12.44	3.938	1800	1440	890	1880	1510	860	1730	1390	610	1430	1150	710
	5/8	11.20	4.375	2230	1790	1070	2320	1860	1040	2140	1710	740	1770	1420	860
	3/4	9.33	5.250	3200	2560	1490	3340	2680	1430	3080	2460	1010	2550	2040	1170
	7/8	8.00	6.125	4370	3490	1910	4560	3650	1710	4200	3360	1210	3480	2780	1410
	1	7.00	7.000	5700	4560	2170	5960	4770	1870	5480	4390	1330	4540	3630	1540
	1-1/8	6.22	7.875	7220	5780	2360	7550	6040	2030	6940	5550	1440	5750	4600	1680
	1-1/4	5.60	8.750	8870	7100	2540	9180	7340	2190	8440	6750	1550	6990	5590	1800
	1-1/2	4.67	10.500	12100	9680	2920	11830	9460	2510	10880	8700	1780	9010	7210	2070
	1-3/4	4.00	12.250	14950	11960	3290	14140	11310	2830	13010	10400	2010	10780	8620	2330
	2	3.50	14.000	17420	13940	3660	16240	12990	3150	14940	11950	2230	12380	9900	2590

TIMBER FASTENERS

TABLE 8.10 — BOLTED JOINTS
ALLOWABLE LOADS IN POUNDS ON ONE BOLT IN DOUBLE SHEAR
THREE MEMBER JOINT

Length Of Bolt In Main Member	Diameter Of Bolt	Length / Diameter L/D	Area Of Bolt A = LXD	Load Parallel To Grain — Steel Side Members	Load Parallel To Grain — Wood Side Members	Load Perpendicular To Grain	Load Parallel To Grain — Steel Side Members	Load Parallel To Grain — Wood Side Members	Load Perpendicular To Grain	Load Parallel To Grain — Steel Side Members	Load Parallel To Grain — Wood Side Members	Load Perpendicular To Grain	Load Parallel To Grain — Steel Side Members	Load Parallel To Grain — Wood Side Members	Load Perpendicular To Grain
				Dense Douglas Fir-Larch			Douglas Fir-Larch			Douglas Fir South			Hem-Fir		
7-1/2	5/8	12.00	4.688	2980	2380	1480	2550	2040	1260	2440	1950	1290	2390	1910	950
	3/4	10.00	5.625	4290	3430	2130	3670	2930	1820	3520	2820	1800	3440	2750	1320
	7/8	8.57	6.563	5840	4670	2840	4990	3990	2430	4790	3830	2360	4680	3750	1730
	1	7.50	7.500	7620	6100	3550	6520	5210	3030	6250	5000	2800	6110	4890	2060
	1-1/8	6.67	8.438	9660	7730	4100	8260	6610	3500	7910	6330	3080	7730	6190	2260
	1-1/4	6.00	9.375	11920	9540	4450	10190	8160	3800	9770	7820	3310	9550	7640	2430
	1-1/2	5.00	11.250	17030	13620	5120	14560	11650	4370	13660	10930	3810	13350	10680	2800
	1-3/4	4.29	13.125	22180	17740	5760	18960	15170	4920	17240	13790	4290	16850	13480	3150
	2	3.75	15.000	26900	21520	6400	23010	18410	5470	20320	16250	4770	19860	15890	3500
8	5/8	12.80	5.000	2980	2380	1430	2550	2040	1220	2440	1950	1270	2390	1910	930
	3/4	10.67	6.000	4290	3430	2080	3670	2940	1780	3520	2820	1760	3440	2760	1300
	7/8	9.14	7.000	5840	4670	2800	5000	4000	2390	4780	3830	2340	4680	3740	1720
	1	8.00	8.000	7630	6100	3570	6520	5220	3050	6260	5010	2900	6120	4890	2130
	1-1/8	7.11	9.000	9660	7720	4270	8260	6610	3650	7910	6330	3290	7730	6180	2410
	1-1/4	6.40	10.000	11920	9540	4740	10190	8160	4050	9780	7820	3530	9560	7650	2590
	1-1/2	5.33	12.000	17100	13680	5460	14620	11700	4670	13860	11090	4060	13550	10840	2980
	1-3/4	4.57	14.000	22780	18220	6150	19480	15590	5250	17960	14370	4570	17560	14040	3360
	2	4.00	16.000	28000	22400	6830	23950	19160	5840	21430	17140	5090	20950	16760	3730
8-3/4	3/4	11.67	6.563	4280	3430	2010	3660	2930	1710	3520	2820	1730	3440	2750	1270
	7/8	10.00	7.656	5840	4670	2730	4990	3990	2330	4790	3830	2310	4680	3750	1690
	1	8.75	8.750	7600	6080	3520	6500	5200	3010	6230	4990	2940	6090	4870	2160
	1-1/8	7.78	9.844	9650	7720	4370	8250	6600	3740	7910	6320	3510	7730	6180	2580
	1-1/4	7.00	10.938	11920	9540	5050	10190	8160	4320	9780	7820	3870	9560	7640	2840
	1-1/2	5.83	13.125	17130	13710	5970	14650	11720	5100	14040	11230	4440	13720	10980	3260
	1-3/4	5.00	15.313	23180	18540	6720	19820	15860	5740	18590	14870	5000	18170	14540	3670
	2	4.38	17.500	29200	23360	7470	24970	19980	6390	22840	18270	5560	22320	17860	4080
9	3/4	12.00	6.750	4290	3430	1980	3670	2940	1690	3520	2810	1720	3440	2750	1270
	7/8	10.29	7.875	5840	4670	2700	5000	4000	2310	4790	3830	2290	4680	3740	1680
	1	9.00	9.000	7630	6100	3500	6520	5220	2990	6260	5010	2930	6120	4900	2150
	1-1/8	8.00	10.125	9660	7720	4380	8260	6610	3740	7920	6340	3560	7740	6190	2610
	1-1/4	7.20	11.250	11920	9540	5120	10190	8160	4380	9760	7810	3960	9540	7630	2910
	1-1/2	6.00	13.500	17160	13730	6140	14680	11740	5250	14070	11260	4570	13750	11000	3360
	1-3/4	5.14	15.750	23210	18570	6910	19850	15880	5910	18710	14970	5150	18290	14630	3780
	2	4.50	18.000	29560	23650	7690	25280	20220	6570	23220	18570	5720	22690	18150	4200
9-1/2	3/4	12.67	7.125	4290	3430	1920	3670	2930	1640	3510	2810	1700	3430	2740	1250
	7/8	10.86	8.313	5850	4680	2660	5000	4000	2270	4800	3840	2260	4690	3750	1660
	1	9.50	9.500	7620	6100	3460	6520	5210	2960	6260	5010	2900	6120	4890	2130
	1-1/8	8.44	10.688	9650	7720	4340	8250	6600	3710	7920	6340	3600	7740	6190	2640
	1-1/4	7.60	11.875	11910	9530	5210	10180	8150	4450	9760	7810	4140	9540	7640	3040
	1-1/2	6.33	14.250	17170	13740	6480	14690	11750	5530	14070	11260	4830	13750	11000	3540
	1-3/4	5.43	16.625	23280	18620	7300	19910	15920	6240	18950	15160	5430	18520	14820	3990
	2	4.75	19.000	29950	23960	8110	25610	20490	6930	23800	19040	6040	23260	18610	4430
10	7/8	11.43	8.750	5830	4660	2600	4980	3990	2220	4790	3830	2230	4680	3740	1640
	1	10.00	10.000	7630	6100	3410	6520	5220	2910	6260	5010	2870	6120	4890	2110
	1-1/8	8.89	11.250	9640	7710	4310	8250	6600	3680	7920	6340	3600	7740	6190	2650
	1-1/4	8.00	12.500	11920	9540	5230	10190	8160	4470	9780	7820	4250	9560	7650	3120
	1-1/2	6.67	15.000	17170	13740	6750	14680	11750	5770	14070	11250	5080	13750	11000	3730
	1-3/4	5.71	17.500	23310	18650	7680	19930	15950	6560	19130	15300	5720	18700	14960	4200
	2	5.00	20.000	30270	24220	8540	25890	20710	7300	24280	19430	6360	23740	18990	4670
10-3/4	7/8	12.29	9.406	5840	4670	2510	4990	3990	2140	4770	3820	2200	4670	3730	1620
	1	10.75	10.750	7630	6100	3320	6520	5220	2840	6250	5000	2820	6110	4890	2070
	1-1/8	9.56	12.094	9660	7730	4240	8260	6610	3620	7920	6330	3550	7740	6190	2610
	1-1/4	8.60	13.438	11900	9520	5170	10180	8140	4420	9770	7820	4310	9550	7640	3160
	1-1/2	7.17	16.125	17150	13720	7050	14660	11730	6020	14060	11250	5450	13740	10990	4000
	1-3/4	6.14	18.813	23310	18650	8260	19940	15950	7060	19170	15330	6150	18740	14990	4510
	2	5.38	21.500	30430	24340	9180	26020	20820	7850	24690	19750	6830	24130	19300	5020
11	7/8	12.57	9.625	5830	4660	2480	4980	3990	2120	4780	3820	2190	4670	3740	1610
	1	11.00	11.000	7620	6090	3310	6510	5210	2830	6260	5010	2810	6120	4900	2060
	1-1/8	9.78	12.375	9650	7720	4200	8250	6600	3590	7910	6330	3540	7730	6190	2600
	1-1/4	8.80	13.750	11920	9530	5150	10190	8150	4400	9780	7820	4310	9550	7640	3160
	1-1/2	7.33	16.500	17140	13710	7120	14660	11730	6080	14070	11250	5560	13750	11000	4080
	1-3/4	6.29	19.250	23380	18710	8450	20000	16000	7220	19160	15330	6290	18730	14990	4620
	2	5.50	22.000	30390	24310	9390	25990	20790	8030	24870	19890	6990	24310	19440	5130

TIMBER FASTENERS

TABLE 8.10 — BOLTED JOINTS
ALLOWABLE LOADS IN POUNDS ON ONE BOLT IN DOUBLE SHEAR
THREE MEMBER JOINT

Length Of Bolt In Main Member	Dia-meter Of Bolt	Length / Dia-meter L/D	Area Of Bolt A = LXD	Mt. Hemlock W. Cedars Load Parallel To Grain Steel Side Members	Wood Side Members	Load Perpendicular To Grain	Ida. W.-Lpole Pine-S. Spr Load Parallel To Grain Steel Side Members	Wood Side Members	Load Perpendicular To Grain	Ponderosa-Sugar Pine Load Parallel To Grain Steel Side Members	Wood Side Members	Load Perpendicular To Grain	Alpine Fir Engel. Spruce Load Parallel To Grain Steel Side Members	Wood Side Members	Load Perpendicular To Grain
7-1/2	5/8	12.00	4.688	2230	1780	1060	2330	1860	1030	2140	1710	730	1770	1420	850
	3/4	10.00	5.625	3210	2570	1480	3350	2680	1420	3090	2470	1000	2560	2050	1170
	7/8	8.57	6.563	4370	3490	1940	4560	3650	1790	4190	3360	1270	3480	2780	1480
	1	7.50	7.500	5700	4560	2300	5960	4770	2000	5480	4390	1420	4540	3630	1650
	1-1/8	6.67	8.438	7210	5770	2530	7540	6030	2180	6930	5550	1550	5740	4600	1800
	1-1/4	6.00	9.375	8900	7120	2720	9310	7450	2340	8560	6850	1660	7090	5680	1930
	1-1/2	5.00	11.250	12450	9960	3130	12450	9960	2690	11450	9160	1910	9490	7590	2220
	1-3/4	4.29	13.125	15710	12560	3520	15030	12020	3030	13820	11060	2150	11450	9160	2500
	2	3.75	15.000	18510	14810	3920	17370	13890	3370	15970	12780	2390	13230	10590	2780
8	5/8	12.80	5.000	2220	1780	1040	2330	1860	1010	2140	1710	720	1770	1420	840
	3/4	10.67	6.000	3210	2570	1450	3350	2680	1400	3080	2460	990	2550	2040	1150
	7/8	9.14	7.000	4360	3490	1920	4550	3640	1830	4180	3350	1300	3470	2770	1500
	1	8.00	8.000	5700	4560	2380	5960	4770	2130	5480	4380	1510	4540	3630	1760
	1-1/8	7.11	9.000	7210	5770	2700	7540	6030	2330	6930	5550	1650	5740	4600	1920
	1-1/4	6.40	10.000	8910	7130	2900	9320	7450	2500	8570	6850	1770	7100	5680	2060
	1-1/2	5.33	12.000	12630	10100	3340	12900	10320	2870	11870	9500	2040	9830	7870	2370
	1-3/4	4.57	14.000	16370	13090	3760	15870	12690	3230	14590	11680	2300	12090	9670	2660
	2	4.00	16.000	19530	15620	4180	18470	14770	3600	16990	13590	2550	14070	11260	2960
8-3/4	3/4	11.67	6.563	3210	2570	1420	3350	2680	1380	3080	2470	980	2550	2040	1140
	7/8	10.00	7.656	4370	3490	1890	4570	3650	1820	4200	3360	1290	3480	2780	1500
	1	8.75	8.750	5680	4540	2420	5940	4750	2250	5460	4370	1600	4530	3620	1860
	1-1/8	7.78	9.844	7200	5760	2890	7530	6020	2540	6920	5540	1800	5740	4590	2100
	1-1/4	7.00	10.938	8910	7130	3180	9310	7450	2730	8570	6850	1940	7100	5680	2250
	1-1/2	5.83	13.125	12800	10240	3650	13350	10680	3140	12280	9830	2230	10180	8140	2590
	1-3/4	5.00	15.313	16940	13550	4110	16950	13560	3540	15590	12470	2510	12910	10330	2910
	2	4.38	17.500	20810	16650	4570	19980	15980	3930	18370	14700	2790	15220	12180	3240
9	3/4	12.00	6.750	3210	2560	1420	3350	2680	1370	3080	2470	970	2550	2040	1130
	7/8	10.29	7.875	4360	3490	1880	4560	3650	1810	4190	3350	1280	3470	2780	1490
	1	9.00	9.000	5710	4570	2410	5960	4770	2270	5480	4390	1610	4540	3630	1870
	1-1/8	8.00	10.125	7220	5780	2920	7540	6030	2620	6940	5550	1860	5750	4600	2150
	1-1/4	7.20	11.250	8900	7120	3260	9310	7440	2810	8560	6850	2000	7090	5670	2320
	1-1/2	6.00	13.500	12820	10260	3760	13410	10720	3230	12330	9860	2290	10220	8170	2660
	1-3/4	5.14	15.750	17050	13640	4230	17230	13780	3640	15850	12680	2580	13130	10500	3000
	2	4.50	18.000	21160	16930	4700	20440	16350	4050	18800	15040	2870	15580	12460	3330
9-1/2	3/4	12.67	7.125	3200	2560	1400	3350	2680	1350	3080	2460	960	2550	2040	1120
	7/8	10.86	8.313	4380	3500	1860	4560	3650	1790	4200	3360	1270	3480	2780	1480
	1	9.50	9.500	5700	4560	2380	5960	4770	2280	5480	4390	1620	4540	3640	1880
	1-1/8	8.44	10.688	7220	5770	2950	7540	6030	2720	6930	5550	1930	5740	4600	2240
	1-1/4	7.60	11.875	8900	7120	3400	9300	7440	2970	8550	6840	2110	7090	5670	2450
	1-1/2	6.33	14.250	12820	10260	3960	13420	10740	3410	12350	9880	2420	10230	8180	2810
	1-3/4	5.43	16.625	17270	13820	4460	17740	14190	3840	16320	13060	2730	13520	10820	3160
	2	4.75	19.000	21690	17350	4960	21340	17070	4270	19620	15700	3030	16260	13010	3520
10	7/8	11.43	8.750	4360	3490	1830	4570	3650	1780	4200	3360	1260	3480	2790	1470
	1	10.00	10.000	5700	4560	2360	5960	4770	2270	5480	4390	1610	4540	3640	1870
	1-1/8	8.89	11.250	7220	5770	2960	7530	6020	2780	6930	5540	1970	5740	4590	2290
	1-1/4	8.00	12.500	8910	7130	3490	9310	7450	3120	8560	6850	2220	7090	5680	2570
	1-1/2	6.67	15.000	12820	10260	4170	13400	10720	3590	12320	9860	2550	10210	8170	2960
	1-3/4	5.71	17.500	17430	13950	4700	18110	14490	4040	16660	13330	2870	13800	11040	3330
	2	5.00	20.000	22130	17700	5220	22130	17710	4490	20360	16290	3190	16870	13490	3700
10-3/4	7/8	12.29	9.406	4350	3480	1810	4560	3650	1750	4200	3360	1240	3480	2780	1440
	1	10.75	10.750	5700	4560	2320	5960	4770	2240	5480	4390	1590	4540	3630	1840
	1-1/8	9.56	12.094	7210	5770	2920	7530	6030	2800	6930	5540	1990	5740	4590	2310
	1-1/4	8.60	13.438	8910	7130	3540	9310	7450	3280	8560	6850	2330	7090	5670	2700
	1-1/2	7.17	16.125	12810	10250	4480	13410	10730	3860	12340	9870	2740	10220	8180	3180
	1-3/4	6.14	18.813	17470	13970	5050	18240	14600	4350	16780	13430	3080	13900	11120	3580
	2	5.38	21.500	22490	18000	5610	23050	18440	4830	21200	16960	3430	17560	14050	3980
11	7/8	12.57	9.625	4350	3480	1800	4560	3640	1750	4190	3350	1240	3470	2780	1440
	1	11.00	11.000	5710	4570	2300	5960	4770	2230	5480	4390	1580	4540	3630	1840
	1-1/8	9.78	12.375	7210	5770	2900	7540	6030	2790	6930	5550	1980	5740	4600	2300
	1-1/4	8.80	13.750	8910	7130	3540	9300	7440	3300	8550	6840	2340	7090	5670	2720
	1-1/2	7.33	16.500	12820	10260	4570	13400	10720	3950	12320	9860	2800	10210	8170	3250
	1-3/4	6.29	19.250	17460	13970	5170	18270	14610	4450	16800	13440	3160	13920	11140	3660
	2	5.50	22.000	22660	18130	5740	23330	18660	4940	21460	17160	3510	17780	14220	4070

TIMBER FASTENERS

TABLE 8.10 — BOLTED JOINTS
ALLOWABLE LOADS IN POUNDS ON ONE BOLT IN DOUBLE SHEAR
THREE MEMBER JOINT

Length Of Bolt In Main Member	Diameter Of Bolt	Length / Diameter L/D	Area Of Bolt A = LXD	Load Parallel To Grain, Steel Side Members (Dense Douglas Fir-Larch)	Load Parallel To Grain, Wood Side Members (Dense Douglas Fir-Larch)	Load Perpendicular To Grain	Load Parallel To Grain, Steel Side Members (Douglas Fir-Larch)	Load Parallel To Grain, Wood Side Members (Douglas Fir-Larch)	Load Perpendicular To Grain	Load Parallel To Grain, Steel Side Members (Douglas Fir South)	Load Parallel To Grain, Wood Side Members (Douglas Fir South)	Load Perpendicular To Grain	Load Parallel To Grain, Steel Side Members (Hem-Fir)	Load Parallel To Grain, Wood Side Members (Hem-Fir)	Load Perpendicular To Grain
11-1/2	1	11.50	11.500	7620	6090	3240	6510	5210	2770	6260	5010	2780	6120	4900	2040
	1-1/8	10.22	12.938	9640	7720	4140	8250	6600	3540	7920	6330	3500	7740	6190	2570
	1-1/4	9.20	14.375	11910	9530	5110	10190	8150	4360	9760	7810	4270	9540	7640	3130
	1-1/2	7.67	17.250	17170	13730	7200	14680	11750	6150	14020	11210	5740	13700	10960	4210
	1-3/4	6.57	20.125	23380	18700	8770	19990	16000	7500	19150	15320	6580	18720	14970	4830
	2	5.75	23.000	30420	24330	9820	26010	20810	8390	24980	19990	7310	24420	19540	5370
12	1	12.00	12.000	7630	6100	3160	6520	5220	2700	6250	5000	2760	6110	4890	2030
	1-1/8	10.67	13.500	9660	7720	4080	8260	6610	3490	7930	6340	3460	7750	6200	2540
	1-1/4	9.60	15.000	11920	9540	5050	10190	8160	4320	9760	7810	4240	9540	7630	3110
	1-1/2	8.00	18.000	17160	13730	7210	14680	11740	6170	14080	11270	5860	13770	11010	4300
	1-3/4	6.86	21.000	23360	18690	9050	19980	15980	7740	19140	15320	6860	18710	14970	5040
	2	6.00	24.000	30510	24410	10250	26100	20880	8760	25010	20010	7630	24450	19560	5600
12-1/4	1	12.25	12.250	7600	6080	3130	6500	5200	2670	6250	5000	2750	6110	4890	2020
	1-1/8	10.89	13.781	9650	7720	4060	8250	6600	3470	7920	6340	3440	7740	6190	2530
	1-1/4	9.80	15.313	11940	9550	5020	10210	8170	4290	9770	7820	4220	9550	7640	3100
	1-1/2	8.17	18.375	17140	13710	7190	14660	11730	6140	14070	11260	5890	13760	11010	4330
	1-3/4	7.00	21.438	23360	18690	9160	19980	15980	7820	19160	15330	7000	18730	14980	5140
	2	6.13	24.500	30500	24400	10460	26080	20870	8940	25030	20020	7790	24470	19570	5720
13	1	13.00	13.000	7630	6100	3020	6520	5220	2580	6260	5010	2710	6120	4890	1990
	1-1/8	11.56	14.625	9630	7700	3950	8240	6590	3370	7900	6320	3400	7730	6180	2500
	1-1/4	10.40	16.250	11930	9540	4920	10200	8160	4200	9790	7830	4160	9570	7650	1850
	1-1/2	8.67	19.500	17160	13730	7140	14670	11740	6100	14080	11260	5960	13760	11010	4380
	1-3/4	7.43	22.750	23370	18700	9390	19990	15990	8020	19140	15320	7380	18710	14970	5420
	2	6.50	26.000	30500	24400	11050	26080	20870	9440	25030	20020	8260	24460	19570	6070
13-1/2	1-1/8	12.00	15.188	9660	7720	3880	8260	6610	3310	7920	6330	3380	7740	6190	2480
	1-1/4	10.80	16.875	11910	9530	4860	10180	8150	4160	9790	7830	4130	9570	7660	3030
	1-1/2	9.00	20.250	17160	13730	7070	14680	11740	6040	14090	11270	5920	13770	11020	4340
	1-3/4	7.71	23.625	23330	18670	9460	19950	15960	8080	19100	15280	7570	18670	14940	5560
	2	6.75	27.000	30550	24440	11370	26120	20900	9710	24990	19990	8580	24420	19540	6300
14	1-1/8	12.44	15.750	9660	7720	3810	8260	6610	3260	7910	6320	3350	7730	6180	2460
	1-1/4	11.20	17.500	11920	9540	4800	10190	8160	4110	9790	7840	4090	9570	7660	3010
	1-1/2	9.33	21.000	17160	13730	7020	14680	11740	6000	14060	11250	5870	13750	11000	4310
	1-3/4	8.00	24.500	23360	18690	9470	19980	15980	8100	19170	15340	7690	18740	14990	5650
	2	7.00	28.000	30510	24410	11630	26100	20880	9940	25030	20020	8900	24460	19570	6530
14-1/4	1-1/8	12.67	16.031	9650	7720	3760	8250	6600	3210	7890	6310	3340	7710	6170	2450
	1-1/4	11.40	17.813	11900	9520	4750	10170	8140	4060	9800	7840	4080	9580	7660	2990
	1-1/2	9.50	21.375	17150	13720	6990	14660	11730	5970	14080	11260	5860	13760	11010	4300
	1-3/4	8.14	24.938	23360	18680	9440	19970	15980	8060	19130	15310	7720	18700	14960	5670
	2	7.13	28.500	30520	24420	11740	26100	20880	10040	25000	20000	9050	24440	19550	6640

TABLE 8.10 — BOLTED JOINTS
ALLOWABLE LOADS IN POUNDS ON ONE BOLT IN DOUBLE SHEAR
THREE MEMBER JOINT

Length Of Bolt In Main Member	Dia-meter Of Bolt	Length / Dia-meter L/D	Area Of Bolt A = LXD	Load Parallel To Grain		Load Perpen-dicular To Grain	Load Parallel To Grain		Load Perpen-dicular To Grain	Load Parallel To Grain		Load Perpen-dicular To Grain	Load Parallel To Grain		Load Perpen-dicular To Grain
				Steel Side Members	Wood Side Members		Steel Side Members	Wood Side Members		Steel Side Members	Wood Side Members		Steel Side Members	Wood Side Members	
				Mt. Hemlock W. Cedars			Ida. W.-Lpole Pine-S. Spr			Ponderosa-Sugar Pine			Alpine Fir Engel. Spruce		
11-1/2	1	11.50	11.500	5710	4570	2280	5960	4770	2210	5490	4390	1570	4540	3640	1820
	1-1/8	10.22	12.938	7210	5770	2880	7530	6030	2770	6930	5540	1960	5740	4590	2280
	1-1/4	9.20	14.375	8900	7120	3510	9290	7430	3340	8540	6840	2370	7080	5660	2750
	1-1/2	7.67	17.250	12770	10220	4720	13370	10690	4130	12300	9840	2930	10190	8150	3400
	1-3/4	6.57	20.125	17450	13960	5400	18260	14610	4650	16790	13430	3300	13910	11130	3830
	2	5.75	23.000	22770	18210	6010	23690	18950	5170	21790	17430	3670	18060	14440	4260
12	1	12.00	12.000	5700	4560	2270	5960	4770	2200	5480	4380	1560	4540	3630	1810
	1-1/8	10.67	13.500	7220	5780	2840	7530	6030	2740	6930	5540	1950	5740	4590	2260
	1-1/4	9.60	15.000	8890	7110	3480	9310	7450	3340	8560	6850	2370	7090	5680	2750
	1-1/2	8.00	18.000	12830	10270	4810	13410	10720	4310	12330	9860	3060	10220	8170	3550
	1-3/4	6.86	21.000	17450	13960	5640	18220	14580	4850	16760	13410	3440	13890	11110	4000
	2	6.00	24.000	22800	18240	6270	23830	19070	5390	21920	17540	3830	18160	14530	4440
12-1/4	1	12.25	12.250	5700	4560	2260	5950	4760	2180	5480	4380	1550	4540	3630	1800
	1-1/8	10.89	13.781	7220	5770	2830	7550	6040	2740	6940	5550	1940	5750	4600	2260
	1-1/4	9.80	15.313	8900	7120	3470	9310	7450	3330	8560	6850	2360	7090	5670	2740
	1-1/2	8.17	18.375	12820	10260	4840	13410	10730	4390	12330	9870	3110	10220	8170	3610
	1-3/4	7.00	21.438	17460	13970	5750	18250	14600	4950	16790	13430	3510	13910	11130	4080
	2	6.13	24.500	22810	18250	6400	23840	19080	5510	21930	17550	3910	18170	14540	4540
13	1	13.00	13.000	5700	4560	2230	5960	4770	2160	5480	4380	1530	4540	3630	1780
	1-1/8	11.56	14.625	7200	5760	2800	7530	6030	2710	6930	5540	1920	5740	4590	2230
	1-1/4	10.40	16.250	8920	7140	3420	9310	7450	3290	8570	6850	2330	7100	5680	2710
	1-1/2	8.67	19.500	12830	10260	4900	13410	10730	4540	12340	9870	3220	10220	8180	3740
	1-3/4	7.43	22.750	17450	13960	6060	18240	14590	5260	16770	13420	3730	13900	11120	4330
	2	6.50	26.000	22810	18240	6790	23830	19060	5840	21920	17530	4150	18160	14530	4810
13-1/2	1-1/8	12.00	15.188	7210	5770	2780	7540	6030	2690	6940	5550	1910	5750	4600	2220
	1-1/4	10.80	16.875	8920	7140	3390	9320	7450	3270	8570	6860	2320	7100	5680	2700
	1-1/2	9.00	20.250	12840	10270	4860	13410	10730	4590	12340	9870	3250	10220	8180	3780
	1-3/4	7.71	23.625	17410	13930	6220	18220	14580	5460	16760	13410	3870	13890	11110	4500
	2	6.75	27.000	22770	18220	7050	23800	19040	6070	21900	17520	4310	18140	14510	5000
14	1-1/8	12.44	15.750	7200	5760	2760	7530	6020	2670	6920	5540	1900	5740	4590	2200
	1-1/4	11.20	17.500	8920	7140	3360	9300	7450	3260	8550	6840	2310	7090	5670	2680
	1-1/2	9.33	21.000	12810	10250	4830	13370	10700	4610	12300	9840	3270	10190	8150	3800
	1-3/4	8.00	24.500	17470	13970	6320	18250	14600	5660	16780	13430	4020	13900	11120	4660
	2	7.00	28.000	22810	18240	7310	23840	19070	6290	21930	17540	4460	18170	14530	5180
14-1/4	1-1/8	12.67	16.031	7190	5750	2740	7530	6030	2660	6930	5540	1890	5740	4590	2190
	1-1/4	11.40	17.813	8930	7140	3350	9300	7440	3250	8550	6840	2310	7090	5670	2680
	1-1/2	9.50	21.375	12830	10260	4810	13410	10730	4610	12340	9870	3270	10220	8180	3790
	1-3/4	8.14	24.938	17440	13950	6350	18250	14600	5740	16790	13430	4080	13910	11130	4730
	2	7.13	28.500	22780	18230	7430	23800	19040	6400	21900	17520	4540	18140	14510	5280

TIMBER FASTENERS

DRIFT BOLTS, DRIFT PINS AND SPIRAL DOWELS

Drift bolts, drift pins, and spiral dowels are simple types of fastening devices used to connect large members such as timber caps to pile bents, stringers to caps, or to connect an assembly of members such as laminations for a composite deck. Spiral dowels are designed to provide both higher initial holding power than ordinary drift bolts and drift pins and also to retain a greater proportion of their holding ability after seasoning or alternate moisture changes have taken place. Spiral dowels, because of their greater holding power can be used to great advantage on structures subject to uplift forces such as a timber trestle exposed to occasional floods.

Drift bolts are rods with a common bolt head formed on one end. A drift pin is simply a steel rod cut to the desired length. Spiral dowels are essentially square rods that have been twisted. They are similar to screws except that the pitch of the thread is very long and they can be driven in instead of turned. These fastenings are illustrated in Figure 8.18.

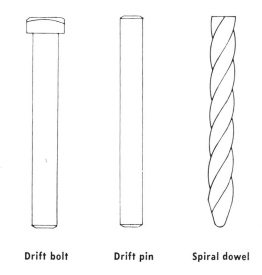

Drift bolt   Drift pin   Spiral dowel

Figure 8.18

Holding Power
The holding power of drift bolts, drift pins and spiral dowels depends on the diameter, penetration, metal strength, and specific gravity of the species into which these fastenings are driven. Because of the limited test data available, a reduction factor of 5 has been applied to the ultimate loads to obtain suggested allowable design loads. This reduction factor is conservative and if the type of construction is such that the loads can be accurately determined and somewhat larger deformations can be tolerated, then a smaller reduction factor may be used. In the example of a timber trestle exposed to occasional floods, the reduction factor could be less since the probability of occurrence of the flood condition is quite low, and no damage would occur even if the loads on the drift bolts, drift pins, or spiral dowels were close to the ultimate. However, engineering judgment should be exercised in the selection of any other reduction factor.

Duration of Load
Allowable loads for drift bolts, drift pins and spiral dowels are for normal condition of loading. For other durations of loading, the allowable loads should be adjusted as outlined on page 21.

Sizes and Lengths
Drift bolts are available in approximately the same range of diameters as bolts, and in lengths as desired. Drift pins may be had in any length or diameter that is available in steel rods.

The following table shows the range of diameters and lengths of stock sizes of spiral dowels. They come in increments of ½″ up to lengths of 8″, and 1″ for lengths over 8″. Other sizes not shown may be obtained by special order. The diameter of a spiral dowel is customarily measured across its greatest dimension after it has been formed. This dimension is not used, however, in determining the net cross sectional area of a spiral dowel.

TABLE 8.11 — Dimensions of Spiral Dowels

Outside Diameter	1/4"	5/16"	3/8"	7/16"	1/2"	5/8"
Minimum Length	2-1/2	3	3-1/2	3-1/2	4	4
Maximum Length	6	6-1/2	10	12	18	24

DRIFT BOLTS AND DRIFT PINS
Lateral Strength in Side Grain
A laterally loaded drift bolt or drift pin joint is similar to a bolted joint except that it lacks the surety of non-separation of the members, because of the eccentricity of the pieces, that is provided by the head and the nut in a bolted joint. Therefore the lateral load for a drift bolt or drift pin, driven into the side grain of wood, should ordinarily be taken as less than for a bolt with nut of the same diameter used under the same conditions. A drift bolt should have greater length than a bolt with nut so that the penetration will compensate in withdrawal resistance for the lack of a nut. A drift pin, having no head, should have relatively long penetration into both pieces.

Lateral Strength in End Grain
The lateral resistance of drift bolts or drift pins driven into end grain is much less than side grain lateral resistance, and it is suggested that 60 per cent of the allowable side grain load perpendicular to grain value of an equal diameter bolt with nut be used for design. To develop this strength the drift bolt or drift pin should penetrate at least 12 diameters into the end grain.

Withdrawal Strength in Side Grain
Suggested allowable withdrawal strengths per inch of penetration of drift bolts or drift pins driven into the side grain of seasoned wood, under

TIMBER FASTENERS

normal conditions of loading, can be determined from the formula:

$$P_s = 777G^2D^{3/4}$$

in which P_s = the allowable withdrawal load from side grain of wood in pounds per inch of penetration,

D = diameter of drift bolt or drift pin in inches.

Withdrawal Strength in End Grain

Although drift bolts and drift pins are quite often used in the end grain of a member, their withdrawal resistance is quite low compared to those driven into the side grain. The formula for determining suggested allowable withdrawal strengths per inch of penetration into end grain is:

$$P_e = 357G^2D^{3/4}$$

in which P_e = the allowable withdrawal load from end grain of wood in pounds per inch of penetration,

D = diameter of drift bolt or drift pin in inches.

The loads obtained by the preceding formula are based on the assumption that the drift bolt or drift pin will be driven in the immediate vicinity of the pith where the specific gravity is comparatively low. For this reason the allowable loads may be increased about 15 per cent when driven outside the vicinity of the pith.

Withdrawal from Side Grain and End Grain Combined

When a drift bolt or drift pin is used so that the penetration is into the end grain of the holding member and through the side grain of the member being held, as in the cap of a trestle bent pinned to the butt of a pile, the penetration into the end grain should provide a withdrawal strength sufficient to develop the side grain withdrawal strength of the member being held.

Condition of Lumber and Service

The allowable lateral load values for drift bolts or drift pins apply to lumber seasoned prior to fabrication and also to lumber fabricated unseasoned which will season in place. Where the lumber remains continuously at or above the fiber saturation point or is subjected to alternate cycles of wetting and drying, the allowable lateral loads should be reduced about 30 per cent.

The allowable withdrawal loads for drift bolts or drift pins are the same for seasoned lumber which will remain dry and for unseasoned lumber which will remain at or above the fiber saturation point. If the lumber is subject to alternate cycles of wetting or drying, however friction and pressure of the wood fibers that grip the shank will be permanently affected and the strength of the joint may be reduced as much as 75 per cent.

Lead Hole

To fully develop the strength of drift bolts and drift pins, and to prevent splitting, they should be driven into pre-bored holes having a diameter 1/16″ less than the drift bolt diameter.

SPIRAL DOWELS

Lateral Strength in Side Grain

The lateral load capacity of a spiral dowel of a specific diameter depends on the depth of penetration of the dowel into the holding member and on the thickness of the side member. Optimum efficiency, strengthwise, is obtained when the spiral dowel penetrates at least 7 diameters into the holding member and when the thickness of the side piece is at least 5 times the diameter of the spiral dowel.

The formula, based on test results, for determining suggested allowable lateral loads, both parallel to grain and perpendicular to grain for spiral dowels driven into the side grain of seasoned wood under normal conditions of loading is:

$$P_L = KD^2$$

in which P_L = the allowable lateral load in pounds for a spiral dowel driven into the side grain of wood under optimum conditions,

D = outside diameter of the spiral dowel in inches.

K = a constant depending on the inherent characteristics of the wood species, see Table 8.4.

Lateral Strength in End Grain

The lateral resistance of spiral dowels driven into end grain, as in the case of drift bolts, is much less than the side grain lateral resistance. Where this condition occurs, 60 per cent of the allowable lateral load in side grain is suggested for design. To develop this strength the spiral dowel should penetrate at least 12 diameters into the end grain.

Withdrawal Strength in Side Grain

The strength of spiral dowels loaded in withdrawal from the side grain of wood is greater than for smooth drift bolts or drift pins due to the additional resistance furnished by the threads.

The dowel rotates during driving and a threaded hole in the wood results with relatively undistorted fibers in contact with the entire surface of the embedded portion of the spiral dowel. This increases the withdrawal resistance and it is suggested that the allowable load for spiral dowels may be determined by increasing the allowable load for drift bolts or drift pins of the same diameters by 45 per cent.

Withdrawal Strength in End Grain

Based on test results, suggested allowable withdrawal loads for spiral dowels from end grain of wood can be obtained by applying an 80 per cent increase to allowable end grain withdrawal loads for drift bolts or drift pins of the same diameters.

Condition of Lumber and Service

The allowable loads, both lateral and in withdrawal, will be affected by the moisture content of the lumber before and after fabrication in essentially the same manner as drift bolts or drift pins.

TIMBER FASTENERS

The reductions that apply to drift bolts or drift pins for the different conditions should also be used for spiral dowels.

Lead Holes
Spiral dowels, like drift bolts and pins, require pre-bored lead holes. The most efficient size of lead hole is about 75 per cent the outside diameter of the spiral dowel. This size hole will permit easy driving and is small enough so that the screw-like action of the spiral dowel can occur.

Tables of Allowable Loads for Drift Bolts, Drift Pins and Spiral Dowels
Allowable withdrawal loads for drift bolts or drift pins and lateral and withdrawal loads for spiral dowels are given in the following tables for convenience. The loads are for seasoned wood that will remain dry in service and are for normal condition of loading. For species included in each Group, see Table 8.4.

TABLE 8.12 — WITHDRAWAL RESISTANCE OF DRIFT BOLTS AND DRIFT PINS

Diameter of Drift Bolt or Drift Pin in inches	Withdrawal Loads in lbs. per inch of Penetration SIDE GRAIN			
	Group I	Group II	Group III	Group IV
1/4	106	71	48	26
5/16	125	84	57	31
3/8	143	97	66	36
7/16	161	109	74	40
1/2	178	120	81	44
9/16	194	131	89	49
5/8	210	142	96	52
3/4	241	163	110	60
7/8	270	183	124	68
1	299	202	137	75
1-1/8	326	221	150	82
1-1/4	353	239	162	88

	END GRAIN			
1/4	49	33	22	12
5/16	57	39	26	14
3/8	66	45	30	16
7/16	74	50	34	18
1/2	82	55	37	20
9/16	89	60	41	22
5/8	96	65	44	24
3/4	111	75	51	28
7/8	124	84	57	31
1	137	93	63	34
1-1/8	150	102	69	37
1-1/4	162	110	75	41

TABLE 8.13 LATERAL RESISTANCE OF SPIRAL DOWELS

Diameter of Spiral Dowel in inches	Lateral Load in Pounds per Spiral Dowel			
	Group I	Group II	Group III	Group IV
1/4	128	111	96	76
5/16	201	173	150	119
3/8	289	250	216	172
7/16	393	340	294	234
1/2	514	444	384	305
9/16	650	562	486	386
5/8	803	693	600	477
3/4	1156	998	863	686
7/8	1573	1359	1175	934
1	2055	1775	1535	1220
1-1/8	2600	2246	1943	1544
1-1/4	3211	2773	2398	1906

TIMBER FASTENERS

TABLE 8.14 — WITHDRAWAL RESISTANCE OF SPIRAL DOWELS

Diameter of Spiral Dowel in inches	Withdrawal Loads in lbs. per inch of Penetration SIDE GRAIN			
	Group I	Group II	Group III	Group IV
1/4	154	104	70	38
5/16	181	122	83	45
3/8	207	140	95	52
7/16	233	158	107	58
1/2	258	174	118	64
9/16	281	190	129	71
5/8	305	206	140	75
3/4	349	236	160	87
7/8	392	265	180	99
1	434	293	199	109
1-1/8	473	320	217	119
1-1/4	512	346	235	128

END GRAIN

1/4	88	59	40	22
5/16	103	70	47	25
3/8	119	81	54	29
7/16	133	90	61	32
1/2	148	99	67	36
9/16	160	108	74	40
5/8	173	117	79	43
3/4	200	135	92	50
7/8	223	151	103	56
1	247	167	113	61
1-1/8	270	184	124	67
1-1/4	292	198	135	74

WOOD SCREWS AND LAG SCREWS

Wood screws and lag screws are fastening devices that serve essentially the same purpose as nails and bolts. Wood screws are somewhat more efficient than nails and have greater lateral and withdrawal strength than nails of a comparable size. Lag screws are sometimes used instead of bolts, particularly where it would be difficult to fasten a bolt or where a nut on the surface would be objectionable. While their lateral strength is not as great as the strength of bolts they still provide an efficient, satisfactory joint.

For both wood screws and lag screws, the diameter, penetration, surface condition, and metal strength are considerations in determining the lateral and withdrawal strength. The specific gravity of the species of wood into which the screws are inserted also has an effect on the strength of the joint. The data presented herein is intended to apply to wood screws and lag screws of steel which are most often used for structural joints. Dimensional data for wood screws and lag screws are tabulated in this chapter.

For other metals, the allowable loads may be adjusted in proportion to the tensile strength of the metal for withdrawal loads and in proportion to the square root of the yield stress for allowable lateral loads.

Number of Wood Screws or Lag Screws

As several screws or lag screws of the same or different sizes may be used to fabricate a joint, allowable loads are determined in the basis of one acting in single shear for lateral loads and per inch of penetration for withdrawal loads. In recent years, research and testing has indicated that the strength of a row of "n" connectors, bolts or lag screws is not necessarily "n" times the strength of one of the fasteners in that row. It thus recognizes the fact that the total load on a row of fasteners is not shared equally between all fasteners. The reader is referred to page 200 for the design of Multiple Fasteners.

Spacing of Wood Screws and Lag Screws

For wood screws, the center-to-center spacing, row spacing, edge distances and end distances need only be sufficient to prevent splitting of the joint.

To develop the full strength of lag screw joints, spacings, end distances and edge distances should be the same as for bolts, as shown on page 213. For lesser spacings the same reductions apply as for bolted joints.

Duration of Load

Allowable loads, both lateral and withdrawal, are for normal conditions of loading. Joints fabricated with wood screws and lag screws are subject to adjustment for different durations of load, as given on page 21.

Specific Gravity of Wood

In common with other fastening devices, the strength of wood screws and lag screws increases when the specific gravity of the wood increases and the different specific gravities of the lumber species are acknowledged by a different constant for each in the equations used to determine allowable working stresses. However, this effect is more pronounced in withdrawal resistance than in lateral strength because of the influence of joint deformation in establishing allowable loads. Therefore, the different species are grouped for greater simplicity in assuming appropriate factors for determining lateral load values. See Table 8.4 for species contained in various group classifications.

WOOD SCREWS

Wood screws are available in a wide assortment of lengths, diameters, head sizes and shapes, and can be obtained in steel, brass, and other metals to satisfy many use requirements. The size of wood screws is expressed by gauge number (diameter) and each gauge is available in different lengths.

Screws have excellent strength because the threaded portion projects into the wood at right angles to the axis of the screw without damaging the wood fibers and the projecting portion of the wood must be sheared through before the screw can be withdrawn. Due to their greater resistance, a lesser number of wood screws is required to provide a joint having the same strength as a nailed joint. However, because of the care required in fabrication and the necessity of boring lead holes, it is often more economical to use a nailed joint.

Lateral Strength

The most efficient use of wood screws is in joints fabricated with the screws inserted in side grain and loaded laterally.

The allowable lateral loads for wood screws are the same whether loaded in a direction parallel to grain of the pieces joined or at angles to the grain. For wood, and under normal conditions of loading, the formula for allowable lateral load on wood screws is:

$$P_L = KD^2$$

in which P_L = the allowable lateral load in pounds when inserted into the side grain of seasoned wood.

K = a constant depending on the inherent characteristics of the wood species, see Table 8.4.

D = diameter of the wood screw shank in inches.

Depth of Penetration

Allowable lateral loads for wood screws are based on a depth of penetration of the threaded end into the holding piece of about seven times the shank diameter and, to be effective, a wood screw should have a minimum penetration of about four times the shank diameter.

For less than the optimum penetration, the lateral load capacity is relatively proportionate.

Metal Side Plates

The deformation of wood screws under load, when two wood members are fastened together, occurs in both pieces. When a metal plate is fastened to a wood member, the deformation under the same load is less since it occurs principally in the wood member. Hence the allowable lateral loads for wood screw joints may be increased 25 per cent when metal side plates are used. The metal side plates must be of sufficient thickness and net cross-section so that the metal is not over-stressed.

Withdrawal Strength

Wood screws loaded in direct withdrawal from side grain are less efficient, strengthwise than when loaded laterally. It is therefore desirable to fabricate structural joints so that wood screws are loaded laterally when practical.

Within limits, the strength of screws loaded in direct withdrawal is dependent for the most part on the diameter of the shank and the length of penetration into the holding piece.

The formula for calculating the withdrawal resistance of a wood screw at normal conditions of loading is

$$P_W = 2844G^2D$$

in which P_W = allowable withdrawal load in pounds per lineal inch of penetration of the threaded portion of the screw into the holding piece,

G = specific gravity of the species, See Table 8.4.

D = diameter of wood screw shank in inches.

End Grain

The lateral and withdrawal resistance of wood screws inserted in end grain is less than for side grain and test results indicate that ultimate loads

TIMBER FASTENERS

are erratic. For these reasons, connections of this type should be avoided whenever possible. If it is necessary to use wood screws in end grain, the allowable lateral load is two-thirds of that in side grain. The end grain withdrawal loads should be reduced to about 75 per cent of the allowable side grain withdrawal loads.

Condition of Lumber and Service

The lateral and withdrawal resistance, as determined by the preceding formulas, applies to wood screws in lumber seasoned to a maximum moisture content of 19 percent that will remain dry in service.

When wood screws are inserted in lumber that is at or above the fiber saturation point, larger deformations, both laterally and in withdrawal, will occur than for the same loads with seasoned lumber although ultimate loads are comparable. Hence, lateral and withdrawal loads for wood screws should be reduced to 67 per cent of the allowable loads for seasoned lumber.

If a joint is fabricated of lumber at or above the fiber saturation point and it is allowed to season after fabrication, the stresses induced by the differential shrinkage in the joint are apt to cause splitting, reducing the allowable loads to about 40 per cent of the values for seasoned wood.

When the wood fibers surrounding a screw are subject to alternate wetting and drying there is a larger joint deformation under load than for seasoned lumber, but the effect is not as severe as for wood that remains continuously wet. For this condition the allowable lateral and withdrawal loads should be reduced to 75 per cent of the values for seasoned wood.

The lateral and withdrawal resistance of wood screws installed in lumber pressure-impregnated with fire-retardant chemicals and kiln-dried after treatment shall be reduced to 90 percent of the tabulated loads. For lumber so treated and not kiln-dried after treatment, the 90 percent value shall be further reduced in accordance with the above paragraphs relating to unseasoned lumber and for alternate wetting and drying.

Lead Holes and Insertion

Wood screws require pre-bored holes of the proper size to prevent splitting and to develop the full strength of the joint.

For wood screws loaded in withdrawal, the lead hole should have a diameter of about 70 per cent the root diameter of the screw.

To develop the full lateral strength, the part of the lead hole receiving the shank should be about seven-eighths the shank diameter and the diameter for the threaded portion should be about seven-eighths the root diameter.

Wood screws should be inserted by turning with a screwdriver. Driving with a hammer tears the wood fibers and injures the screw thread, seriously reducing the load carrying capacity of the screw. Soap, or other lubricants, may be used to facilitate insertion of the screws.

LAG SCREWS

Lag screws are generally made of hot rolled steel and are readily available in a range of sizes, suitable to most wood joints. Lag screw size is expressed in terms of diameter and length and each diameter is available in several lengths.

Lateral Loading Parallel to Grain

From the formula which follows, values for the lateral resistance of lag screws loaded parallel to grain are determined. These are basal values that are predicated on three assumptions and these values are further adjusted for conditions that prevail in use. The basic assumptions are:

1. That the piece under the head of the lag screw is $3\frac{1}{2}$ times the diameter of the lag screw shank. (Thickness of side member).

2. That the junction of the unthreaded shank and the threaded portion of the lag screw coincides with the contact plane of the member being joined. Figure 8.19. (Penetration of shank portion).

3. That the penetration of the threaded portion, not including the tapered tip, of the lag screw into the holding piece is approximately 7, 8, 10 or 11 times the shank diameter for Group I, Group II, Group III and Group IV woods respectively (see Table 8.4).

The basic formula for these conditions is:

$$P_L = KD^2$$

in which P_L = allowable lateral load parallel to grain in pounds,

D = diameter of lag screw shank in inches

K = a constant depending on the inherent characteristics of the wood species

When there is a variation from any of these basic assumptions, the formula must be multiplied by a factor for each variation, the magnitude of the factor depending on the amount of the variation.

The tabulated values for lag screws that conclude this chapter and which cover the most widely used range of sizes have been adjusted for variances from these three basic assumptions and reflect the use of standard cut washers.

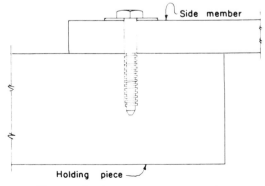

Figure 8.19 — Lag Screw Joint.

Lateral Loading Perpendicular to Grain

When lag screws are loaded perpendicular to grain, the allowable lateral load is affected by the lag screw diameter, resulting from the change in side grain bearing value for small bearing areas as described on page 78.

To obtain the allowable lateral load perpendicular to grain, the parallel to grain value of a lag screw is multiplied by a diameter factor. Following is a tabulation of these factors for different lag screw diameters:

Lag Screw Diameter	Multiplying Factors
3/16″	1.0
1/4″	.97
5/16″	.85
3/8″	.76
7/16″	.71
1/2″	.65
5/8″	.60
3/4″	.55
7/8″	.52
1″	.50

Angle to Grain Loading

The allowable load for angles of load to grain between parallel and perpendicular is determined through the Hankinson formula, see page 79. By using the parallel to grain value "P_L" and the perpendicular to grain value as "F_c" and "$F_{c\perp}$" respectively in this formula, the allowable load for a lag screw at an angle to grain is obtained. This value may be quickly and accurately found by using the nomograph, Figure 7.7, on page 79.

Withdrawal Strength

The formula for withdrawal resistance of lag screws inserted in the side grain of wood under normal condition of loading is:

$$P_W = 1800\ G^{3/2} D^{3/4}$$

in which P_W = allowable withdrawal load in pounds per lineal inch of penetration of the threaded portion of the lag screw into the holding piece,

G = the average specific gravity of the species at oven-dry volume and weight.

D = diameter of lag screw shank in inches.

When the screws penetrate more than about 10 diameters into the holding member, the tensile strength of the metal, from which the screw is made, limits the maximum withdrawal strength that otherwise might accrue from deep penetration.

End Grain

As in the case for wood screws, the lateral and withdrawal resistance of lag screws inserted in end grain is less than for side grain, and connections of this type should be avoided whenever possible. If it is necessary to use lag screws in end grain, the allowable lateral load is two-thirds of the side grain load capacity. The end grain withdrawal loads should be reduced to about 75 per cent of the allowable side grain withdrawal loads.

Condition of Lumber and Service

The lateral and withdrawal resistance, as determined by the preceding formulas, applies to lag screws in lumber seasoned to a maximum moisture content of 19 percent that will remain dry in service.

For lumber unseasoned at time of fabrication which dries to a maximum moisture content of 19 percent before full design load is applied, the full allowable lag screw loads may be used for a lag screw joint having a single lag screw and loaded parallel or perpendicular to grain; or multiple rows of lag screws loaded parallel to grain with separate splice plate for each row. For other types of joints in unseasoned lumber, the allowable lag screw loads shall be 40 percent of the tabulated loads.

For lumber partially seasoned when fabricated, proportional intermediate loads may be used.

For lumber pressure-impregnated with fire-retardant chemicals and kiln-dried after treatment, 90 percent of the tabulated lag screw loads shall apply. For lumber so treated and not kiln-dried after treatment, the 90 percent value shall be further reduced in accordance with the above paragraph relating to unseasoned lumber.

Metal Side Plates

The allowable loads parallel and perpendicular to grain for lag screws with metal side plates are comparable to the basic wood side member to lag screw diameter relationship of 3½. However the thinner metal side plate results in more penetration of the shank into the holding piece and more depth of embedment for a given lag screw size. This results in an increase in the lateral holding power which is reflected in the tabulation of allowable load for lag screws with metal side plates that concludes this chapter.

For perpendicular to grain loading, the parallel to grain loads should be multiplied by the appropriate diameter factor on page 235.

These load values apply only when the depth of penetration of the lag screw in the holding member is 9 diameters or more. For lesser penetrations the loads should be reduced in proportion to the lesser penetration to the required penetration.

For parallel to grain loading, the deformation under load is less with metal side plates than for wood side members since it is limited principally to the wood holding member. This permits a 25 per cent increase in allowable loads when metal side plates are used.

For perpendicular to grain loading the bearing strength of the wood is the critical factor and no increase can be permitted.

TIMBER FASTENERS

The thickness of the metal side plate, unless the metal becomes over-stressed, has very little effect on the allowable loads and the thickness may be varied without requiring a modification of load values.

Lead Holes and Insertion

Pre-bored holes for lag screws should have the same diameter as the shank for the length of the shank and from 60 to 75 per cent of the shank diameter for the threaded portion. The higher percentage applies to lag screws of larger diameters. Extra long lag screws may require slightly larger lead holes, to prevent splitting and to facilitate turning.

Lag screws should be inserted by turning with a wrench. Driving with a hammer tears the wood fibers and injures the screw thread, seriously reducing the load carrying capacity of the screw. Soap, or other lubricants, may be used to facilitate insertion of lag screws.

Tables of Allowable Lateral and Withdrawal Loads for Wood Screws and Lag Screws

A tabulation of allowable lateral and withdrawal loads for wood screws and lag screws for seasoned wood under normal conditions of loading concludes this chapter. The tabulated loads for lag screws incorporate the various adjustments for thickness of side member and for conditions where the shank extends into the holding member. For species included in each Group see Table 8.4.

TABLE 8.15 — LATERAL RESISTANCE OF WOOD SCREWS IN SIDE GRAIN

Allowable Lateral Load in pounds per Screw

Size or Gauge of Wood Screw	Diameter, inches	Group I Side Plate		Group II Side Plate		Group III Side Plate		Group IV Side Plate	
		Wood	Steel	Wood	Steel	Wood	Steel	Wood	Steel
6	.138	91	114	75	94	62	77	48	60
7	.151	109	137	90	113	74	92	57	72
8	.164	129	161	107	133	87	109	68	85
9	.177	150	188	124	155	102	127	79	99
10	.190	173	217	143	179	117	146	91	114
12	.216	224	280	185	231	151	189	118	147
14	.242	281	351	232	290	190	237	148	184
16	.268	345	431	284	356	233	291	181	226
18	.294	415	519	342	428	280	350	218	272
20	.320	492	614	406	507	332	415	258	323
24	.372	664	830	548	685	448	560	349	436

TABLE 8.16 — WITHDRAWAL RESISTANCE OF WOOD SCREWS IN SIDE GRAIN

Size or Gauge of Wood Screw	Diameter, inches	Allowable Withdrawal Load, lbs. per in. of Penetration			
		Group I	Group II	Group III	Group IV
6	.138	151	102	69	37
7	.151	165	112	76	41
8	.164	179	121	82	46
9	.177	193	131	89	48
10	.190	208	141	93	51
12	.216	236	160	108	60
14	.242	264	179	121	65
16	.268	293	198	134	74
18	.294	321	217	147	80
20	.320	350	237	161	88
24	.372	407	275	187	102

TIMBER FASTENERS

TABLE 8.17 — LATERAL RESISTANCE OF LAG SCREWS IN SIDE GRAIN
Wood Side Members

Side Member Thickness (inches)	Length of Lag Screw (inches)	Diameter of Lag Screw Shank (inches)	Total Lateral Load Per Lag Screw in Single Shear (Pounds)							
			GROUP I		GROUP II		GROUP III		GROUP IV	
			Parallel to Grain	Perpendicular to Grain	Parallel to Grain	Perpendicular to Grain	Parallel to Grain	Perpendicular to Grain	Parallel to Grain	Perpendicular to Grain
1-1/2	4	1/4	200	190	170	170	130	120	100	100
		5/16	280	230	210	180	150	130	120	100
		3/8	320	240	240	180	170	130	140	100
		7/16	350	250	270	190	190	140	150	110
		1/2	390	250	290	190	210	140	170	110
		5/8	470	280	360	210	260	150	200	120
	5	1/4	230	220	200	190	180	170	160	150
		5/16	330	280	290	250	230	200	190	160
		3/8	430	330	370	280	260	200	210	160
		7/16	540	380	400	290	290	210	230	160
		1/2	580	380	440	280	310	200	250	160
		5/8	710	420	530	320	380	230	310	180
	6	1/4	270	260	230	220	200	200	180	180
		5/16	380	320	330	280	290	250	260	220
		3/8	480	370	420	320	360	280	290	220
		7/16	590	420	510	360	400	280	320	230
		1/2	700	460	600	390	430	280	340	220
		5/8	860	510	710	430	510	310	410	250
	7	1/4	280	270	240	230	210	210	190	180
		5/16	400	340	350	300	310	270	280	230
		3/8	520	400	450	340	410	310	360	270
		7/16	640	460	560	390	500	350	420	290
		1/2	760	500	660	430	560	360	450	290
		5/8	910	550	790	470	640	380	510	310
2-1/2	6	3/8	450	340	370	280	270	200	210	160
		7/16	570	400	430	310	310	220	250	180
		1/2	620	410	470	310	340	220	270	180
		5/8	730	440	550	330	390	240	320	190
		3/4	820	450	620	340	440	240	360	200
		7/8	930	490	710	370	500	260	400	210
		1	1040	520	790	390	560	280	450	230
	7	3/8	500	380	430	330	370	280	300	220
		7/16	660	470	570	410	420	300	340	240
		1/2	830	540	650	420	460	300	370	240
		5/8	1000	600	750	450	540	320	430	260
		3/4	1110	610	840	460	600	330	480	270
		7/8	1260	660	950	500	680	360	550	290
		1	1420	710	1070	540	770	380	620	310
	8	3/8	550	420	480	360	430	320	380	290
		7/16	720	510	630	440	550	390	440	310
		1/2	890	580	770	500	600	390	480	310
		5/8	1230	740	970	580	700	420	560	340
		3/4	1430	790	1080	600	780	430	620	340
		7/8	1590	830	1200	630	860	450	690	360
		1	1800	900	1360	680	970	490	780	390
	9	3/8	600	460	520	390	460	350	410	310
		7/16	790	560	680	480	610	430	540	380
		1/2	970	630	840	540	750	490	600	390
		5/8	1310	790	1130	680	860	520	690	420
		3/4	1670	920	1340	740	960	530	770	420
		7/8	1920	1000	1450	760	1040	540	830	430
		1	2170	1090	1640	820	1180	590	940	470
3-1/2	8	3/8	450	340	390	300	350	270	280	210
		7/16	620	440	530	380	410	290	330	230
		1/2	800	520	640	410	460	300	370	240
		5/8	1030	620	780	470	560	340	450	270
		3/4	1180	650	890	490	640	350	510	280
		7/8	1300	680	980	510	700	370	560	290

TIMBER FASTENERS
TABLE 8.17 — LATERAL RESISTANCE OF LAG SCREWS IN SIDE GRAIN
Wood Side Members

Total Lateral Load Per Lag Screw in Single Shear (Pounds)

Side Member Thickness (inches)	Length of Lag Screw (inches)	Diameter of Lag Screw Shank (inches)	GROUP I Parallel to Grain	GROUP I Perpendicular to Grain	GROUP II Parallel to Grain	GROUP II Perpendicular to Grain	GROUP III Parallel to Grain	GROUP III Perpendicular to Grain	GROUP IV Parallel to Grain	GROUP IV Perpendicular to Grain
3-1/2 Continued	8	1	1420	710	1070	540	770	380	620	310
		1-1/8	1570	790	1190	590	850	420	680	340
		1-1/4	1690	840	1270	640	910	460	730	370
	9	3/8	500	380	430	330	380	290	340	260
		7/16	670	470	580	410	520	370	420	300
		1/2	860	560	740	480	590	380	470	310
		5/8	1310	790	1000	600	720	430	580	350
		3/4	1510	830	1140	630	820	450	660	360
		7/8	1670	870	1260	660	900	470	730	380
		1	1820	910	1380	690	980	490	790	390
		1-1/8	2000	1000	1510	750	1080	540	870	430
		1-1/4	2160	1080	1630	820	1170	580	940	470
	10	3/8	580	440	500	380	450	340	400	300
		7/16	770	540	660	470	590	420	520	370
		1/2	970	630	830	540	750	490	600	390
		5/8	1440	860	1240	750	900	540	730	440
		3/4	1890	1040	1430	790	1020	560	820	450
		7/8	2090	1090	1580	820	1130	590	910	470
		1	2270	1130	1710	860	1230	610	980	490
		1-1/8	2440	1220	1840	920	1320	660	1060	530
		1-1/4	2630	1310	1990	990	1420	710	1140	570
	11	3/8	620	470	540	410	480	360	420	320
		7/16	830	590	720	510	640	460	570	400
		1/2	1070	690	920	600	820	540	730	470
		5/8	1580	950	1370	820	1110	660	890	530
		3/4	2070	1140	1740	960	1250	690	1000	550
		7/8	2530	1320	1910	990	1370	710	1100	570
		1	2740	1370	2070	1040	1480	740	1190	590
		1-1/8	2950	1470	2230	1110	1590	800	1280	640
		1-1/4	3100	1550	2340	1170	1680	840	1350	670
5-1/2	11	1/2	800	520	700	450	570	370	460	300
		5/8	1260	750	980	590	700	420	560	340
		3/4	1530	840	1160	640	830	460	660	370
		7/8	1760	910	1330	690	950	490	760	400
		1	1970	990	1490	740	1070	530	860	430
		1-1/8	2150	1080	1630	810	1160	580	930	470
		1-1/4	2270	1140	1720	860	1230	620	990	490
	12	1/2	860	560	740	480	660	430	570	370
		5/8	1320	790	1140	690	870	520	700	420
		3/4	1880	1040	1420	780	1020	560	820	450
		7/8	2160	1120	1630	850	1170	610	940	490
		1	2420	1210	1830	920	1310	660	1050	530
		1-1/8	2650	1320	2000	1000	1430	720	1150	570
		1-1/4	2810	1400	2120	1060	1520	760	1220	610
	13	1/2	930	600	800	520	720	470	630	410
		5/8	1410	850	1220	730	1040	630	840	500
		3/4	1990	1090	1710	940	1220	670	980	540
		7/8	2580	1340	1950	1020	1400	730	1120	580
		1	2900	1450	2190	1100	1570	780	1260	630
		1-1/8	3160	1580	2390	1200	1710	860	1370	690
		1-1/4	3370	1680	2540	1270	1820	910	1460	730
	14	1/2	1000	650	870	560	780	500	680	450
		5/8	1500	900	1300	780	1160	700	990	590
		3/4	2090	1150	1810	990	1440	790	1150	630
		7/8	2780	1450	2290	1190	1640	850	1320	680
		1	3390	1700	2560	1280	1840	920	1470	740
		1-1/8	3700	1850	2800	1400	2000	1000	1610	800
		1-1/4	3940	1970	2970	1490	2130	1060	1710	850

TABLE 8.18 — LATERAL RESISTANCE OF LAG SCREWS IN SIDE GRAIN
Metal Side Plates 1/2″ in thickness

Total Lateral Load Per Lag Screw in Single Shear (Pounds)

Length of Lag Screw (inches)	Diameter of Lag Screw Shank (inches)	GROUP I Parallel to Grain	GROUP I Perpendicular to Grain	GROUP II Parallel to Grain	GROUP II Perpendicular to Grain	GROUP III Parallel to Grain	GROUP III Perpendicular to Grain	GROUP IV Parallel to Grain	GROUP IV Perpendicular to Grain
3	1/4	240	185	210	160	160	125	130	100
	5/16	355	240	265	180	190	130	155	105
	3/8	420	255	315	190	225	140	180	110
	7/16	480	270	360	205	260	145	210	115
	1/2	535	280	405	210	290	150	235	120
	5/8	645	310	480	235	350	170	280	135
4	1/4	275	215	235	185	210	165	185	145
	5/16	415	280	355	240	295	200	235	160
	3/8	575	350	485	295	345	210	275	170
	7/16	725	405	550	310	395	220	315	175
	1/2	810	420	615	320	440	230	350	185
	5/8	980	470	740	355	530	255	425	205
5	1/4	285	220	245	190	220	170	195	150
	5/16	435	295	375	255	340	230	300	205
	3/8	615	375	535	325	470	285	375	230
	7/16	820	460	710	395	535	300	430	240
	1/2	1040	545	840	435	600	310	480	250
	5/8	1310	630	990	475	710	340	570	275
6	1/4	285	220	250	190	220	170	195	150
	5/16	445	305	385	260	345	235	305	205
	3/8	635	385	550	335	490	300	435	265
	7/16	855	480	735	415	660	370	545	305
	1/2	1100	570	950	495	765	395	600	320
	5/8	1650	795	1290	620	925	445	740	355
7	3/8	645	390	555	340	495	300	440	265
	7/16	870	485	750	420	670	375	590	330
	1/2	1130	590	975	510	875	455	740	385
	5/8	1710	825	1480	710	1130	540	905	435
	3/4	2400	1060	1840	810	1320	580	1060	465
8	1/2	1140	590	985	510	880	455	775	405
	5/8	1750	840	1510	725	1320	635	1060	510
	3/4	2470	1090	2130	940	1560	685	1250	550
	7/8	3280	1370	2490	1030	1780	740	1430	595
	1	3680	1470	2780	1110	1990	795	1600	640
9	5/8	1770	850	1530	735	1370	655	1210	580
	3/4	2510	1110	2170	955	1790	780	1440	635
	7/8	3360	1400	2880	1200	2060	855	1650	685
	1	4280	1710	3230	1290	2310	925	1860	740
	1-1/8	4710	1890	3560	1420	2550	1020	2050	820
	1-1/4	5100	2040	3850	1540	2760	1100	2210	885
10	3/4	2550	1120	2200	970	1970	865	1630	720
	7/8	3430	1430	2960	1230	2340	975	1880	780
	1	4420	1770	3680	1470	2640	1050	2120	845
	1-1/8	5410	2160	4090	1630	2930	1170	2350	940
	1-1/4	5870	2350	4440	1770	3180	1270	2550	1020
11	3/4	2570	1130	2220	980	1990	875	1760	770
	7/8	3470	1440	3000	1250	2620	1090	2100	875
	1	4490	1800	3880	1550	2960	1180	2370	950
	1-1/8	5630	2250	4600	1840	3290	1320	2640	1060
	1-1/4	6630	2650	5010	2000	3580	1430	2880	1150
12	3/4	2580	1140	2230	980	1990	880	1760	770
	7/8	3490	1450	3020	1260	2700	1120	2320	965
	1	4520	1810	3900	1560	3270	1310	2620	1050
	1-1/8	5670	2270	4900	1960	3640	1450	2920	1170
	1-1/4	6940	2780	5550	2220	3980	1590	3190	1280
13	3/4	2580	1140	2230	980	1990	880	1760	775
	7/8	3510	1460	3030	1260	2710	1130	2390	995
	1	4550	1820	3930	1570	3520	1410	2870	1150

TIMBER FASTENERS
TABLE 8.18 — LATERAL RESISTANCE OF LAG SCREWS IN SIDE GRAIN
CONTINUED   Metal Side Plates 1/2" in thickness

Length of Lag Screw (inches)	Diameter of Lag Screw Shank (inches)	Total Lateral Load Per Lag Screw in Single Shear (Pounds)							
		GROUP I		GROUP II		GROUP III		GROUP IV	
		Parallel to Grain	Perpendicular to Grain	Parallel to Grain	Perpendicular to Grain	Parallel to Grain	Perpendicular to Grain	Parallel to Grain	Perpendicular to Grain
13	1-1/8	5710	2280	4930	1970	3980	1590	3200	1280
	1-1/4	6990	2800	6040	2420	4360	1750	3500	1400
14	3/4	2580	1140	2230	980	1990	880	1760	770
	7/8	3510	1460	3030	1260	2710	1130	2390	995
	1	4570	1830	3950	1580	3530	1410	3110	1250
	1-1/8	5750	2300	4960	1990	4330	1730	3480	1390
	1-1/4	7030	2810	6070	2430	4750	1900	3810	1520
15	3/4	2580	1140	2230	980	1990	880	1760	770
	7/8	3510	1460	3030	1260	2710	1130	2390	995
	1	4590	1830	3960	1580	3540	1420	3130	1250
	1-1/8	5770	2310	4980	1990	4460	1780	3750	1500
	1-1/4	7070	2830	6110	2440	5140	2050	4120	1650
16	3/4	2580	1140	2230	980	1990	880	1760	770
	7/8	3510	1460	3030	1260	2710	1130	2390	995
	1	4590	1830	3960	1580	3540	1420	3130	1250
	1-1/8	5790	2320	5000	2000	4480	1790	3950	1580
	1-1/4	7120	2850	6150	2460	5500	2200	4430	1770

TABLE 8.19 — WITHDRAWAL RESISTANCE OF LAG SCREWS IN SIDE GRAIN

Shank Diameter of Lag Screw (inches)	Species Group (See Table 8.4) Pounds per inch of Penetration			
	Group I	Group II	Group III	Group IV
1/4	311	232	173	110
5/16	367	274	205	130
3/8	421	314	235	149
7/16	473	353	264	168
1/2	522	390	291	185
9/16	570	426	318	202
5/8	618	461	344	219
3/4	708	528	395	251
7/8	795	593	443	282
1	878	656	490	311
1-1/8	960	716	535	340
1-1/4	1038	775	579	368

TABLE 8.20 — Dimensions of Standard Lag Screws:

[All dimensions in inches]

D = Nominal diameter.
Ds = D = Diameter of shank.
DR = Diameter at root of thread.
W = Width of bolt head across flats.

H = Height of bolt head.
L = Nominal length of bolt.
S = Length of shank.
T = Length of thread for effective embedment.

E = Length of tapered tip.
N = Number of threads per inch.

Nominal length of screw (L) in inches*	Item	Dimensions of lag bolt with nominal diameter (D) of—											
		1/4	5/16	3/8	7/16	1/2	9/16	5/8	3/4	7/8	1	1-1/8	1-1/4
	Ds = D	0.250	0.3125	0.375	0.4375	0.500	0.5625	0.625	0.750	0.875	1.000	1.125	1.250
	DR	.173	.227	.265	.328	.371	.435	.471	.579	.683	.780	.887	1.012
	E	3/16	1/4	1/4	9/32	5/16	3/8	3/8	7/16	1/2	9/16	5/8	3/4
	H	11/64	13/64	1/4	19/64	21/64	3/8	27/64	1/2	19/32	21/32	3/4	27/32
	W	3/8	1/2	9/16	5/8	3/4	7/8	15/16	1-1/8	1-5/16	1-1/2	1-11/16	1-7/8
	N	10	9	7	7	6	6	5	4-1/2	4	3-1/2	3-1/4	3-1/4
	D²	.0625	.0976	.1406	.1914	.2500	.3164	.3906	.5625	.7656	1.0000	1.2656	1.5625
	D³/⁴	.354	.418	.479	.538	.594	.649	.703	.806	.905	1.000	1.0925	1.182
1	S	1/4	1/4	1/4	1/4	1/4	....	....	....	....	....	....	....
	T	9/16	1/2	1/2	15/32	7/16	....	....	....	....	....	....	....
1½	S	3/8	3/8	3/8	3/8	3/8	....	....					
	T	15/16	7/8	7/8	27/32	13/16	....	....					
2	S	1/2	1/2	1/2	1/2	1/2	1/2	1/2	....				
	T	1-5/16	1-1/4	1-1/4	17/32	1-3/16	1-1/8	1-1/8	....				
2½	S	1	7/8	7/8	3/4	3/4	3/4	3/4	....	....	....	....	....
	T	1-5/16	1-3/8	1-3/8	1-15/32	1-7/16	1-3/8	1-3/8	....	....	....	....	....
3	S	1	1	1	1	1	1	1	1	1	1	....	....
	T	1-13/16	1-3/4	1-3/4	1-23/32	1-11/16	1-5/8	1-5/8	1-9/16	1-1/2	1-7/16	....	....
4	S	1-1/2	1-1/2	1-1/2	1-1/2	1-1/2	1-1/2	1-1/2	1-1/2	1-1/2	1-1/2	1-1/2	1-1/2
	T	2-5/16	2-1/4	2-1/4	2-7/32	2-3/16	2-1/8	2-1/8	2-1/16	2	1-15/16	1-7/8	1-3/4
5	S	2	2	2	2	2	2	2	2	2	2	2	2
	T	2-13/16	2-3/4	2-3/4	2-23/32	2-11/16	2-5/8	2-5/8	2-9/16	2-1/2	2-7/16	2-3/8	2-1/4
6	S	2-1/2	2-1/2	2-1/2	2-1/2	2-1/2	2-1/2	2-1/2	2-1/2	2-1/2	2-1/2	2-1/2	2-1/2
	T	3-5/16	3-1/4	3-1/4	3-7/32	3-3/16	3-1/8	3-1/8	3-1/16	3	2-15/16	2-7/8	2-3/4
7	S	3	3	3	3	3	3	3	3	3	3	3	3
	T	3-13/16	3-3/4	3-3/4	3-23/32	3-11/16	3-5/8	3-5/8	3-9/16	3-1/2	3-7/16	3-3/8	3-1/4
8	S	3-1/2	3-1/2	3-1/2	3-1/2	3-1/2	3-1/2	3-1/2	3-1/2	3-1/2	3-1/2	3-1/2	3-1/2
	T	4-5/16	4-1/4	4-1/4	4-7/32	4-3/16	4-1/8	4-1/8	4-1/16	4	3-15/16	3-7/8	3-3/4
9	S	4	4	4	4	4	4	4	4	4	4	4	4
	T	4-13/16	4-3/4	4-3/4	4-23/32	4-11/16	4-5/8	4-5/8	4-9/16	4-1/2	4-7/16	4-3/8	4-1/4
10	S	4-3/4	4-3/4	4-3/4	4-3/4	4-3/4	4-3/4	4-3/4	4-3/4	4-3/4	4-3/4	4-3/4	4-3/4
	T	5-1/16	5	5	4-31/32	4-15/16	4-7/8	4-7/8	4-13/16	4-3/4	4-11/16	4-5/8	4-1/2
11	S	5-1/2	5-1/2	5-1/2	5-1/2	5-1/2	5-1/2	5-1/2	5-1/2	5-1/2	5-1/2	5-1/2	5-1/2
	T	5-9/32	5-1/4	5-1/4	5-7/32	5-3/16	5-1/8	5-1/8	5-1/16	5	4-15/16	4-7/8	4-3/4
12	S	6	6	6	6	6	6	6	6	6	6	6	6
	T	5-13/16	5-3/4	5-3/4	5-23/32	5-11/16	5-5/8	5-5/8	5-9/16	5-1/2	5-7/16	5-3/8	5-1/4

* Length of thread on intervening bolt lengths is the same as that of the next shorter bolt length listed. The length of thread on standard bolt lengths in excess of 12 inches is equal to 1/2 the bolt length.

TIMBER FASTENERS
TIMBER CONNECTORS

Timber connectors are devices that give a high degree of efficiency to timber joints and make possible the utilization of a higher proportion of the strength of the member than is possible with most other types of fastenings.

Split rings and some other types of timber connectors, were introduced into America in 1933 and have been widely used since. Improvements and the development of new types have been accomplished so that the diversified requirements of connectors for timber construction are quite completely met.

Of the several types of timber connectors, the split ring and shear plate are those most commonly used, and it is these two types that are covered herein. Other types are: spike grids and clamping plates. Figure 8.20 illustrates these devices.

There are two sizes of each of the split ring and shear plate types that are generally available. In similar sizes, the split rings and shear plates have allowable load values in the same range. Each has a preferred use in making structural joints in timber.

Working loads for timber connectors are based on tests and recommendations of the U. S. Forest Products Laboratory, Timber Engineering Company, and others. All of the needed design data for each size and type of timber connector, allowable working loads, connector spacings, end distances and edge distances, are presented at the end of this chapter.

Split Ring Timber Connectors
The most used of all timber connectors are the split rings. They are readily available in diameters of 2½ in. and 4 in., though they have been produced in larger diameters. They are installed in pre-cut conforming grooves in the contact faces of lumber being joined. The depth of the groove

in the face of each piece is equal to one-half of the width of the split ring so that an equal amount of the width of the connector is embedded in each face of the two pieces joined. The inner surface of the split ring bears on the core left by grooving and the outer face bears on the outer wall of the groove. As the diameter of the groove is slightly larger than that of the connector, the split ring connector is expanded when in position, making the simultaneous bearings positive. See Figure 8.21.

Most of the split rings now used are made from steel bars having a double wedge cross-section, though some are available made from plain rectangular bars. Those with the double wedge shape fit more snugly into their conforming grooves and have less inelastic and therefore less total joint deformation under load. For maximum efficiency of split ring joints it is necessary that faces of members joined be in contact. If these faces become separated, and nuts on bolts are not tightened, the joint no longer conforms to the basis for design, nor is it practicable to make an assumption of the reduction in strength which may develop.

Shear Plate Timber Connectors
Shear plates are popularly used for wood-to-steel connections, as with gusset plates or column to foundation anchor straps. They also make a very strong demountable wood-to-wood connection possible. Only one shear plate is used in a wood-to-steel joint, but two are required, one placed in each lumber face, in a wood-to-wood connection. See Figure 8.22. Like split rings, they are installed in conforming grooves, but they are embedded deeper into the wood than split rings of similar size. Shear plates fit flush with the face of the piece when in position. Their strength is developed by bearing of the outer face of the connector against the wall of the groove. Joint forces may be limited in transmittal from shear plate to shear plate, or shear plate to steel gusset

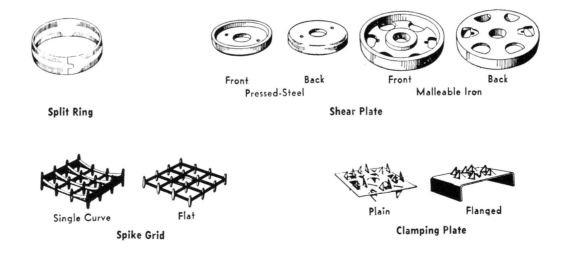

Split Ring

Front   Back
Pressed-Steel

Front   Back
Malleable Iron

Shear Plate

Single Curve   Flat

Spike Grid

Plain   Flanged

Clamping Plate

Figure 8.20 — Timber Connectors.

or strap, by steel-to-steel bearing on the bolt, or by the shear strength of the bolt. Shear plates are manufactured in 2⅝ in. and 4 in. diameters.

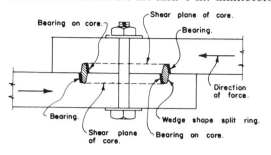

Figure 8.21 — Split Ring Timber Connector.

Factors Affecting Strength of Timber Connectored Joints

The principal factors that affect the strength of timber connector joints are:

Allowable load for one connector
Condition of lumber at time of fabrication
Condition of service
Thickness of members
Metal side members (with shear plates)
Angle of load to grain
Duration of load
Number of connectors
Spacing of connectors
End distance
Edge distance
Net section

These and other special conditions are discussed in detail in this Chapter.

Allowable Load for One Connector

Allowable connector loads for split rings and split rings and shear plates are based on average proportional limit joint stresses modified to provide stresses well below the proportional limit stress of the joint.

The load charts at the end of this chapter show the allowable normal loads for one connector unit and bolt in single shear. The connector unit consists of one split ring, a pair of shear plates, or a single shear plate used with a steel sideplate.

The load charts are broken vertically into three species groups (A, B and C) which include the species most often used with timber connectors. A note at the bottom of each chart provides a factor which, when multiplied by the values obtained from the chart for Group C species, provides appropriate values for species included in Group D. Select the group from Table 8.22 according to the species of lumber specified and use the portion of the chart applying to this group. Within each group there are several curves, each representing a curve conforming to the condition existing in the joint. Each curve is plotted according to the Hankinson Formula with load in pounds and angle of load to grain as the variables. Select the proper angle at bottom or top of the chart, proceed vertically to the selected curve and proceed horizontally to read the allowable normal load. Lumber thicknesses less than those shown

on the load data charts for the corresponding number of loaded faces are not recommended.

Condition of Lumber

Tests show that the moisture content, both before and after fabrication, of the lumber used with timber connectors will affect the connector load capacity. Allowable loads are based on connectors used in wood that is seasoned to a moisture content of approximately 15 per cent, to a depth of ¾ inch from the surface, at the time of fabrication.

For connectors used in lumber which is fabricated before it is seasoned to a depth of ¾ inch from the surface and which later is seasoned either before erection or while in the structure, 80 per cent of the basic loads apply for all connectors.

For lumber partially seasoned when fabricated, proportional intermediate connector values may be used.

For connectors used in lumber which is fabricated in a seasoned or unseasoned condition and will remain wet in service, 67 percent of the basic loads apply for all connectors.

For connectors used in lumber which has been pressure-impregnated with fire-retardant chemicals and kiln-dried after treatment, 90 percent of the basic loads apply for all connectors. For lumber so treated and not kiln-dried after treatment, 72 percent of the basic loads apply for all connectors.

If by some circumstance, lumber that has been fabricated while unseasoned is left unused overly long and allowed to season to a very low moisture content before assembly, it is possible that the rate of shrinkage across the grain as compared to practically none along the grain may cause the grooves for the timber connectors to become considerable out of round and prevent proper installation of the connectors. Such a condition does not destroy the usefulness of the members

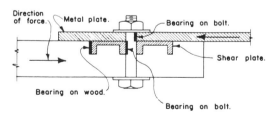

Wood to Metal Connection.

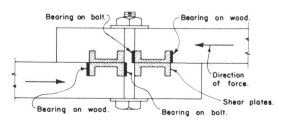

Wood to Wood Connection.

Figure 8.22 — Shear Plate Timber Connector.

TIMBER FASTENERS

as it is possible to regroove for the connectors and to restore the timber connector capacity of the joint to a value equal to that of a joint originally fabricated in seasoned lumber by filling the gap left on the inside of the connector groove with a hard setting, permanent compound. Tests of this repair feature showed that the filling compound need only be placed in the member, described later in this chapter as the "loaded member."

Thickness of members

The thickness of the member in which timber connectors are embedded and whether the connectors are in one face only or back to back in both faces of the piece have an effect on the allowable connector load. Minimum to optimum thicknesses for these conditions have been determined by tests and these conditions are recognized in the tabulations of connector values.

In the design of a timber connector joint the thickness of either of the members being joined may be governed by the needed connector capacity rather than the stress in the member or, where a member needs to be of minimum thickness, an additional connector can be used to compensate for the limited connector capacity.

Metal Side Members

When a timber connector joint is to be made between a wood member and a metal side plate, only a shear plate connector can be used. Though limited by the allowable unit strength of the metal, tests show that for a 4 inch shear plate there is an 18 per cent greater connector capacity with a dense grade of Douglas fir and an 11 per cent increase in capacity for other grades when used with a metal side plate than for this size shear plate in a wood-to-wood joint. These increases are applicable when the shear plate is loaded parallel to the grain of the wood member and are progressively less to no increase when the loading is perpendicular to the grain of the wood member. For this reason, separate data pages are provided for the 4 inch shear plate, covering its use in a wood-to-metal connection and a wood-to-wood joint, respectively.

When metal side members are used they should be designed in accordance with the applicable metal specifications and must always be of sufficient thickness and net cross-section to prevent over-stress in the metal.

For design, the allowable unit stresses shown in the *Manual of Steel Construction* by the American Institute of Steel Construction, Inc. should be used.

Loaded Member and Loading Member

In a joint where the force is transferred directly by timber connectors between two members that meet at an angle, the connector bearing is usually parallel to the grain in one member and at the joint angle, "θ," with regard to the grain of the other. The member loaded at an angle to the grain is referred to as the "loaded member" and under most all conditions it is the member that governs the design of the timber connector joint.

The other member, from which the load is transmitted, is called the "loading member."

Because the loaded member governs the design of the joint, it is important to determine which is the loaded member of any two members meeting at an angle. This is readily done by considering the forces in the joint and the relative positions of the lapped members. Examples follow:

1. In a wood-to-wood joint like that in Figure 8.23, whether with one vertical piece between two horizontal pieces, or one horizontal piece between two vertical pieces, the horizontal piece, member A, will be the loaded member and will govern the joint analysis with the connectors loaded at the angle "θ" across the

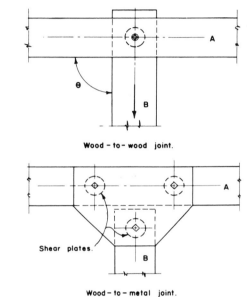

Wood – to – wood joint.

Wood – to – metal joint.

Figure 8.23 — Timber Connector Joints.

grain of the pieces. The vertical member B is the loading member with the connectors bearing parallel to the grain of this piece. In a similar wood-to-metal joint member A is the loaded member and B is the loading member.

2. The best construction for a heel joint, Figure 8.24, is for the member A to bear directly on the support, transferring the vertical com-

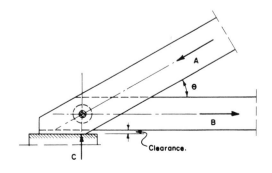

Figure 8.24 — Heel Joint.

TIMBER FASTENERS

ponent of the force from A directly to the support and leaving the horizontal component from member A to be resisted by member B. As the only force exerted on member B is axial, the potential load capacity of the connector in member B is the maximum parallel to grain value. Hence, B is the loading member and A is the loaded member. The design of the joint is predicated on the load from member B being resisted by the connector in member A at the angle "θ" across the grain of member A.

3. In a multiple member joint, Figure 8.25, the vertical component of forces from the two pieces of member A are resisted by member B and the horizontal component of forces from member A are resisted by each piece of member C. Considering the connections of vertical and horizontal members to the diagonal member separately, member B is regarded as a loading member with the load on the connectors parallel to the grain in that member. The two pieces of member A are the loaded members with a connector in each loaded by the force from B at angle "θ_2" across the grain of pieces A. To complete the joint analysis, the two pieces of member C

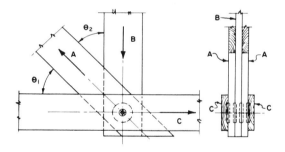

Figure 8.25 — Multiple Member Joint. Wood to Wood Connection.

are loading members with the load on each connector acting parallel to the grain in these pieces. The pieces of member A are again the loaded member with the connector in each loaded by the horizontal joint force imparted from C at angle "θ_1" across the grain of the pieces of member A.

4. In a multiple member joint using steel side plates, Figure 8.26, the conponents of forces are all transmitted through the steel plates leaving the joint forces in all members axial to the members and the shear plates are therefore all bearing parallel to the grain of each member. In cases such as this there are no loaded members in the joint analysis and connectors are designed on the basis that all members are loading members.

Duration of Load
As in the case of other types of metal fastening devices, a strength property of wood usually governs the load capacity and the effect of duration of load must be considered in the design of timber

connector joints. Following custom, the tabulated allowable connector loads are for normal condi-

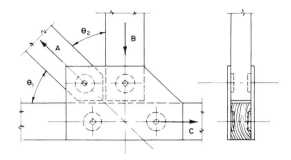

Figure 8.26 — Multiple Member Joint. Wood to Metal Connection.

tions of loading and these loads should be adjusted for other durations of load. For convenience, the duration of load adjustment factors are also tabulated on the data pages.

In the case of shear plate timber connectors, the bearing strength of the metal shear plate on the bolt or the shear value of the bolt may limit the maximum value of these timber connectors when the angle of load to the grain, "θ", of the piece approaches 0°. Though the allowable loads tabulated herein for parallel to grain loading on shear plates frequently exceed the allowable unit stress for metal, these excessive values are nevertheless shown so that load capacities for connectors loaded at angles to the grain can be determined. The maximum loads, as limited by the strength of the metal, are given in footnotes below the table. These limiting values are based on unit stresses as follows:

Stress	Allowable Value (Lbs./inch²)
Net section in tension	20,000
Single shear	12,500
Single shear bearing	22,500
Double shear bearing	28,125

For wind or earthquake loading these limiting values may be increased by one-third.

Number of Connectors
In recent years, research and testing has indicated that the strength of a row of "n" connectors, bolts or lag screws is not necessarily "n" times the strength of one of the fasteners in that row. It thus recognizes the fact that the total load on a row of fasteners is not shared equally between all fasteners. The reader is referred to Page 200 for the design of Multiple Fasteners.

In many cases the number of connectors used at a joint will exceed the actual requirements, since a fractional number of connectors cannot be used. Furthermore, in a multiple member joint it is often necessary to use more connectors than required in order to keep the joint symmetrical. Where excess connectors must be used for these

TIMBER FASTENERS

practical reasons, the potential capacity of the timber connectors in the joint is not utilized. This will permit reduced spacing between connector and smaller edge and end distances surrounding the connectors. It is therefore useful, in the procedure for connector joint design given herein, to determine the actual percentage of the connector capacity that is used. To do this, the number of connectors required by the load, in units and portions of units, is divided by the number of connectors actually used.

Spacing Between Connectors
The center to center spacing between pairs of connectors on the face of a member is the distance measured on the line joining their centers. Spacing is an important factor in the joint design as it controls the area of wood needed to develop the joint, and this in turn can supersede the stress in the members in determining the minimum width of the pieces being joined.

When timber connectors are fully loaded parallel to the grain, $\theta = 0°$, as in the chord member splice of Figure 8.27, the spacing, "a," between connectors parallel to the length of the pieces is the important dimension and the spacing, "b," across the width of the piece need only be the required minimum.

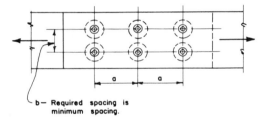

b— Required spacing is minimum spacing.

Figure 8.27 — Connector Spacing. Parallel to Grain Loading.

Conversely, when timber connectors are fully loaded and the angle of the load, "θ", is between 60° and 90° to the grain of the loaded member, as illustrated in Figure 8.28, the spacing of the connectors, "a," parallel to the length of the loaded member need only be the required minimum and the spacing, "b," across the grain of the loaded member is the important dimension.

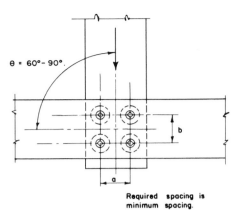

$\theta = 60° - 90°$

Required spacing is minimum spacing.

Figure 8.28 — Connector Spacing. Perpendicular to Grain Loading.

When the design load on the timber connectors turns out to be not more than 50 per cent of their potential capacity, the center to center spacings "a" and "b" need only be the required minimums regardless of the angle of the load to the grain of the loaded member. Required maximum and minimum spacings for the four timber connectors dealt with in this chapter are given in the table below.

For connector loadings intermediate between 50 per cent and 100 per cent of the connector capacity, the center to center spacing is proportionate.

When the angle of the axis on which the connectors are spaced, "ϕ," is neither parallel nor perpendicular to the length of the loaded piece, the center to center spacing, "R," of two fully loaded connectors will fall on an ellipse whose major and minor axes are determined by the dimensions "a" and "b." This is illustrated in Figure 8.29.

When the load on the connectors is less than their full capacity, the dimension of the major axis of the ellipse shortens until it is equal to that of the minor axis at a connector load of 50 per cent or less of the full capacity.

Connector Size and Capacity Used	Parallel and Perpendicular to Grain Spacing for Angle of Load to Grain of:			
	$\theta = 0°$		$\theta = 60°-90°$	
	a	b	a	b
2½″ Split ring and 2⅝″ shear plate: For 100% connector capacity For 50% of connector capacity	6¾″ 3½″	3½″ 3½″	3½″ 3½″	4¼″ 3½″
4″ Split ring and 4″ shear plate: For 100% connector capacity For 50% of connector capacity	9″ 5″	5″ 5″	5″ 5″	6″ 5″

TIMBER FASTENERS

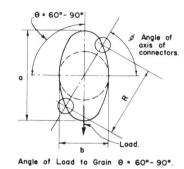

Angle of Load to Grain θ = 0°.

Angle of Load to Grain θ = 60° - 90°.

**Figure 8.29 — Center to Center Spacing.
Angles of Load to Grain.**

All of these spacing variables may seem complicated, but the spacing charts included at the end of this chapter for each of the connectors simplify the design procedure by showing these spacing requirements graphically.

On the right hand page of the data for each connector, is the spacing chart. Each chart has five parabolic curves representing recommended spacing for full load at the particular angle of load to grain noted on the curve. For intermediate angles of load, straight line interpolation may be used. If the spacing for full load is desired, select the proper angle of load to grain curve and find where it intersects the radial lines representing angle of axis to grain, the distance from that point to the lower left hand corner is the spacing. It is probably more convenient, however, in laying out this spacing to use the parallel to grain and perpendicular to grain components or measurements of the spacing. The parallel to grain component may be read at the bottom of the chart by projecting downward from the point on the curve. The perpendicular component of the spacing may be read at the left hand side of the chart by projecting horizontally from the point on the curve.

The sixth curve on the chart is a quarter-circle. This curve represents the spacing for 50% of full load for any angle of load to grain and also the minimum spacing permissible. For percentages between 50% and 100% of full load for an angle of load to grain, interpolate radially on a straight

line between the 50% curve and the curve corresponding to the proper angle of load to grain.

Reductions in load for edge distance and end distance are not additive to spacing reductions but are coincident.

End Distance
Timber connectors located near the ends of pieces must have an end distance, from the center of the connector to the end of the piece, sufficient to prevent a shear failure of the wood. If the end of the piece is cut at an angle, the end distance is measured parallel to the length of the piece on a line that is one-fourth of the connector diameter from the center of the connector and on the side nearest to the obtuse angle of the end cut. The methods of measuring the required end distance are shown in Figure 8.30.

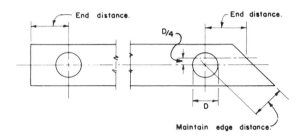

Figure 8.30 — End Distances.

Tests have shown that end distances longer than an optimum dimension do not add to connector capacity. On the other hand, connector capacity decreases nearly uniformly as end distance is progressively shortened to one-half of the optimum end distance. At this short length, which is considered a limit for good practice, the load capacity of a timber connector was found to be 62½ per cent of its maximum capacity. Converting this relationship to design purposes, the end distance may vary proportionately between optimum and minimum dimensions as the used capacity of a connector differs between 100 per cent and 62½ per cent.

The required end distance for connectors in a tension member is greater than that required in a compression member when the connector bearing is parallel to the grain of the piece. Such is the case with loading members.

When a connector is bearing at an angle of 90° to the grain of the piece it is in, the member is stressed locally in cross-grain tension. With the connector near the end of the piece, the end distance of either a tension or compression member must provide sufficient area to resist this stress and prevent splitting. The end distance for this condition coincides with that required for a tension member with the connector bearing parallel to grain.

From the preceding, it is obvious that the end distance required for a connector in a tension

TIMBER FASTENERS

member is constant for all angles of load to the grain of the piece. Also, the required end distance for a connector in a compression member is less when it is bearing parallel to the grain than when it is bearing at 90° to the grain of the piece and end distance is proportionate for intermediate angles.

Where a loading compression or tension member connects to a loaded member at an angle, the capacity of the connector joint is limited by the connector bearing at an angle to the grain in the loaded piece, and the potential capacity of the connector in the loading member, which is bearing parallel to the grain, cannot be utilized. Hence, the required end distance for the connector in the loading member may be proportioned, between optimum and minimum, by the ratio of potential connector capacity in the loaded member to that in the loading member. This ratio is cumulative with the connector capacity between 100 per cent and 62½ per cent.

When stitch bolts are used near the end of tension members the required end distance need only be equal to the maximum requirement for compression members since the stitch bolt alleviates any tendency toward splitting and shear failure.

End distance requirements for tension and compression members are tabulated on this page, but they can be determined directly and for all of the variables, from the charts on the data pages concluding this chapter.

Edge Distance

Edge distance is the perpendicular distance from the center of a connector to the edge of a piece. To begin with, there are two basic edge distances for a fully loaded timber connector. One of these is the basic minimum recommended edge distance, for each connector size, which is always applicable on the unloaded edge of the piece. The other is the basic larger edge distance, for each connector size, that is required only on the loaded edge of a piece. The larger edge distance on the loaded edge of the piece is variable depending on the angle of load to the grain of the piece and on the percentage used of connector capacity. The terms "unloaded edge" and "loaded edge" are explained further.

At parallel to grain loading, components of the connector load thrust toward the edges of the piece, but these thrusts are of low intensity and the minimum recommended edge distance is ample on each side of the connector. For this direction of loading, the two edges of the piece are unloaded edges. See Figure 8.31.

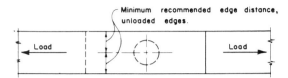

Figure 8.31 — Edge Distances.

Tests show that with an edge distance practically flush with the diameter of a connector the ultimate connector capacity at parallel to grain loading is reduced to about 80 per cent. Regardless of this, a reduction of edge distance, for any reason, below the recommended minimum is not considered good practice.

In a joint between members that meet at an angle, the timber connector edge distance in the direction of the load from the loading member is increasingly important as the angle "θ" increases to 45° or more, and the larger recommended edge distance is required at full connector capacity. This is the "loaded edge" condition. On the opposite side, away from the direction of load, is the "unloaded edge" and the edge distance need only be the recommended minimum.

For intermediate angles of load to grain the edge distance can be proportioned between the recommended minimum at $\theta = 0°$ and the larger required edge distance at $\theta = 45°-90°$.

When the angle of load to grain is 45° or more, the amount of edge distance may be proportioned between that recommended for full connector capacity and the basic minimum edge distance when the connector load is 83 per cent of capacity. Proportioning of the edge distance may also be made for connectors loaded between 100 per cent and 83 per cent of capacity when the direction of load is between $\theta = 0°$ and $\theta = 45°$.

Connector Size and Capacity Used	End Distances		
	Tension Member	Compression Member	
	Angle of Load to Grain	Angle of Load to Grain	
	$\theta = 0°\text{-}90°$	$\theta = 0°$	$\theta = 90°$
2½″ Split ring and 2⅝″ shear plate:			
For 100% connector capacity	5½″	4½″	5½″
For 62½% of connector capacity	2¾″	2½″	2¾″
4″ Split ring and 4″ shear plate:			
For 100% connector capacity	7″	5½″	7″
For 62½% of connector capacity	3½″	3¼″	3½″

TIMBER FASTENERS

These factors lead to the following rules:

1. The minimum basic recommended edge distance for each size of connector is applicable to both edges of a loading member, to the unloaded edge of a loaded member and to the loaded edge of a loaded member when the connector is not used to more than 83 per cent of its potential capacity.

2. The largest basic recommended edge distance is applicable only to the loaded edge of a loaded member when the connector is used to full capacity and the angle of load to grain is 45° or more.

3. The edge distance may be proportioned between the basic recommended minimum and the largest required, for angles of load to grain intermediate between $\theta = 0°$ and $\theta = 45°$ and may be further adjusted when the used connector capacity is intermediate between 100 per cent and 83 per cent.

The table on this page lists the basic recommended edge distance for timber connectors.

However, the data pages at the end of this chapter have charts that solve the edge distance requirements quickly and easily.

Net Section

In the design of structures employing timber connectors, the strength of the member between the joints, and the strength of the net section at the joint must be considered in addition to the strength of the joint itself. The net section is determined by subtracting from the full cross-sectional area of the member, the projected area of the portion of the connector within the member and the portion of the bolt hole not within the connector projected area. See Figure 8.32. In tension and compression members the required net area, in square inches, may be determined by dividing the total load, in pounds, which is transferred through the critical plane of the member by the appropriate constant in Table 8.21. When determining the required net area in this manner, the cross-sectional area of knots occurring in the critical plane outside the area of connectors and bolts should also be deducted. Where connectors are staggered, adjacent connectors, with parallel-to-grain spacing equal to

or less than one connector diameter, should be considered as occurring at the same critical section.

Table 8.21 Constants for use in determining required net section in square inches.

Duration of loading	Thickness of wood member in inches	Constants for each connector load group			
		Group A*	Group B*	Group C*	Group D*
Normal	4 inches or less	2350	2000	1650	1300
	Over 4 inches	1850	1600	1300	1050
Permanent	4 inches or less	2100	1800	1500	1200
	Over 4 inches	1700	1450	1200	950
Snow	4 inches or less	2700	2300	1900	1500
	Over 4 inches	2150	1850	1500	1200
Wind or earthquake ..	4 inches or less	3100	2650	2200	1750
	Over 4 inches	2500	2150	1750	1400

*For woods in this group, see Table No. 8.22.

In using the clear wood fiber strength at the net section it is assumed that the cross-section will not be additionally reduced by knots in the joint area. If it is anticipated that material will not be selected so as to exclude knots in the joint area, a more conservative fiber strength value should be used. Such a value is determined by reducing to $\frac{7}{8}$, the allowable unit stress in bending for the grade of lumber used.

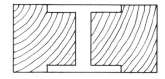

Figure 8.32 — Projected Area of Connectors and Bolts.

Connector Size and Angle of Load to Grain θ	Edge Distance		
	Loaded Edge Connector Capacity Used		Unloaded Edge Connector Capacity Used
	100%	83% or less	100% or less
2½″ Split ring and 2⅝″ shear plate:			
$\theta = 0°$ angle of load to grain	1¾″	1¾″	1¾″
$\theta = 45°$-90° angle of load to grain	2¾″	1¾″	1¾″
4″ Split ring and 4″ shear plate:			
$\theta = 0°$ angle of load to grain	2¾″	2¾″	2¾″
$\theta = 45°$-90° angle of load to grain	3¾″	2¾″	2¾″

TIMBER FASTENERS

The preceding recommendations apply to sawn lumber. When timber connectors are used in glued laminated structural lumber, the strength of the net section is determined by multiplying the net area by the appropriate allowable compression parallel to the grain value assigned to the laminated member used.

TABLE 8.22 — Connector load grouping of species when stress-graded.

Connector load grouping	Species	
Group A ...	Ash, Commercial White Beech Birch, Sweet & Yellow Douglas Fir-Larch (Dense)	Hickory & Pecan Oak, Red & White Maple, Black & Sugar Southern Pine (Dense)
Group B ...	Douglas Fir-Larch Southern Pine	Sweetgum & Tupelo
Group C ...	California Redwood (Close grain) Douglas Fir South Eastern Hemlock- Tamarack Eastern Spruce Hem-Fir Idaho White Pine Lodgepole Pine	Mountain Hemlock Northern Pine Ponderosa Pine- Sugar Pine Red Pine Sitka Spruce Southern Cypress Spruce-Pine-Fir Yellow Poplar
Group D ...	Balsam Fir California Redwood (Open grain) Coast Sitka Spruce Cottonwood, Eastern Eastern White Pine	Engelmann Spruce Northern White Cedar Subalpine Fir Western Cedars Western White Pine

Bolting Requirements

The ratio between the allowable load for a timber connector and bolt acting together and the allowable load for the bolt alone is not constant for different sizes of connectors, thicknesses of members and angles of load to grain, because of the interaction between bolt and connector. Bolt sizes to be used with the different sizes and types of connectors are given in the table of working values on the data pages, and except for some shear plate conditions where the stress in the metal governs the maximum load, an increase in bolt sizes over those given will not result in increased connector loads.

Holes for bolts should be bored 1/16 inch larger than the bolt diameter. Bolts must have an appropriate washer under the head and the nut except that washers may be omitted when metal side plates are used. Appropriate sizes for different kinds of washers, when bearing on wood, are given on the data pages.

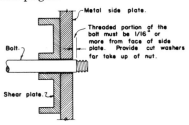

Figure 8.33 — Bolt Length Requirements for Metal Side Plates.

Lag Screws in Lieu of Bolts

When lag screws are used with connectors, the full allowable load (the load for one connector unit with bolt) may be used for 2½-inch and 4-inch split rings and 4-inch shear plates when

TABLE 8.23 — Projected Area of Connectors and Bolts (For Use in Determining Net Sections)

Connector Size	Bolt Diameter (Inches)		Total Projected Area in Square Inches of Connectors and Bolts in Net Lumber Thickness of									
			1½"	2½"	3⅛"	3½"	5⅛"	5½"	6¾"	7½"	8¾"	9½"
SPLIT RINGS												
2½	½	One Face	1.73	2.30	2.65	2.86	3.77	3.98	4.69	5.11	5.81	6.23
	½	Two Faces	2.62	3.18	3.54	3.75	4.66	4.87	5.58	6.00	6.70	7.12
4	¾	One Face	3.05	3.86	4.37	4.68	6.00	6.30	7.32	7.93	8.94	9.55
	¾	Two Faces	4.89	5.70	6.21	6.51	7.83	8.14	9.15	9.76	10.78	11.39
SHEAR PLATES												
2⅝ Light Gage	¾	One Face	1.93	2.75	3.25	3.56	4.88	5.18	6.20	6.81	7.82	8.43
	¾	Two Faces	2.65	3.46	3.97	4.28	5.60	5.90	6.92	7.52	8.54	9.15
2⅝ Regular	¾	One Face	2.06	2.87	3.38	3.68	5.00	5.31	6.32	6.93	7.95	8.56
	¾	Two Faces	2.90	3.71	4.22	4.52	5.84	6.15	7.16	7.77	8.79	9.40
4	¾	One Face	3.28	4.09	4.60	4.90	6.22	6.53	7.54	8.15	9.17	9.78
	¾	Two Faces	—	6.15	6.66	6.96	8.28	8.59	9.60	10.21	11.23	11.84
4	⅞	One Face	3.39	4.32	4.91	5.26	6.78	7.14	8.31	9.01	10.18	10.89
	⅞	Two Faces	—	6.30	6.89	7.24	8.76	9.12	10.29	10.99	12.16	12.87

TIMBER FASTENERS

the minimum penetration of the lag screw into the member receiving the point is 7 diameters for Group I woods, 8 diameters for Group II, 10 diameters for Group III, and 11 diameters for Group IV. For 2⅝-inch shear plates, the full allowable load may be used when the minimum penetration is 4 diameters for Group I woods, 5 diameters for Group II, 7 diameters for Group II, and 8 diameters for Group IV. (See Table 8.22.)

The allowable load for 2½-inch and 4-inch split rings and 2⅝-inch and 4-inch shear plates when used with lag screws varies uniformly from the full allowable load with penetration, as specified in the previous paragraph, to 75 per cent of the full allowable load with penetration of 3 diameters for Group I woods, 3½ diameters for Group II, 4 diameters for Group III, and 4½ diameters for Group IV. When metal side plates are used with 2⅝-inch shear plates, the full allowable load may be used for the minimum penetrations specified.

Structural Considerations
In the design of timber connector joints, the joint may determine the width and thickness of the members. The location of splices and splice details require special consideration. Members may be subject to combined bending and axial forces. Lastly, proper maintenance of timber connectored structures is required. These items are briefly discussed herein.

Width of Members
Where more than two connectors are used in one face of a member, the spacing is determined by considering two connectors at a time. For example, in a joint having connectors on three bolts, three spacings are involved and the spacings are investigated separately between pairs.

The forces in the members composing a timber connectored joint may be considerably larger in one member than in another. For this reason it is desirable to arrange the connectors in a multiple connector joint so that the member having the smallest force can have the narrowest width to permit the use of the most economical size member. Figure 8.34 shows how widths of members can be increased or decreased depending on the location of the connectors.

Splices
When two members of different thickness are spliced, the thicker one should be dapped to the thickness of the thinner one, see Figure 8.35. The use of a filler piece would introduce an additional joint line, with resultant double joint elongation at the filler piece and an eccentric flow of forces through the joint.

All the pieces of a multi-piece member, when spliced, should be spliced in the same panel; otherwise the elongation of the joint in the spliced piece will cause an unsymmetrical flow of forces between the pieces.

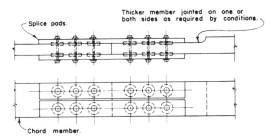

Figure 8.35 — Splice with Members of Different Thickness.

Tension and Compression
Members in truss type framing are either compression members or tension members and in addition, may be subjected to bending loads resulting in combined stresses. The members in these frames, when in axial compression, are designed as either simple solid columns or spaced

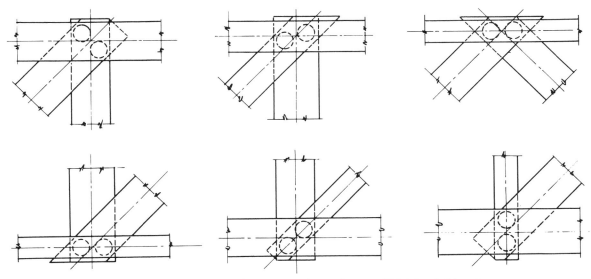

Figure 8.34 — Effect of Connector Location on Width of Members.

TIMBER FASTENERS

columns, depending on the arrangement of the members. For a detailed discussion of compression members, including compression members subjected to bending loads, see page 52.

Members stressed in axial tension may also support bending loads, as when a ceiling or a hoist is attached to the tension chord of a truss. When this condition occurs, the member is designed for combined bending and axial tension and should be proportioned so that

$$\frac{P/A}{F_t} + \frac{M/S}{F_b} \text{ does not exceed unity.}$$

where

P = total axial load. pounds.

A = area of cross section of member, square inches.

P/A = tension stress induced by axial load. pounds per square inch.

M = total bending moment. inch pounds.

S = section modulus of member.

M/S = flexual stress induced by bending load. pounds per square inch.

F_b = allowable unit stress in pounds per square inch that would be permitted if flexure only existed.

F_t = allowable unit stress in pounds per square inch that would be permitted if tension only existed.

The area of a tension or compression member at a joint may be influenced by the net section requirement as discussed in this chapter.

Maintenance of Timber Structures

It may be important to service a timber connectored structure during the first year or so after erection, particularly if the moisture content of the lumber when installed is not in equilibrium with the surrounding atmosphere.

Lumber in service eventually attains a moisture content commensurate with its condition of ex- posure regardless of its moisture content at the time of installation. In covered structures the final moisture content will range from about 8 to 15 per cent depending on whether the structure is completely covered and heated in winter or whether the structure is only semi-protected and is unheated. Geographical, climatic differences also influence the residential moisture content of wood.

As lumber seasons below its fiber saturation point, about 27 per cent moisture content, it shrinks. For this reason it is particularly important that timber connectored structures, when built of unseasoned lumber, be inspected and nuts on bolts retightened if necessary during the early life of the structure so that the capacity of the connectors is not reduced by a separation of the timber faces in a joint as a result of the shrinkage.

Rapid drying is frequently the cause of end checks and splits. If they do occur in the immediate area of a timber connectored joint their possible effect on joint strength can be estimated by whether the opening of the end split is equal to the amount of shrinkage or is greater. If the opening is greater, it indicates a possible wedging action from the connector force. This can be corrected by boring a hole across the end of the piece and installing a stitch bolt. No attempt should be made to tighten the stitch bolt enough to close the split more than the amount that would occur from natural shrinkage. To attempt to completely close the split would tend to crush the wood fibers around the connector and introduce secondary cross-grain stresses.

If a large variance in moisture content of pieces of lumber in a structure is anticipated, the effect of potential end splitting at joints can be avoided to a large degree by generous end distances, straight end cuts, and pre-installed stitch bolts. In tension and compression splices, separate splice plates for each row of connectors and saw kerfs between longitudinal rows of connectors are advantageous.

Splits or checks have little influence, except for appearance, on the strength of a member stressed in axial compression unless so extensive as to split the piece practically in two. Splits or checks have even less influence on a member stressed in axial tension unless they are at an angle to the grain of the piece and tend to extend across a face so as to separate the piece in two.

TIMBER FASTENERS

Bolted connections in space frame spanning 120 feet. —Lane Community College, Eugene, Oregon

TIMBER FASTENERS

2½″ Split Rings

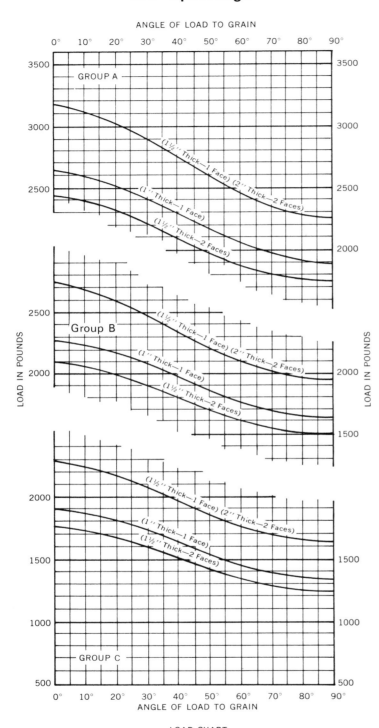

ANGLE OF LOAD TO GRAIN

LOAD CHART
FOR NORMAL LOADING
ONE 2½″ SPLIT RING AND BOLT IN SINGLE SHEAR

Note: For Group D connector values, multiply Group C values by 0.86.

2½″ SPLIT RING DATA

Split Ring — Dimensions
Inside Diameter at center when closed	2½″
Inside diameter at center when installed	2.54″
Thickness of ring at center	0.163″
Thickness of ring at edge	0.123″
Depth	¾″

Lumber, Minimum dimensions allowed
Width	3½
Thickness, rings in one face	1″
Thickness, rings opposite in both faces	1½″

Bolt, diameter	½″
Bolt hole, diameter	9/16″

Projected Area for portion of one ring within a member, square inches 1.10

Washers, minimum
Round, Cast or Malleable Iron, diameter	2⅛″
Square Plate Length of Side	2″
Thickness	⅛″

(For trussed rafters and similar light construction standard wrought washers may be used.)

SPLIT RING SPECIFICATIONS

Split rings shall be manufactured from hot rolled S. A. E. — 1010 carbon steel. Each ring shall form a closed true circle with the principal axis of the cross section of the ring metal parallel to the geometric axis of the ring. The ring shall fit snugly in the prepared groove. The metal section of each ring shall be beveled from the central portion toward the edges to a thickness less than that at mid-section. It shall be cut through in one place in its circumference to form a tongue and slot.

PERCENTAGES FOR DURATION OF MAXIMUM LOAD

Two Months Loading, as for snow	115%
Seven Days Loading	125%
Wind or Earthquake Loading	133⅓ %
Impact Loading	200%
Permanent Loading	90%

DECREASES FOR MOISTURE CONTENT CONDITIONS

Condition when Fabricated	Seasoned	Unseasoned	Unseasoned
Condition when Used	Seasoned	Seasoned	Unseasoned or Wet
Split Rings	0%	20%	33%

Courtesy Timber Engineering Company

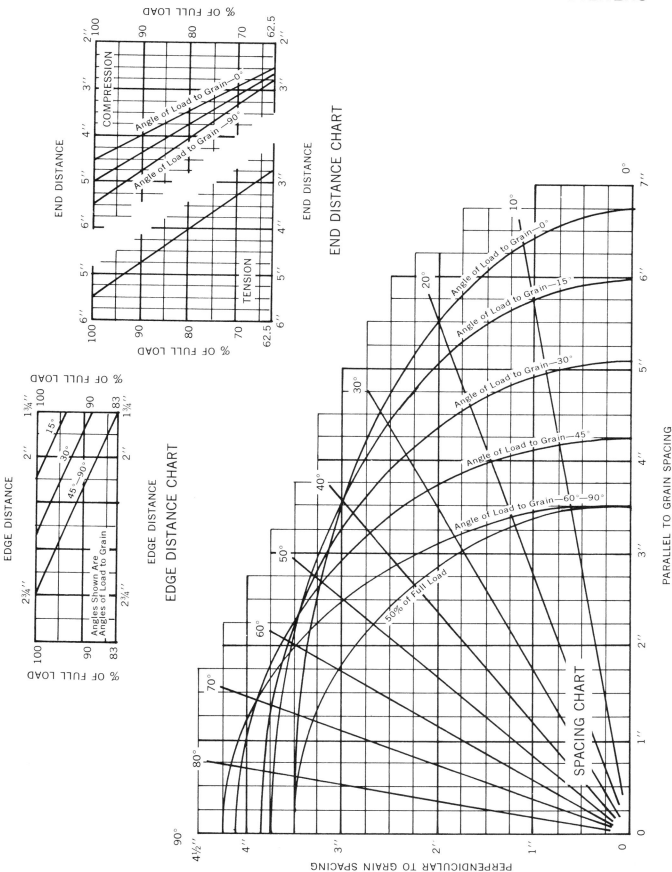

COMPRESSION

Angle of Load to Grain—0°

Angle of Load to Grain —90°

END DISTANCE

% OF FULL LOAD

TENSION

END DISTANCE

END DISTANCE CHART

EDGE DISTANCE

15°
30°
45°—90°

Angles Shown Are
Angles of Load to Grain

EDGE DISTANCE

% OF FULL LOAD

EDGE DISTANCE CHART

Angle of Load to Grain—0°
Angle of Load to Grain—15°
Angle of Load to Grain—30°
Angle of Load to Grain—45°
Angle of Load to Grain—60°—90°

50% of Full Load

SPACING CHART

PARALLEL TO GRAIN SPACING

PERPENDICULAR TO GRAIN SPACING

TIMBER FASTENERS
4'' Split Rings

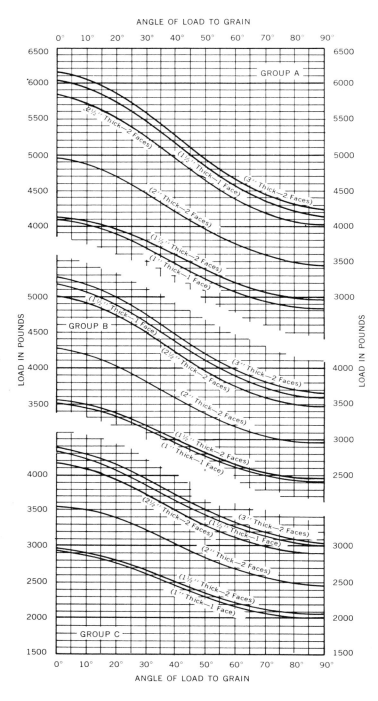

**LOAD CHART
FOR NORMAL LOADING
ONE 4'' SPLIT RING AND BOLT IN SINGLE SHEAR**

Note: For Group D connector values, multiply Group C values by 0.86.

4'' SPLIT RING DATA

Split Ring — Dimensions
Inside Diameter at center when closed .... 4''
Inside diameter at center when installed .... 4.06''
Thickness of ring at center .... 0.193''
Thickeness of ring at edge .... 0.133''
Depth .... 1''

Lumber, Minimum dimensions allowed
Width .... 5½''
Thickness, rings in one face .... 1''
Thickness, rings opposite in both faces .... 1½''

Bolt, diameter .... ¾''
Bolt hole, diameter .... 13/16''

Projected Area for portion of one ring within a member, square inches 2.24

Washers, minimum
Round, Cast or Malleable Iron, diameter .... 3''
Square Plate
Length of Side .... 3''
Thickness .... 3/16''
(For trussed rafters and similar light construction standard wrought washers may be used.)

SPLIT RING SPECIFICATIONS

Split rings shall be TECO split rings as manufactured by the Timber Engineering Company. Split rings shall be manufactured from hot rolled S.A.E. — 1010 carbon steel. Each ring shall form a closed true circle with the principal axis of the cross section of the ring metal parallel to the geometric axis of the ring. The ring shall fit snugly in the prepared groove. The metal section of each ring shall be beveled from the central portion toward the edges to a thickness less than that at mid-section. It shall be cut through in one place in its circumference to form a tongue and slot.

PERCENTAGES FOR DURATION OF MAXIMUM LOAD

Two Months Loading, as for snow .... 115 %
Seven Days Loading .... 125 %
Wind or Earthquake Loading 133⅓%
Impact Loading .... 200 %
Permanent Loading .... 90 %

DECREASES FOR MOISTURE CONTENT CONDITIONS

Condition when Fabricated	Seasoned	Unseasoned	Unseasoned
Condition when Used	Seasoned	Seasoned	Unseasoned or Wet
Split Rings	0%	20%	33%

Courtesy Timber Engineering Company

TIMBER FASTENERS

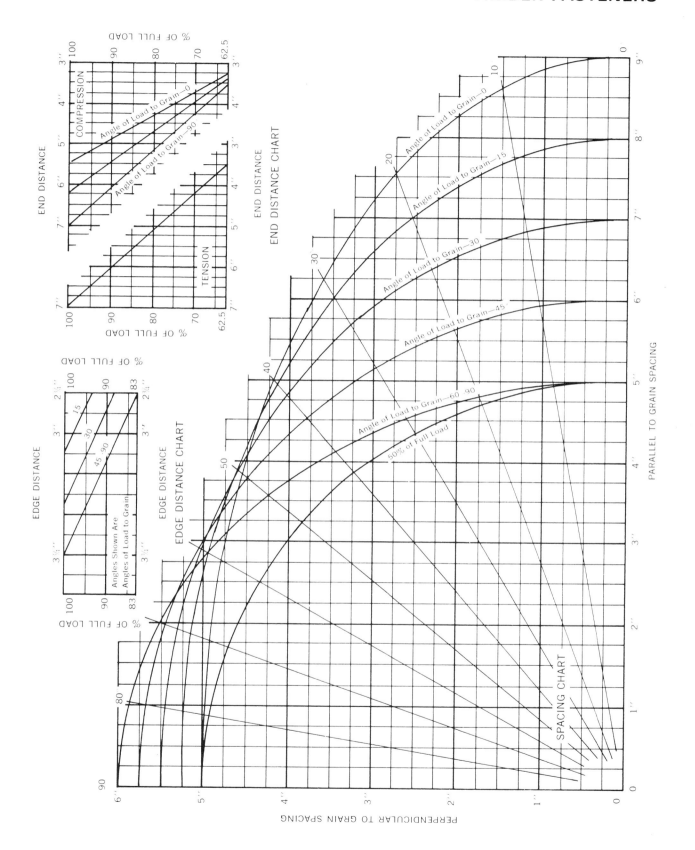

TIMBER FASTENERS

2⅝'' Shear Plates

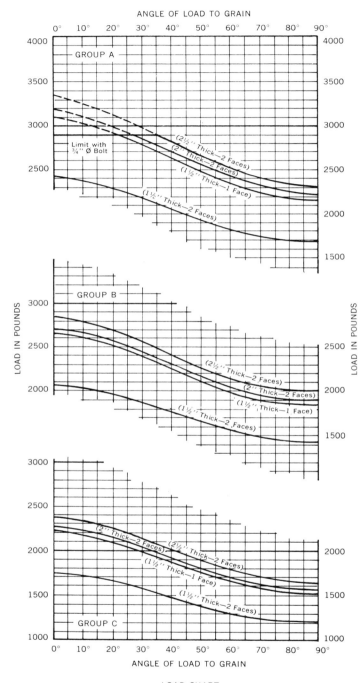

ANGLE OF LOAD TO GRAIN

GROUP A

Limit with ¾'' Ø Bolt

(2½'' Thick—2 Faces)
(2'' Thick—2 Faces)
(1½'' Thick—1 Face)
(1½'' Thick—2 Faces)

GROUP B

(2½'' Thick—2 Faces)
(2'' Thick—2 Faces)
(1½'' Thick—1 Face)
(1½'' Thick—2 Faces)

(2'' Thick—2 Faces)
(2½'' Thick—2 Faces)
(1½'' Thick—1 Face)
(1½'' Thick—2 Faces)

GROUP C

LOAD IN POUNDS

ANGLE OF LOAD TO GRAIN

LOAD CHART
FOR NORMAL LOADING
ONE 2⅝'' SHEAR-PLATE UNIT AND BOLT IN SINGLE SHEAR

Note: For Group D connector values, multiply Group C values by 0.86.

2⅝'' SHEAR PLATE DATA

Shear Plates, Dimensions	Pressed Steel	
Material	Reg.	Lt. Ga.
Diameter of plate	2.62''	2.62''
Diameter of bolt hole	.81''	.81''
Depth of plate	.42''	.35''
Lumber, minimum dimensions		
Face, width	3½''	3½''
Thickness, plates in one face only	1½''	1½''
Thickness, plates opposite in both faces	1½''	1½''

Steel Shapes or Straps (Thickness required
when used with shear plates)
Thickness of steel side plates shall be
determined in accordance with
A.I.S.C. recommendations.

Hole, diameter in steel straps or shapes	13/16''	13/16''
Bolt, diameter	¾''	¾''
Bolt Hole, diameter in timber	13/16''	13/16''

Washers, standard, timber to timber
connections only
Round, cast or malleable iron, diameter .... 3''   3''
Square Plate
    Length of side .... 3''   3''
    Thickness .... ¼''   ¼''
(For trussed rafters and other light
structures standard wrought washers
may be used.)

Projected Area, for one shear plate, square
inches 1.18   1.00

SHEAR PLATE SPECIFICATIONS

Pressed Steel Type — Pressed steel shear-plates shall be manufactured from hot-rolled S. A. E. — 1010 carbon steel. Each plate shall be a true circle with a flange around the edge extending at right angles to the face of the plate and extending from one face only, the plate portion having a central bolt hole and two small perforations on opposite sides of the hole and midway from the center and circumference.

PERCENTAGES FOR DURATION OF MAXIMUM LOAD

Two Months Loading, as for snow	*115 %
Seven Days Loading	*125 %
Wind or Earthquake Loading	*133⅓%
Impact Loading	*200 %
Permanent Loading	90 %

    *Do not exceed limitations for maximum allowable loads for shear plates given elsewhere on this page.

DECREASES FOR MOISTURE CONTENT CONDITIONS

Condition when Fabricated	Seasoned	Unseasoned	Unseasoned
Condition when Used	Seasoned	Seasoned	Unseasoned or Wet
Shear Plates	0%	20%	33%

MAXIMUM PERMISSIBLE LOADS ON SHEAR PLATES

The allowable loads for all loadings except wind shall not exceed 2900 lbs for 2⅝'' shear plates with ¾'' bolts. The allowable wind load shall not exceed 3870 lbs.

Courtesy Timber Engineering Company

TIMBER FASTENERS

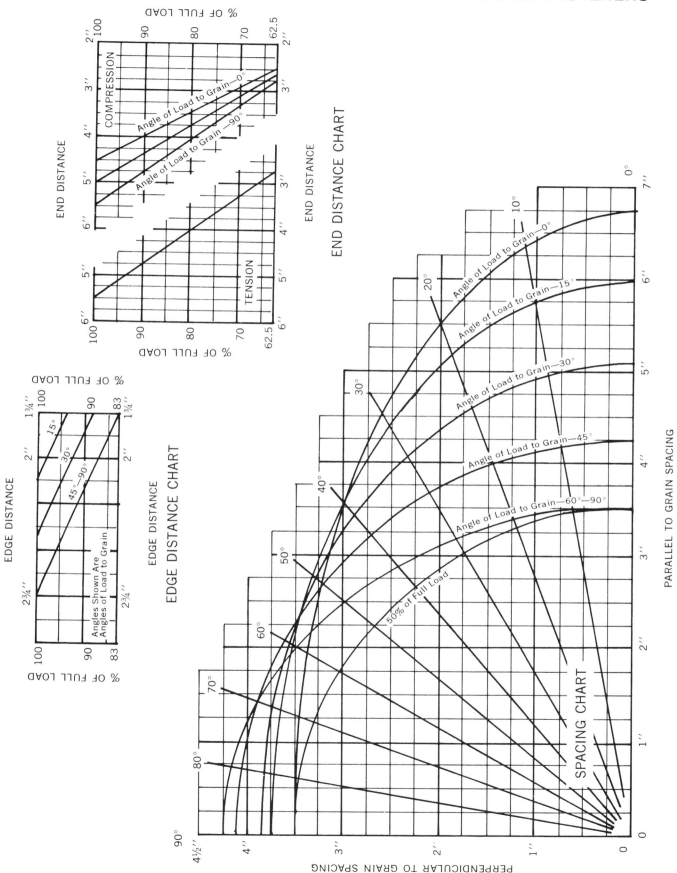

END DISTANCE

COMPRESSION

Angle of Load to Grain—0°

Angle of Load to Grain—90°

% OF FULL LOAD

TENSION

END DISTANCE CHART

END DISTANCE

EDGE DISTANCE

15°

30°

45°—90°

% OF FULL LOAD

Angles Shown Are
Angles of Load to Grain

EDGE DISTANCE

EDGE DISTANCE CHART

Angle of Load to Grain—0°

Angle of Load to Grain—15°

Angle of Load to Grain—30°

Angle of Load to Grain—45°

Angle of Load to Grain—60°—90°

50% of Full Load

SPACING CHART

PARALLEL TO GRAIN SPACING

PERPENDICULAR TO GRAIN SPACING

TIMBER FASTENERS

4" Shear Plates (Wood-to-Wood)

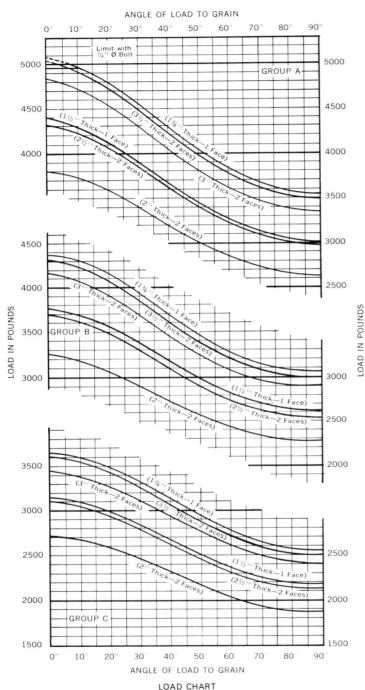

ANGLE OF LOAD TO GRAIN

LOAD CHART
FOR NORMAL LOADING
ONE 4" SHEAR-PLATE UNIT AND BOLT IN SINGLE SHEAR

Note: For Group D connector values, multiply Group C values by 0.86.

4" SHEAR PLATE DATA

Shear Plates, Dimensions	Malleable Iron	Malleable Iron
Material		
Diameter of plate	4.03"	4.03"
Diameter of bolt hole	.81"	.94"
Depth of plate	.64"	.64"
Lumber, minimum dimensions		
Face, width	5½"	5½"
Thickness, plates in one Face only	1½"	1½"
Thickness, plates opposite in both faces	1¾"	1¾"
Bolt, diameter	¾"	⅞"
Bolt Hole, diameter in timber	13/16"	15/16"
Washers, standard, timber to timber connections only		
Round, cast or malleable iron, diameter	3"	3½"
Square Plate		
Length of side	3"	3"
Thickness	¼"	¼"
(For trussed rafters and other light structures standard wrought washers may be used.)		
Projected Area, for one shear plate, square inches	2.58	2.58

SHEAR PLATE SPECIFICATIONS

Malleable Iron Types — Malleable iron shear plates shall be manufactured according to A.S.T.M. Standard Specifications A 47-33, Grade 35018, for malleable iron castings. Each casting shall consist of a perforated round plate with a flange around the edge extending at right angles to the face of the plate and projecting from one face only, the plate portion having a central bolt hole reamed to size with an integral hub concentric to the bolt hole and extending from the same face as the flange.

PERCENTAGES FOR DURATION OF MAXIMUM LOAD

Two Months Loading, as for snow	*115 %
Seven Days Loading	*125 %
Wind or Earthquake Loading	*133⅓%
Impact Loading	*200 %
Permanent Loading	90%

*Do not exceed limitations for maximum allowable loads for shear plates given elsewhere on this page.

DECREASES FOR MOISTURE CONTENT CONDITIONS

Conditions when Fabricated	Seasoned	Unseasoned	Unseasoned
Condition when Used	Seasoned	Seasoned	Unseasoned or Wet
Shear Plates	0%	20%	33%

MAXIMUM PERMISSIBLE LOADS ON SHEAR PLATES

The allowable loads for all loadings except wind shall not exceed 4970 lbs for 4" shear plates with ¾" bolts and 6760 lbs for 4" shear plates with ⅞" bolts. The allowable wind loads shall not exceed 6630 lbs when used with a ¾" bolt and 9020 lbs when used with a ⅞" bolt.

TIMBER FASTENERS

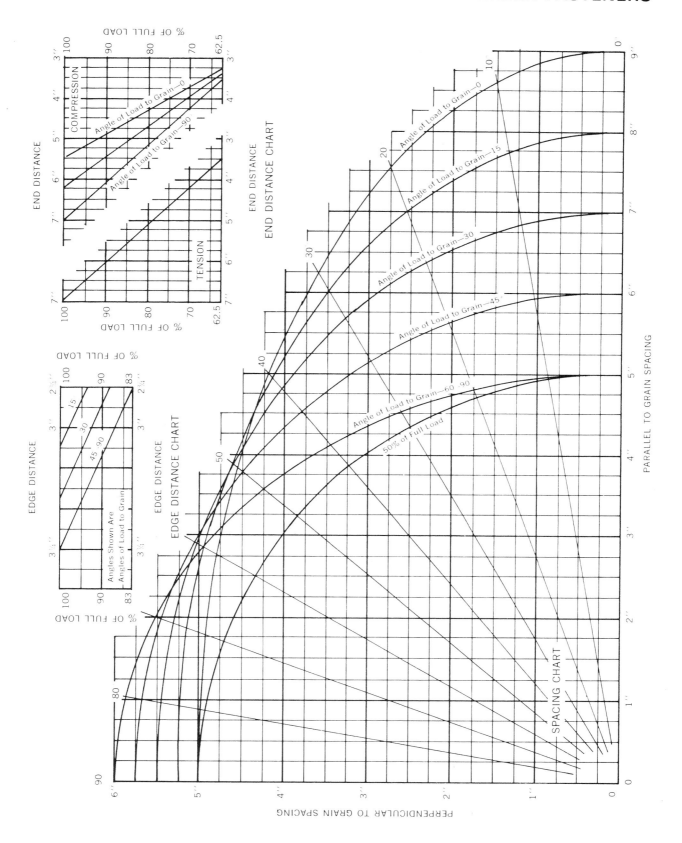

END DISTANCE

COMPRESSION

Angle of Load to Grain—0

Angle of Load to Grain—90

TENSION

% OF FULL LOAD

END DISTANCE

END DISTANCE CHART

EDGE DISTANCE

Angles Shown Are
Angles of Load to Grain

EDGE DISTANCE

EDGE DISTANCE CHART

% OF FULL LOAD

Angle of Load to Grain—0

Angle of Load to Grain—15

Angle of Load to Grain—30

Angle of Load to Grain—45

Angle of Load to Grain—60–90

50% of Full Load

SPACING CHART

PARALLEL TO GRAIN SPACING

PERPENDICULAR TO GRAIN SPACING

TIMBER FASTENERS

4" Shear Plates (Wood-to-Steel)

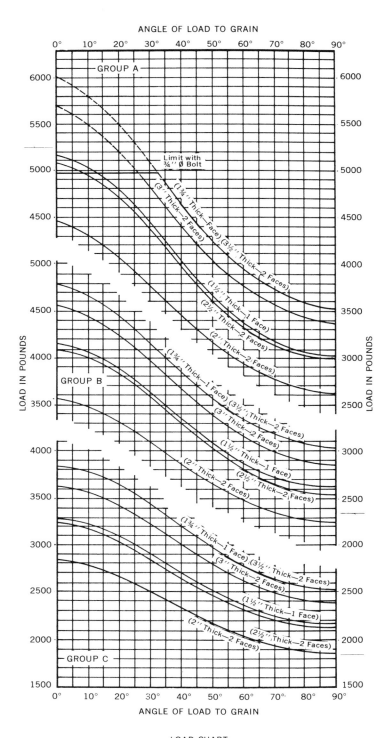

ANGLE OF LOAD TO GRAIN

LOAD CHART
FOR NORMAL LOADING
ONE 4" SHEAR-PLATE UNIT AND BOLT IN SINGLE SHEAR

Note: For Group D connector values, multiply Group C values by 0.86.

4" SHEAR PLATE DATA

Shear Plates, Dimensions		
Material	Malleable Iron	Malleable Iron
Diameter of plate	4.03"	4.03"
Diameter of bolt hole	.81"	.94"
Depth of plate	.64"	.64"
Lumber, minimum dimensions		
Face, width	5½"	5½"
Thickness, plates in one face only	1½"	1½"
Thickness, plates opposite in both faces	1¾"	1¾"

Steel Shapes or Straps
(Thickness required when used with shear plates)
Thickness of steel side plates shall be determined in accordance with A.I.S.C. recommendations.

Hole, diameter in steel straps or shapes	13/16"	15/16"
Bolt, diameter	¾"	⅞"
Bolt Hole, diameter in timber	13/16"	15/16"
Projected Area, for one shear plate, square inches	2.58	2.58

SHEAR PLATE SPECIFICATIONS

Malleable Iron Types — Malleable iron plates shall be manufactured according to A.S.T.M. Standard Specifications A 47-33, Grade 35018, for malleable iron castings. Each casting shall consist of a perforated round plate with a flange around the edge extending at right angles to the face of the plate and projecting from one face only, the plate portion having a central bolt hole reamed to size with an integral hub concentric to the bolt hole and extending from the same face as the flange.

PERCENTAGES FOR DURATION OF MAXIMUM LOAD

Two Months Loading, as for snow ....*115 %
Seven Days Loading ....*125 %
Wind or Earthquake Loading *133⅓%
Impact Loading ....*200 %
Permanent Loading ....90 %

*Do not exceed limitations for maximum allowable loads for shear plates given below.

DECREASES FOR MOISTURE CONTENT CONDITIONS

Condition when Fabricated	Seasoned	Unseasoned	Unseasoned
Condition when Used	Seasoned	Seasoned	Unseasoned or Wet
Shear Plates	0%	20%	33%

MAXIMUM PERMISSIBLE LOADS ON SHEAR PLATES

The allowable loads for all loadings except wind shall not exceed 4970 lbs for 4" shear plates with ¾" bolts and 6760 lbs for 4" shear plates with ⅞" bolts. The allowable wind loads shall not exceed 6630 lbs when used with a ¾" bolt and 9020 lbs when used with a ⅞" bolt.

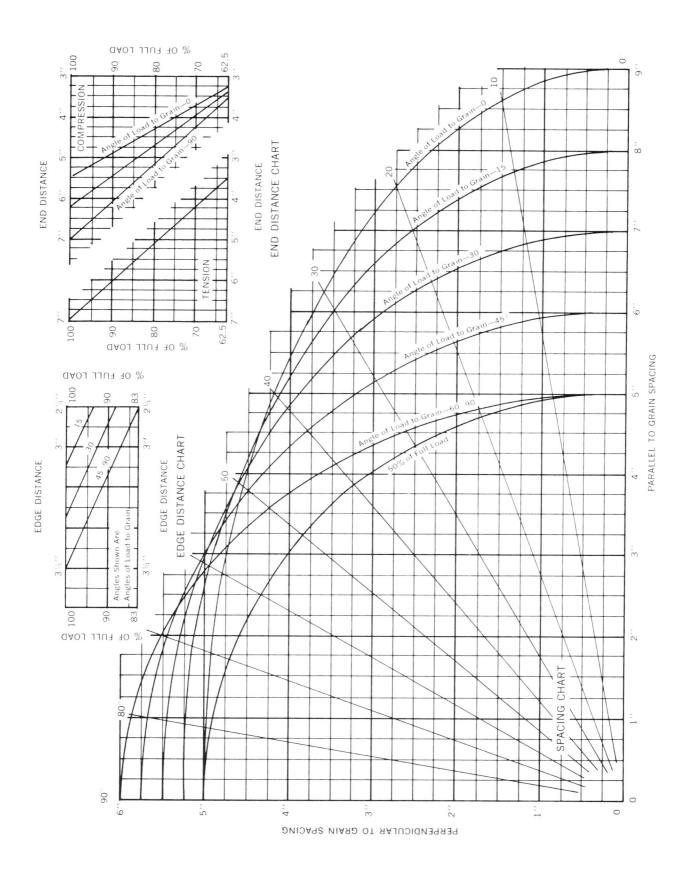

TIMBER FASTENERS

FRAMING ANCHORS

Two special fastening devices frequently used to simplify and strengthen framed connections, are framing anchors and joist and beam hangers. Framing anchors are a comparatively new device but joist and beam hangers have long been in use.

Framing Anchors

Framing anchors, generally manufactured from 18 gauge zinc coated sheet steel, are usually of three basic types, with right and left hand bends making them suitable, within their load capacity, for most all joints with dimension lumber 2 to 4 inches thick. Special 10¼ gauge short nails, of ample strength without protruding through 2 inch lumber, are usually furnished with the framing anchors. The nails fit snugly in the holes punched in the framing anchors to minimize inelastic slip. Originally introduced in hurricane areas, framing anchors are now widely used where simple joints that are stronger than provided by nails alone are needed. A principal advantage of framing anchors is that the nails are always loaded laterally, the most efficient direction strengthwise. Figure 8.36 shows the types of a widely used framing anchor.

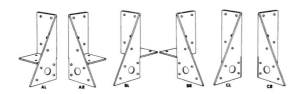

Figure 8.36 — Framing Anchor Types.

Tests have been made of the load capacity of framing anchors and suggested allowable working loads for different directions and durations of loading based on these tests are tabulated herein for one framing anchor.

Framing anchors are adaptable to a wide range of use and Figure 8.38 illustrates some applications in frame construction.

Joist and Beam Hangers

These devices, used to support the ends of joists and beams, eliminate the need for ledger strips or notching, and also provide more head room as they permit the joists to be framed level with the top of the supporting members. Joist and beam hangers, available for use with light and heavy timber members are manufactured from sheet or strap steel, depending on the size. Several types of these hangers are illustrated in Figure 8.37.

As there is no standardization of width and thickness of metal used in manufacturing such hangers, allowable loads must be ascertained from the manufacturer of the product used.

Joist hangers for dimension lumber of 2 inch thickness are generally manufactured of galvanized sheet metal of 16 or 18 gauge and are from ¾ to 1½ inches wide. For 3 inch and thicker joists and girders, strap steel ⅛ inch or more in thickness and up to 2½ inches wide is used. Joist hangers for heavy timbers are sometimes fabricated of an angle and strap welded together.

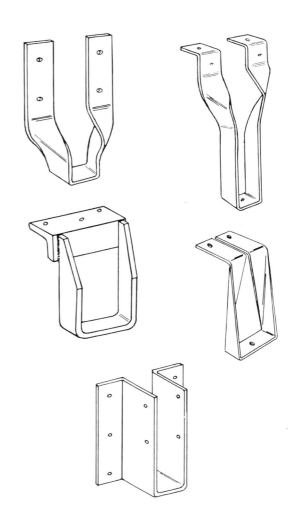

Figure 8.37 — Joint Hanger Types.

Joist hangers may rely entirely on the lateral strength of the nails for light loads, or the strap may be bent over the top of the girder and the bearing strength of the wood utilized for heavy loads.

For very large sizes and heavy loads joist hangers must be individually designed to provide sufficient bearing to avoid crushing the wood and must be of sufficient cross-section to support the reaction load.

FRAMING ANCHORS

TABLE 8.24 — Allowable Load in Pounds for One Framing Anchor When Fully Nailed:

(Loads shown are illustrative of comparative allowable directional loads for one patented framing anchor fastened to Douglas Fir or other species with equivalent specific gravity. Consult manufacturer for recommended allowable loads for specific framing anchors).

Condition of Loading	Direction of Load					
	A	B	C	D	E	F
Wind, Earthquake and Impact	450	825	420	300	450	675
All others	300	530	290	200	300	450

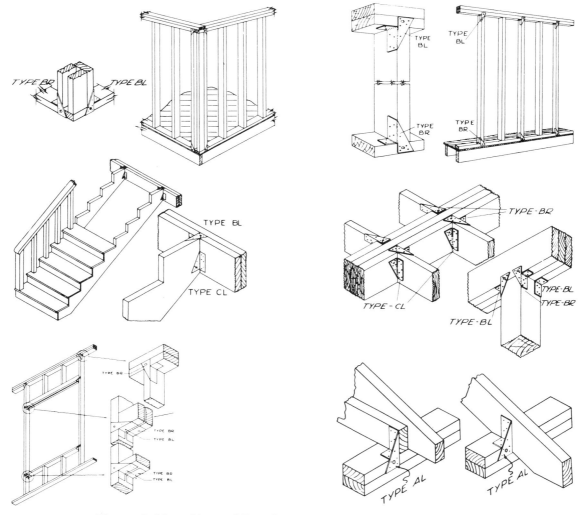

Figure 8.38 — Uses of Framing Anchors in Frame Construction.

CHAPTER IX

Tanks and Pipe

TANKS AND PIPE

Tanks, vats and pipe of wood have many applications, and their usefulness and adequacy have been demonstrated by many years of continuous and satisfactory service. Advantages of wood tanks and pipe are their initial economy, low maintenance costs and long service life. Of special importance is the suitability of these pipes, tanks and vats for storage, processing and transmission of corrosive liquids. As large pipe and tanks are normally shipped knocked down and erected at the site, transportation costs and problems are minimized. The knocked down feature is very advantageous when erection is to be within a finished building.

Wood tanks, vats and pipe are not subject to corrosion or rust and are unaffected by electrolysis, as wood is a non-conductor. Since the expansion or contraction of wood with heat or cold is negligible, wood pipe does not require expansion joints, and extreme changes in temperature will not cause damage or bursting. Where fluctuations in temperature must be kept at a minimum, the low thermal conductivity of wood reduces heat loss and may even eliminate the need of additional insulation. Preservatively treated tanks and pipe can be used for domestic water supplies without affecting the quality and taste of the water, and there are records of treated wood pipe in service for more than fifty years without apparent deterioration.

Some of the many uses for wood tanks, vats and pipe are:

Tanks and Vats
> Water storage
> Air pollution control
> Wineries
> Food processing and storage
> Dyeing
> Petroleum refining
> Pulp and paper manufacture
> Soap manufacture
> Tanneries
> Glue manufacture
> Textiles
> Mineral refining
> Pickle manufacture
> Ink manufacture
> Railroads
> Rolling mills
> Chemical plants

Pipe
> Water transmission lines
> Culverts
> Storm sewers
> Sanitary sewers
> Irrigation systems
> Flumes
> Industrial piping
> Mill tailings disposal
> Hydrolectric penstocks
> Insulation (cover for pipe linings)

TANKS
The principal difference between tanks and vats is one of use, since the construction is the same for both. Tanks are generally associated with the storage of liquids while vats are used for processing purposes, such as dye vats and pickling vats in rolling mills. Wood tanks and vats are built in many different shapes and sizes. Principal among these is the cylindrical shape, used either vertically or horizontally. Tanks of very large capacity are most always cylindrical and are used vertically. Tanks having an elliptical cross section are similar in details and construction to cylindrical tanks except for shape. A variation of the cylindrical tank is the half round (half cylinder) and round bottom tank with vertical sides. Round bottom tanks have advantages of being easily made liquid tight, they drain well and are well adapted to mechanical agitation. There are also plain rectangular tanks shaped like a box. Several special purpose variations in the bottoms of cylindrical tanks are available. They may be level or sloping and they may have double bottoms; a main bottom and a false one. The false bottom may also be level, sloping or conical and may be perforated, depending on the use for the tank. Figure 9.2 illustrates some of the various shapes of wood tanks.

Tanks may be open top or may be built with a fixed top or head, or with a loose flat cover if inside a building, or a framed roof if outside. Covers are used to protect against contamination, the weather and from freezing, or to contain fumes, also as a safety measure. Liquids protected by wood covers will have less tendency to evaporate or to freeze, due to the insulating properties of wood.

The walls of cylindrical, elliptical and rectangular type wood tanks consist of staves. Very little strength is required of the staves; their principal function being to provide a liquid tight container. For this reason it is essential that the edges of staves be carefully jointed to assure a tight fit. The bottoms of these tanks when used vertically are tightly joined planks, fitted into a croze (dado) machined in the inner face of the staves a specified distance from the end of the stave called the chime. See Figure 9.1. If the tanks are to be completely tight, a head is fitted in the same

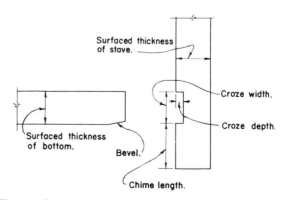

Figure 9.1 — Tank Stave and Bottom Detail.

TANKS AND PIPE

way the bottom is built. Cylindrical type tanks used horizontally have bulkheads fitted into each end, similar to the way a bottom is fitted in a vertically placed tank. Half round or round bottom tanks are built of staves and may use bulkheads fitted into a croze; short length half round or round bottom tanks may have bulkheads clamped to their ends which also may serve as the tank supports.

Steel hoops formed from round steel rods are used to hold the staves in place, to compress the joints to make them liquid tight, and to resist the outward thrust of the liquid against the sides of the tank. For cylindrical tanks or the round portion of other tanks the staves should be finished convex to the outside surface to give full contact with the hoops. Horizontal tie rods are used to hold the sides and ends of rectangular tanks and the ends of half round and round bottom tanks in place and to resist the forces at the ends caused by the pressure of the liquid.

Capacity of Wood Tanks

Wood tanks have been built ranging in size from small rectangular tanks used in film developing to large capacity cylindrical water storage tanks up to 1,000,000 gallons capacity. The table below gives the capacity in gallons of cylindrical tanks based on the inside diameter. Capacities of square, rectangular and other shape tanks in gallons may be computed by multiplying the volume in cubic feet by the factor 7.48.

Hoops

The most important part of the design of wood tanks is the determination of the size and spacing of the steel hoops or the tie rods. The outward pressure of the liquid contents against the walls of the tank increases uniformly from zero at the surface of the liquid to a maximum at the bottom of the tank.

TABLE 9.1 — Capacity of Cylindrical Tanks

Outside Diameter in feet	Nominal Lumber Stock Thickness	Inside Diameter ft.	inches	Capacity U.S. Gallons per ft. of depth	Nominal Lumber Stock Thickness	Inside Diameter ft.	inches	Capacity U.S. Gallons per ft. of depth
3	2″	2	8¾	43.8	3″	2	6¾	38.6
4	2″	3	8¾	81.71	3″	3	6¾	74.6
5	2″	4	8¾	131.4	3″	4	6¾	122.31
6	2″	5	8¾	192.8	3″	5	6¾	181.8
7	2″	6	8¾	266	3″	6	6¾	253
8	2″	7	8¾	351	3″	7	6¾	336
9	2″	8	8¾	447	3″	8	6¾	431
10	2″	9	8¾	556	3″	9	6¾	537
11	2″	10	8¾	676	3″	10	6¾	655
12	2″	11	8¾	808	3″	11	6¾	785
13	2″	12	8¾	952	3″	12	6¾	927
14	2″	13	8¾	1107	3″	13	6¾	1081
15	2″	14	8¾	1275	3″	14	6¾	1246
16	2″	15	8¾	1454	3″	15	6¾	1423
17	2″	16	8¾	1644	3″	16	6¾	1612
18	2″	17	8¾	1847	3″	17	6¾	1812
19	2″	18	8¾	2061	3″	18	6¾	2024
20	2″	19	8¾	2287	3″	19	6¾	2248
20	3″	19	6¾	2248	4″	19	4¾	2215
22	3″	21	6¾	2732	4″	21	4¾	2695
24	3″	23	6¾	3262	4″	23	4¾	3221
26	3″	25	6¾	3839	4″	25	4¾	3795
28	3″	27	6¾	4463	4″	27	4¾	4416
30	3″	29	6¾	5135	4″	29	4¾	5084
32	3″	31	6¾	5853	4″	31	4¾	5799
34	3″	33	6¾	6618	4″	33	4¾	6561
36	3″	35	6¾	7430	4″	35	4¾	7370
38	3″	37	6¾	8290	4″	37	4¾	8225
40	3″	39	6¾	9196	4″	39	4¾	9128
42	3″	41	6¾	10150	4″	41	4¾	10080
44	3″	43	6¾	11150	4″	43	4¾	11070
46	3″	45	6¾	12200	4″	45	4¾	12120
48	3″	47	6¾	13290	4″	47	4¾	13210
50	3″	49	6¾	14430	4″	49	4¾	14350
50	4″	49	4¾	14350	6″	49	1	14150
55	4″	54	4¾	17400	6″	54	1	17190
60	4″	59	4¾	20740	6″	59	1	20510
65	4″	64	4¾	24380	6″	64	1	24130
70	4″	69	4¾	28310	6″	69	1	28040
75	4″	74	4¾	32540	6″	74	1	32260
80	4″	79	4¾	37050	6″	79	1	36740

TANKS AND PIPE

Since it is customary for all of the hoops to be of the same cross sectional area, the spacing between the hoops will be greater at the top of the tank where the outward pressure is least than at the bottom where the outward pressure is greatest. The hoop spacing, which is usually limited to a maximum of 18 inches, depends on the cross sectional area of the hoop, the allowable unit stress of the hoop steel, the distance from the top of the tank to the hoop under consideration, and the unit weight of the liquid. Following is a formula recommended by tank manufacturers that can be used to determine the required hoop spacing in inches for vertical cylindrical tanks:

$$S = \frac{12F}{wRh}$$

where S = hoop spacing in inches measured as one half the distance between the hoop next above and the hoop next below the hoop under consideration,
F = allowable load on hoop in pounds,
R = outside radius of tank in feet,
h = distance from top of tank to hoop in feet,
w = weight of liquid in lbs. per cu. ft.

Tank manufacturers recommend that the allowable unit stress used for the hoop steel not exceed ⅓ of the ultimate strength of the steel. For a steel having an ultimate strength in the range of 55,000 to 65,000 lbs. per sq. in., an allowable unit stress of 18,000 lbs. per sq. in. would be used.

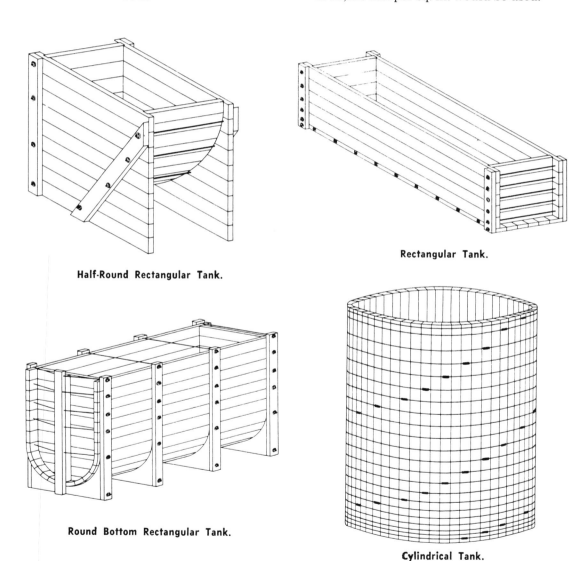

Half-Round Rectangular Tank.

Rectangular Tank.

Round Bottom Rectangular Tank.

Cylindrical Tank.

Figure 9.2 — Types of Douglas Fir Tanks.

Hoops are fastened by means of special lugs as shown in Figure 9.3. Hoop lengths are usually made with a button head on one end and cold rolled threads at the other, with the threaded end upset so that the threaded portion has the same strength as the body of the hoop. Where cut threads are used, the strength of the hoop must be calculated from the net cross section at the root of the threads.

Hoops are usually made in single lengths for small diameter tanks and in multiple lengths for large diameter tanks. The following tabulation represents the usual number of lengths in a hoop used for various tank diameters:

Outside Tank Diameter	Number of Lengths in a Hoop
to 7'6"	1 or 2
7'7" to 15'6"	2 or 3
15'7" to 22'0"	3 or 4
22'1" to 26'0"	4 to 6
26'1" and over	5 or more

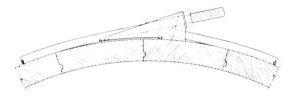

Figure 9.3 — Lug for Tank and Pipe Hoops.

should be designed as beams as outlined on pages 71 to 107. The bottom planking is designed as outlined on pages 163 to 171. For large capacity tanks, the combination of a concrete bottom and wood stave construction where the tanks are installed at ground level is generally the most economical. The concrete bottom, which serves as the bottom of the tank as well as the foundation, eliminates the usual foundation and other supports. This type of tank is particularly adaptable where sloping or conical shaped bottoms are required. The table of unit weights of various chemical solutions on page 277 can be used in designing tanks and for computing the total weight of the contents of a tank.

Supporting Structures

Supporting structures for elevated tanks should be designed to resist the vertical loads from the contents and lateral forces from wind or earthquake, in accordance with standard engineering procedures. Information on design to resist lateral forces is given on pages 173 to 195.

Tank Lumber

As the function of the tank staves, bottom planks or bulkheads is to contain the liquid stored in the tank, it is important that the right grade of lumber is used so as to provide liquid tightness. All species covered in the *Standard Grading Rules for Western Lumber* of the Western Wood Products Association may be graded in accordance with the *Standard Grading Rules for West Coast Lumber* of the West Coast Lumber Inspection Bureau (WCLIB). The WCLIB grading rules contain two grades of Tank Stock: "UNDER FOUR INCH" and "FOUR INCH and

Bottom Planks and Chime Joists

The bottom planks of vertical tanks carry the full weight of the contents. It is also essential that these planks fit accurately and have tight joints to prevent leakage. They should be planed to a uniform thickness and the ends cut to the shape of the circumference of the tank so that they fit properly in the croze of the staves. To insure an exact fit, the edges of the bottom planks should be held in alignment by wood dowels spaced not over 4 feet apart for 2 inch nominal thickness plank and not over 5 feet apart for 3 inch nominal and thicker plank. A dowel should also be approximately 6 inches from each end of the planks. The thickness required of the bottom planks depends on the weight they must support and the spacing of the cross members (chime joists) supporting the planks. If a tank rests on a slab or on the ground, it is important that the chime joists are deep enough to provide a good ventilation space of about 1½ inches between the bottom of the staves and the base on which the tank rests. The chime joists may be supported on mud sills or other foundation as illustrated in Figure 9.4, or on a structural framework for elevated tanks. The size of the chime joists depends on the joist span and spacing. Chime

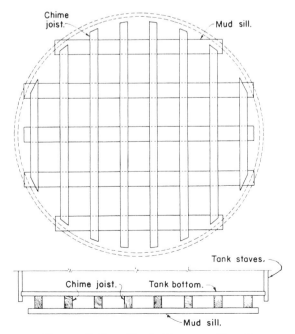

Figure 9.4 — Tank Support Details.

TANKS AND PIPE

THICKER". Pieces of this grade are entirely clear or have only a few minor and unimportant characteristics, such as small sound and tight knots, surface checks and small pitch pockets, none of which extends through the piece and affects its usefulness. If the tank is used where there are conditions conducive to decay, the lumber should be preservatively treated by a pressure process.

Tank Linings

Unlined wood tanks provide natural protection against the corrosive effect of most acid and alkaline solutions. They also protect against the action of organic solvents, sulfur compounds, flourides, organic acids, industrial wastes, salt water, water and other corrosive liquids and gases. Wood is composed principally of cellulose and lignin. Cellulose is resistant to oxidizing and alkaline agents but not to acids, and lignin is resistant to acids but not to oxidizing and alkaline agents. Therefore, wood tanks can be used satisfactorily for acids having a pH of not less than 2.0 and alkalies having a pH of not more than 11.0 at room temperature. Although in some cases these limits are exceeded, and tank life is necessarily shortened, wood tanks may still provide the best answer to a particular problem. Some liquids such as nitric acid, chromic acid, permanganate, hypochlorites or alkali in the presence of atmospheric oxygen will attack wood in its entirety depending on the concentration and temperature. At room temperature a 5 per cent solution of nitric acid, 1 per cent sodium hydroxide, or a 5 per cent solution of sodium hypochlorite will be detrimental to the wood. All of these are outside the range of pH values given. Data on the gain or loss of strength of wood exposed to chemicals is given on page 5.

To increase the useful life of a wood tank used for storage of corrosive liquids the interior of the tank can be lined with a corrosion resistant material. The use of a lining limits the requirement of wood merely to strength and resistance to decay, and the life expectancy of the tank becomes a function of the resistance of the lining to attack by the contents. The type of lining used will depend on the nature of the contents, since some liquids are corrosive to certain materials while others are not. One of the materials having a long history as a tank lining is lead for use in holding sulfuric acid in concentrations up to 96 per cent at room temperature. At concentrations of 85 per cent, lead resists sulfuric acid up to 425°F. The resistance of lead to sulfuric acid is due to the protective action of the thin film of lead sulfate formed. Excessive turbulence increases the rate of corrosion by causing the formation of a constantly renewed film of lead sulfate. Other tank linings used are: brick, asphalt, pitch, paint and flexible plastic liners.

Many of the polymers are available as tank linings, making wood tanks adaptable to almost any application. Some of these polymers, such as nitrile rubber latex, can be applied by brush or spray, while others, such as polyethylene, are available in sheet form. As these lining materials are of relatively recent development, service life histories are not available, but accelerated tests indicate that long service life can be expected. The following table shows the expected service life of lined and unlined wood tanks based on past experience when used for storage of various chemicals. Also shown is a performance record of wood tanks used for containing various corrosive chemicals.

Maintenance of Wood Tanks

A mimimum of maintenance is required for wood tanks, but a reasonable amount of care and periodic inspections will result in better service and longer life.

There should be an adequate circulation of air around and particularly under tanks on supports to reduce conditions conducive to decay for water storage tanks and to avoid the accumulation of fumes when tanks are used for storage and processing of corrosive liquids. Clearance around the tank should be sufficient to allow easy access for inspecting, cleaning and tightening the hoops.

Hoops should be inspected periodically and tightened if required. The hoops are tightened in several steps, working around the tank and from hoop to hoop so that the slack is taken up uniformly around the entire tank.

Leaks in joints between staves, if they occur, can be stopped by tightening the hoops. If a leak still persists it may be stopped by making a series of narrow openings in the staves on both sides of the joint and parallel to it with a chisel and driving wood wedges into the openings, which will force the edges of the staves together. The openings for the wedges should be about an inch or two inches deep, depending on the thickness of the staves, but should not penetrate completely through. They should be located about an inch away from the joint and should extend a short distance beyond the location of the leak.

The schedule for cleaning of tanks is governed by the solution and environment. Water storage tanks require cleaning at infrequent intervals, while tanks used in pickling may require cleaning as often as once a week. When cleaning is necessary the tank should be drained, all scale and foreign matter removed, and the tank flushed with water. To keep the joints tight, tanks used to contain water or other liquids should be kept filled with water when not in use. The outside should also be washed down to remove spillage and to soak the wood which aids in keeping the joints tight.

When tanks are to contain corrosive liquids the hoops should be protected from contact with the liquids and the corrosive atmosphere. Allowance for corrosion can be made by increasing the cross sectional area of the hoops beyond that required to resist the outward pressure. There are several methods that can be used to protect the hoops depending on the degree of protection required.

TABLE 9.2 — Performance record of wood tanks containing corrosive chemicals

INDUSTRY	Number, size of tanks, thickness	Years in service when inspected	Condition when inspected	Strength of solution	Temperature of solution	REMARKS
ACETIC ACID Food Products Plant	10 tanks — 8' x 8', 2''	23 Yrs.	Good	10%	75°-120°F.	Tanks are not lined.
Vinegar Plant	2 tanks — 14' x 12', 3'	18 Yrs.	Good	10%	70°F.	Tanks are not lined.
Food Preserving Plant	1 tank — 12' x 8', 2''	8 Yrs. in present use	Good	10%	75°F.	This tank purchased second hand. Operator does not know how old it was when secured. Tank is not lined.
Pickle Plant	10 tanks — 10' x 10', 2''	30 Yrs.	Good	5-10% variable	75°F.	Tanks are not lined.
Vinegar Plant	2 tanks — 14' x 12' 3'' nom. stock	18 Yrs.	Good	6%	70°F.	These tanks are used for cider vinegar. Are not lined.
ARSENIC ACID Ortho Spray Chemical Factory	2 tanks — 21' x 10', 3''	13 Yrs.	Good	.01%	36°-90°F.	Acid carried in combination with 0.1% solution of copper sulphate. Tanks are not lined.
FLUOSILICIC ACID Chemical Plant	2 tanks — 20' x 20', 3''	4 Yrs.	Good	8-15%	40°-100°F.	Tanks are not lined. Hoops corrode relatively quickly. Tried lead shields under hoops which gave better service. However, rubber hose placed around hoops affords best protection.
HYDROGEN FLUORIDE Steel Plant	2 tanks — 14' x 6' x 4', 3''	5 Yrs.	Good	3%	36°-90°F.	Tank has false wood lining, and acid-resisting brick on bottom to take mechanical wear occasioned by handling steel shapes.
OCEAN WATER Sea Food Cannery	27 tanks — 20' x 6' x 4', 2''	8 Yrs.	Good	Sea water	70°F.	Tanks are not lined.
SULPHURIC ACID Steel Pickling Plant	2 tanks — 16' x 6' x 4', 3''	5 Yrs.	Good	5-12%	36°-190°F.	Tank has false wood lining and bottom of acid-resisting brick to take mechanical wear from pickling cast iron shapes.
Plating Works	3 tanks — 12' x 4½' x 4', 3''	20 Yrs.	Fair	pH 5.8	36°-80°F.	These tanks were not lined
Tannery	3 tanks — 6' x 3', 3''	27 Yrs.	Good	1½%	36°-120°F.	Tanks are not lined. Tanks were used for 13 years for water storage prior to their present use. Total service 40 years.
Chemical Plant	1 tank — 14' x 10', 3'' nom. stock	21 Yrs.	Good	2%	40°-180°F.	Tank is not lined. Sulphuric acid carried in combination with 1½% solution of hydrochloric acid.
Galvanizer	2 rectangular tanks — 5' wide x 4' deep x 30' long, 6'' tank stock	25 Yrs.	Fair			Sulphuric acid tanks with 2'' wood liner 120° F. 15 to 17% sulphuric acid.
Galvanizer	1 rectangular tank — 5' wide x 4' deep x 30' long, 6'' tank stock	30 Yrs.	Poor			Sulphuric acid tanks with 2'' wood liner 120° F. 15 to 17% sulphuric acid. Reline sides and bottom each 2 years.
Tannery	10 tanks — 12' x 6', 2½''	36 Yrs.	Good	Dilute (Under 5%)	36°-80°F.	Tanks are not lined.
ALUMINUM SULPHATE Fiberboard Mill	3 — open board wet machine vats, 3''	1 tk. — 3 Yrs. 1 tk. — 2 Yrs. 1 tk. — 1 Yr.	Good	2-4%	50°-100°F.	The solution used in treating paper and cotton stock. Tanks are not lined.
AMMONIUM NITRATE Plating Works	1 tank — 5' x 4' x 4', 3''	3 Yrs.	Good	8 oz. per gal. about 6% solution.	Room temp.	Solution used in metal plating. Tank is not lined.
COPPER PYRITES Mining Company	2 tanks — 20' x 10' 1 tank — 16' x 16', 3''	21 Yrs.	Good	13-15% Copper	Normal Normal	Tanks are not lined. This compound made up of copper pyrites, iron sulphide (triolite) and copper sulphide (chalcocite) $CuFeS_2$ and $FeS.2Cu_2S$.
Mining Company COPPER SULPHATE	2 tanks — 50' x 10' 3''	28 Yrs	Good	15% Copper	Normal	Tanks are not lined. Compound is same as above.
Chemical Plant	1 tank — 10' x 8', 2½''	13 Yrs.	Good	5%	36°-170°F.	Tank is not lined.
Chemical Plant	2 tanks — 10' x 8', 2½''	13 Yrs.	Good	1-5%	36°-170°F.	Tanks are not lined. A 1% solution of sulphuric acid is added in the tanks to the copper sulphate solution.
POTASSIUM CYANIDE Mining Company	3 tanks — 35' x 6' 2 tanks — 20' x 15', 3''	20 Yrs.	Good	1%	Normal	Tanks are not lined. These tanks were used in one location for 3 years, then dismantled, shipped to another mine, re-erected and used for same purpose.
Mining Company SODIUM CHLORIDE	9 tanks — 60' x 16', 4''	20 Yrs.	Good	0.50-2.0%	Normal	Tanks are not lined.
Olive Cannery	24 tanks — 8' x 6' 20 tanks — 10' x 8' 2 tanks — 12' x 12', 3'' nom. stock	15 Yrs.	Good	Dilute	70°F.	Tanks are not lined. These tanks have been used in present application for 15 years. Prior to that time they were used for unknown period of years as wine storage tanks.
Fish Cannery CALCIUM HYDROXIDE	15 tanks — 6' x 4' x 3', 2''	15 Yrs.	Good	5%	40°-90°F.	Tanks are not lined.
Mining Company	2 tanks — 12' x 10', 3''	10 Yrs.	Good	2-3%	Normal	Tanks are not lined. Prior to this present 10 year usage, these tanks were used for other purposes, presumably for neutral solutions.
SODIUM HYDROXIDE Olive Cannery	4 tanks — 8' x 3½', 3'' staves, concrete bottoms	11 Yrs.	Good	2-10% Lye mix.	70°-185°F. Max. temp applied twice every 6 days.	Tanks are not lined.
Olive Cannery	56 tanks — 13' x 5' x 1½', 2''	8 Yrs.	Good	1-2%	40°-212°F. Max. temp. applied twice every 6 days.	Tanks are not lined. Solution is olive cure lye.
Paper Manufacturing Plant	15 Screen boxes — 2½' x 12' x 2', 2''	9 Yrs. and under	Good	0.10-0.25%	Normal	Boxes are not lined.

TANKS AND PIPE

TABLE 9.3 — Expected Service Life of Lined and Unlined Wood Tanks

Chemical	Concentration %	Temperature range of contents F°	Type of lining	Expected service life
Hydrochloric acid	20	60 to 120	Rubber	20 years
" "	28 to 30	61 to 120	Tar and asphalt	Less than 2 years
" "	"	Room	Heavy pitch	More than 10 years
" "	5	36 to 90	None	More than 3 years
" "	3 to 5	Room	Acid resistant paint	More than 5 years
" "	Less than 1	40 to 150	Acid resistant paint	More than 10 years
Sulfuric acid	95	36 to 200	Lead	Long life - More than 50 years
" "	20	60 to 120	Asphalt and tar	More than 10 years
" "	5	Room	None	More than 5 years
" "	0.0001	Room	None	More than 30 years
Acetic acid	40-80	Room	None	More than 45 years
Vinegar	....	....	None	More than 8 years
Lactic acid	25 to 27	150	None	More than 3 years
Fatty acids			None	Virtually unaffected
Calcium hydroxide	2 to 3		None	More than 10 years
" "	Concentrated		None	Destroys
Magnesium hydroxide	8 to 10	170	None	More than 17 years
Ortho arsenic acid	Less than 0.01	Less than 100	None	More than 10 years
Nitric acid	5 to 8	36 to 90	Asphalt brick	More than 20 years
Phosphoric acid	30	36 to 90	None	More than 3 years
Sodium meta antimanate	....	60 to 70	None	16 years
Nickel Carbonate	....	....	None	15 to 20 years

Paint may be used when it is established that its particular composition is impervious to the chemical and its fumes. Brush or trowel coatings of the acid and alkali resistant polymers that are used for tank linings provide effective protection. Wood lagging strips, placed under the hoops to hold them away from the staves, will make them accessible for painting or application of a protective coating. Galvanizing is also used as a protective coating, but it is a sacrificial type as zinc will eventually oxidize, exposing the hoop steel. Rubber hose, plastic hose or lead tubing are probably the most effective means of protecting the steel hoops.

PIPE

Two general types of wood pipe are manufactured. These are: machine banded pipe, which is spirally wrapped in a machine especially designed for this purpose, and continuous stave pipe, which is assembled on the job and is banded with hoops.

Machine Banded Pipe

Machine banded pipe is manufactured in lengths up to 20 feet and comes with end joints and couplings ready for installation. End joints may be of several types as shown in Figure 9.5. The inserted joint type has one end of the pipe reamed out to form a mortise and the other end is shaped into a tenon. Lengths are assembled by driving the mortise of one pipe over the machine turned tenon of the adjacent section. This type of joint is frequently used on pipes up to 14 inches in diameter and for low pressure heads. A second type of end joint is the machine banded collar which is recommended by pipe manufacturers for pipes up to 14 inches in diameter and for pressure heads of 150 to 400 feet. The collars are banded in the same manner as the pipe except the bands are spaced to provide 50 per cent greater strength than required for the pipe. The collars are milled for a perfect fit over the tenons and are generally 6 to 8 inches long. A third type, the reinforced inserted joint, is the same as an inserted joint except the wire banding on the mortise end is replaced by one or two metal hoops. Used for pipe diameters 14 to 24 inches, this type is suitable for pressure heads of 150 to 400 feet. A fourth type of end joint, the individual banded collar, where individual hoops take the place of the wire wrapping, is often used. The collared joint is stronger and easier to repair than the inserted type joint. Special cast iron or steel collars are also sometimes used for extremely high pressure pipe.

Continuous Stave Pipe

Continuous stave pipe is constructed with random length staves of from 7 to 24 feet, placed in a continuous line from one end of the pipe to the other. Liquid tight end joints in the staves are made with galvanized steel or exterior type plywood tongues inserted in slots cut in the ends of the staves or with specially constructed malleable iron butt joints as shown in Figure 9.6.

Capacities

The capacity of wood pipe of a given size is related to the pressure head and the velocity of flow of

TANKS AND PIPE

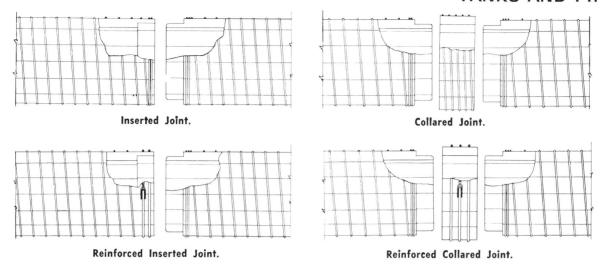

Inserted Joint.   **Collared Joint.**

Reinforced Inserted Joint.   **Reinforced Collared Joint.**

Figure 9.5 — Types of End Joints for Machine Banded Pipe.

the liquid through the pipe. Wood pipe is manufactured in many sizes. Machine banded pipe is produced in sizes from 2 to 24 inches inside diameter and continuous stave pipe is made in sizes from 6 inches to 20 feet inside diameter. Machine banded pipe is available for pressure heads from 50 to 400 feet in 50 foot increments of head. Continuous stave pipe is banded for 10 foot intervals of head for heads up to 400 feet. In the very large diameters the maximum head is somewhat lower.

Design
The strength of wood pipe depends principally on the strength of the wrapping or banding. As wood pipe is manufactured to resist pressure heads in uniform increments of head, the design of a pipe line is a fairly simple matter. The required pipe diameter can be obtained by use of standard hydraulic formulas when the quantity of flow and velocity are known. In specifying wood pipe it is only necessary to indicate the pipe diameter and the required pressure head.

Pipe Lumber
Lumber used for pipe staves must have essentially the same limitations on growth characteristics as tank stave lumber, since it has a similar function. All species covered in the *Standard Grading Rules for Western Lumber* of the Western Wood Products Association may be graded in accordance with the *Standard Grading Rules for West Coast Lumber* of the West Coast Lumber Inspection Bureau (WCLIB). The WCLIB grading rules contain only one grade of Pipe Stave Stock: "PIPE STAVE STOCK". Pieces of this grade may have a few minor and unimportant characteristics, such as sound and tight one-inch knots and small pitch pockets, none of which extends through the piece.

Pipe staves are run to a pattern with the outer and inner faces milled to circular arcs corresponding to the outer and inner diameter of the

pipes to provide full contact with the banding and a smooth inside surface. The edges are carefully jointed to a line to assure a tight fit and the staves of continuous stave pipe are held in exact position during erection by the tongue and groove on the edges. Pipe staves are generally manufactured in 2″, 3″ and 4″ nominal thickness and in widths of 4 inches and wider.

Curvature
Machine banded pipe, manufactured in straight sections, can be given curvature in place. To do this, short pipe sections are used and joints are not driven up tight on the outside of the curve, leaving a gap in the outside of the joints of not more than one-fourth of an inch. The following table shows the minimum radius of curvature for various pipe diameters using the short pipe lengths indicated.

Continuous stave pipe can very easily and economically be built to conform to the natural contour of the ground or to curvature without having to use special fittings. The procedure for curving continuous stave pipe is to assemble a length on a tangent, partly tighten with a few bands and then force it into the curve. The staves are then driven up tight and the remaining bands

TABLE 9.4 — Radius of Curvature — Continuous Stave Pipe

Inside Diameter of Pipe in Feet	Suggested Minimum Radius of Curvature in Feet
2	115
3	155
4	195
5	240
6	290
7	345
8	420
9	500
10	580
12	660
14	745
16	830
18	915
20	1000

TANKS AND PIPE

TABLE 9.5 — Radius of Curvature — Machine Banded Pipe

Length of pipe section feet	Radius of curve in feet for inside pipe diameter in inches of													
	2	3	4	5	6	8	10	12	14	16	18	20	22	24
2	32	40	49	57	66	82	98	115	131	148	164	181	197	213
3	48	60	74	86	99	123	147	173	197	222	246	272	296	320
4	64	80	98	114	132	164	196	230	262	296	328	362	394	426
5	80	100	123	143	165	205	245	288	328	370	410	453	493	533
6	96	120	147	171	198	246	294	345	393	444	492	543	591	639

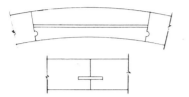
Galvanized Steel Butt Joint.

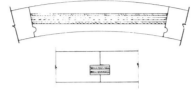
Plywood Butt Joint.

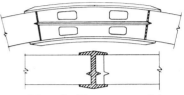
Special Malleable Iron Butt Joint.

Figure 9.6 — Types of End Joints for Continuous Stave Pipe.

placed and tightened. If the pipe is supported by anchored cradles, the curved sections are built right in the cradles. Small pipe can be fitted to moderate curves simply by forcing it into position, but larger pipe requires the use of block and tackle for positioning. Minimum suggested radius of curvature for various diameters of continuous stave pipe are given in the above table. These are for average field conditions. Somewhat smaller radii can be used under ideal conditions.

Pipe Foundations and Cradles
Except for very large diameter pipes, cradles are not required for buried pipe where the ground is reasonably firm. Where pipe is buried on soft ground, a foundation should be provided to hold the pipe to its required grade. Pipe lines erected in a ditch should be back filled and tamped up to mid-height of the pipe.

There are several types of cradles. The simplest, which is suitable for continuous stave pipe up to about 40 inches in diameter, is simply a 4" x 8", or similar size, shaped to fit the curvature of the pipe, resting on a larger timber which in turn rests on mud sills. This and another type of cradle used for larger diameter pipes are shown in Figure 9.8. Where pipe is subjected to a heavy overburden it is generally reinforced with braces as shown in Figure 9.7. Since the cradles are subject to severe conditions of exposure, their service life can be increased considerably by pressure treatment with an approved preservative.

Pipe Fittings
Many different types of fittings are manufactured for wood pipe. Dead end plugs, made of wood, are used for closing the ends of machine banded wood stave pipe lines for either temporary or permanent installations. Pipe reducers are used to connect pipes of different diameters and are either tapered lengths of wood pipe having a reduction in diameter of approximately two inches

for each five feet of length, or tapered lengths of cast iron pipe varying in lengths from 7 to 30 inches, depending on the diameter and the amount of reduction. Service connections to wood pipe can be made with brass tapping nipples for service connections ½ inch to 1½ inches in diameter, lock nut connections for sizes ¾ inch to 3½ inches in diameter, and saddle connections for larger diameters. Gate valves for shutting off and controlling the flow of liquid through pipes are manufactured in sizes to fit the different diameters of wood pipe and may be either hub-end, into which the tenon end of the pipe is fitted, or flanged, which utilizes a flange to sleeve adapter. Specially designed blow-off valves are made for the removal of accumulations of silt, rocks and other debris from low points in the pipe line and for draining of low sections between summits. Air

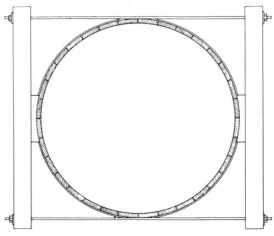
Figure 9.7 — Bracing for Pipe Buried In Trench.

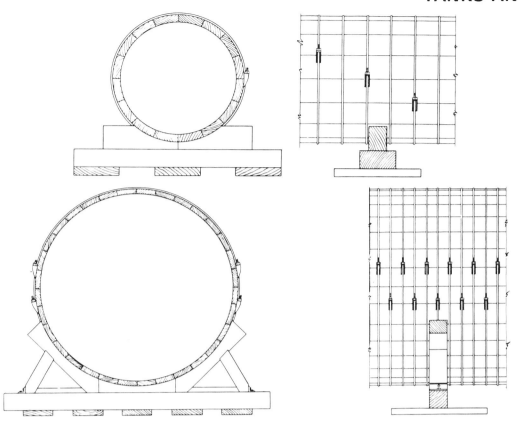

Figure 9.8 — Types of Pipe Cradles.

relief and vacuum valves are provided for the release of accumulated air at the summit and to protect the pipe from negative pressures caused by a break or a sudden opening of valves along the line.

Pipe for Mine Tailings Disposal
The design of pipe for mine tailings disposal requires a slightly different approach from the design for ordinary liquids. Mine tailings consist of a mixture of water and solids. The water with fine solids suspended in it serves as the vehicle for transporting the large solids. Because of the severe service conditions encountered experience has proven Douglas fir pipe to be the most suitable for this use.

The velocity of flow through the pipe should be limited to not more than six feet per second to avoid turbulence. The inside diameter of the pipe should be made 30 to 40 per cent larger than needed to transmit the volume of tailings to be disposed of. This provides room for a sand deposit to be formed in the bottom of the pipe and this deposit reduces the wear on the staves from the abrasive action of the tailings.

Where it is necessary to introduce a sharp bend in the pipe, experience has shown that tees for 90 degree bends and wyes for lesser bends give better service than ells and elbows. The run side of the tee or wye is blanked off with the take off on the branch side. This forms a water cushion

at the turn, cutting down wear and turbulence.

With these provisions, Douglas fir tailing disposal pipe can be expected to have a service life sufficient to transport fifty million tons of tailings.

TABLE 9.6 — Unit Weights of Various Aqueous Solutions

Liquid	Solution	Weight in lbs. per cu. ft.	Weight in lbs. per gallon
Acetic acid	5%	63.06	8.43
	10%	63.06	8.43
	20%	64.31	8.60
	30%	64.94	8.68
	50%	66.18	8.85
Aluminum chloride	5%	64.94	8.68
	10%	66.81	8.93
	20%	71.81	9.60
	30%	77.43	10.35
Aluminum sulfate	10%	69.31	9.27
	20%	76.80	10.27
Ammonium hydroxide	10%	59.94	8.07
	20%	57.44	7.68
	30%	55.57	7.43
Ammonium nitrate	5%	63.69	8.51
	10%	64.94	8.68
	20%	68.06	9.10
	30%	70.56	9.43
	50%	76.80	10.27

TANKS AND PIPE

TABLE 9.6 (continued) Unit Weights of Various Aqueous Solutions

Liquid	Solution	Weight in lbs. per cu. ft.	Weight in lbs. per gallon	Liquid	Solution	Weight in lbs. per cu. ft.	Weight in lbs. per gallon
Calcium chloride	10%	67.44	9.02	Potassium carbonate	10%	68.06	9.10
	20%	73.68	9.85		20%	74.30	9.93
	30%	79.92	10.68		30%	81.17	10.85
Copper nitrate	10%	68.06	9.10		50%	96.16	12.86
	20%	74.30	9.93	Potassium chloride	10%	66.19	8.85
Copper sulfate	10%	69.31	9.27		20%	70.56	9.43
	20%	76.18	10.18	Potassium chromate	5%	64.94	8.68
Ethyl alcohol	5%	61.82	8.26		10%	67.44	9.02
	10%	61.19	8.18		20%	73.68	9.85
	20%	61.19	8.18		30%	79.92	10.68
	30%	60.57	8.10	Potassium hydroxide	5%	65.56	8.76
	50%	58.07	7.76		10%	68.06	9.10
	100%	49.33	6.59		20%	74.30	9.93
Ferric chloride	5%	64.94	8.68		30%	80.55	10.77
	10%	66.81	8.93		50%	94.28	12.60
	20%	71.81	9.60	Potassium iodide	10%	67.44	9.02
	30%	78.67	10.52		20%	73.05	9.77
Formic acid	5%	63.06	8.43		30%	79.30	10.60
	10%	64.31	8.60		50%	96.78	12.94
	20%	65.56	8.76	Potassium sulfate	10%	67.44	9.02
	30%	66.81	8.93	Sodium arsenate	5%	63.69	8.51
	50%	69.93	9.35		10%	64.94	8.68
Glycerin	5%	63.06	8.43		20%	68.06	9.10
	10%	63.69	8.51		30%	71.18	9.52
	20%	65.56	8.76	Sodium carbonate	5%	65.56	8.76
	30%	66.81	8.93		10%	68.68	9.18
	50%	70.56	9.43	Sodium chloride	2%	63.06	8.43
	100%	76.18	10.18		5%	64.31	8.60
Hydrochloric acid	2%	63.06	8.43		10%	66.81	8.93
	5%	63.69	8.51		20%	71.81	9.60
	10%	65.56	8.76	Sodium hydroxide	2%	63.69	8.51
	20%	68.68	9.18		5%	65.56	8.76
	30%	71.81	9.60		10%	69.31	9.27
	40%	74.93	10.02		20%	76.18	10.18
Magnesium chloride	10%	67.44	9.02		30%	83.05	11.10
	20%	73.05	9.77		50%	95.53	12.77
	30%	79.30	10.60	Sulfuric acid	2%	63.06	8.43
Magnesium sulfate	10%	68.68	9.18		5%	63.06	8.43
	20%	76.18	10.18		10%	66.81	8.93
	30%	84.29	11.27		20%	71.18	9.52
Nitric acid	5%	64.31	8.60		30%	76.18	10.18
	10%	65.56	8.76		50%	87.41	11.69
	20%	69.93	9.35		75%	104.27	13.94
	30%	73.68	9.85		100%	114.27	15.28
	50%	81.80	10.94	Tannic acid	2%	63.06	8.43
	100%	94.28	12.60		5%	63.69	8.51
Oxalic acid	5%	63.69	8.51		10%	64.94	8.68
	10%	64.94	8.68	Zinc chloride	10%	67.44	9.02
Petroleum	100%	54.95	7.35		20%	74.30	9.93
Phosphoric acid	5%	64.31	8.60		30%	80.55	10.77
	10%	65.56	8.76		50%	98.03	13.11
	20%	69.31	9.27				
	30%	73.68	9.85				
	50%	83.67	11.19				

CHAPTER X

Wood Preservation

WOOD PRESERVATION

General

All wood used under conditions conducive to attack by wood destroying fungi (decay), wood boring insects (termites), marine borers (limnoria) or to damage by fire should be pressure treated. Treatment should be with a preservative known to be toxic to the harmful organisms or insects or with a fire retardant that has been tested and listed by Underwriters Laboratories, Inc.

Preservatives

Wood preservatives are described in the "P" section of the *American Wood Preservers Association Book of Standards, Standards of the American Society for Testing and Materials,* and standards published by the Federal Government.

A suitable preservative must be toxic to wood destroyers, permanent, safe to handle and use, harmless to wood or metal, and economical. It is necessary to force the preservative into the wood under pressure to attain the high degree of permanence and toxicity required.

Preservatives fall into three general classifications: Creosote and Cresote Solutions: Recommended for use under severe use conditions. These preservatives have low volatility and are insoluble in water.

Pentachlorophenol: There are three common solvents in which Pentachlorophenol is dissolved in predetermined proportions for use as a preservative.

Heavy petroleum oils.
Light hydrocarbon oils or mineral spirits.
Volatile solvents.

All have low volatility and are insoluble in fresh water. The latter two types may be paintable. Choice of solvent depends upon the ultimate use of the treated product.

Water Borne Preservatives: A combination of preservative chemicals dissolved in water and forced into the wood under pressure. They are designed to form compounds of low water solubility as the water evaporates from the treated wood.

A dual treatment first with a water borne salt approved for ground contact, and then with creosote, is now available for marine structures where the crustacean borers (limnoria) are prevalent.

Fire Retardants

Wood that has been pressure treated with a fire retardant chemical will not support its own combustion and will cease to char when the source of heat is removed. This characteristic permits the designer to utilize the many inherent natural advantages of wood with added fire resistance when desired. Frequently building code provisions are more liberal and lower insurance rates may apply when fire retardant lumber is used. Fire retardant treatments are available in two types: One for interior use not subjected to leaching, and the other for exterior areas or where leaching

may be expected. Underwriters Laboratory, Inc. ratings should be referenced.

Design Practices

The allowable unit stresses for lumber apply to lumber pressure-impregnated by an approved process and preservative. The allowable unit stresses for lumber should be reduced 10 percent for lumber pressure-impregnated with fire-retardant chemicals. The resulting stresses are subject to duration of load adjustment as shown on page 21. Treated timber structures do not suffer progressive loss in strength due to decay or other wood destroying agents. The design weights used for pressure treated wood are obtained by increasing the weights for untreated wood by an amount equal to the preservative retention specified.

Treating Glued Laminated Material

Glued laminated material may be pressure treated, either before or after gluing. However, when treatment is done after gluing, oil borne preservatives are usually preferable and an exterior type glue must be used. Designers should keep in mind that for members to be treated after gluing, the size and shape is limited by the size of the treating cylinders which are usually six to eight feet in diameter with lengths ranging up to 150 feet. When material is pressure treated before gluing, some dimensional changes may occur and a final surfacing is necessary to provide a uniform gluing surface. Pressure treated wood reacts dimensionally to changes in moisture content about the same as untreated wood. Wood treated with an oil borne preservative reacts more slowly to moisture changes than does wood treated with water borne preservatives or with organic material in evaporative solvents.

Fabrication

All practical fabrication should be accomplished prior to pressure treating so that the material enters the treating cylinder in its final manufactured form. Fabrication should include boring holes, dapping, cutting and grooving. Cutting into wood in any way after treatment exposes untreated wood and should be avoided if possible. Refer to the paragraph on Field Practices.

Incisings

Woods which are difficult to penetrate should be incised. When required or recommended in treating standards, material should be incised prior to treatment by a method that will provide at least the minimum penetration specified without damage and with the least loss in strength, with the exception that incising may be waived when it will make the material unfit for the use intended.

Incising is accomplished by special machines which separate the wood fibers with a series of knife-like teeth so that the preservative material can penetrate the wood more easily. When properly done, incising has little effect on structural strength and does help minimize checking due to rapid changes of moisture content.

WOOD PRESERVATION

Pressure Process
Two basic processes known as the full cell and the empty cell process are used.

The full cell process leaves the treated wood cells as full of preservative as possible. It is used for all water borne treatments and for oil treatments, particularly for marine structures, where the aim is to have as high retention as possible in the treated wood.

The empty cell process leaves the cell walls in a nearly saturated condition and spreads a given quantity of preservative over a larger volume of treated wood. It is used with most oil type preservatives, providing more economical treatment with improved appearance and handling characteristics.

Field Practices
Pressure treated timber should be handled carefully so the protective zone of preservative is not damaged or ruptured.

Untreated wood that is exposed after pressure treatment should be treated in accordance with the *American Wood Preservers Association Standard M4-62.*

Retentions
The amount of retention of any preservative is expressed in pounds of preservative retained in each cubic foot of the wood treated. With a few exceptions, retention requirements are based on the amount of preservative in a given zone in the treated wood.

Minimum retentions for commodities are specified in the *American Wood Preservers Book of Standards.* When retentions for both above ground and ground contact are shown in a commodity standard, the heavier retention should be used if there is any question as to the final use of the product.

Specifications
Each of the recognized pressure treatments has certain advantages, and specifications for the type of chemical and its application should be determined by the end use of the material.

A recommended specification should state the type of preservative permitted and the minimum retention desired with pressure treating in accordance with the *American Wood Preservers Association Book of Standards.* Other referenced specifications include American Wood Preservers Institute and Federal issues but all are based upon the AWPA standards. Fire retardant specifications must conform to requirements of the Underwriters or Factory Mutual Laboratories for a given rating.

The American Wood Preservers Institute serves as a consulting and educational arm of the wood preserving industry. Its primary function is to assist engineers, architects, designers, contractors, builders and governmental agencies in making the best use of pressure treated wood products.

CHAPTER XI

Fire Protection

FIRE PROTECTION

INTRODUCTION

Without fire, many conveniences of modern living would be non-existent. It is because people have learned to use heat and power under controlled conditions that we have comfortable warmth in winter and cool interiors in summer, and can enjoy modern day leisures and conveniences. However, the elements that give such heat and power exert constant pressure against encircling restraint so that any laxness or breakdown can allow them to escape with resulting loss of life or of property.

Since buildings are inanimate they cannot initiate fires. For the same reason they cannot extinguish fire and it is therefore a fallacy to consider buildings fireproof. Many disastrous fires have occurred in buildings advertised as "fireproof," such as the large life losses in hotel fires of the 1940's and warehouse fires where not only the contents were lost but the buildings collapsed.

Life and property loss from fire spread and structural failure can be reduced by attention to the arrangement of the building in a manner to retard the spread and growth of fire, to details of the structure that make it less susceptible to damage, and to adequate provision for egress of occupants, and ingress of firemen.

Poor housekeeping, carelessness and complacency are a major cause of fire. Typical of these are:

Carelessness with —
    Smoking and matches
    Welding
    Accumulation and burning of refuse
    Housekeeping
    Flammable liquids and chemicals
    Materials subject to spontaneous ignition

Complacency about —
    Abuses of electrical systems
    Improper installation of equipment
    Machinery bearings
    Materials placed in lockers and cupboards
    Hazardous processes
    Materials subject to spontaneous ignition

There are many causes of fire, but the above serve as a reminder of the need for close attention to details for maximum safety to life and property. Windows, for fire ventilation and for attack on the fire with hose streams and even as a secondary means for exit, are an example of a detail worthy of consideration. There are records of suffocation when people have been unable to escape through small-paned metal sash windows.

Any discussion of fire losses would be remiss without a reminder that large losses are often the result of delay in sending in the fire alarm. An immediate alarm should precede local first aid measures.

In the economic design of buildings there are **protective details that relate to life and others** that relate to property. Contemplated occupancy, with its related hazard, will influence needed protection. For a building that will be occupied by many people, major emphasis is on exits, whereas buildings housing commodities emphasize the volume or value at risk within the areas separated. The "fire endurance" or "fire resistance" of the structural elements and parts of buildings give a large measure of protection. As these terms have a particular meaning, as used in this chapter, they are defined on page 286.

Buildings codes customarily set forth the requirements for buildings in terms of occupancy types and hourly ratings and building code regulations must be met where structures are built within their jurisdiction. This portion of the Western Woods Use Book does not attempt to outline building code requirements. Herein the designer is furnished useful information that may be suited to buildings of many classifications and occupancies.

SAFE EXITS
General

The number, size and position of exits, consisting of passageways, halls, stairways and doors, are important to life safety as buildings must be emptied promptly and without panic.

Though codes vary somewhat in exit requirements, similar and adequate exits are provided by adherence to such regulations. The variance between codes makes it impractical to give specific details in this book, but fire safety is essential and good practice must be followed in design, even where there is no code jurisdiction. Safe exitways, both horizontal and vertical, can be provided for any occupancy. The following are basic considerations and apply to all types of construction.

Residential Exits

The size, height and occupancy of a building have much to do with exit requirements. The small size, few occupants, familiarity with the premises and many windows provide maximum safety for the householder. Hence, it is not customary for codes to specify exit requirements for other than multi-family residences, though it is wise to provide at least two means of egress to the outside and the location of a stairway should be planned with emergency evacuation in mind.

Capacity of Exitways

The needed number and width of exitways are determined by the anticipated population and occupancy hazard of a building. The width of exitways is measured in units, representing the free passage of one file of persons. As the number of exitway units is related to the speed at which a building can be emptied, buildings of high hazard occupancy are allotted fewer people per exitway unit than buildings of low occupancy hazard. One frequently used code uses a 22 inch unit of exit width with a minimum of 50 and a maximum of 100 people for each unit of exit doorway width. For each unit of stairway width, 30 people are the minimum and 60 the maximum per run. In each case, the minimum number is associated with high fire hazard and the maximum with a low hazard occupancy.

FIRE PROTECTION

Location of Exits

Doors and stairways should be so arranged that the maximum travel distance to reach these exits does not exceed distances associated with occupancy hazard. A maximum distance for low occupancy hazard is about 150 feet and this distance is reduced proportionately to about 75 feet when the hazard is high.

There should be at least two well separated exits from every floor.

Stairways

Exitways must be arranged with continuity from the uppermost level to the ground floor and lead directly to the outside so that there are no dead ends to confuse or trap people.

A ramp may be used instead of a stairway or vertical exit. Ramps are particularly suited to hospitals and like institutions as bedridden patients can be rolled out in their beds. Also, ramps are safer than a limited number of steps.

It is not necessary to increase the units of width of lower floor stairways to accommodate the population of upper floors because the maximum movement of people from the floor served by the stairway will have occurred before those from the floor above arrive. Of course, the stairways for each floor must be adequate for the floor they serve and not less in width than required for any upper floor also being served.

The height of stair risers should be uniform for each stairway and the treads uniform in width. A landing is necessary wherever a door opens onto a stairway and for any run of over eight feet. Landings must be the same width as stairs, and should not be less than 44" in the direction of the run.

Stairways and other vertical openings could be a flue for smoke, hot gases and fire. This makes it necessary to use solid risers and treads to form a barrier and to provide closed doors at each floor level. Also, walls and partitions enclosing stairwalls should be resistive to rapid fire penetration. The space under a required exit stairway should be completely closed, which eliminates a closet or storage space where a fire may start unnoticed. Exterior fire escapes are not a satisfactory substitute for protected stairways. This is because they may be rendered unusable by smoke and flame issuing from openings at lower levels, or they may become hazardous to use from ice or snow.

Horizontal Exits

A horizontal exit, consisting of a protected opening through or around a fire wall that separates floor areas, will provide a quick refuge from either side and lessen the necessity for hasty evacuation of the floor. However, to be counted as a part of the required exitways, the wall or walls must provide adequate fire resistance, and the floor area on either side must be large enough to accommodate all occupants. Doors are required at openings and an exitway from both sides must be provided so that occupants will not be trapped.

Exit Doors

It is a basic principle that doors must swing in the direction of exit travel when the occupant load served exceeds 50 and be arranged so that they can always be readily opened from the side from which egress is made. Exit doorways needed for the ground floor of a building are in addition to those required for stairways emptying at that level.

Doorways at the foot and head of each stairway must be equal in width to the stairway served, and the doors need to be durable under fire exposure. A panel of wire-glass, to allow users to observe conditions before entering onto stairs, is desirable in each door. Doors must be hung so that they are self closing with their normal position closed. Doorways to or through horizontal exits are like those used for stairways.

Aisles and Corridors

Any aisle or corridor leading to an exit must have a clear width equal to the required exit width. The finish of the walls and ceilings of corridors should have flame spread characteristics no greater than smooth panels of lumber, except that for occupancies where inmates are not free to move about for reasons of health or forcible restraint, material of a lesser flame spread characteristic is usually required. Lumber and wood products may be specially treated or painted to achieve this. Treatments and paints are discussed in greater detail further in this chapter.

STRUCTURAL PROTECTION

General

The fire endurance of the structural elements of buildings is measured by the time required to produce failure when exposed to fire. Similarly the resistiveness of a separation, such as a wall, is measured by the time required for fire to penetrate from the exposed to the unexposed face, or raise the temperature of the unexposed face beyond a certain limit. Standard methods of testing to determine these ratings have been established so that materials of unknown character can be compared with those of known qualities. The first recognition of the structural fire endurance of buildings was in the use of heavy timber framing for the textile mill buildings of New England. This system of framing was evolved about the middle of the nineteenth century as a result of experiences with disastrous mill building fires. It is probable that the resistive tests now used were originally developed as a means of determining the adequacy of materials intended to compete with the established system of framing mill buildings with timbers.

Relative fire endurance values are determined by controlled test conditions. These conditions do not prevail in actual fires as there are fluctuations in heat intensity, differences in maximum temperatures produced by burning materials and a time lapse from incipient start to the point where there is sufficient heat and volume to affect the structure. These variables usually give greater actual fire endurance to structural elements than tests indicate.

FIRE PROTECTION

There are various degrees of fire endurance and resistance required by building codes for different building occupancies and building areas. Building codes customarily classify the elements of structures by hourly ratings, and building code regulations must be met where structures are built within their jurisdiction.

"Fire Endurance" and "Fire Resistance"

The terminology used in this chapter, which may also appear in others, is similar to terminology found in building codes. However, terms and their meanings are not the same in all codes and may differ from the definitions given here. Similar terms have an entirely different meaning to the insurance business.

"Fire endurance" is defined for use herein as: The ability of a structural material or combination of materials, while being exposed to high fire temperatures, to sustain structural loads for a sufficient length of time to be significant to the safety of the structure.

"Fire resistance" is defined for use herein as: The resistance, rated in time, of a component of a building, such as a wall or floor, to penetration by fire or heat for a duration long enough to offer significant protection.

Fire Endurance of Structural Materials

The fire endurance value of the skeletal frame or an element of a structure may mean the difference between structural collapse with but little possibility of salvage, or a minimum of damages with early suppression of the fire and a maximum of building and content salvage. The degree to which a structural element of any material will stand up under load when exposed to fire, in other words, its endurance, is dependent upon inherent insulative qualities enhanced by cross sectional size. Materials which readily conduct heat depend upon the protection of a thick covering of other products such as plaster or concrete.

The burning contents of buildings may create temperatures averaging 1700°F. and higher. All structural materials are affected in some manner at such temperatures. In the lower half of the range to 1700°F., metals begin to loose their strength, the cement in concrete begins dehydration and wood chars. In the upper half of this range, metal becomes so plastic it will not support its own weight, cement is completely dehydrated and wood flames.

Unprotected steel and iron collapse quickly when exposed to fire. Hot cast iron cracks from cold water. Concrete and wood behave differently, dehydration of concrete and charring of wood begin at practically the same temperature and proceed at about the same rate. The progress becomes increasingly slower as the calcined concrete and charred wood insulate the inner portion of the section. Concrete is liable to damage from fire by unequal expansion of the component materials, or by spalling if cold water is suddenly thrown on it. Wood, especially wood char, absorbs water thrown on it. This increases its resistance to burning. Damage to wood progresses only in proportion to the length of exposure to fire, with the unburned portion retaining its strength. When timber joints are assembled with timber connectors, these may be expected to carry the load as long or longer than the members, due to the fact that the connectors are insulated from the heat by the surrounding wood.

Wood normally does not burn unless the fibers are at zero moisture content, a condition that is non-existent in normal usage. Hence, external heat must remove the normal surface moisture before combustion can take place. When exposed to fire, a portion of the moisture in wood is evaporated and a portion is forced inward. This action progressively retards drying and rate of burning, as the moisture content towards the core of the piece is continuously increasing. The burning of wood decomposes it into water vapor, carbon dioxide and ash. Smooth wood surfaces will not persist in active flaming combustion unless adjacent air temperatures are sustained substantially above 1000°F. although glowing combustion might still persist.

An example of the manner in which a large wood member behaves under exposure to fire is shown in *Comparative Fire Test of Timber and Steel Beams, Technical Report No. 3*, published by the National Forest Products Association. The comparative test was conducted by the Southwest Research Institute, San Antonio, Texas.

TEST CRITERIA

The objective of this test project was to determine the comparative performance of fully loaded timber and exposed structural steel roof framing members to fire temperatures reasonably simulating those existing in actual fires. The following test criteria were established to provide a practical and equitable procedure for the collection of factual data:

1. The test structure should be sufficiently large that the timber and steel members to be evaluated could be of a size and span representing full-scale roof framing.

2. The test enclosure should be such that both framing systems could be exposed simultaneously to equivalent fire conditions, and so arranged that each system could react independently.

3. A roof load calculated to develop the design capacity of each member should be applied throughout the period of fire exposure.

4. Exposure temperatures in the test enclosure should follow those set forth in the Standard Time-Temperature Curve, as specified in *American Society for Testing Materials Designation E-119*, which is the standard reference in testing for fire endurance.

TEST STRUCTURE AND EQUIPMENT
Test Structure
The test was conducted at Southwest Research Institute, in a structure measuring 20 feet in width and 60 feet in length. It was a reinforced concrete frame building enclosed by concrete-block panel walls provided with ports for mounting gas burners and with vents for combustion control. The upper half of the interior wall was surfaced with two inches of insulating block. For this test, a wall with pilasters was constructed at the three-quarter point to provide end-support for the beams.

Roof Framing System
The two beams to be evaluated were installed as the supporting members of the roof structure. The clear span for the roof framing members was 43 feet, 3 inches, with each beam supporting half of the total roof load.

The left panel was supported by a 16-inch rolled steel beam (16 WF 40) designed for the applied roof load in accordance with recommendations of the American Institute of Steel Construction. The right panel was supported by a 7″ x 21″ glued-laminated timber beam, using casein glue and without chemical treatment, designed in accordance with the *National Design Specification for Stress-Grade Lumber and Its Fastenings,* recommended by the National Forest Products Association, and the design standards of the American Institute of Timber Construction. Both beams were supplied with 2 inches of camber to offset initial deflection.

The roof deck construction consisted of bulb-tee sections spaced at 32⅝ inches on center and attached to the top edges of the beams and to the exterior walls. One-half-inch gypsum form board was placed on the bulb tees to receive the lightweight concrete deck which was poured to a depth of 2½ inches. To provide lateral support to meet design calculations for the steel beam, two tee sections (T2 x 2 x 3.56) were attached to the top edge of the steel beam at third points. Attachment of all tee sections to the framing members was by fillet weld to the steel and lag screws to the wood.

The 7″ x 21″ wood beam was selected because it met the requirements of the design. The induced stress was 1552 pounds per square inch and the calculated deflection was 2.32 inches or $l/224$. This deflection is within limits commonly specified in building codes and was the controlling factor in selecting the wood beam.

The 16 WF 40 steel beam was selected because it met the requirements of the design and is a stock item. The calculated deflection was 1.51 inches or $l/344$. The induced stress was 12,524 pounds per square inch. This beam was designed to recognize the effect of depth to span ratio by installing lateral supports at the third-points in the span.

The two sections of the roof deck were entirely separated by a longitudinal joint, 2 inches wide, which was covered with a flexible insulating blanket. This allowed each panel to move inde-

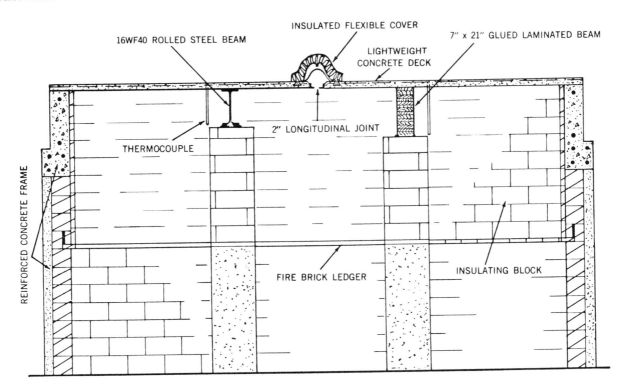

Figure 11.1 — A section through the test structure showing construction details.

FIRE PROTECTION

pendently for a vertical distance of 36 inches without loss of heat in the structure. A typical cross section of the test structure showing the roof deck construction is shown in Figure 11.1.

Roof Load

The total design load on the roof consisted of an applied live load equivalent to 30 pounds per square foot of roof surface, plus the dead load weights of the deck construction and the test beams. This resulted in a total load of 12,346 pounds for the wood beam and 12,432 pounds for the steel beam. The slight difference in total load is due to the lesser weight of the wood beam.

The live load consisted of bagged sand carefully weighted and positioned over each beam in the amount necessary to provide the 30 pounds per square foot required.

TEST RESULTS AND CONCLUSIONS

This test compared the fire endurance of an untreated, heavy timber beam with that of an unprotected, heavy steel beam having equivalent structural capacity. The results indicate that the fire exposure was unbiased and that it conformed to the ASTM Standard Time-Temperature Curve.

Although the recorded temperatures adjacent to the steel beam did not represent as severe an exposure as that for the wood beam, the average test chamber temperatures were within the specified limits of accuracy defined in ASTM Designation E 119. Thus, it is evident that the objective of the test was achieved in an impartial and factual manner.

There are three significant results of the test: 1) The deflection pattern for the steel beam; 2) the amount of undamaged wood remaining in the glue-laminated beam at the time of failure of the steel; and 3) the relative endurance of the two framing systems under design load.

A statement of these results and the conclusions indicated are as follows:

1. Six minutes after the burners had been lighted, the temperature near the steel member was 894°F. and the deflection was 2 inches. At 14 minutes, when this temperature was 1194°F., the deflection had increased to 8¼ inches. This relatively uniform increase continued for 20 minutes, when the deflection reached 11¾ inches at a temperature of 1279°F.

   After 20 minutes of fire exposure, the deflection rate increased rapidly until it had reached 35½ inches at 29 minutes. The temperature near the steel at this time was 1422°F.

   Although the steel supported panel fell into the test chamber after 30 minutes of exposure, it is evident that its structural integrity was in doubt long before this.

   The deflection-temperature relationships, in-

dicated by these results, are in agreement with the generally recognized behavior of steel structural members when exposed to building fires. That is, unprotected steel begins to lose strength at 800° to 900°F., and will fail to support load over 1200°F.

2. The wood beam continued to support its full design load, throughout the test, with a maximum deflection of only 2¼ inches at 30 minutes. The uniform deflection rate of the wood beam demonstrates the dependability of heavy timber framing under fire conditions.

   At the conclusion of the test, the wood beam was sawed through at a representative section, revealing a depth of char penetration of approximately ¾-inch on each side and ⅝-inch on the bottom.

   While penetration of char at the glue line was slightly greater, the deflection record demonstrates that the integrity of the casein adhesive bond was maintained during fire exposure.

   Thus, after 30 minutes of fire exposure, during which temperatures in excess of 1500°F. were recorded, 75 per cent of the original wood section remained undamaged and the beam continued to support its full design load.

3. A glued-laminated heavy timber beam and a heavy structural steel beam, supporting equivalent applied loads, were exposed to identical fire conditions. The fire exposure conformed to the recognized standard used for evaluating the fire performance of structural materials.

   Both framing members, exposed to the fire, were stock items without protective covering.

   The wood beam had received no chemical fire retarding treatment.

   The test results clearly demonstrate that the fire endurance of an unprotected and untreated heavy timber beam is substantially greater than that for a comparable unprotected steel beam. Under fire conditions, a structural steel framing member may be expected to fail through excessive deflection long before significant damage has occurred in a timber member.

Sustained high temperatures will reduce the strength of wood fibers. The degree of temperature, length of exposure and medium for transmission of heat are all related to the amount of loss of strength. However, wood fibers exposed to a short duration of above normal temperature will recover full strength and the insulating quality of wood makes it improbable that high temperature will penetrate the uncharred portion of wood members during exposure to building fires.

For these reasons the relative structural endurance of a material under fire attack, and its economy, is a better measure of its ultimate value than a designation of "combustible" or "noncombustible".

FIRE PROTECTION

Fire Resistive Construction

The fire resistance values of assemblies are determined by tests or, as an alternate, long experience. The building components must be able to resist penetration by heat or fire and, while heated to maximum temperatures, sustain the effects of rapid cooling and pressure from a hose-stream.

Fire resistive components serve to contain a fire to the area of its origin and also as protection from exposure fires. They serve in such dual capacities as exterior walls between closely spaced buildings, as interior separations between occupancies, as walls around stairwells and exitways, as furnace room enclosures, or as separations around a floor area of high fire hazard and other vertical or horizontal separations.

Timber Buildings

Buildings that are built of lumber are usually referred to as one of three general types. Based on their details of construction, they are designated as: Wood Frame, Ordinary Construction, and Heavy Timber Construction (also called Mill Construction). See following text for details of construction.

The occupancy, representing low, moderate and high combustible contents, or nominal to high populations, is an indication of the desired fire endurance and fire resistance for a building.

Wood Frame, as exemplified by traditional residential construction, is very popular. Single-story schools and churches, many motels, office, commercial, storage, industrial and like occupancies use wood frame construction for one, two or three stories, where combustible contents are low in density and occupancy and exposure hazards are nominal.

A wood frame building constructed to provide one hour fire protection throughout is an excellent and economical building. The added fire resistance is sometimes desirable or required where exposure or occupancy fire hazard is more than average.

Ordinary Construction is popular in motels, small hotels, warehouses, industrial, commercial and mercantile buildings with moderate combustible storage. As the protection offered by this type of construction is in the highly fire resistive exterior walls, its greatest use is in congested areas.

Heavy Timber Construction has its greatest use in assembly buildings, gymnasiums, sports arenas, warehouses and larger industrial and commercial buildings where fire losses to contents are potentially greater. Heavy timber construction offers both fire endurance and fire resistance, and is used extensively for maximum protection.

Traditional Wood Frame Construction

Wood frame construction is that type in which exterior walls, bearing walls and partitions, floor and roof construction are wholly or partly of wood. Very few of the parts that comprise this system of framing are structurally designed and many parts are capable of supporting loads much greater than any that will be imposed on them.

Furthermore, there is a repetitious spacing of joists, studs, rafters and other parts that adds much to the structural factor of safety of this kind of construction. This is because the over loading or damaging of one or more of the framing parts will not cause a building failure. This same principle enhances the fire safety of conventional wood framing. Elements of light framing such as floors, partitions, and roof framing, are frequently used with other types of construction.

It is often advisable and sometimes required, that portions of buildings provide a specific period of fire resistance to protect occupancies or exitways. The structural core may be the traditional system of wood framing with wall, ceiling and similar surfaces of specified materials and thicknesses.

Ordinary Construction

Ordinary construction differs from light frame buildings by the fire resistive separation provided between adjacent properties as protection against horizontal exposure hazards. This type of construction is intended for use primarily in congested industrial and commercial areas or where structures are built to the lot line.

Exterior walls are bearing walls and those near the property line are normally of masonry having a fire resistive rating depending upon the degree of exposure. Walls that are set back from property lines a sufficient distance to provide access and reduce exposure are often of one hour fire resistance. Doors, windows or other openings are only used through the exterior walls when they are set back from the property line or on an open area. When the walls are in close proximity to lot lines, such doors are "fire doors" and windows have wire-glass. Walls that front on a wide street often have lesser fire resistive requirements than the property line walls and inner court walls are usually of one hour rated construction.

Framing of wood joists, either unprotected or with fire resistive protection are customarily used for the interior of buildings of ordinary construction. Where protected framing is used, it should be normally not less than ¾ or one hour fire resistive. Except for necessary protection around stairwells, elevator shafts and other vertical openings, the choice of using fire resistive or unprotected framing will depend on the size of the building and the occupancy.

Heavy Timber Construction (Mill Construction)

Heavy timber construction is a superior type of construction. The large size members have great fire endurance and many buildings, exposed to severe interior fires, have been rehabilitated at minimum cost by sand blasting the char away.

With properly enclosed and protected vertical openings, and fire stops in concealed vertical and horizontal framing, it is doubtful that fire could spread beyond the area of its origin. The details of heavy timber usually leave no concealed spaces under floors as the beams and girders are left exposed as a desirable architectural feature and for economy. Supporting columns are similarly left exposed.

FIRE PROTECTION

Partitions creating corridors or separation of principal areas are of one hour fire resistive construction. Any of the one hour rated systems of constructing stud wall partitions are suitable. Such partition walls are frequently built of tight, laminated or double plank wood construction.

Floor systems are a choice of tongue and grooved or splined planks with finish flooring on top, or laminated deck. The design of the plank and the laminated floors are shown elsewhere in this book. However, laminated decks must be laid with staggered joints so that there is no continuous line of joints across the deck, and laminated decks should not be spiked to supporting girders.

Floors are frequently given a pitch of about one inch in twenty feet to discharge points so as to relieve the structure of the weight of water from discharge of automatic sprinklers or hose streams. This detail also helps to keep water from damaging materials on lower floors in the event of fire.

Interior structural framing is thoroughly tied together horizontally, laterally, and vertically up to the roof by steel straps, steel dogs, anchor straps, anchor bolts, wood splice pads, or other means that the ingenuity of the designer can devise.

To qualify as a "heavy timber" building the size of the various structural members and elements must meet minimum requirements even if the parts are larger than needed to support the imposed loads. The required framing details and minimum sizes shown following are based on maximum structural endurance if exposed to fire. Sawn or glued laminated members of comparable size may be used.

Definition of Heavy Timber Construction

Heavy Timber Construction is that type in which fire resistance is attained by placing limitations of minimum sizes on wood structural members and on minimum thickness and composition of wood floors and roofs; by avoidance of concealed spaces under floors and roofs; by use of approved fastenings, construction details, and adhesives for structural members; and by providing the required degree of fire resistance in exterior and interior walls.

FRAMING MEMBERS

Columns

1. Wood columns may be sawn or glued-laminated and shall be not less than 8 inches nominal in any dimension when supporting floor loads, and not less than 6 inches nominal in width, and 8 inches nominal in depth when supporting roof and ceiling loads only.

2. Columns shall be continuous or superimposed throughout all stories by means of reinforced concrete or metal caps with brackets, or shall be connected by properly designed steel or iron caps with pintles and base plates, or by timber splice plates affixed to the columns by means of metal connectors

housed within the contact faces, or by other approved methods.

Floor Framing

1. Beams and girders of wood may be sawn or glued-laminated and shall be not less than 6 inches nominal in width and not less than 10 inches nominal in depth.

2. Framed or glued-laminated arches which spring from the floor line and support floor loads shall be not less than 8 inches nominal in any dimension.

3. Framed timber trusses supporting floor loads shall have members of not less than 8 inches nominal in any dimension.

Roof Framing

1. Framed or glued-laminated arches for roof construction which spring from the floor line and do not support floor loads shall have members not less than 6 inches nominal in width and 8 inches nominal in depth for the lower half of the height, and not less than 6 inches nominal in any dimension for the upper half of the height.

2. Framed or glued-laminated arches for roof construction which spring from the top of walls or wall abutments and framed timber trusses and other roof framing which do not support floor loads shall have members not less than 4 inches nominal in width and not less than 6 inches nominal in depth. Spaced members may be composed of two or more pieces not less than 3 inches nominal in thickness when blocked solidly throughout their intervening spaces or when such spaces are tightly closed by a continuous wood cover plate of not less than 2 inches nominal in thickness, secured to the underside of the members. Splice plates shall be no less than 3 inches nominal in thickness. When protected by approved automatic sprinklers under the roof deck, such framing members shall be not less than 3 inches nominal in width.

Construction Details

1. Wall plate boxes of self-releasing type, or approved hangers, shall be provided where beams and girders enter masonry. An air space of ½-inch shall be provided at the top, end and sides of the member unless approved durable or treated wood is used.

2. Girders and beams shall be closely fitted around columns and adjoining ends shall be cross-tied to each other, or intertied by caps or ties, to transfer horizontal loads across the joint. Wood bolsters may be placed on tops of columns which support roof loads only.

3. Where intermediate beams are used to support floors, they shall rest on top of the girders, or shall be supported by ledgers or blocks securely fastened to the sides of the girders, or they may be supported by approved metal hangers into which the ends of the beams shall be fitted closely.

4. Columns, beams, girders, arches and trusses of material other than wood shall have a fire resistance rating of not less than one hour.

5. Wood beams and girders supported by walls required to have a fire resistance rating of two hours or more shall have not less than 4 inches of solid masonry between their ends and the outside face of the wall, and between adjacent beams.

6. Adequate roof anchorage shall be provided.

FLOOR DECKS

Floors shall be without concealed spaces. They shall be of sawn or glued-laminated plank, splined, or tongued and grooved, of not less than 3 inches nominal in thickness, or of planks not less than 4 inches nominal in width set on edge and well spiked together. The planks shall be laid so that no continuous line of joints will occur except at points of support and they shall not be spiked to supporting girders. Planks shall be covered with 1-inch nominal tongued and grooved flooring laid crosswise or diagonally or with ½ inch plywood. Planks and flooring shall not extend closer than ½ inch to walls to provide an expansion joint, and the joint shall be covered at top or bottom.

ROOF DECKS

Roofs shall be without concealed spaces and roof decks shall be sawn or glued-laminated, splined or tongued-and-grooved plank, not less than 2 inches nominal, in thickness, or of planks not less than 3 inches nominal in width set on edge and spiked together as required for floors, or of 1⅛ inch thick tongued and grooved plywood bonded with exterior glue. Other types of decking may be used when approved by the building official.

WALLS
Bearing Walls

Bearing portions of exterior and interior walls shall be of approved non-combustible material or fire-retardant treated wood and shall have a fire resistance rating of not less than 2 hours, except that where a horizontal separation of 3 feet or less is provided, bearing portions of exterior walls shall have a fire resistance rating of not less than 3 hours.

Non-Bearing Walls

Non-bearing portions of exterior walls shall be of approved non-combustible materials or fire-retardant treated wood except as otherwise noted and:

1. Where a horizontal separation of 3 feet or less is provided, non-bearing exterior walls shall have a fire resistance rating of not less than 3 hours.

2. Where a horizontal separation of more than 3 feet but less than 20 feet is provided, non-bearing exterior walls shall have a fire resistance rating of not less than 2 hours.

3. Where a horizontal separation of 20 feet to 30 feet is provided, non-bearing exterior walls shall have a fire resistance rating of not less than one hour.

4. Where a horizontal separation of 30 feet or more is provided, non-bearing exterior walls are not required to have a fire resistance rating and may be construction conforming to the heavy timber sizes specified herein for roofs.

5. Where a horizontal separation of 20 feet or more is provided, wood columns and arches conforming to heavy timber sizes may be used externally.

Fire Stops

To prevent the vertical spread of lethal gases and fire within any building, fire stops must be placed to cut off concealed draft openings between stories in walls, partitions, and furred spaces. A spacing of not more than 10 feet in a vertical or horizontal direction is recommended. Concealed spaces must not open into attics. To prevent horizontal spread of gases and fire, concealed spaces in floors should not exceed approximately 100 square feet without fire stops unless solidly filled with incombustible material.

It is recommended that draft stops in attic spaces be installed. A distance of 75 feet in any direction, or an area of about 5000 square feet is suggested as maximum for determining the location of draft stops.

Vertical Openings

The need for enclosure of stairwells has already been mentioned. Elevator shafts and other floor to floor connections likewise need to be enclosed and to have doors at each floor opening. Without this protection, rising hot gases will spread rapidly throughout a building.

Draft Curtain

In buildings having automatic sprinkler systems, draft curtains that are about 24 inches deep and enclosing ceiling areas not exceeding 16,000 square feet will add to the efficiency of the system. Sprinklers, ineffective because of distance from the fire source, are not needlessly activated. This conserves water and excessive water damage is prevented. In some buildings, beams, arches and similar structural elements may be of a depth and spacing to serve wholly or partially as draft curtains.

In unsprinklered, single-story buildings of large area, draft curtains can retard the spread of fire, especially if each curtained area is provided with adequate vents. An area of 10,000 square feet is suggested for curtained ceiling areas. Where roofs are supported by trusses, curtains are easily constructed by solidly facing a truss, if located at the desired spacing, with tightly jointed boards. The facing should be fitted from the under side of the roof to the bottom chord. Where possible, curtains should be arranged to take advantage of the natural venting characteristics of a roof system.

FIRE PROTECTION

Roof vents that automatically open with a rise in temperature will hold fire, for a short time, to the area of its origin by exhausting the hot combustible gases as they are generated. Sky lights and monitors will often act as a venting system.

Fire Resistance

Building codes specify fire resistance requirements for floors, ceilings, roofs, walls and partitions in order to establish a measure of containment of fire within a room or building. Fire resistance is the resistance, rated in time, of a component of a building, such as a wall or floor, to penetration by fire or heat for a duration long enough to offer significant protection.

The standard test for measuring fire resistance is the *American Society for Testing and Materials' Test Method E-119.* Ratings of assemblies are determined by test procedures somewhat simulating actual fire conditions. Floor/ceiling and roof/ceiling assemblies are tested flat while carrying their full design load. Walls are tested vertically either as bearing walls under their full load, or as nonbearing walls under no load. The resistance rating is expressed in hours or minutes that the construction withstands the test. So it approximates the time the assembly would be expected to withstand actual fire conditions.

A one-hour rating, for example, is taken to mean that an assembly similar to that tested will not collapse nor transmit flame or a high temperature, while supporting its full load, for at least one hour after the fire commences.

Many tests have been made on various combinations of materials on wood joisted floors, wood stud walls, and solid panel constructions by numerous reputable agencies in accordance with the standard ASTM E-119 methods. Building codes usually accept these test results and permit the use of listed assemblies which meet all building code requirements.

Space limitation does not permit the listing and description of the many wood assemblies which have successfully qualified for fire resistive ratings ranging from less than one hour to more than two hours. The reader is referred to the applicable building code, the *Fire Resistance Index of the Underwriters' Laboratories, Inc.,* and *Fire Resistance,* a booklet published by the Gypsum Association.

Flame Spread

Fire endurance and resistance to fire penetration are two factors that have long been given consideration in providing fire safety and protection. Flame spread, or the rate at which fire may spread over the surface of a material is important mostly to life safety.

Any system for rating the flame spread characteristics of materials must use an arbitrary scale of measurement. The "tunnel" test system, generally accepted, establishes a scale by assigning zero value to cement asbestos board and 100 to red oak. It is interesting that some materials have been tested and rated to over 2000 on this scale.

The "tunnel" test is made in a long rectangular tube with a gas burner at one end. The top of the tunnel is a lid to the underside of which a 25 foot long panel of the specimen material is fastened. Small windows spaced along the side of the tunnel permit observation and timing of the spread of the flame from the large fire source to the other end of the specimen. Accelerated testing conditions cause the red oak control specimens to ignite from end to end in about 5½ minutes, approximately the time it takes the average person to walk ¼ of a mile.

As the purpose of these tests is to measure the relative flame spread characteristics of materials, other tests should be devised to determine maximum flame spread ratings acceptable for specific uses of materials. With life safety in mind, a special test was used for determining the extent to which the spread and increase of fire will contribute to life hazard when wood paneling is used on walls and ceilings. To correlate these tests with the tunnel test, red oak paneling was one of several species tested on a simulated room.

Though a temperature that is lethal to humans has never been ascertained, 300°F. was assumed as hazardous for the room tests. Experiments by the U. S. Air Force show that a person can be exposed to 247°F., or 35° hotter than boiling water, with no adverse after effects. Hence, the assumption is probably close. The test procedure used an ignition source fire that raised the room temperature to 155°F. at breathing level and near to the source. The source fire readily ignited the paneling but did not obscure the objective of the test. Maximum room temperatures developed in 4 to 5 minutes, and were generally well below the 300°F. at a reasonable distance from the fire and at the breathing level. The 300°F. was infrequently exceeded by a small amount close to the fire.

It was noted that when the ignition fuel was consumed, the exposed wall and a portion of the ceiling had been involved in flame, and char at the point of maximum exposure was approximately ¼ inch deep. It was significant that when the source fire was burned out, the wood paneling ceased to flame, which substantiates a previous statement that a minimum air temperature of 1000°F., adjacent to a smooth wood surface, must be maintained to produce continued combustion of flat wood surfaces.

Conclusions for these tests indicate that solid wood paneling does not constitute a life hazard and its presence has little significance compared with the effect of life safety of the combustible contents represented by most occupancies. This is manifested by the fact that adding only 2½ pounds of fuel to the igniting fire in the room, without paneling present, produced a greater increase of temperature at the breathing level than did the 293 sq. ft. of wood panelling, about

600 pounds of wood, applied to the walls and ceilings.

Most of the finish materials customarily affixed to the interior of buildings have flame spread ratings below 225. Lumber paneling tests appreciably below this value, and Douglas fir rates about 100 on the flame spread scale. In other than one and two-family residences where it is impractical to control combustible materials, paneling with ratings higher than 225 should be used with caution if permitted at all.

Where, for special reasons, severe limitations are made on the use of wall and ceiling finish materials, wood trim and wainscoting may still be used. The wood trim is of small quantity and wood wainscoting, being the bottom portion of the wall, will be in a low temperature zone.

Fire Retardant Treated Lumber
The principal advantage of fire retardant treated lumber is that it does not support combustion.

Structures of wood frame or ordinary construction can be economically built to larger areas and heights without increasing hazards when the lumber is fire retardant treated. A substantial increase in building area and additional story height is recommended for buildings using fire retardant treated lumber throughout over those that would normally be built using untreated wood.

The natural strength, endurance and the non-flaming character of treated lumber exposed to fire make this a superior material where building codes require non-combustible construction, or where it is especially needed.

A flame spread rating of about 15-25 is achieved for the normal retentions of fire retardant chemicals.

Fire Retardant Paints and Coatings
Fire retardant paints and coatings are useful in reducing the flame spread characteristics of combustible materials. Approved, applied fire retardants test to flame spread ratings of from 55 to below 25. Some applied fire retardants are also known to have a high insulation value that will retard the heating of materials that are adversely affected, strengthwise, by high temperatures.

Conditions of exposure should be taken into account in selecting a fire retardant, as moisture or even high humidity may cause depreciation of the efficiency of some types.

Automatic Sprinklers
Automatic sprinklers are an extremely important fire protection device. As the name implies, they provide a method of automatically distributing water over a fire in sufficient quantities to hold it in check and usually extinguish it entirely. Two systems, known as "dry pipe" and "wet pipe", are commonly used. Each uses sprinkler heads that are opened by the melting of a fusible link. The heads are spaced along pipes that are ordinarily attached to the ceiling. The sealed piping of the "dry pipe" system contains only air. When a sprinkler head opens the air is released and the water that has been held in check begins to flow. The dry pipe system is used mostly where there is a possibility of water in pipes being frozen. The wet pipe system has water under pressure in the pipes at all times.

The amount of water discharged by a sprinkler depends upon the pressure, as the size of the opening is about the same in all sprinklers. A working or flowing pressure of fifteen pounds is considered a minimum for proper action. At this pressure the sprinkler will discharge about twenty-two gallons per minute and over a floor area of more than 100 square feet. In the average building each sprinkler is spaced to cover about 80 square feet.

Automatic sprinkler systems are designed to extinguish fires at the point of origin and are not intended to control a fire involving the total floor area of a building, as water supply and pressure may not be sufficient to operate many heads, although automatic sprinklers are so effective that they usually control fires beyond the conditions for which they were designed. Automatic sprinklers increase the degree of life safety for occupants of buildings and also serve to alleviate unusually restrictive building requirements.

In designing a sprinkler system for a building, the following principles should be observed

1. All portions of the building or property should be equipped with sprinklers. This includes attics, basements, or any space between the ground and first floor, additions, stairs, elevator towers or enclosures.

2. The distribution of water must be unobstructed so that the seat of the fire may be reached by the water spray. This may require the placing of sprinklers inside enclosures, under decks, platforms, etc.

3. The pressure and volume of the water must be adequate for the number of sprinklers that will operate. This water supply must be maintained until the fire is extinguished or under control.

A sprinkler system is of no value if the water supply is not in service, or if a valve is closed. The sprinklers should be kept clean and never covered with paint or similar material, for this may affect their sensitiveness, time and temperature of operation, or even render them entirely inoperative, and stock should never be piled around the sprinklers so as to obstruct the distribution of the water.

CHAPTER XII

Sound Control

SOUND CONTROL

PRINCIPLES OF NOISE CONTROL
Noise Control by Design
Traffic noise or other sounds originating outside the building are controlled through site selection; landscaping; floor plan and the exterior building construction. Those noises originating inside the building are controlled by the floor plan, tenant placement, proper isolation of mechanical equipment and the construction of interior walls and floors.

Noise Transmission Control Within a Building
Noise is transmitted from one room to another as airborne, as structure-borne or as impact noise and measures should be taken to insulate against each. Airborne noise, such as speech or music, is transmitted through air as pressure waves and induces vibration in walls, floors, and ceilings. The difference in the vibrational energy induced in the near side and in the far side of a wall determines that partition's effectiveness in insulating against noise transmission. Thus the importance of isolating one wall surface from the other — or a ceiling from a floor. Leaks through cracks or other openings which provide a path for airborne sound will seriously reduce the effectiveness of a sound barrier.

Structure-borne noise originates from the vibrations of fans, compressors, pipes, ducts, etc. that are not properly isolated from the building structure. Since sound travels more readily through the building framework than through air gaps, structure-borne noise may carry through an entire building. Finally, footsteps on a floor create localized but sometimes annoying impact noise in a room below. These noises are most easily controlled by a cushioned floor surface.

Sound Transmission Ratings
There is a growing tendency for lenders, mortgage insuring agencies and building code officials to require wall and floor constructions that have a rated resistance to sound transmission, based on laboratory tests. Ratings for a wide variety of wood-framed walls and floor-ceiling assemblies are illustrated here to help designers and builders selectively accomplish noise control.

A wall or floor system's resistance to the transmission of speech, music or other airborne sound is measured over the most important part of the hearing range (from 125 to 4000 cycles per second) to insure that it is effective against low, intermediate and high frequencies. However, for convenience in specifying sound insulating properties, a single figure sound transmission class (STC) is determined from the measurements and reported as the overall rating of the partition. The higher the number, the better the sound barrier and values of 45 to 55 are commonly cited for good barriers.

The way in which the STC of a wall or floor determines acoustical privacy is illustrated.

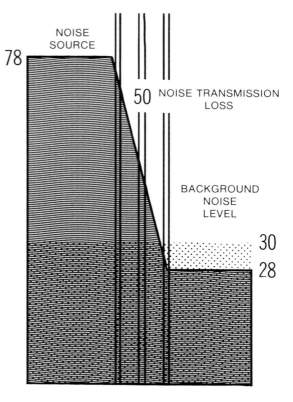

A good sound barrier should reduce the noise originating in one room to below the background noise level in an adjacent room.

25	Normal speech can be understood quite easily
30	Loud speech can be understood fairly well
35	Loud speech audible but not intelligible
42	Loud speech audible as a murmur
45	Must strain to hear loud speech
48	Some loud speech barely audible
50	Loud speech not audible

This chart from the Acoustical and Insulating Materials Association illustrates the degree of noise control achieved with barriers having different STC numbers.

SOUND CONTROL

Superiority of Wood Framing for Sound-Rated Partitions

Reliance on lightweight construction systems challenges designers to insulate against noise by means other than the massiveness of walls and floors. Excellent sound insulation can be provided with wood frame constructions. Some advantages are:

1. Wood framing systems damp vibration better than other framing.

2. They are effective over full range of frequencies. Material costs and installation costs are generally less than for other systems.

3. Wood framing is available when and where needed.

4. Wood framing adjusts easily to building imperfections and requires less calking than some systems.

5. Wood-framed walls are stiffer for a given thickness and weight than competitive partitions.

6. It is easier to fasten cabinets and other wall hung equipment to wood framing.

7. Double wood stud walls tolerate oversights in workmanship better than other constructions.

Facts About Installation

Good sound barriers require careful attention to detail. Wood framing makes this easier to accomplish but adequate supervision of workmanship is still vital to prevent sound leaks.

Cost saving with wood-framed systems permits the extra margin of care required to get the best results from any system.

Careful installation cannot remedy oversights in design. It is important to isolate major noise sources; to match occupancies (as bedroom — bedroom) on opposite sides of a wall or floor; and to continue sound barriers between apartments from ground to roof.

For specific design and construction practices that help control noise transmission, see the references on page 304, particularly (2).

Acoustical Properties of Wood Stud Systems

The wall and floor constructions described here should permit the designer or builder to select a system that best fits his requirements for sound insulation and fire resistance to his limitations on cost. Additional latitude is provided by the fact that the constructions shown can be modified in minor ways without changing their sound insulating properties. For example, the following differences in construction do not significantly affect a wall or floor's resistance to sound transmission:

1. Untreated or fire retardant treated wood.

2. Width of stud (3- or 4-inch nominal) or depth of joist (8- or 12-inch nominal)

3. Thickness of gypsum board (½- or ⅝-inch)

4. Thickness of subfloor (½- or ⅝-inch)

5. Glass fiber or mineral wool thermal insulation batts as absorptive material

6. Resilient channels on one vs. both sides of a wall

7. Species and grade of wood for studs or joists. Any available species of Western Wood — Douglas Fir, Western Larch, Hem-Fir, Engelmann Spruce, Ponderosa Pine, Lodgepole Pine, Western Red Cedar, Incense Cedar, Idaho White Pine or Sugar Pine may be specified.

Major modification in thickness or cumulative changes can, of course, alter the sound insulation provided.

Fire Resistance Rating

The nation's major building codes have established certain fire protection requirements in structures to safeguard life and public welfare. Included in these are requirements for fire resistance of wall and floor systems. The fire resistance rating of a partition is a measure of the time required for fire to penetrate a wall or a floor-ceiling assembly — as for example, a 1-hour wall. Thus, the rating denotes the partition's capacity to confine fire at its source.

The most recent *Building Materials List* of the Underwriters' Laboratories (see page 8, Reference 10) shows 32 wood-framed floor-ceiling assemblies with a 1-hour fire rating. A few typical constructions are illustrated on page 298.

Fire retardant treated wood framing (FR-S) is accepted by many building departments as equivalent to "non-combustible." Fire retardant treated studs are approved under most codes for nonbearing partitions in high-rise construction.

When specified, framing lumber should be fire retardant treated in accordance with *American Wood Preservers Association Standard C20-70, (Structural Lumber-Fire Retardant Treatment by Pressure Processes).* Reference to the Underwriters' FR-S is sufficient. The industry generally follows AWPA standards for pressure treatment but the UL label guarantees performance.

Wood Frame Walls, Floors for Sound Insulation

The wall and floor constructions illustrated in this brochure have been tested and rated for sound insulation by recognized acoustical laboratories. They permit selection of a wall or floor construction to provide a desired level of sound insulation and fire resistance at reasonable cost.

SOUND CONTROL

The wall and floor constructions illustrated were compiled by the U.S. Forest Service (Wood Construction Research) based on that unit's extensive studies of sound insulation in wood-framed buildings. The Western Wood Products Association and the Forest Service are grateful to the many sponsors of laboratory tests who have given permission to include their data. The source references listed on page 304 contain further helpful information on noise control.

The values shown are those obtained in carefully controlled laboratory tests. As such, they indicate the potential sound insulation of such construction.

If reasonable precautions are taken to prevent sound leaks and flanking of noise around, over and under the floor or wall, the field performance should be within 2-5 points of the laboratory value for walls and within 3 points of that for floors.

Because the quality of workmanship and site conditions may vary widely, the Association cannot guarantee or assume responsibility for performance at the rated values.

Sample Specifications

"Floor joists, headers, lintels, ceiling joists and rafters shall be surfaced 4 sides (S4S) seasoned No. 2 grade Douglas Fir-Larch (Para. 62.12) unless otherwise noted on the plans.

"All studding, blocking and plates shall be surfaced 4 sides (S4S) seasoned No. 3 grade Douglas Fir-Larch or Hem-Fir unless otherwise noted on the plans."

typical one-hour fire resistive floor-ceiling assemblies

Double Lumber Floor. Ceiling Nailed Directly to Joists

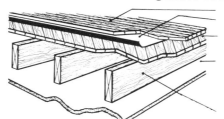

1″ wood flooring
Building paper
1x6 T&G boards or ½″ Standard grade plywood with exterior glue
⅝″ Type X gypsum board ceiling or ½″ special fire resistive gypsum board ceiling. May be attached to resilient acoustical channels or nailed directly to joists
Joists 16″ o.c.**

Double Plywood Floor. Ceiling Suspended in T-Bar Grid

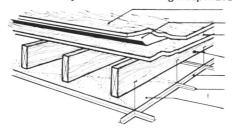

⅝″ T&G Underlayment grade plywood
Building paper
½″ Standard grade plywood with exterior glue
Joists 16″ o.c.**
T-bar grid ceiling system
Main runners 48″ o.c.
Cross-tees 24″ o.c.
½″x48″x24″ mineral acoustical ceiling panels (install with hold-down clips)

Gypsum Underlayment Compound on Plywood Subfloor. Ceiling Resilient Acoustical Channels

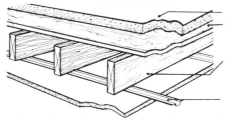

Gypsum Underlayment Compound
½″ T&G Underlayment grade plywood

Joists 16″ o.c.**

⅝″ Type X or ½″ fire resistive type gypsum board ceiling on resilient acoustical channels

two-hour fire resistive floor-ceiling assembly

Double Wood Floor. Double Gypsum Board Ceiling

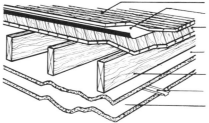

1″ wood flooring
Building paper
1x6 T&G boards

⅝″ Type X gypsum board nailed directly to joists

Joists 16″ o.c.**

Resilient acoustical channels

⅝″ Type X gypsum board, second layer applied on channels

**Fire tests conducted with 2″x10″ joists.

Modern Urban Living Makes Adequate Sound Control Essential   70-unit Condominium, Verdes West, Palos Verdes Hills, California

SOUND CONTROL
wood frame partition systems for sound control

PARTITION SYSTEM		WALL NUMBER	WALL FACE
single stud walls Basic construction is 2″ x 4″ studs 16″ o.c. with double top plate and single or double bottom plate. Faces are ⅝″ thick fire resistive type gypsum board applied, taped and finished in accordance with manufacturer's recommendations. Resilient channels are applied to studs 24″ o.c. as shown with a ½″x3″ gypsum nailing strip at the bottom. Absorptive material is paper-backed glass fiber or mineral wool batts stapled in the stud space as illustrated. Sound deadening board is sound-rated organic fiber board with a 15-18 pcf density. **no. 3**		1	Single gypsum board each side, applied with screws; no resilient channels
		2	Single gypsum board laminated and nailed[2] over sound board each side; no channels
		3	Single gypsum board applied with screws 1 side; opposite side on resilient channels
		4	Single gypsum board laminated and nailed[2] over sound board, opposite side on resilient channels
		5	Single gypsum board on resilient channels each side
		6	Double ½″ gypsum board, base sheet vertical; face sheet horizontal; applied on resilient channels one side
double stud walls with a common plate Basic construction is a double row of 2″x3″ or 2″x4″ studs, each row 16″ o.c. and each row aligned with an opposite edge of the 2″x6″ top and bottom plates. The rows of studs are offset 2″ to 8″ to prevent any chance contact. Other details and materials are as described for single stud walls. **no. 11**		7	Single gypsum board each side, applied with screws (2x3 studs—16″ o.c.); no resilient channels
		8 [3]	Single gypsum board laminated and nailed[2] over sound deadening board each side (2x4 studs—16″ o.c.); no resilient channels
		9 [4]	Single gypsum board nailed one side. Single gypsum on resilient channels opposite
		10	Single gypsum board laminated and nailed[2] over sound deadening board 1 side. Single gypsum board on resilient channels opposite (2x3 studs—16″ o.c.)
		11	Double gypsum board (½″ over ⅝″) nailed one side; single gypsum board on resilient channels opposite (2x4 studs—24″ o.c.)
double stud walls on separate plates Basic construction is a double wall of 2″x3″ studs on separate plates about 1″ apart. Studs of each frame are 16″ o.c. with the studs in one frame offset 2″ to 8″ from those of the other. Other details and materials are as described for single stud walls. **no. 13**		12	Single gypsum board each side applied with screws
		13	Single gypsum board laminated and nailed[2] over sound board each side
		14	Same as wall 13
		15	Single gypsum board laminated and nailed[2] over sound board 1 side; single gypsum board on resilient channels opposite
		16	Double gypsum board; nailed each side
		17	Double gypsum board each side; outer layer laminated and nailed[2]; base layer nailed
		18	Double gypsum board laminated and nailed[2] one side. Single gypsum board on resilient channels opposite

SOUND CONTROL

ABSORPTIVE MATERIAL	STC	STC TEST DESIGNATION	STC REF. SEE PAGE 8	FIRE RATING	FIRE TEST DESIGNATION	WEIGHT p.s.f.
None	34	G&H 30 FT USG	12	1 Hr	UL 5¹	6½
None	45	G&H 75 FT SIM	9	1 Hr	U of C 8/21/64	8
1½″ glass fiber	50	OR-64-16	4	1 Hr	T-3127 OSU	6½
1½″ glass fiber	52	KAL 736-2-69	6	1 Hr	(Est)	7
3″ glass fiber	53	KAL 736-3-69	6	1 Hr	(Est)	7
2″ mineral wool	59	TL-67-239	12	2 Hr	T-4799 OSU	12
2″ mineral wool	49	G&H 155 FT-USG	12	1 Hr	(Est)	7
None	49	G&H 24 FT IBI	7	1 Hr	(Est)	10
1½″ glass fiber	50	TL 68-17	12	1 Hr	(Est)	8
1½″ glass fiber	53	KAL 736-5-69	6	1 Hr	(Est)	8
1½″ glass fiber	56	KAL 736-7-69	6	1 Hr	(Est)	10
2″ mineral wool	51	G&H 106 FT—USG	12	1 Hr	(Est)	7½
None	53	G&H 46 FT—USG	12	1 Hr	(Est)	9
3″ mineral wool	60	TL 71-233	14	1 Hr	(Est)	9
3″ mineral wool	58	TL 71-243	14	1 Hr	(Est)	8
None	51	TL 69-214	12	2 Hr	(Est)	12½
3″ mineral wool	59	TL 71-255	14	2 Hr	(Est)	12½
3″ mineral wool	57	TL 71-278	14	1 Hr	(Est)	10

³Where an interior shear wall is required, ⅜-inch plywood may be substituted for the sound deadening board with little change in the STC. Reference (1) describes such a wall (KAL 262-5) having an STC of 47.
⁴An alternate shear wall can be provided by using a base sheet of ⅜-inch plywood under the gypsum board on the side opposite the resilient channels. Reference (1) describes such a wall (KAL 262-6) having an STC of 50.

SOUND CONTROL
conventional wood floor joist systems for sound control

FLOOR SYSTEM	FLOOR NUMBER	FLOOR COVERING
conventional	1	⅛″ vinyl asbestos tile on ⅜″ plywood underlayment
	2	.075″ vinyl sheet on ⅜″ plywood underlayment
CARPET & PAD / ⅝″ PLYWOOD SUBFLOOR / 2 x 8 JOISTS 16″ O.C. / 3″ GLASS FIBER / **FLOOR NO. 3**	3	Carpet and pad directly over subfloor
	4	²⁵⁄₃₂″ oak strip floor over subfloor
The basic construction is illustrated by floor No. 3 although floors 4 and 5 have 2″x10″ joists and ½″ subfloor. Except in floor No. 1, the ceiling is fire-resistive type gypsum board applied with screws to resilient channels 24″ o.c. Standard carpet is 44-ounce (sq. yd.) gropoint over 40-ounce hair pad.	5	Carpet and pad added to No. 4
conventional With Floated Floor Over	6	Wood block (⁵⁄₁₆″) laminated to underlayment
	7	Carpet and pad
½″ UNDERLAYMENT / ½″ SOUND BOARD / ⅝″ SUBFLOOR / 2 x 10 JOISTS 16″ O.C. / 3″ GLASS FIBER	8	Vinyl flooring laminated to underlayment applied over sound board with 4-inch circular globs of glue
	9	Vinyl covering like 8 with sleepers glued between sound board and underlayment
	10	Oak strip flooring (²⁵⁄₃₂″) nailed to 2x3 sleepers glued over sound board strips 1⅞″ glass fiber between sleepers
The basic construction is illustrated. Sound deadening board (15-18 p.c.f.) is laid over a ⅝″ plywood subfloor, with or without stapling, and ½″ T&G underlayment grade plywood glued over the sound board. The ceiling is ⅝″ fire-resistive type gypsum board on resilient channels; absorptive material is 3-inch thick glass fiber batts.	11	Vinyl flooring (0.07″) on ⅝″ T&G plywood underlayment glued to 2x2 sleepers glued to subfloor 16″ o.c. Sand fill over subfloor to depth of sleepers (1½″). Balance as in basic construction
conventional With lightweight Concrete or Gypsum Cement Added	12	Ceiling nailed to joists; no absorptive material; with carpet and pad....................................
FLOOR NO. 14 / 1⅝″ LT. WT. CONCRETE / ⅝″ SUBFLOOR / 3″ MINERAL WOOL / 2 x 10 JOISTS 16″ O.C. / ⅝″ GYPSUM BOARD ON R.C.	13	Ceiling nailed to joists; 3″ glass fiber with carpet and pad....................................
	14	**Basic construction**—(no floor covering) with carpet and pad....................................
The basic construction is illustrated by floor No. 14. The floor topping is 1⅝″ thick cellular (foamed) concrete (100 p.c.f.). Ceilings are fire-resistive type gypsum board on resilient channels, 24 inches o.c. Absorptive material is 3″ thick mineral wool batts. Floor coverings for impact tests are 44-ounce carpet over 40-ounce hair pad or vinyl floor covering, approximately 0.07 inches thick. Note variations from basic construction drawn in plans 12-16.	15	Add ½″ sound board between concrete and subfloor with vinyl tile.................................... with carpet and pad....................................
	16	Basic construction—but with ¾″ thick gypsum concrete in place of 1⅝″ thick cellular concrete; ½″ gypsum ceiling without floor covering.........................

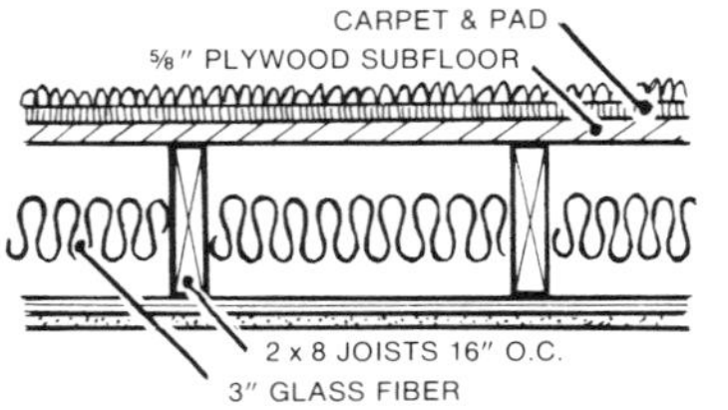

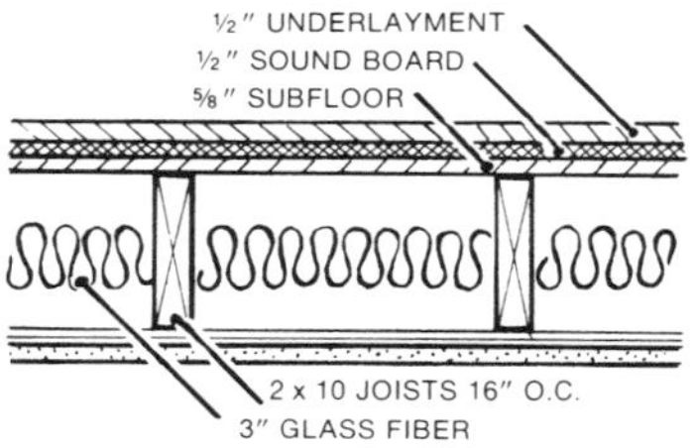

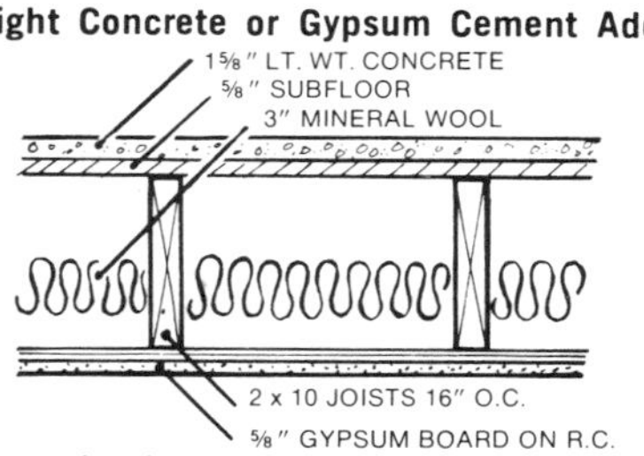

The improved resistance to airborne sound transmission gained by isolating the ceiling with resilient channels and adding absorptive material is evident by comparing floors 2 to 5 with No. 1. A 10-point increase in STC reduces the loudness of transmitted noise by one-half. Improved resistance to impact noise transmission is gained by adding carpet and pad as is evident by comparing floor No. 3 with No. 2 or floor No. 5 with 4. An IIC of 51 is often recommended as an acceptable level of impact insulation.

SOUND CONTROL

GYPSUM BOARD CEILING	ABSORPTIVE MATERIAL	STC	IIC	TEST REFERENCE	REFERENCE SOURCE SEE PAGE 8	WEIGHT p.s.f.
½" nailed direct to joists	None	37	34	NBS 728 A	3	9
⅝" on resilient channels	3" glass fiber	46	44	KAL 224, 1&2	1	9
⅝" on resilient channels	3" glass fiber	47	69	KAL 224, 3&4	1	8½
½" on resilient channels	3" mineral wool	50	46	CK 6512-9	12	9
½" on resilient channels	3" mineral wool	50	71	CK 6512-8	12	9½
⅝" on resilient channels	3" glass fiber	54	51	KAL-736-10,11	6	11½
⅝" on resilient channels	3" glass fiber	55	72	TL 70-71' IN 70-10	13	10½
⅝" on resilient channels	3" glass fiber	58	55	TL 70-72' IN 70-11	13	11
⅝" on resilient channels	3" glass fiber	57	56	TL 70-61' IN 70-9	13	11½
⅝" on resilient channels	3" glass fiber	55	51	KAL-736-8,9	6	11½
⅝" on resilient channels	3" glass fiber	59	56	TL 71-279 IN 71-19	14	22
⅝" nailed	None	47	68	G&H 1ST-USDA 1MT-LCR'	11	21
⅝" nailed	None	47	66	KAL 224 29, 30	1	20½
⅝" on resilient channels	3" glass fiber	58	67	G&H 2ST-USDA	11	20½
⅝" on resilient channels	3" glass fiber	59	52 72	G&H 9ST-USDA	11	21½ 22
½" on resilient channels	3" mineral wool	58	44	G&H 1MT-USG	12	15½

The three floor coverings used on floors 6, 7, and 8 provide equivalent airborne sound insulation, but the carpet and pad provide the best impact sound insulation.
Floors 9 and 10 add wood sleepers over the sound board, but comparisons of floors 9 with 8 and 10 with 6 reveal that this addition does not improve sound insulation.

'With permission of Lightcrete, Inc.

²Estimated from related tests.

SOUND CONTROL
Long Span Joists

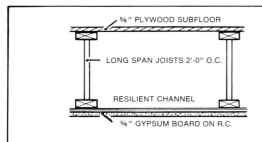

Long span joists 12 to 14 inches deep with wood 2x4 flanges and tubular steel web, spaced 24 inches o.c. Plywood subfloor is ¾" thick nailed to flanges with face grain perpendicular to joists. Concrete topping is cellular (foamed) concrete (100 p.c.f.). Ceiling is ⅝" thick fire-resistive type gypsum board applied to resilient channels 24 inches o.c. Carpet is 44-ounce gropoint on 40-ounce hair pad.

FLOOR NUMBER	VARIATIONS FROM BASIC CONSTRUCTION DRAWN	STC	IIC	TEST REFERENCE	REFERENCE SOURCE	WEIGHT p.s.f.
17	Carpet and pad over ⅜" plywood underlayment; no absorptive material	48	62	TL 70-48 IN 70-7	12	7½
18	Carpet and pad over 1⅝" concrete (100 p.c.f.); no absorptive material	58	80	TL 70-44 IN 70-6	12	21½

1. American Plywood Association. 1967. *Plywood in Apartments.* Tacoma, Washington 98401.

2. Berendt, R.D., Winzer, G.E. and Burroughs, C.B. 1967. *A Guide to Airborne, Impact and Structure-Borne Noise Control in Multi-family Dwellings.* Prepared by the Nat. Bur. of Standards for the FHA, U.S. Dept. of Housing & Urban Development, U.S. Govt. Printing Office ($2.50), Washington, D.C. 20402.

3. Berendt, R.D. and Winzer, G.E., 1964 *Sound Insulation of Wall, Floor and Door Constructions.* NBS Monograph 77, U.S. Dept. of Commerce, Nat. Bur. of Standards, U.S. Govt. Printing Office ($0.40), Washington, D.C. 20402.

4. Georgia-Pacific — Gypsum Division. 1969. *Sound Advice.* Portland, Oregon 97204.

5. Gypsum Association. 1971. *Design Data.* 1971-72 edition. Chicago, Ill. 60606.

6. Iowa State University and U.S. Forest Service. (Division For. Economics and Marketing Research) Washington, D.C. 20250.

7. Insulation Board Institute.

1967. *Noise Control with Insulation Board.* (Now called Acoustical and Insulating Materials Association, Park Ridge, Illinois 60068.)

8. Owens-Corning Fiberglass Corp. 1969. *Solutions to Noise Control Problems.* Toledo, Ohio 43601.

9. Simpson Timber Company. 1964. *Product Data.* Seattle, Washington 98101.

10. Underwriters' Laboratories, Inc. 1971. *Building Materials List* — 1971. 207 E. Ohio Street, Chicago, Illinois 60611.

11. U.S. Forest Service. (Wood Construction Research) Seattle, WA. 98105.

12 U.S. Gypsum Company. 1969. *Technical Data — Drywall Products and Systems.* Chicago, Illinois 60606.

13. Weyerhaeuser — Dierks Division. 1970. *Weyerhaeuser — Dierks Sound Deadening Systems.* Hot Springs, Ark. 71901.

14. Western Wood Products Association. Yeon Building, Portland, Oregon 97204.

Appendix

APPENDIX

The following book abbreviations and symbols are in general use throughout this book. Deviations from these notations are identified where they occur.

ABBREVIATIONS

Btu	British thermal unit
c-c	center to center
C_L	centerline
cu	cubic
DL	dead load
EMC	equilibrium moisture content
fbm	foot board measure
ft, ft², ft³, ft⁴, . . .	feet, square feet, cubic feet, feet to the fourth power, etc.
ga	gage
in., in.², in.³, in.⁴, . . .	inches, square inches, cubic inches, inches to the fourth power, etc.
in.-lb	inch-pound
k	kip (one thousand pounds)
lb	pound
lin	lineal
LL	live load
max	maximum
MC	moisture content
min	minimum
mph	miles per hour
NA	neutral axis
o.c.	on centers
pcf	pounds per cubic foot
plf	pounds per lineal foot
pli	pounds per lineal inch
psf	pounds per square foot
psi	pounds per square inch
SL	snow load
sq	square
TL	total load
WL	wind load
yd	yard

SYMBOLS

A	area of cross section
b	breadth (width) of rectangular member
C	coefficient, constant, or factor
C_c	curvature factor
C_d	depth effect factor
C_f	form factor
C_s	slenderness factor
c	distance from neutral axis to extreme fiber
D	diameter
d	depth of rectangular member, or least dimension of compression member
E	modulus of elasticity
e	eccentricity
F_b	allowable unit stress for extreme fiber in bending
f_b	actual unit stress for extreme fiber in bending
F_c	allowable unit stress in compression parallel to grain
F_c'	allowable unit stress in compression parallel to grain adjusted for l/d ratio
f_c	actual unit stress in compression parallel to grain
$F_{c\perp}$	allowable unit stress in compression perpendicular to grain

$f_{c\perp}$	actual unit stress in compression perpendicular to grain
F_r	allowable unit radial stress
f_r	actual unit radial stress
F_{rc}	allowable unit radial stress in compression
f_{rc}	actual unit radial stress in compression
F_{rt}	allowable unit radial stress in tension
f_{rt}	actual unit radial stress in tension
F_t	allowable unit stress in tension parallel to grain
f_t	actual unit stress in tension parallel to grain
F_v	allowable unit horizontal shear stress
f_v	actual unit horizontal shear stress
h	rise
I	moment of inertia
L	span length of beam, or unsupported length of column, ft
l	span length of beam, or unsupported length of column, in.
M	bending moment
m	unit bending moment
P	total concentrated load, or axial compression load
P/A	induced axial load per unit of cross-sectional area
Q	statical moment of an area about the neutral axis
R	radius of curvature
R_H	horizontal reaction
R_V	vertical reaction
r	radius of gyration
S	section modulus
T	total axial tension load
t	thickness
V	total vertical shear
W	total uniform load
w	uniform load per unit of length
Δ_A	allowable deformation or deflection
Δ_a	actual deformation or deflection
$\parallel$	parallel
$\perp$	perpendicular
π	pi
$>$	greater than
$\geq$	greater than or equal to
$<$	less than
$\leq$	less than or equal to

LUMBER ABBREVIATIONS

AAR — Association of American Railroads
AD — Air-dried
ADF — After deduction freight
ALS — American Lumber Standards
AVG — Average
AW&L — All widths and lengths
BD — Board
BD. FT — Board feet
BDL — Bundle
BEV — Bevel
BH — Boxed heart
B/L, BL — Bill of lading
BM — Board Measure
B&S — Beams and Stringers
BSND — Bright Sapwood no defect
BTR — Better

CB — Center Beaded
CF — Cost and freight
CIF — Cost, insurance and freight
CIFE — Cost, insurance, freight, exchange
C/L — Carload
CLG — Ceiling
CLR — Clear
CM — Center matched
CS — Caulking seam
CSG — Casing
CV — Center V
DET — Double end trimmed
DF — Douglas Fir
DF-L — Douglas Fir-Larch
DIM — Dimension
DKG — Decking
D/S, DS — Drop siding
D&M — Dressed and matched
E — Edge or modulus of elasticity
EB1S — Edge bead one side
EB2S — Edge bead two sides
E&CB2S — Edge & center bead two sides
EV1S — Edge vee one side
EV2S — Edge vee two sides
E&CV1S — Edge & center vee one side
E&CV2S — Edge & Center vee two sides
EE — Eased edged
EG — Edge (vertical) grain
EM — End matched
ES — Engelmann spruce
f — Allowable fiber stress in bending (also Fb)
FAS — Free alongside (vessel)
FG — Flat or slash grain
FLG — Flooring
FOB — Free on board (Named point)
FOHC — Free of heart center
FRT — Freight
Ft — Foot
FT. BM — Feet board measure (also FBM)
FT. SM — Feet surface measure
H.B. — Hollow back
HEM — Hemlock
H&M — Hit and miss
H or M — Hit or miss
IC — Incense cedar
IN — Inch or inches
IND — Industrial
IWP — Idaho white pine
J&P — Joists and Planks
JTD — Jointed
KD — Kiln-dried
L — Larch
LBR — Lumber
LCL — Less than carload
LF — Light Framing
LFVC — Loaded full visible capacity
LGR — Longer
LGTH — Length
LIN — Lineal
LNG — Lining

LP — Lodgepole pine
M — Thousand
MBF — Thousand board feet
M. BM — Thousand (ft.) board measure
MC — Moisture content
MG — Mixed grain
MLDG — Moulding
MOE — Modulus of elasticity of "E"
MOR — Modulus of Rupture
MSR — Machine Stress Rated
NBM — Net board measure
N1E — Nose one edge
PAD — Partly Air Dried
PARA — Paragraph
PART — Partition
PAT — Pattern
PET — Precision end trimmed
PP — Ponderosa pine
P&T — Posts and Timbers
RC — Red Cedar
RDM — Random
REG — Regular
RGH — Rough
R/L, RL — Random lengths
R/S — Resawn
R/W, or RW — Random widths
R/W, R/L — Random width, Random length
SB1S — Single bead one side
SDG — Siding
SEL — Select
SG — Slash or flat grain
S/L or SL — Shiplap
STD.M. — Standard matched
SM — Surface measure
SP — Sugar pine
SQ — Square
STK — Stock
STPG — Stepping
STR — Structural
S&E — Side and edge
S1E — Surfaced one edge
S2E — Surfaced two edges
S1S — Surfaced one side
S2S — Surfaced two sides
S4S — Surfaced four sides
S1S&CM — Surfaced one side and center matched
S2S&CM — Surfaced two sides and center matched
S4S&CS — Surfaced four sides and caulking seam
S1S1E — Surfaced one side, one edge
S1S2E — Surfaced one side, two edges
S2S1E — Surfaced two sides, one edge
TBR — Timber
T&G — Tongued and grooved
VG — Vertical (edge) grain
WDR — Wider
WF — White fir
WT — Weight
WTH — Width
WRC — Western Red Cedar
WWPA — Western Wood Products Association

APPENDIX

TABLES OF BOARD MEASURE

NOMINAL SIZE OF PIECE	BOARD FEET CONTENT WHEN LENGTH IN FEET EQUALS											
	2	4	6	8	10	12	14	16	18	20	22	24
1 x 2	1/3	2/3	1	1 1/3	1 2/3	2	2 1/3	2 2/3	3	3 1/3	3 2/3	4
1 x 3	1/2	1	1 1/2	2	2 1/2	3	3 1/2	4	4 1/2	5	5 1/2	6
1 x 4	2/3	1 1/3	2	2 2/3	3 1/3	4	4 2/3	5 1/3	6	6 2/3	7 1/3	8
1 x 6	1	2	3	4	5	6	7	8	9	10	11	12
1 x 8	1 1/3	2 2/3	4	5 1/3	6 2/3	8	9 1/3	10 2/3	12	13 1/3	14 2/3	16
1 x 10	1 2/3	3 1/3	5	6 2/3	8 1/3	10	11 2/3	13 1/3	15	16 2/3	18 1/3	20
1 x 12	2	4	6	8	10	12	14	16	18	20	22	24
2 x 2	2/3	1 1/3	2	2 2/3	3 1/3	4	4 2/3	5 1/3	6	6 2/3	7 1/3	8
2 x 3	1	2	3	4	5	6	7	8	9	10	11	12
2 x 4	1 1/3	2 2/3	4	5 1/3	6 2/3	8	9 1/3	10 2/3	12	13 1/3	14 2/3	16
2 x 6	2	4	6	8	10	12	14	16	18	20	22	24
2 x 8	2 2/3	5 1/3	8	10 2/3	13 1/3	16	18 2/3	21 1/3	24	26 2/3	29 1/3	32
2 x 10	3 1/3	6 2/3	10	13 1/3	16 2/3	20	23 1/3	26 2/3	30	33 1/3	36 2/3	40
2 x 12	4	8	12	16	20	24	28	32	36	40	44	48
2 x 14	4 2/3	9 1/3	14	18 2/3	23 1/3	28	32 2/3	37 1/3	42	46 2/3	51 1/3	56
3 x 4	2	4	6	8	10	12	14	16	18	20	22	24
3 x 6	3	6	9	12	15	18	21	24	27	30	33	36
3 x 8	4	8	12	16	20	24	28	32	36	40	44	48
3 x 10	5	10	15	20	25	30	35	40	45	50	55	60
3 x 12	6	12	18	24	30	36	42	48	54	60	66	72
3 x 14	7	14	21	28	35	42	49	56	63	70	77	84
3 x 16	8	16	24	32	40	48	56	64	72	80	88	96
4 x 4	2 2/3	5 1/3	8	10 2/3	13 1/3	16	18 2/3	21 1/3	24	26 2/3	29 1/3	32
4 x 6	4	8	12	16	20	24	28	32	36	40	44	48
4 x 8	5 1/3	10 2/3	16	21 1/3	26 2/3	32	37 1/3	42 2/3	48	53 1/3	58 2/3	64
4 x 10	6 2/3	13 1/3	20	26 2/3	33 1/3	40	46 2/3	53 1/3	60	66 2/3	73 1/3	80
4 x 12	8	16	24	32	40	48	56	64	72	80	88	96
4 x 14	9 1/3	18 2/3	28	37 1/3	46 2/3	56	65 1/3	74 2/3	84	93 1/3	102 2/3	112
4 x 16	10 2/3	21 1/3	32	42 2/3	53 1/3	64	74 2/3	85 1/3	96	106 2/3	117 1/3	128
6 x 6	6	12	18	24	30	36	42	48	54	60	66	72
6 x 8	8	16	24	32	40	48	56	64	72	80	88	96
6 x 10	10	20	30	40	50	60	70	80	90	100	110	120
6 x 12	12	24	36	48	60	72	84	96	108	120	132	144
6 x 14	14	28	42	56	70	84	98	112	126	140	154	168
6 x 16	16	32	48	64	80	96	112	128	144	160	176	192
6 x 18	18	36	54	72	90	108	126	144	162	180	198	216
6 x 20	20	40	60	80	100	120	140	160	180	200	220	240
6 x 22	22	44	66	88	110	132	154	176	198	220	242	264
6 x 24	24	48	72	96	120	144	168	192	216	240	264	288
8 x 8	10 2/3	21 1/3	32	42 2/3	53 1/3	64	74 2/3	85 1/3	96	106 2/3	117 1/3	128
8 x 10	13 1/3	26 2/3	40	53 1/3	66 2/3	80	93 1/3	106 2/3	120	133 1/3	146 2/3	160
8 x 12	16	32	48	64	80	96	112	128	144	160	176	192
8 x 14	18 2/3	37 1/3	56	74 2/3	93 1/3	112	130 2/3	149 1/3	168	186 2/3	205 1/3	224
8 x 16	21 1/3	42 2/3	64	85 1/3	106 2/3	128	149 1/3	170 2/3	192	213 1/3	234 2/3	256
8 x 18	24	48	72	96	120	144	168	192	216	240	264	288
8 x 20	26 2/3	53 1/3	80	106 2/3	133 1/3	160	186 2/3	213 1/3	240	266 2/3	293 1/3	320
8 x 22	29 1/3	58 2/3	88	117 1/3	146 2/3	176	205 1/3	234 2/3	264	293 1/3	322 2/3	352
8 x 24	32	64	96	128	160	192	224	256	288	320	352	384
10 x 10	16 2/3	33 1/3	50	66 2/3	83 1/3	100	116 2/3	133 1/3	150	166 2/3	183 1/3	200
10 x 12	20	40	60	80	100	120	140	160	180	200	220	240
10 x 14	23 1/3	46 2/3	70	93 1/3	116 2/3	140	163 1/3	186 2/3	210	233 1/3	256 2/3	280
10 x 16	26 2/3	53 1/3	80	106 2/3	133 1/3	160	186 2/3	213 1/3	240	266 2/3	293 1/3	320
10 x 18	30	60	90	120	150	180	210	240	270	300	330	360
10 x 20	33 1/3	66 2/3	100	133 1/3	166 2/3	200	233 1/3	266 2/3	300	333 1/3	366 2/3	400
10 x 22	36 2/3	73 1/3	110	146 2/3	183 1/3	220	256 2/3	293 1/3	330	366 2/3	403 1/3	440
10 x 24	40	80	120	160	200	240	280	320	360	400	440	480

TABLES OF BOARD MEASURE

BOARD FEET CONTENT WHEN LENGTH IN FEET EQUALS

NOMINAL SIZE OF PIECE	2	4	6	8	10	12	14	16	18	20	22	24
12 x 12	24	48	72	96	120	144	168	192	216	240	264	288
12 x 14	28	56	84	112	140	168	196	224	252	280	308	336
12 x 16	32	64	96	128	160	192	224	256	288	320	352	384
12 x 18	36	72	108	144	180	216	252	288	324	360	396	432
12 x 20	40	80	120	160	200	240	280	320	360	400	440	480
12 x 22	44	88	132	176	220	264	308	352	396	440	484	528
12 x 24	48	96	144	192	240	288	336	384	432	480	528	576
14 x 14	32 2/3	65 1/3	98	130 2/3	163 1/3	196	228 2/3	261 1/3	294	326 2/3	359 1/3	392
14 x 16	37 1/3	74 2/3	112	149 1/3	186 2/3	224	261 1/3	298 2/3	336	373 1/3	410 2/3	448
14 x 18	42	84	126	168	210	252	294	336	378	420	462	504
14 x 20	46 2/3	93 1/3	140	186 2/3	233 1/3	280	326 2/3	373 1/3	420	466 2/3	513 1/3	560
14 x 22	51 1/3	102 2/3	154	205 1/3	256 2/3	308	359 1/3	410 2/3	462	513 1/3	564 2/3	616
14 x 24	56	112	168	224	280	336	392	448	504	560	616	672
16 x 16	42 2/3	85 1/3	128	170 2/3	213 1/3	256	298 2/3	341 1/3	384	426 2/3	469 1/3	512
16 x 18	48	96	144	192	240	288	336	384	432	480	528	576
16 x 20	53 1/3	106 2/3	160	213 1/3	266 2/3	320	373 1/3	426 2/3	480	533 1/3	586 2/3	640
16 x 22	58 2/3	117 1/3	176	234 2/3	293 1/3	352	410 2/3	469 1/3	528	586 2/3	645 1/3	704
16 x 24	64	128	192	256	320	384	448	512	576	640	704	768
18 x 18	54	108	162	216	270	324	378	432	486	540	594	648
18 x 20	60	120	180	240	300	360	420	480	540	600	660	720
18 x 22	66	132	198	264	330	396	462	528	594	660	726	792
18 x 24	72	144	216	288	360	432	504	576	648	720	792	864
20 x 20	66 2/3	133 1/3	200	266 2/3	333 1/3	400	466 2/3	533 1/3	600	666 2/3	733 1/3	800
20 x 22	73 1/3	146 2/3	220	293 1/3	366 2/3	440	513 1/3	586 2/3	660	733 1/3	806 2/3	880
20 x 24	80	160	240	320	400	480	560	640	720	800	880	960
22 x 22	80 2/3	161 1/3	242	322 2/3	403 1/3	484	564 2/3	645 1/3	726	806 2/3	887 1/3	968
22 x 24	88	176	264	352	440	528	616	704	792	880	968	1056
24 x 24	96	192	288	384	480	576	672	768	864	960	1056	1152

COVERAGE ESTIMATOR

The following table provides factors for determining the exact amount of material needed for the five basic types of wood paneling. Multiply square footage to be covered by the tabulated factor (length x width x factor).

	Nominal Size	WIDTH Overall	WIDTH Face	AREA FACTOR*		Nominal Size	WIDTH Overall	WIDTH Face	AREA FACTOR*
SHIPLAP 	1 x 6	5½	5⅛	1.17	PANELING PATTERNS	1 x 6	5⅞₆	5⅛₆	1.19
	1 x 8	7¼	6⅞	1.16		1 x 8	7⅛	6¾	1.19
	1 x 10	9¼	8⅞	1.13		1 x 10	9⅛	8¾	1.14
	1 x 12	11¼	10⅞	1.10		1 x 12	11⅛	10¾	1.12
TONGUE AND GROOVE	1 x 4	3⅜	3⅛	1.28		1 x 4	3½	3½	1.60
	1 x 6	5⅜	5⅛	1.17	BEVEL SIDING	1 x 6	5½	5½	1.33
	1 x 8	7⅛	6⅞	1.16		1 x 8	7¼	7¼	1.28
	1 x 10	9⅛	8⅞	1.13		1 x 10	9¼	9¼	1.21
	1 x 12	11⅛	10⅞	1.10		1 x 12	11¼	11¼	1.17
S4S 	1 x 4	3½	3½	1.14					
	1 x 6	5½	5½	1.09					
	1 x 8	7¼	7¼	1.10					
	1 x 10	9¼	9¼	1.08					
	1 x 12	11¼	11¼	1.07					

*Allowance for trim and waste should be added.

APPENDIX

DECIMAL EQUIVALENTS

	DECIMAL OF A FOOT					DECIMAL OF AN INCH	
FRACTION	DECIMAL	FRACTION	DECIMAL	FRACTION	DECIMAL	FRACTION	DECIMAL
1/16	0.0052	4-1/16	0.3385	8-1/16	0.6719	1/64	0.015625
1/8	0.0104	4-1/8	0.3438	8-1/8	0.6771	1/32	0.03125
3/16	0.0156	4-3/16	0.3490	8-3/16	0.6823	3/64	0.046875
1/4	0.0208	4-1/4	0.3542	8-1/4	0.6875	1/16	0.0625
5/16	0.0260	4-5/16	0.3594	8-5/16	0.6927	5/64	0.078125
3/8	0.0313	4-3/8	0.3646	8-3/8	0.6979	3/32	0.09375
7/16	0.0365	4-7/16	0.3698	8-7/16	0.7031	7/64	0.109375
1/2	0.0417	4-1/2	0.3750	8-1/2	0.7083	1/8	0.125
9/16	0.0459	4-9/16	0.3802	8-9/16	0.7135	9/64	0.140625
5/8	0.0521	4-5/8	0.3854	8-5/8	0.7188	5/32	0.15625
11/16	0.0573	4-11/16	0.3906	8-11/16	0.7240	11/64	0.171875
3/4	0.0625	4-3/4	0.3958	8-3/4	0.7292	3/16	0.1875
13/16	0.0677	4-13/16	0.4010	8-13/16	0.7344	13/64	0.203125
7/8	0.0729	4-7/8	0.4063	8-7/8	0.7396	7/32	0.21875
15/16	0.0781	4-15/16	0.4115	8-15/16	0.7448	15/64	0.234375
1-	0.0833	5-	0.4167	9-	0.7500	1/4	0.250
1-1/16	0.0885	5-1/16	0.4219	9-1/16	0.7552	17/64	0.265625
1-1/8	0.0938	5-1/8	0.4271	9-1/8	0.7604	9/32	0.28125
1-3/16	0.0990	5-3/16	0.4323	9-3/16	0.7656	19/64	0.296875
1-1/4	0.1042	5-1/4	0.4375	9-1/4	0.7708	5/16	0.3125
1-5/16	0.1094	5-5/16	0.4427	9-5/16	0.7760	21/64	0.328125
1-3/8	0.1146	5-3/8	0.4479	9-3/8	0.7813	11/32	0.34375
1-7/16	0.1198	5-7/16	0.4531	9-7/16	0.7865	23/64	0.359375
1-1/2	0.1250	5-1/2	0.4583	9-1/2	0.7917	3/8	0.375
1-9/16	0.1302	5-9/16	0.4635	9-9/16	0.7969	25/64	0.390625
1-5/8	0.1354	5-5/8	0.4688	9-5/8	0.8021	13/32	0.40625
1-11/16	0.1406	5-11/16	0.4740	9-11/16	0.8073	27/64	0.421875
1-3/4	0.1458	5-3/4	0.4792	9-3/4	0.8125	7/16	0.4375
1-13/16	0.1510	5-13/16	0.4844	9-13/16	0.8177	29/64	0.453125
1-7/8	0.1563	5-7/8	0.4896	9-7/8	0.8229	15/32	0.46875
1-15/16	0.1615	5-15/16	0.4948	9-15/16	0.8281	31/64	0.484375
2-	0.1667	6-	0.5000	10-	0.8333	1/2	0.500
2-1/16	0.1719	6-1/16	0.5052	10-1/16	0.8385	33/64	0.515625
2-1/8	0.1771	6-1/8	0.5104	10-1/8	0.8438	17/32	0.53125
2-3/16	0.1823	6-3/16	0.5156	10-3/16	0.8490	35/64	0.546875
2-1/4	0.1875	6-1/4	0.5208	10-1/4	0.8542	9/16	0.5625
2-5/16	0.1927	6-5/16	0.5260	10-5/16	0.8594	37/64	0.578125
2-3/8	0.1979	6-3/8	0.5313	10-3/8	0.8646	19/32	0.59375
2-7/16	0.2031	6-7/16	0.5365	10-7/16	0.8698	39/64	0.609375
2-1/2	0.2083	6-1/2	0.5417	10-1/2	0.8750	5/8	0.625
2-9/16	0.2135	6-9/16	0.5469	10-9/16	0.8802	41/64	0.640625
2-5/8	0.2188	6-5/8	0.5521	10-5/8	0.8854	21/32	0.65625
2-11/16	0.2240	6-11/16	0.5573	10-11/16	0.8906	43/64	0.671875
2-3/4	0.2292	6-3/4	0.5625	10-3/4	0.8958	11/16	0.6875
2-13/16	0.2344	6-13/16	0.5677	10-13/16	0.9010	45/64	0.703125
2-7/8	0.2396	6-7/8	0.5729	10-7/8	0.9063	23/32	0.71875
2-15/16	0.2448	6-15/16	0.5781	10-15/16	0.9115	47/64	0.734375
3-	0.2500	7-	0.5833	11-	0.9167	3/4	0.750
3-1/16	0.2552	7-1/16	0.5885	11-1/16	0.9219	49/64	0.765625
3-1/8	0.2604	7-1/8	0.5938	11-1/8	0.9271	25/32	0.78125
3-3/16	0.2656	7-3/16	0.5990	11-3/16	0.9323	51/64	0.796875
3-1/4	0.2708	7-1/4	0.6042	11-1/4	0.9375	13/16	0.8125
3-5/16	0.2760	7-5/16	0.6094	11-5/16	0.9427	53/64	0.828125
3-3/8	0.2813	7-3/8	0.6146	11-3/8	0.9479	27/32	0.84375
3-7/16	0.2865	7-7/16	0.6198	11-7/16	0.9531	55/64	0.859375
3-1/2	0.2917	7-1/2	0.6250	11-1/2	0.9583	7/8	0.875
3-9/16	0.2969	7-9/16	0.6302	11-9/16	0.9635	57/64	0.890625
3-5/8	0.3021	7-5/8	0.6354	11-5/8	0.9688	29/32	0.90625
3-11/16	0.3073	7-11/16	0.6406	11-11/16	0.9740	59/64	0.921875
3-3/4	0.3125	7-3/4	0.6458	11-3/4	0.9792	15/16	0.9375
3-13/16	0.3177	7-13/16	0.6510	11-13/16	0.9844	61/64	0.953125
3-7/8	0.3229	7-7/8	0.6563	11-7/8	0.9896	31/32	0.96875
3-15/16	0.3281	7-15/16	0.6615	11-15/16	0.9948	63/64	0.984375
4-	0.3333	8-	0.6667	12-	1.0000	1-	1.000

GLOSSARY

The following glossary is reprinted from the WWPA "Standard Grading Rules for Western Lumber" in order to provide the reader with a readily available reference to the definitions of words and terms used in grading lumber.

■**700.00**

Throughout these rules various words and terms are used with meanings specifically applicable to lumber. In the use of these rules a full understanding of the words and terms in this Glossary is essential. An index to the Glossary follows:

■**702.00   BURL** — A distortion of grain, usually caused by abnormal growth due to injury of the tree. The effect of burls is assessed in relation to knots.

■**704.00   CHECKS** — A separation of the wood normally occurring across or through the rings of annual growth and usually as a result of seasoning.

(a) A surface check occurs only on one surface of a piece.

(b) A through check extends from one surface of a piece to the opposite or adjoining surface.

(c) Small checks are not over 1/32" wide and not over 4" long.

(d) Medium checks are not over 1/32" wide and not over 10" long.

(e) Large checks are larger than medium.

(f) A roller check is a crack in the wood structure caused by a piece of cupped lumber being flattened in passing between the machine rollers.

A light roller check is a perceptible opening not over 2' long.

A medium roller check is a perceptible opening over 2' long but not exceeding 4' in length.

A heavy roller check is over 4' in length.

■**706.00   COMPRESSION WOOD** — Abnormal wood that forms on the under side of leaning and crooked coniferous trees. It is characterized, aside from its distinguishing color, by being hard and brittle and by its relatively lifeless appearance. It is not permitted in readily identifiable and damaging form in stress grades nor where specifically limited.

■**708.00   DECAY** — A disintegration of the wood substance due to action of wood-destroying fungi, and is also known as dote, rot and unsound wood.

(a) Heart center decay is a localized decay developing along the pith in some species and is readily identifiable and easily detected by visual inspection. Heart center decay develops in the living tree and does not progress further after the tree is cut.

(b) White specks are small white pits or spots in wood caused by the fungus "Fomes pini." It develops in the living tree and does not develop further in wood in service. Where permitted in these rules it is so limited that it has no more effect on the intended use of the pieces than other characteristics permitted in the same grade. Pieces containing white speck are no more subject to decay than pieces which do not contain it.

(c) Honeycomb is similar to white speck but the pockets are larger. Where permitted in the rules it is so limited that it has no more effect on the intended use of the piece than other characteristics permitted in the same grade. Pieces containing honeycomb are no more subject to decay than pieces which do not contain it.

(d) Peck is channeled or pitted areas or pockets as sometimes found in cedar and cypress. Wood tissue between pecky areas remains unaffected in appearance and strength. All further growth of the fungus causing peckiness ceases after the trees are felled.

■**710.00   EDGE** — There are three meanings for edge: (1) The narrow face of rectangular-shaped pieces. (2) The corner of a piece at the intersection of two longitudinal faces. (3) Usually in stress grades that part of the wide face nearest the corner of the piece.

(a) Eased edges means slightly rounded surfacing on pieces of lumber to remove sharp corners. Lumber 4" or less in thicknesss is frequently shipped with eased edges unless otherwise specified. Lumber of 1" and 2" thickness may be rounded to a radius of no more than 1/16" and ⅛" respectively.

(b) Square edged means free from wane and without eased edges.

(c) Free of wane means without wane but may have eased edges. (See WANE definition.)

(d) Square corners means without eased edges but may permit wane allowance.

■**712.00   GRAIN** — The fibers in wood and their direction, size, arrangement, appearance or quality.

(a) For requirements and method of measuring medium grain, close grain and dense material, see Para. 170.00.

(b) Slope of grain is the deviation of the line of fibers from a straight line parallel to the sides of the piece. For method of measurement, see Para. 230.00.

GLOSSARY

(c) Summerwood is the portion of the annual growth ring formed during the latter part of the yearly growth ring. It is darker in color, more dense, and stronger mechanically than springwood.

(d) Springwood is the portion of the annual growth ring formed during the early part of the yearly growth period. It is lighter in color, less dense, and not as strong mechanically as summerwood.

(e) Vertical grain (VG) (Edge grain (EG) (Rift grain) lumber is a piece or pieces sawn at approximately right angles to the annual growth rings so that the rings form an angle of 45 degrees or more with the surface of the piece.

(f) Flat grain (FG) (Slash grain SG) lumber is a piece or pieces sawn approximately parallel to the annual growth rings so that all or some of the rings form an angle of less than 45 degrees with the surface of the piece.

(g) Mixed grain (MG) lumber may be either or both vertical and flat grain.

(h) Spiral grain is a deviation in the slope of grain caused when the fibers in a tree take a spiral course around the trunk of the tree instead of the normal vertical course.

(i) Diagonal grain is a deviation in the slope of grain caused by sawing at an angle with the bark of the tree.

■**714.00　HEART** — The portion of the tree contained within the sapwood. It is sometimes used to mean the pith.

(a) Boxed heart means with the pith enclosed in the piece.

(b) Heart center is the pith or center core of the log.

(c) Free of heart center (FOHC) means without pith (side cut). When a piece has been sawn so as to eliminate the pith (heart center), an occasional piece showing pith on the surface for not more than ¼ the length may be accepted.

(d) Heartwood and sapwood of equivalent character are of equal strength. No requirement of heartwood need be made when strength alone is the governing factor.

(e) Heartwood is more durable than sapwood, and for wood which is to be exposed to decay-producing conditions without preservative treatment, the minimum percentage of heartwood to be present in all pieces in a shipment of any species may be specified.

(f) Sapwood takes preservative treatment more readily than heartwood, and is equally durable when treated. For lumber and timbers to be treated, there should be no heartwood requirement nor limitation on sapwood.

■**716.00　HOLES** — Holes may extend partially or entirely through a piece and may be from any cause. Holes that extend only partially through the piece may also be designated as surface pits. Unless otherwise specified holes are measured the same as knots. Holes are classified by size as follows:

(a) A pin hole is not over 1/16" in diameter.

(b) A medium (small) hole is not over ¼" in diameter.

(c) A large hole is not over 1" in diameter.

(d) A very large hole is over 1" in diameter.

■**718.00　KNOTS** — A portion of a branch or limb that has become incorporated in a piece of lumber. In lumber, knots are classified as to form, size, quali-

ty and occurrence. A red knot is one that results from a live branch growth in the tree and is intergrown with the surrounding wood. A black knot is one that results from a dead branch which the wood growth of the tree has surrounded.

(a) A round knot is a knot cut at right angles to the length of the knot (limb).

(b) An oval knot is a knot cut at slightly more than right angles to the length of the knot (limb).

(c) A spike knot is a knot cut either lengthwise of the knot or diagonally across it.

(d) A pin knot is not over ½".

(e) A small knot is not over ¾".

(f) A medium knot is not over 1½".

(g) A large knot is over 1½".

(h) A sound knot contains no decay. It may be red or black.

(i) A pith knot is sound in all respects except it contains a pith hole not over ¼" in diameter.

(j) A hollow knot is an apparently sound knot in all respects except it contains a hole over ¼" in diameter, and a through opening in a hollow knot may be of a size equal to other holes permitted.

(k) An unsound knot contains decay.

(l) A "firm" knot is solid across its face but contains incipient decay.

(m) A tight knot is so fixed by growth, shape or position that it retains its place in the piece. It may be red or black.

(n) An intergrown knot is one whose growth rings are partially or completely intergrown on one or more faces with the growth rings of the surrounding wood.

(o) A watertight knot has its growth rings completely intergrown with those of the surrounding wood on one surface and is sound on that surface.

(p) An encased knot is one which is not intergrown with the growth rings of the surrounding wood.

(q) A "loose" or "not firmly fixed" knot is one not held tightly in place by growth, shape or position.

(r) A "fixed" knot will retain its place in dry lumber under ordinary conditions but can be moved under pressure though not easily pushed out.

(s) A knot cluster is two or more knots grouped together as a unit with the fibers of the wood deflected around the entire unit.

(t) A star-checked knot has radial checks.

(u) Well-scattered knots are not in clusters and each knot is separated from any other by a distance at least equal to the diameter of the smaller of the two.

(v) Well-spaced knots means that the sum of the sizes of all knots in any 6" of length of a piece must not exceed twice the size of the largest knot permitted. More than one knot of maximum permissible size must not be in same 6" of length and the combination of knots must not be serious.

■**720.00　MANUFACTURING IMPERFECTIONS** — Means all imperfections or blemishes which are the result of manufacturing, such as the following:

(a) Chipped grain is a barely perceptible irregularity in the surface of a piece caused when particles of wood are chipped or broken below the line of cut. It is too small to be classed as torn grain and as usually found is not considered unless in excess of 25% of the surface is involved.

(b) Torn grain is an irregularity in the surface of a piece where wood has been torn or broken out by surfacing. Torn grain is described as follows:

Very light torn grain — not over 1/64" deep.
Light torn grain — not over 1/32" deep.
Medium torn grain — not over 1/16" deep.
Heavy torn grain — not over ⅛" deep.
Very heavy torn grain — over ⅛" deep.

(c) Raised grain is an unevenness between springwood and summerwood on the surface of dressed lumber. Slight raised grain is an unevenness somewhat less than 1/64". Very light raised grain is not over 1/64". Light raised grain is not over 1/32". . Medium raised grain is not over 1/16". Heavy raised grain is not over ⅛".

(d) Loosened grain is a grain separation or loosening between springwood and summerwood without displacement. Very light loosened grain is not over 1/64" separation. Light loosened grain is not over 1/32". separation. Medium loosened grain is not over 1/16" separation. Heavy loosened grain is not over ⅛" separation. Very heavy loosened grain is over ⅛" separation.

(e) Skips are areas on a piece that failed to surface clean. Skips are described as follows with equivalent areas being permissible:

Very light skip is not over 1/64" deep. *[and **approximately 6" in length.**]
Light skip is not over 1/32" deep. *[on face, may **be 12" in length and on edge may be 2' long.**]
Medium skip is not over 1/16" deep. *[on face, **may be 12" in length and on edge may be 2' long.**]
Heavy skip is not over ⅛" deep.
***Provisions in brackets apply to all except dimension lumber.**

(f) Hit and miss is a series of skips not over 1/16" deep with surfaced areas between.

(g) Hit or miss means completely surfaced or partly surfaced or entirely rough. Scantness may be 1/16".

(h) Mismatch is an uneven fit in worked lumber when adjoining pieces do not meet tightly at all points of contact or when the surfaces of adjoining pieces are not in the same plane.

Slight mismatch is a barely evident trace of mismatch.

Very light mismatch is not over 1/64".
Light mismatch is not over 1/32".
Medium mismatch is not over 1/16".
Heavy mismatch is not over ⅛".

(i) Machine burn is a darkening of the wood due to overheating by machine knives or rolls when pieces are stopped in machine.

(j) Machine bite is a depressed cut of the machine knives at the end of the piece. Very light machine bite is not over 1/64" deep. Light machine bite is not over 1/32" deep. Medium machine bite is not over 1/16" deep. Heavy machine bite is not over ⅛" deep. Very heavy machine bite is over ⅛" deep.

(k) Machine gouge is a groove cut by the machine below the desired line. Slight machine gouge is less than 1/64" deep. Very light machine gouge is not over 1/64" deep. Light machine gouge is not over 1/32" deep. Medium machine gouge is not over 1/16" deep. Heavy machine gouge is not over ⅛" deep.

(l) A machine offset is an abrupt dressing variation in the edge surface which usually occurs near the end of the piece and without reducing the width or without changing the plane of the wide surface. Very light machine offset is a variation not over 1/64". Light machine offset is a variation not over 1/32". Medium machine offset is a variation not over 1/16". Heavy machine offset is a variation not over ⅛". Very heavy machine offset is a variation over ⅛".

(m) Chip marks are shallow depressions or indentations on or in the surface of dressed lumber caused by shavings or chips getting embedded in the surface during dressing. Slight chip marks are less than 1/64" deep. Very light chip marks are not over 1/64" deep. Light chip marks are not over 1/32" deep. Medium chip marks are not over 1/16" deep. Heavy chip marks are not over ⅛" deep.

(n) Knife marks are the imprints or markings of the machine knives on the surface of dressed lumber. Very slight knife marks are visible only from a favorable angle and are perfectly smooth to the touch. Slight knife marks are readily visible but evidence no unevenness to the touch.

(o) Wavy dressing involves more uneven dressing than knife marks. Very slight wavy dressing evidences unevenness that is barely perceptible to the touch. Slight wavy dressing evidences perceptible unevenness that is somewhat less than 1/64" deep. Very light wavy dressing is not over 1/64" deep. Light wavy dressing is not over 1/32" deep. Medium wavy dressing is not over 1/16" deep. Heavy wavy dressing is not over ⅛" deep. Very heavy wavy dressing is over ⅛" deep.

■722.00   **CLASSIFICATION OF MANUFACTURING IMPERFECTIONS —**

(a) Standard "A" Manufacture admits: Very light torn grain; occasional slight chip marks; very slight knife marks.

(b) Standard "B" Manufacture admits: Very light torn grain; very light raised grain; very light loosened grain; slight chip marks; average of one slight chip mark per lineal foot but not more than two in any lineal foot; slight knife marks; very slight mismatch.

(c) Standard "C" Manufacture admits: Medium torn grain; light raised grain; light loosened grain; very light machine bite; very light machine gouge; very light machine offset; light chip marks if well-scattered; occasional medium chip marks; very slight knife marks; very slight mismatch.

(d) Standard "D" Manufacture admits: Heavy torn grain; medium raised grain; very heavy loosened grain; light machine bite; light machine gouge; light machine offset; medium chip marks; slight knife marks; very light mismatch.

(e) Standard "E" Manufacture admits: Torn grain; raised grain; very heavy loosened grain; medium machine bite; machine gouge; medium machine offset; chip marks; knife marks; light wavy dressing; light mismatch.

(f) Standard "F" Manufacture admits: Very heavy torn grain; raised grain; very heavy loosened grain; heavy machine bite; machine gouge; heavy machine offset; chip marks; knife marks; medium wavy dressing; medium mismatch.

■724.00   **MOISTURE CONTENT** — The weight of the water in wood expressed in percentage of the weight of the oven-dry wood.

GLOSSARY

■726.00 **OCCASIONAL PIECES** — Means not more than 10% of the pieces in a parcel or shipment.

■728.00 **PITCH** — Is an acculumation of resinous material.

(a) Light pitch is the light but evident presence of pitch.

(b) Medium pitch is a somewhat more evident presence of pitch than is the light.

(c) Heavy pitch is a very evident accumulation of pitch showing by its color and consistency.

■730.00 **PITCH STREAK** — Is a well-defined accumulation of pitch in the wood cells in a more or less regular streak. It should not be confused with dark grain. Pitch streaks are described approximately as follows, with equivalent areas being permissible:

(a) Very small pitch streak ⅜" in width and 15" in length.

(b) Small pitch streak 1/12 the width and 1/6 the length of the piece.

(c) Medium pitch streak 1/6 the width and ⅓ the length of the piece.

(d) A large pitch streak is not over ¼ the width by ½ the length of the surface.

(e) A very large pitch streak is over ¼ the width by ½ the length of the surface.

(f) A pitch seam is a shake or check which contains pitch.

■732.00 **PITH** — Pith is the small soft core in the structural center of a log.

(a) Very small pith is not over ⅛" wide and occupies on face surface not over ¼ square inch (⅛" wide by 2" long, or 1/16" by 4").

(b) Small pith occupies not over ¾ square inch (¼" by 3", 3/16" by 4", ⅛" by 6", or 1/16" by 12").

(c) Free of pith means that pith on or within the body of the piece is prohibited.

■734.00 **POCKET** — A well-defined opening between the rings of annual growth which develops during the growth of the tree. It usually contains pitch or bark.

Pockets are described approximately as follows with equivalent areas being permissible:

(a) Very small pocket — 1/16" in width and 3" in length, or ⅛" in width and 2" in length.

(b) Small pocket — 1/16" in width and 6" in length, or ⅛" in width and 4" in length, or ¼" in width and 2" in length.

(c) Medium pocket — 1/16" in width and 12" in length, or ⅛" in width and 8" in length, or ⅜" in width and 4" in legnth.

(d) An large pocket is not over 4 square inches in area.

(e) A very large pocket is over 4 square inches in area.

■736.00 **PLUGS AND FILLERS** — Wood plugs and fillers are inserted into pieces of lumber to improve their appearance and usefulness. Lumber containing plugs and fillers may be shipped providing the order, acknowledgement and invoice carry reference to the inserts. Quality of the inserts and workmanship must be in keeping with the quality of the grade. In di-

mension and other lumber graded for strength, inserts are limited to the same size and location as knots.

■738.00 **SAPWOOD** — Outer layers of growth between the bark and the heartwood which contain the sap.

(a) Bright sapwood shows no stain and is not limited in any grade except as specifically provided.

(b) Sapwood restrictions waived means that any restrictions in a rule on the amount of sapwood permitted in pieces graded under that rule are not to apply.

(c) Bright sapwood no defect (BSND) means that bright sapwood is permitted in each piece in any amount.

■740.00 **SHAKE** — A lengthwise separation of the wood which usually occurs between or through the rings of annual growth.

(a) A light shake is not over 1/32" wide.

(b) A medium shake is not over ⅛" wide.

(c) A surface shake occurs on only one surface of a piece.

(d) A through shake extends from one surface of a piece to the opposite or to an adjoining surface.

(e) A pith shake (or heart shake or heart check) extends through the growth rings from or through the pith towards the surface of a piece, and can be distinguished from a season check by the fact that its greatest width is nearest the pith, whereas the greatest width of a season check in a pith-centered piece is farthest from the pith.

(f) A ring shake occurs between the growth rings to partially or wholly encircle the pith.

■742.00 **SPLITS** — A separation of the wood due to the tearing apart of the wood cells.

(a) A very short split is equal in length to ½ the width of the piece.

(b) A short split is equal in length to the width of the piece and in no case exceeds 1/6 the length.

(c) A medium split is equal in length to twice the width of the piece and in no case exceeds 1/6 the length.

(d) A long split is longer than a medium split.

■744.00 **STAINED WOOD** —

(a) Stained Heartwood and Firm Red Heart — Stained Heartwood or Firm Red Heart is a marked variation from the natural color. It may range from pink to brown. It should not be confused with natural red heart. Natural color is usually uniformly distributed through certain annual rings, whereas stains are usually in irregular patches. In grades where it is permitted, it has no more effect on the intended use of the piece than other characteristics permitted in the grade.

(b) Stained Sapwood — Stained Sapwood similarily has no effect on the intended use of the pieces in which it is permitted but affects appearance in varying degrees.

(1) Light stained sapwood is so slightly discolored that it does not materially affect natural finishes.

(2) Medium stained sapwood has a pronounced difference in coloring which sometimes affects its usefulness for natural finishes but not for paint finishes.

(3) Heavy stained sapwood has so pronounced a

GLOSSARY

difference in color that the grain may be obscured but the lumber containing it is acceptable for paint finishes.

(c) Discoloration through exposure to the elements is admitted in all grades of framing and sheathing lumber.

■**746.00 STRESS GRADES** — Lumber grades having assigned working stress and modulus of elasticity values in accordance with accepted basic principles of strength grading, and the provisions of sections 5.3.1 and 5.3.2 of Voluntary Product Standard 20-70.

■**748.00 TRIM** —

(a) Trimming of lumber is the act of crosscutting a piece to a given length.

(b) Double end trimmed (DET) lumber is trimmed reasonably square by a saw on both ends.

(c) Precision end trimmed (PET) lumber is trimmed square and smooth on both ends to uniform length with a manufacturing tolerance of 1/16" over or under in length in 20% of the pieces.

(d) Square end trimmed lumber is trimmed square permitting slight manufacturing tolerance of 1/64" for each nominal 2" of thickness or width.

■**750.00 WANE** — Bark or lack of wood from any cause, except eased edges, on the edge or corner of a piece of lumber.

■**752.00 WARP** — Any deviation from a true or plane surface, including bow, crook, cup and twist or any combination thereof. Warp restrictions are based on the average form of warp as it occurs normally, and any variation from this average form, such as short kinks, shall be appraised according to its equivalent effect. Pieces containing two or more forms shall be appraised according to the combined effect in determining the amount permissible. In these rules warp is classified as very light, light, medium and heavy, and applied to each width and length as set forth in the various grades in accordance with the following provisions and tables:

(a) Bow is a deviation flatwise from a straight line drawn from end to end of a piece. It is measured at the point of greatest distance from the straight line. The amount permitted according to the grade is as follows: If under 2" thick, three times as much as crook permitted for 2" faces. If 2" thick and under 3", twice as much as crook permitted for 2" faces. If 3" thick and over, the same as the amount of crook permitted for that thickness.

(b) Crook is a deviation edgewise from a straight line drawn from end to end of a piece. It is measured at the point of greatest distance from the straight line. For amount permitted, see tables on Pages ,

(c) Cup is a deviation in the face of a piece from a straight line drawn from edge to edge of a piece. It is measured at the point of greatest distance from the straight line. For amount permitted, see cup table.

CUP TABLE

Cup	Face Width					
	2"&3"	4"	5"&6"	8"	10"	12"
Very Light	1/32"	1/32"	1/32"	1/16"	3/32"	1/8"
Light	1/32"	1/32"	1/16"	1/8"	3/16"	1/4"
Medium	1/32"	1/16"	1/8"	3/16"	1/4"	3/8"
Heavy	1/16"	1/8"	3/16"	1/4"	3/8"	1/2"

14" and Wider proportionately more.

(d) Twist is a deviation flatwise, or a combination of flatwise and edgewise, in the form of a curl or spiral, and the amount is the distance an edge of a piece at one end is raised above a flat surface against which both edges at the opposite end are resting snugly. For amount permitted, see tables on Page

CROOK TABLE for FRAMING and ALTERNATE BOARD RULES

Length In Feet	Crook	Width						
		2"	3"	4"	5" & 6"	8"	10"	12"
4 & 6	Very Light	1/8	1/8	1/8	1/8	1/16	1/16	1/16
	Light	1/4	1/4	1/4	3/16	1/8	1/16	1/16
	Medium	3/8	3/8	3/8	1/4	3/16	1/8	1/8
	Heavy	1/2	1/2	1/2	3/8	1/4	3/16	3/16
8	Very Light	1/4	1/4	3/16	1/8	1/8	1/16	1/16
	Light	3/8	3/8	3/8	5/16	1/4	3/16	1/8
	Medium	1/2	1/2	1/2	1/2	3/8	1/4	3/16
	Heavy	3/4	3/4	3/4	5/8	1/2	3/8	1/4
10	Very Light	3/8	5/16	1/4	3/16	3/16	1/8	1/8
	Light	3/4	5/8	1/2	7/16	3/8	1/4	3/16
	Medium	1 3/8	1	3/4	5/8	1/2	7/16	3/8
	Heavy	1 3/4	1 1/4	1 1/8	1	7/8	3/4	5/8
12	Very Light	1/2	3/8	3/8	5/16	1/4	1/4	3/16
	Light	1	3/4	11/16	5/8	1/2	7/16	3/8
	Medium	1 1/2	1 1/8	1	7/8	13/16	3/4	9/16
	Heavy	2	1 1/2	1 3/8	1 1/4	1 1/8	1	13/16
14	Very Light	5/8	1/2	7/16	3/8	5/16	1/4	3/16
	Light	1 1/4	1	7/8	3/4	5/8	1/2	3/8
	Medium	2	1 1/2	1 1/4	1 1/8	1	7/8	3/4
	Heavy	2 3/4	2	1 3/4	1 1/2	1 1/4	1 1/8	1
16	Very Light	3/4	5/8	1/2	7/16	3/8	5/16	1/4
	Light	1 5/8	1 1/4	1	7/8	3/4	5/8	1/2
	Medium	2 1/2	1 7/8	1 1/2	1 3/8	1 1/8	1	7/8
	Heavy	3 1/4	2 1/2	2	1 3/4	1 1/2	1 1/4	1 1/8
18	Very Light	1	3/4	5/8	1/2	7/16	3/8	5/16
	Light	2	1 3/8	1 1/8	1	7/8	3/4	5/8
	Medium	3	2 1/16	1 5/8	1 1/2	1 1/4	1 1/8	1
	Heavy	4	2 3/4	2 1/4	2	1 3/4	1 1/2	1 1/4
20	Very Light	1 1/8	7/8	3/4	5/8	1/2	7/16	3/8
	Light	2 1/4	1 1/2	1 3/8	1 1/4	1	1 5/8	3/4
	Medium	3 3/8	2 1/4	2 1/16	1 7/8	1 1/2	1 5/16	1 1/8
	Heavy	4 1/2	3	2 3/4	2 1/2	2	1 3/4	1 1/2
22	Very Light	1 1/4	1	7/8	3/4	5/8	1/2	7/16
	Light	2 1/2	1 3/4	1 5/8	1 1/2	1 1/4	1	7/8
	Medium	3 3/4	2 5/8	2 7/16	2 1/4	1 7/8	1 1/2	1 1/4
	Heavy	5	3 1/2	3 1/4	3	2 1/2	2	1 3/4
24	Very Light	1 1/2	1 1/8	1	7/8	3/4	5/8	1/2
	Light	3	2	1 7/8	1 3/4	1 1/2	1 1/4	1
	Medium	4 1/2	3	2 3/4	2 5/8	2 1/4	1 7/8	1 5/8
	Heavy	6	4	3 3/4	3 1/2	3	2 1/2	2 1/4

GLOSSARY

CROOK TABLE for SELECTS and FINISH

Length	4"	6"	8"	10"	12"
8 Feet					
C Sel. (Choice IWP) & Btr. Superior	1/4	1/4	3/16	3/16	1/8
D Sel. (Quality IWP) Prime	3/8	3/8	5/16	5/16	1/4
10 Feet					
C Sel. (Choice IWP) & Btr. Superior	3/8	5/16	5/16	1/4	3/16
D Sel. (Quality IWP) Prime	9/16	9/16	1/2	7/16	3/8
12 Feet					
C Sel. (Choice IWP) & Btr. Superior	9/16	1/2	7/16	3/8	5/16
D Sel. (Quality IWP) Prime	7/8	3/4	11/16	5/8	9/16
14 Feet					
C Sel. (Choice IWP) & Btr. Superior	3/4	11/16	9/16	1/2	3/8
D Sel. (Quality IWP) Prime	1 1/8	1 1/16	15/16	7/8	3/4
16 Feet					
C Sel. (Choice IWP) & Btr. Superior	1	7/8	3/4	5/8	1/2
D Sel. (Quality IWP) Prime	1 1/2	1 3/8	1 1/4	1 1/8	1

In the grades of Selects and Finish, crook is limited to the amount shown in the above table for the appropriate length, width and grade. Pieces differing in length and width from these basic sizes may have crook in proportion to the amounts shown. Crook is limited to occasional pieces of any item.

CROOK TABLE for COMMON BOARDS

Length	4"	6"	8"	10"	12"
8 Feet					
No. 2 & Btr. Com.	1/2	7/16	3/8	5/16	1/4
No. 3 Com.	13/16	3/4	11/16	5/8	1/2
No. 4 Com.	1	15/16	7/8	13/16	3/4
10 Feet					
No. 2 & Btr. Com.	13/16	11/16	9/16	1/2	3/8
No. 3 Com.	1 1/4	1 3/16	1 1/16	1	13/16
No. 4 Com.	1 9/16	1 7/16	1 3/8	1 1/4	1 3/16
12 Feet					
No. 2 & Btr. Com.	1 1/8	1	7/8	11/16	9/16
No. 3 Com.	1 13/16	1 11/16	1 9/16	1 7/16	1 1/8
No. 4 Com.	2 1/4	2 1/8	2	1 13/16	1 11/16
14 Feet					
No. 2 & Btr. Com.	1 9/16	1 5/16	1 1/8	15/16	3/4
No. 3 Com.	2 1/2	2 5/16	2 1/8	1 15/16	1 9/16
No. 4 Com.	3 1/16	2 7/8	2 11/16	2 1/2	2 5/16
16 Feet					
No. 2 & Btr. Com.	2	1 3/4	1 1/2	1 1/4	1
No. 3 Com.	3 1/4	3	2 3/4	2 1/2	2
No. 4 Com.	4	3 3/4	3 1/2	3 1/4	3

Crook is limited to the amount shown in the above table for the appropriate length, width and grade. Pieces differing in length and width from these basic sizes may have crook in proportion to the amounts shown. Crook is limited to occasional pieces of any item.

TWIST TABLE

Length In Feet	Twist	2"	3" & 4"	5" & 6"	8"	10"	12"
4	Very Light	1/16	1/8	3/16	1/4	5/16	3/8
	Light	1/8	1/4	3/8	1/2	5/8	3/4
	Medium	3/16	3/8	1/2	3/4	7/8	1 1/8
	Heavy	1/4	1/2	3/4	1	1 1/4	1 1/2
6	Very Light	3/32	3/16	5/16	3/8	7/16	9/16
	Light	3/16	3/8	1/2	3/4	7/8	1 1/8
	Medium	9/32	1/2	3/4	1 1/8	1 3/8	1 5/8
	Heavy	3/8	3/4	1 1/8	1 1/2	1 7/8	2 1/4
8	Very Light	1/8	1/4	3/8	1/2	5/8	3/4
	Light	1/4	1/2	3/4	1	1 1/4	1 1/2
	Medium	3/8	3/4	1 1/8	1 1/2	1 7/8	2 1/4
	Heavy	1/2	1	1 1/2	2	2 1/2	3
10	Very Light	5/32	5/16	7/16	5/8	3/4	15/16
	Light	5/16	5/8	7/8	1 1/4	1 1/2	1 7/8
	Medium	1/2	7/8	1 3/8	1 7/8	2 3/8	2 3/4
	Heavy	5/8	1 1/4	1 7/8	2 1/2	3 1/8	3 3/4
12	Very Light	3/16	3/8	9/16	3/4	15/16	1 1/8
	Light	3/8	3/4	1 1/8	1 1/2	1 7/8	2 1/4
	Medium	9/16	1 1/8	1 5/8	2 1/4	3 3/8	3 3/8
	Heavy	3/4	1 1/2	2 1/4	3	3 3/4	4 1/2
14	Very Light	7/32	7/16	5/8	7/8	1 1/16	1 5/16
	Light	7/16	7/8	1 1/4	1 3/4	2 1/8	2 5/8
	Medium	5/8	1 1/4	1 7/8	2 5/8	3 1/4	3 7/8
	Heavy	7/8	1 3/4	2 5/8	3 1/2	4 3/8	5 1/4
16	Very Light	1/4	1/2	3/4	1	1 1/4	1 1/2
	Light	1/2	1	1 1/2	2	2 1/2	3
	Medium	3/4	1 1/2	2 1/4	3	3 3/4	4 1/2
	Heavy	1	2	3	4	5	6
18	Very Light	5/16	9/16	13/16	1 1/8	1 7/16	1 11/16
	Light	9/16	1 1/8	1 5/8	2 1/4	2 3/4	3 3/8
	Medium	7/8	1 5/8	2 1/2	3 3/8	4 1/4	5
	Heavy	1 1/8	2 1/4	3 3/8	4 1/2	5 5/8	6 3/4
20 and Longer	Very Light	5/16	5/8	15/16	1 1/4	1 9/16	1 7/8
	Light	5/8	1 1/4	1 7/8	2 1/2	3 1/8	3 3/4
	Medium	1	1 7/8	2 3/4	3 3/4	4 5/8	5 5/8
	Heavy	1 1/4	2 1/2	3 3/4	5	6 1/4	7 1/2